PSYCHOLOGY THROUGH LITERATURE

✳ ✳ ✳

PSYCHOLOGY

THROUGH LITERATURE

An Anthology

✳ ✳ ✳

EDITED BY

CAROLINE SHRODES
DEPARTMENT OF ENGLISH, SAN FRANCISCO STATE COLLEGE

JUSTINE VAN GUNDY
DEPARTMENT OF ENGLISH, SAN FRANCISCO STATE COLLEGE

RICHARD W. HUSBAND
DEPARTMENT OF PSYCHOLOGY, IOWA STATE COLLEGE

New York · OXFORD UNIVERSITY PRESS

COPYRIGHT 1943 BY OXFORD UNIVERSITY PRESS, INC.

Fifth printing, 1950

19532

PRINTED IN THE UNITED STATES OF AMERICA

Contents

❈

THE LEARNING PROCESS 229

PART TWO

ADJUSTMENT AND MALADJUSTMENT OF THE PERSONALITY

DREAMS AND THE UNCONSCIOUS 249

THE NEUROSES 281

THE PSYCHOSES 325

Preface

❋

THE purpose of this anthology is to lead the student of human motivation and behavior to a better understanding of himself and his world through the vicarious experience that literature affords. It is designed primarily to enrich an introductory course in psychology or mental hygiene, fields in which too often the young person, bewildered by formal classifications and strange terminology, fails to recognize the relation between academic discussions and the forces that condition the growth of his own personality. It may also be found useful as a book of readings for a course in creative writing in which stress may be placed on the understanding and sharing of human experience rather than upon techniques of writing and literary form.

An undergraduate's personal experience is extremely limited. He is a product of his conditioning: his physical constitution, the health of his parents, the degree of their compatibility, the extent to which they accept and understand him, their economic and social status, the mores of the neighbors—in short, biological, psychological, and sociological factors have all contributed to the shaping of his personality. But these need not be limiting forces. The subtle process of identification which literature affords will permit him sympathetically to enter the lives of others and become immeasurably enriched through his analysis of their motives and drives, hopes and fears, loves and hates. He will thus come better to understand the elements of his own personality and the conflicting forces that impel men as individuals and as members of society.

Implicit in literature are all of the facts of psychology. The facts constitute the center of the experience which is literature. But the facts alone are not truth. They become true to the scientist as his imagination plays upon them and weaves them together into a consistent and organic whole. They become true to the poet or the dramatist when his imagination has ordered them into a living organism. But the layman cannot readily enter into the imagination of the scientist, for the scientist separates human knowledge, and only those who share his technical equipment can see the whole. All persons are privileged, however, to enter into the imaginative experience of the artist, for art relates all knowledge to human experience. Art, like poetry, 'attaches emotion to the idea; the idea is the fact!' All those who possess the capacity of the artist, not as creator or craftsman, but as human being, can share his understanding. The artist writing as a man to men calls into exercise our universal heritage of sympathy and love, fear and hate. He alone can communicate to the emotions as well as to the intellect our common experience of life. While the scientist draws upon the fact and the case study, thus treating of the partial and the exceptional, the artist, dealing with the same material, by an imaginative process of selection and synthesis, presents a 'higher fact,' that truth which is universal and functional. In this collection, therefore, we shall let the artist be our guide. At one time he may use the methods of the empiricist, recording human behavior in action; at another time he employs introspection, setting down the thoughts of human beings. But always he is the creator whose power it is to impress the reader with the universality of basic human experience.

In our process of selection we have tried to find the story, poem, essay, or chapter from biography or fiction that seems most comprehensively and effectively to dramatize psychological concepts fundamental to our daily lives. We have avoided material that employs the vocabulary of psychology and, not content to describe, self-consciously interprets. In all cases we have attempted to choose selections which speak for themselves. It is hoped that they will not merely illuminate and clarify the substance of text or lecture but will provide concrete materials for discussion and analysis so that the student cannot fail to perceive the immediate bearing of these ideas on his own life.

The classification of selections under general topics which separate the biological, psychological, and sociological motive forces may seem arbitrary in the light of our awareness that man is part of all that he has met, and that all that he has met is interwoven in the fabric of the total personality. It has seemed useful, however, to classify each selection in accordance with its central focus. The prefaces and the index will suggest how various selections may be reconsidered under a variety of main headings. Although titles in the bibliography are listed for convenience under the main divisions of the anthology, it is obvious that multiple insights into the human personality may be found in every significant piece of literature.

Since the abnormal and exceptional in human behavior have contributed to our understanding of the normal and representative, we have not confined our attention to the latter. It is true that the majority of people do not undergo the emotional conflicts of a character in a Dostoyevsky novel, but it does not thereby follow that a Lise or an Ivan is untrue to life. In experiencing their extreme torment, before which our own loves, hates, and fears may dwindle to insignificance, we come better to understand our own emotions. The Aristotelian theory of catharsis propounded over two thousand years ago, no less than the concepts of Freud, suggests that sharing another's experience may purge us of our own hates and fears and permit us to release in pity some of our aggressive drives. If we understand why people are impelled to brutality or self-torture or antisocial behavior, we can less easily revel in our own superiority and self-righteously condemn the victims of such impulses. Only when we learn to assign adequate causes to man's behavior and perceive the significance of his acts in the context of his total personality, shall we ourselves be substituting for irrational and emotional reactions the cognitive, investigative powers of our higher faculties.

The fact that some of these selections were written before the science of human behavior became an acknowledged sphere of learning does not in any way invalidate them; rather it attests the more surely to the immediacy and relevance of the materials of psychology to actual life. We recognize in Sophocles, Shakespeare, and Hardy, as well as in contemporary writing, patterns of emotions common to us today. The artist has imposed design on the raw materials of life, and in his detached view we may find insights into the problems of our own lives. Through the vicarious experiences of literature, we may approach that inward and outward integration of self which it is the purpose of psychology to foster. We may see that neither the individual nor his environment is static and unalterable, but subject to change and interaction, and that man has some power to direct both himself and his world.

Part One

THE FORMATION OF THE PERSONALITY

THE PHYSICAL HERITAGE

Our minds are perpetually wrought on by the temperament of our bodies; which makes me suspect they are nearer allied than either our philosophers or school-divines will allow them to be.

—DRYDEN

CERTAIN physical characteristics—one's personal appearance, the state of his health, a physical deformity—may influence an individual's personality and determine the nature of his attitudes toward himself and others. The color of one's hair, the shape of his nose, the size of his bones—innumerable physical details—may be important as they serve to attract or repel people. Physical defects often assume undue significance because of a sensitiveness induced in childhood by the attitude of parents, companions, or teachers. Fears, repression, introversion, despondency, self-pity, emotional outbursts, efforts at compensation, and day dreaming may become more serious obstacles to satisfactory adjustment to one's world than are the physical defects themselves. It is difficult to surmise how much of Byron's moodiness, his emotional violence, and instability may have had their origin in the defect of a club foot which caused his erratic mother alternately to caress and abuse him. Byron was able to compensate for his handicap, first through building up physical superiority as a swimmer and later by winning sensational recognition as romantic hero and poet. The great ungainly bulk of Dr. Johnson, his scrofula, and his squinting eyes must have made him repellent to many people whose admiration he craved. It seems probable that his moodiness and his verbal bludgeoning of friend and foe were in part expressions of the frustrations traceable to his physical unattractiveness. One who declared that his idea of heaven was to spend the day riding in a post chaise with a pretty woman cannot have been indifferent to the fact that nature had not endowed him with the fascinations of a Lord Chesterfield. Dr. Johnson ascribes much of Alexander Pope's acerbity of temper and vindictiveness to the suffering induced by his poor health and the physical deformity that made him a queer little dwarf of a man. The insignificant statures of Napoleon, Mussolini, and Hitler may well be taken into consideration as factors that impelled these men to compensatory dreams of world conquest. The great passion for physical activity displayed by Theodore Roosevelt and his worship of a militant virility as a national virtue doubtless had origins in the feelings of inferiority from which he suffered as a sickly child who deliberately built up a strong body through vigorous self-discipline.

3

Whether one accepts a physical handicap and adjusts himself to it or allows it to warp his mind and emotions, its presence must leave a deep mark on the individual's personality.

❊

OF HUMAN BONDAGE

SOMERSET MAUGHAM

[In his autobiographical novel, *Of Human Bondage,* Somerset Maugham portrays vividly the effect of a physical handicap on a sensitive child. The cruelty children often display toward those of their fellows who in any way deviate from their standards has been frequently observed. Philip's club foot made him a 'freak' whom it was great sport to torment. When his efforts to engage in the normal activities of the boys were thwarted and their taunts induced overwhelming shame, he turned to the world of fantasy and to wishful restoration of a happier past.]

Next morning when the clanging of a bell awoke Philip he looked around his cubicle in astonishment. Then a voice sang out, and he remembered where he was.

'Are you awake, Singer?'

The partitions of the cubicle were of polished pitch-pine, and there was a green curtain in front. In those days there was little thought of ventilation, and the windows were closed except when the dormitory was aired in the morning.

Philip got up and knelt down to say his prayers. It was a cold morning, and he shivered a little; but he had been taught by his uncle that his prayers were more acceptable to God if he said them in his nightshirt than if he waited till he was dressed. This did not surprise him, for he was beginning to realise that he was the creature of a God who appreciated the discomfort of his worshippers.

Then he washed. There were two baths for the fifty boarders, and each boy had a bath once a week. The rest of his washing was done in a small basin on a wash-stand, which, with the bed and a chair, made up the furniture of each cubicle. The boys chatted gaily while they dressed. Philip was all ears. Then another bell sounded, and they ran downstairs. They took their seats on the forms on each side of the two long tables in the school-room; and Mr. Watson, followed by his wife and the servants, came in and sat down. Mr. Watson read prayers in an impressive manner, and the supplications thundered out in his loud voice as though they were threats personally addressed to each boy. Philip listened with anxiety. Then Mr. Watson read a chapter from the Bible, and the servants trooped out. In a moment the untidy youth brought in two large pots of tea and on a second journey immense dishes of bread and butter.

Philip had a squeamish appetite, and the thick slabs of poor butter on the bread turned his stomach, but he saw other boys scraping it off and followed their example. They all had potted meats and such like, which they had brought in their play-boxes; and some had 'extras,' eggs or bacon, upon which Mr. Watson made a profit. When he had asked Mr. Carey whether Philip was to have these, Mr. Carey replied that he did not think boys should be spoilt. Mr. Watson quite agreed with him—he considered nothing was better than bread and butter for growing lads—but some parents, unduly pampering their off-spring, insisted on it.

Philip noticed that 'extras' gave boys a certain consideration, and made up his mind, when he wrote to Aunt Louisa, to ask for them.

After breakfast the boys wandered out into the playground. Here the day-boys were gradually assembling. They were sons of the local clergy, of the officers at the Depot, and of such manufacturers or men of business as the old town possessed. Presently a bell rang, and they all trooped into school. This consisted of a large, long room at opposite ends of which two under-masters conducted the second and third forms, and of a smaller one, leading out of it, used by Mr. Watson, who taught the first form. To attach the preparatory to the senior school these three classes were known officially, on speech days and in reports, as upper, middle, and lower second. Philip was put in the last. The master, a red-faced man with a pleasant voice, was called Rice; he had a jolly manner with boys, and the time passed quickly. Philip was surprised when it was a quarter to

eleven and they were let out for ten minutes' rest.

The whole school rushed noisily into the playground. The new boys were told to go into the middle, while the others stationed themselves along opposite walls. They began to play *Pig in the Middle*. The old boys ran from wall to wall while the new boys tried to catch them: when one was seized and the mystic words said— one, two, three, and a pig for me—he became a prisoner and, turning sides, helped to catch those who were still free. Philip saw a boy running past and tried to catch him, but his limp gave him no chance; and the runners, taking their opportunity, made straight for the ground he covered. Then one of them had the brilliant idea of imitating Philip's clumsy run. Other boys saw it and began to laugh; then they all copied the first; and they ran round Philip, limping gro-tesquely, screaming in their treble voices with shrill laughter. They lost their heads with the delight of their new amusement, and choked with helpless merriment. One of them tripped Philip up and he fell, heavily as he always fell, and cut his knee. They laughed all the louder when he got up. A boy pushed him from be-hind, and he would have fallen again if another had not caught him. The game was forgotten in the entertain-ment of Philip's deformity. One of them invented an odd, rolling limp that struck the rest as supremely ridiculous, and several of the boys lay down on the ground and rolled about in laughter; Philip was completely scared. He could not make out why they were laughing at him. His heart beat so that he could hardly breathe, and he was more frightened than he had ever been in his life. He stood still stupidly while the boys ran round him, mimicking and laughing; they shouted to him to try and catch them; but he did not move. He did not want them to see him run any more. He was using all his strength to prevent himself from crying.

Suddenly the bell rang, and they all trooped back to school. Philip's knee was bleeding, and he was dusty and dishevelled. For some minutes Mr. Rice could not control his form. They were excited still by the strange novelty, and Philip saw one or two of them furtively looking down at his feet. He tucked them under the bench.

In the afternoon they went up to play football, but Mr. Watson stopped Philip on the way out after dinner.

'I suppose you can't play football, Carey?' he asked him.

Philip blushed self-consciously.

'No, sir.'

'Very well. You'd better go up to the field. You can walk as far as that, can't you?'

Philip had no idea where the field was, but he answered all the same.

'Yes, sir.'

The boys went in charge of Mr. Rice, who glanced at Philip and, seeing he had not changed, asked why he was not going to play.

'Mr. Watson said I needn't, sir,' said Philip.

'Why?'

There were boys all round him, looking at him curiously, and a feeling of shame came over Philip. He looked down without answering. Others gave the reply.

'He's got a club-foot, sir.'

'Oh, I see.'

Mr. Rice was quite young; he had only taken his degree a year before; and he was suddenly embarrassed. His instinct was to beg the boy's par-don, but he was too shy to do so. He made his voice gruff and loud.

'Now then, you boys, what are you waiting about for? Get on with you.'

Some of them had already started and those that were left now set off, in groups of two or three.

'You'd better come along with me, Carey,' said the master. 'You don't know the way, do you?'

Philip guessed the kindness, and a sob came to his throat.

'I can't go very fast, sir.'

'Then I'll go very slow,' said the master, with a smile.

Philip's heart went out to the red-faced, commonplace young man who said a gentle word to him. He suddenly felt less unhappy.

But at night when they went up to bed and were undressing, the boy who was called Singer came out of his cubicle and put his head in Philip's.

'I say, let's look at your foot,' he said.

'No,' answered Philip.

He jumped into bed quickly.

'Don't say no to me,' said Singer. 'Come on, Mason.'

The boy in the next cubicle was looking round the corner, and at the words he slipped in. They made for Philip and tried to tear the bed-clothes off him, but he held them tightly.

'Why can't you leave me alone?' he cried.

Singer seized a brush and with the back of it beat Philip's hands clenched on the blanket. Philip cried out.

'Why don't you show us your foot quietly?'

'I won't.'

In desperation Philip clenched his fist and hit the boy who tormented him, but he was at a disadvantage, and the boy seized his arm. He began to turn it.

'Oh, don't, don't,' said Philip. 'You'll break my arm.'

'Stop still then and put out your foot.

Philip gave a sob and a gasp. The boy gave the arm another wrench. The pain was unendurable.

'All right. I'll do it,' said Philip.

He put out his foot. Singer still kept his hand on Philip's wrist. He looked curiously at the deformity.

'Isn't it beastly?' said Mason.

Another came in and looked too.

'Ugh,' he said, in disgust.

'My word, it is rum,' said Singer, making a face. 'Is it hard?'

He touched it with the tip of his forefinger, cautiously, as though it were something that had a life of its own. Suddenly they heard Mr. Watson's heavy tread on the stairs. They threw the clothes back on Philip and dashed like rabbits into their cubicles. Mr. Watson came into the dormitory. Raising himself on tiptoe he could see over the rod that bore the green curtain, and he looked into two or three of the cubicles. The little boys were safely in bed. He put out the light and went out.

Singer called out to Philip, but he did not answer. He had got his teeth in the pillow so that his sobbing should be inaudible. He was not crying for the pain they had caused him, nor for the humiliation he had suffered when they looked at his foot, but with rage at himself, because, unable to stand the torture, he had put out his foot of his own accord.

And then he felt the misery of his life. It seemed to his childish mind that this unhappiness must go on for ever. For no particular reason he remembered that cold morning when Emma had taken him out of bed and put him beside his mother. He had not thought of it once since it hap- pened, but now he seemed to feel the warmth of his mother's body against his and her arms around him. Sud- denly it seemed to him that his life was a dream, his mother's death, and the life at the vicarage, and these two wretched days at school, and he would awake in the morning and be back again at home. His tears dried as he thought of it. He was too unhappy, it must be nothing but a dream, and his mother was alive, and Emma would come up presently and go to bed. He fell asleep.

But when he awoke next morning it was to the clanging of a bell, and the first thing his eyes saw was the green curtain of his cubicle.

*　　*　　*

As time went on Philip's deformity ceased to interest. It was accepted like one boy's red hair and another's un- reasonable corpulence. But mean- while he had grown horribly sensitive. He never ran if he could help it, be- cause he knew it made his limp more conspicuous, and he adopted a pecul- iar walk. He stood still as much as he could, with his club-foot behind the other, so that it should not at- tract notice, and he was constantly on the lookout for any reference to it. Because he could not join in the games which other boys played, their life remained strange to him; he only interested himself from the outside in their doings; and it seemed to him that there was a barrier between them and him. Sometimes they seemed to think that it was his fault if he could not play football, and he was unable to make them understand. He was left a good deal to himself. He had been inclined to talkativeness, but gradually he became silent. He began to think of the difference between himself and others.

The biggest boy in his dormitory, Singer, took a dislike to him, and Philip, small for his age, had to put up with a good deal of hard treatment. About half-way through the term a mania ran through the school for a game called Nibs. It was a game for two, played on a table or a form with steel pens. You had to push your nib with the fingernail so as to get the point of it over your opponent's, while he manoeuvred to prevent this and to get the point of his nib over the back of yours; when this result was achieved you breathed on the ball of your thumb, pressed it hard on the two nibs, and if you were able then to lift them without dropping either, both nibs became yours. Soon nothing was seen but boys playing this game, and the more skilful acquired vast stores of nibs. But in a little while Mr. Watson made up his mind that it was a form of gambling, forbade the game, and confiscated all the nibs in the boys' possession. Philip had been very adroit, and it was with a heavy heart that he gave up his winnings; but his fingers itched to play still, and a few days later, on his way to the football field, he went into a shop and bought a pennyworth of J pens. He carried them loose in his pocket and enjoyed feeling them. Presently Singer found out that he had them. Singer had given up his nibs too, but he had kept back a very large one, called a Jumbo, which was almost unconquerable, and he could not resist the opportunity of getting Philip's Js out of him. Though Philip knew that he was at a disadvantage with his small nibs, he had an adventurous disposition and was willing to take the risk; besides he was aware that Singer would not allow him to refuse. He had not played for a week and sat down to the game now with a thrill of excitement. He lost two of his small nibs quickly, and Singer was jubilant, but the third time by some chance the Jumbo slipped round and Philip was able to push his J across. He crowed with triumph. At that moment Mr. Watson came in.

'What are you doing?' he asked.

He looked from Singer to Philip, but neither answered.

'Don't you know that I've forbidden you to play that idiotic game?'

Philip's heart beat fast. He knew what was coming and was dreadfully frightened, but in his fright there was a certain exultation. He had never been swished. Of course it would hurt, but it was something to boast about afterwards.

'Come into my study.'

The headmaster turned, and they followed him side by side. Singer whispered to Philip:

'We're in for it.'

Mr. Watson pointed to Singer.

'Bend over,' he said.

Philip, very white, saw the boy quiver at each stroke, and after the third he heard him cry out. Three more followed.

'That'll do. Get up.'

Singer stood up. The tears were streaming down his face. Philip stepped forward. Mr. Watson looked at him for a moment.

'I'm not going to cane you. You're a new boy. And I can't hit a cripple. Go away, both of you, and don't be naughty again.

When they got back into the schoolroom a group of boys, who had learned in some mysterious way what was happening, were waiting for them. They set upon Singer at once with eager questions. Singer faced them, his face red with the pain and the marks of tears still on his cheeks. He pointed with his head at Philip, who was standing a little behind him.

'He got off because he's a cripple,' he said angrily.

Philip stood silent and flushed. He felt that they looked at him with contempt.

'How many did you get?' one boy asked Singer.

But he did not answer. He was angry because he had been hurt.

'Don't ask me to play Nibs with you again,' he said to Philip. 'It's jolly nice for you. You don't risk anything.'

'I didn't ask you.'

'Didn't you!'

He quickly put out his foot and tripped Philip up. Philip was always rather unsteady on his feet, and he fell heavily to the ground.

'Cripple,' said Singer.

For the rest of the term he tormented Philip cruelly, and, though Philip tried to keep out of his way, the school was so small that it was impossible; he tried being friendly and jolly with him; he abased himself so far as to buy him a knife; but though Singer took the knife he was not placated. Once or twice, driven beyond endurance, he hit and kicked the bigger boy, but Singer was so much stronger that Philip was helpless, and he was always forced after more or less torture to beg his pardon. It was that which rankled with Philip: he could not bear the humiliation of apologies, which were wrung from him by pain greater than he could bear. And what made it worse was that there seemed to be no end to his wretchedness; Singer was only eleven and would not go to the upper school till he was thirteen. Philip realized that he must live two years with a tormentor from whom there was no escape. He was only happy while he was working and when he got into bed. And often there recurred to him then that queer feeling that his life with all its misery was nothing but a dream, and that he would awake in the morning in his own little bed in London.

❀

KING HENRY THE SIXTH

WILLIAM SHAKESPEARE

[The compensatory mechanisms which one may build into his character to make up for physical handicaps were well understood by Shakespeare, who has given us remarkable insight into the problem in the character of Richard III. In two passages, first in Henry the Sixth and again in Richard the Third, he has traced Richard's resolution to be a villain to his realization that his physical deformity will never permit him to play the coveted role of lover, that he is perforce a social outcast and can assert his personality only through attaining ruthless power over the lives of others.]

GLOUCESTER. Thy son I kill'd for his presumption.

KING HENRY. Hadst thou been kill'd, when first thou didst presume,
Thou hadst not liv'd to kill a son of mine.
And thus I prophesy: that many a thousand,
Which now mistrust no parcel of my fear,
And many an old man's sigh, and many a widow's,
And many an orphan's water-standing eye,
Men for their sons', wives for their husbands'
And orphans for their parents' timeless death,
Shall rue the hour that ever thou wast born.
The owl shriek'd at thy birth, an evil sign;
The night-crow cried, aboding luckless time;
Dogs howl'd, and hideous tempest shook down trees!
The raven rook'd her on the chimney's top,
And chattering pies in dismal discords sung.
Thy mother felt more than a mother's pain,
And yet brought forth less than a mother's hope;
To wit, an indigest deformed lump,
Not like the fruit of such a goodly tree.
Teeth hadst thou in thy head when thou wast born,
To signify thou camest to bite the world:
And, if the rest be true which I have heard,
Thou camest—

GLOUCESTER. I'll hear no more: die, prophet, in thy speech: (Stabs him.
For this, amongst the rest, was I ordain'd.

KING HENRY. Ay, and for much more slaughter after this.
O, God forgive my sins, and pardon thee!
(Dies.

GLOUCESTER. What! will the aspiring blood of Lancaster
Sink in the ground? I thought it would have mounted.
See how my sword weeps for the poor king's death!
O! may such purple tears be always shed
From those that wish the downfall of our house.
If any spark of life be yet remaining,
Down, down to hell; and say I sent thee thither, (Stabs him again.
I, that have neither pity, love, nor fear.
Indeed, 'tis true, that Henry told me of;
For I have often heard my mother say
I came ino the world with my legs forward.
Had I not reason, think ye, to make haste,
And seek their ruin that usurp'd our right?
The midwife wonder'd, and the women cried,
'O! Jesus bless us, he is born with teeth.'
And so I was; which plainly signified
That I should snarl and bite and play the dog.
Then, since the heavens have shap'd my body so,
Let hell make crook'd my mind to answer it.
I have no brother, I am like no brother;
And this word 'love,' which greybeards call divine,
Be resident in men like one another
And not in me; I am myself alone.
Clarence, beware; thou keep'st me from the light:
But I will sort a pitchy day for thee;
For I will buzz abroad such prophecies
That Edward shall be fearful of his life;
And then, to purge his fear, I'll be thy death.
King Henry and the prince his son are gone:
Clarence, thy turn is next, and then the rest,
Counting myself but bad till I be best.
I'll throw thy body in another room,
And triumph, Henry, in thy day of doom.
(Exit, with the body.

❉

KING RICHARD THE THIRD

William Shakespeare

GLOUCESTER. Now is the winter of our discontent
Made glorious summer by this sun of York;
And all the clouds that lour'd upon our house
In the deep bosom of the ocean buried.
Now are our brows bound with victorious wreaths;
Our bruised arms hung up for monuments;
Our stern alarums changed to merry meetings;
Our dreadful marches to delightful measures.
Grim-visag'd war hath smooth'd his wrinkled front;
And now,—instead of mounting barbed steeds,
To fright the souls of fearful adversaries,—
He capers nimbly in a lady's chamber
To the lascivious pleasing of a lute.
But I, that am not shap'd for sportive tricks,
Nor made to court an amorous looking-glass;
I, that am rudely stamp'd, and want love's majesty
To strut before a wanton ambling nymph;
I, that am curtail'd of this fair proportion,
Cheated of feature by dissembling nature,
Deform'd, unfinish'd, sent before my time
Into this breathing world, scarce half made up,
And that so lamely and unfashionable
That dogs bark at me, as I halt by them;
Why, I, in this weak piping time of peace,
Have no delight to pass away the time,
Unless to see my shadow in the sun
And descant on mine own deformity:
And therefore, since I cannot prove a lover,
To entertain these fair well-spoken days,
I am determined to prove a villain,
And hate the idle pleasures of these days.
Plots have I laid, inductions dangerous,
By drunken prophecies, libels, and dreams,
To set my brother Clarence and the king
In deadly hate the one against the other;
And if King Edward be as true and just
As I am subtle, false, and treacherous,
This day should Clarence closely be mew'd up,
About a prophecy, which says, that G
Of Edward's heirs the murderer shall be.
Dive, thoughts, down to my soul: here Clarence comes.

❉

AND MAN

William Saroyan

[Most of us are fortunate in having no serious physical handicaps that set us apart from the group. And yet everyone is aware of physical growth and change. From childhood to youth, maturity, and age, these changes condition our emotional experiences and the attitudes of others toward us. The growth

From *Young Man on the Flying Trapeze and Other Stories* by William Saroyan. Reprinted by permission of Random House, Inc.

of a boy in adolescence, the relation between the physical changes that are taking place in him and his emotional awareness of himself and his world are presented in Saroyan's story. Especially significant is the boy's feeling of shame over his large ugly nose and his compensatory wishful thinking in which the girl he admires sees not the ugly features but the splendid image of himself his imagination has created.]

One morning, when I was fifteen, I got up before daybreak, because all night I hadn't been able to sleep, tossing in bed with the thought of the earth and the strangeness of being alive, suddenly feeling myself a part of it, definitely, solidly. Merely to be standing again, I had thought all night. Merely to be in the light again, standing, breathing, being alive. I left my bed quietly in the darkness of early morning and put on my clothes, a blue cotton shirt, a pair of corduroy pants, stockings and shoes. It was November and it was beginning to turn cold, but I did not wish to put on more clothes. I felt warm enough. I felt almost feverish, and with more clothes I knew it would not happen. Something was going to happen, and I felt that if I put on too much clothes it would dwindle away and all that I would have would be the remembrance of something expected, then lost.

All through the sleeplessness of the night I could feel turning in me, like a multitude of small and large wheels, some swift and wordless thought, on the verge of articulation, some vast remembrance out of time, a fresh fullness, a new solidity, a more graceful rhythm of motion emerging from the hurried growth that had taken place in me during the summer.

With the beginning of spring that year came the faint and fragmentary beginning of this thought, burning in my mind with the sound of fire eating substance, sweeping through my blood with the impatience and impetuosity of a deluge. Before the beginning of this thought I had been nothing more than a small and sullen boy, moving through the moments of my life with anger and fear and bitterness and doubt, wanting desperately to know the meaning and never quite being able to do so. But now in November I was as large physically as a man, larger, for that matter, than most men. It was as if I had leaped suddenly from the form of myself as a boy to the vaster form of myself as a man, and to the vaster meaning of myself as something specific and alive. Look at him, my relatives were saying, every part of his body growing, especially his nose. And they made sly jokes about my private organs, driving me out of my head with shame. How about it? they asked, even the ladies. Is it growing? Do you dream of big women, hundreds of them?

I don't know what you're talking about, I used to say. But I did know. Only I was ashamed. Look at that nose, they used to say. Just look at that enormous nose on his face.

During the summer I sometimes stopped suddenly before a mirror to look at myself, and after a moment I would turn away, feeling disgusted with my ugliness, worrying about it. I couldn't understand how it was that I looked utterly unlike what I imagined myself to be. In my mind I had another face, a finer, a more subtle and dignified expression, but in the mirror I could see the real reflection of myself, and I could see that it was ugly, thick, bony, and coarse. I thought it was something finer, I used to say to myself. I hadn't bothered before about looking at myself. I had thought that I knew precisely how I looked, and the truth distressed me, making me ashamed. Afterwards I stopped caring. I am ugly, I said. I know I am ugly. But it is only my face.

And I could believe that my face was not the whole of it. It was simply a part of myself that was growing with the rest, an outward part, and therefore not as important as the inward part. The real growth was going on inside, not simply within the boundaries of my physical form, but outward through the mind and through the imagination to the real largeness of being, the limitless largeness of consciousness, of knowing and feeling and remembering.

I began to forget the ugliness of my face, turning again to the simplicity and kindliness of the face I believed to be my own, the face of myself in the secrecy of my heart, in the night light of sleep, in the truth of thought.

It is true that my face seems ugly, I said, but it is also true that it is not ugly. I know it is not, because I have seen it with my own eyes and shaped it with my own thought, and my vision has been clear and my thought has been clean. I cannot be ugly.

But how was anyone to understand the real truth, how was anyone to see the face that I saw, and know that it was the real reflection of my being? This worried me a lot. There was a girl in my class at high school whom I worshipped, and I wanted this girl to see that my face, the face she saw, was not the truthful one, that it was merely a part of the growth that was

going on. And I wanted her to be able to see with me the truthful face, because I felt that if she did see it, she would understand my love for her, and she would love me.

All through the night I had tossed with the thought of myself somehow alive on the earth, somehow specific and at the same time a substance that was changing and would always change, from moment to moment, imperceptibly, myself entering one moment thus, and emerging thus, over and over again. I wanted to know what it was in me that was static and permanent and endurable, what it was that belonged not to myself alone but to the body of man, to his legend, to the truth of his motion over the earth, moment after moment, century after century. All through the night it seemed that I would soon learn, and in the morning I left my bed, standing in the darkness and the stillness, feeling the splendor of having form and weight and motion, having, I hoped, meaning.

I walked quietly through the darkness of the house and emerged, standing for a moment in the street, acknowledging the magnificence of our earth, the large beauty of limitless space about our insignificant forms, the remoteness of the great celestial bodies of our universe, our oceans, our mountains, our valleys, the great cities we had made, the strong and clean and fearless things we had done. The small boats we had made and sent over the wild waters, the slow growth of railroads, the slow accumulation of knowledge, the slow but everlasting seeking after God, in the vastness of the universe, in the solidity of our own earth, in the glory of our own small beings, the simplicity of our own hearts.

Merely to be standing, merely to be

breathing that day was a truth in the nature of an inexplicable miracle. After all these years, I thought . . . I myself standing here in the darkness, breathing, knowing that I live. I wanted to say something in language, with the words I had been taught in school, something solemn and dignified and joyous . . . to express the gratitude I felt to God. But it was impossible. There were no words with which to say it. I could feel the magnificence coming through the cold clean air, touching my blood, racing through it, dancing, but there were no words with which to say it.

There was a fire hydrant in our street, and I had always wanted to hurdle it, but I had always been afraid to try. It was made of metal and I was made of flesh and blood and bone, and if I did not clear the fire hydrant, leaping swiftly, my flesh would smash against it, paining me, perhaps breaking a bone in one of my legs.

Suddenly I was leaping over the hydrant, and, clearing it, I was thinking, I can do it now. I can do anything now.

I hurdled the fire hydrant six or seven times, leaping away over it, hearing myself landing solidly on the earth, feeling tremendous.

Then I began to walk, not slowly, not casually, but vigorously, leaping now and then because I couldn't help it. Each time I came to a tree, I leaped and caught a limb, making it bend with my weight, pulling myself up and letting myself down. I walked into the town, into the streets where we had put up our buildings, and suddenly I saw them for this first time, suddenly I was really *seeing* them, and they were splendid. The city was almost deserted, and I seemed to be alone in it, seeing it as it really was, in all its fineness, with all its mean-

ing, giving it its real truth, like the truth of my hidden face, the inward splendor. The winter sun came up while I walked and its light fell over the city, making a cool warmth. I touched the buildings, feeling them with the palms of my hands, feeling the meaning of the solidity and the precision. I touched the plate-glass windows, the brick, the wood and the cement.

When I got home, everyone was awake, at the breakfast table. Where have you been? they asked. Why did you get up so early?

I sat in my chair at the table, feeling great hunger. Shall I tell them? I thought. Shall I try to tell them what is happening? Will they understand? Or will they laugh at me?

Suddenly I knew that I was a stranger among them, my own people, and I knew that while I loved them, I could not go out to them, revealing the truth of my being. Each of us is alone, I thought. Each is a stranger to the other. My mother thinks of me as a pain she once suffered, a babe at her breast, a small child in the house, a boy walking to school, and now a young man with an ugly face, a restless and half-mad fellow who moves about strangely.

We ate mush in those days. It was cheap and we were poor, and the mush filled a lot of space. We used to buy it in bulk, by the pound, and we had it for breakfast every morning. There was a big bowl of it before me, about a pound and a half of it, steaming, and I began to swallow the food, feeling it sinking to my hunger, entering my blood, becoming myself and the change that was going on in me.

No, I thought. I cannot tell them. I cannot tell anyone. Everyone must see for himself. Everyone must seek the truth for himself. It is here, and each man must seek it for himself. But the girl, I thought. I should be able to tell her. She was of me. I had taken her name, her form, the outward one and the inward one, and I had breathed her into me, joining her meaning to my meaning, and she was of my thought, of my motion in walking over the earth, and of my sleep. I would tell her. After I had revealed my hidden face to her, I would speak to the girl about ourselves, about our being alive together, on the same earth, in the same moment of eternity. I had never spoken to the girl. I had loved her secretly, worshipping her, worshipping the very things she touched, her books, her desk, the earth over which she moved, the air about her, but I had never had the courage to speak to her. I wanted my speaking to mean so much, to be so important to each of us, that I was afraid even to think of breaking the silence between us.

I went for a little walk, I replied.

Everyone began to laugh at me, even my mother. What's the matter with you? they asked. Why can't you sleep? Are you in love again? Is that it? Are you dreaming of some girl?

I sat at the table, swallowing the hot food, hearing them laughing at me. I cannot tell them, I thought. They are laughing at me. They think it is something to laugh about. They think it is a little joke.

I began to blush, thinking of the girl and worrying about something to say that would satisfy and silence them, stopping their laughter. Then they began to laugh louder than ever, and I couldn't help it, I began to laugh too.

Yes, they laughed. It must be some girl. Look how handsome he is getting to be. Dreaming about a girl always does that.

I ate all the mush in the bowl and got up from the table. If I try to tell them the truth, I thought, they will laugh more than ever.

I'm going to school, I said, and I left the house. But I knew that I would not go to school that day. I had decided not to go in the middle of the night, when I was unable to sleep. In school, in that atmosphere, it would never happen. I would never be able to understand what it was that turned in me, circling toward truth, and it would be lost, maybe forever. I decided to walk into the country, and be alone with the thought, helping it to emerge from the bewilderment and confusion of my mind, and the fever of my blood, carrying it to silence and simplicity, giving it a chance to reach its fullness and be whole.

Walking through the country, moving quietly among the leafless grape vines and fig trees, the thought became whole, and I knew the truth about myself and man and the earth and God.

At the proper hour I returned home, as if I were coming home from school, and the following day I went to school. I knew I would be asked for an excuse and an explanation for my absence, and I knew that I would not lie about it. I could tell them that I had been at home, sick with a cold, but I didn't want to do it. There would be a punishment, but I didn't care about that. Let them punish me if they liked. Let old man Brunton give me a strapping. I had walked into the country, into the silence, and I had found the truth. It was more than anything they would ever be able to teach. It was something that wasn't in any of their books. Let them punish me. I wanted also to impress the girl. I wanted her to understand that I had strength, that I could tell the truth and be punished for it, that I would not make up a cheap lie just to get out of a strapping. My telling the truth ought to mean something to her, I thought. Being so much a part of myself, she would be able to see beneath the surface and understand what I had done, and why.

After the roll was taken, my name was called and our teacher said: You were not at school yesterday. Have you brought an excuse?

No, I said, I have not.

Suddenly I felt myself to be the object of the laughter of everyone in the class-room, and I could imagine everyone thinking: What a stupid fellow! I looked at this girl whom I loved so much and I saw that she too was laughing, but I would not believe it. This sometimes happens. It happens when a man has given another person his own dignity and meaning, and the other person has not acquired that dignity and meaning. I saw and heard the girl laughing at me, but I would not believe it. I hadn't intended to entertain her. I hadn't intended to entertain anyone, and the laughter made me angry.

Why were you away from school? said the teacher. Where were you?

I was in the country, I said, walking.

Now the laughter was greater than ever, and I saw the girl I secretly loved laughing with the others, as if I meant nothing to her, as if I hadn't made her a part of myself. I began to feel ill and defiant, and there was warm perspiration on the palms of my hands.

The teacher stood over me, trembling. One must, perhaps, be a teacher to be able to appreciate precisely how angry she felt. For years she had been asking boys why they had been ab-

sent from school, and for years the boys had replied that they had been at home, ill. She had known that in most cases they had not told the truth, but the tradition had been maintained and everything had remained solid in her world. Now everything was being shattered, and she was standing over me, trembling with rage. I think she tried to shake me, and I would not let her do it, holding myself solidly. For a moment she budged at me, hating me, and then she said, You Armenians, you, you . . . and I thought she would burst into tears. I felt sorry for her, for the stupidity she had preserved in herself after so many years of trying to teach school, a woman almost fifty years of age.

And I hadn't meant to hurt her. That hadn't been my object at all. I had meant simply to tell the truth. I had meant to reveal to the girl my true face, the face which had been shaped by the dignity and simplicity of man and which she had helped to shape, and I had meant to reveal to her the truth of my presence on earth. And then her laughter, just like the laughter of the others . . . it mangled something in me, and I stood in the midst of the noise, embarrassed and bewildered, bleeding, and breaking to pieces. God damn it, I thought. This is not true. God damn it, this is a lie.

But I knew that I was deceiving myself. And I knew that I would never be able to speak to the girl about my love for her, and the meaning of that love to me, and to the earth and the universe, and to man.

I was sent to the principal of the school, and he stood over me, grumbling in a deep voice. You, he said, you are a disgrace to this school. You are a disgrace to your own race. You break rules. Then you come to school flaunting your crime. What have you to say for yourself.

Nothing, I said.

Why did you do it? he asked

I wanted to walk, I said.

You could have waited till Saturday, he said.

No, I said. I had to walk yesterday.

Can you think of any reason why I shouldn't strap you? he asked.

That's up to you, I said.

I was angry. I felt bitter about the girl, and I wasn't afraid of the principal, or of the strapping I knew he would give me. It was all over. I would have to walk alone with the secret. I would have to accept the sickness in me that the girl had made by laughing, but the truth would remain whole and I would have it to keep forever, walking alone, in the secrecy of my heart.

The strapping made me cry, big as I was, strong as I was. While I cried, though, I knew that it wasn't the strapping that was hurting me . . . it was this other thing, this incredible blindness everywhere. I cried bitterly, and when I returned to class my eyes were red and I was ashamed, and the whole class was laughing at me, even the girl.

After school, walking alone, I tried to heal the wound in my heart, and I began to think again of the swift and bright truth of being, the truth I had earned for myself by walking alone through the silence of the earth, and walking, thinking of it, I could feel myself becoming whole again, and I could hear myself laugh-ing through the vastness of the secret space I had discovered.

The truth was the secret, God first, the word, the word God, out of all things and beyond, spaceless and timeless, then the void, the silent emptiness, vaster than any mortal mind could conceive, abstract and precise and real and lost, the sub-stance in the emptiness, again precise and with weight and solidity and form, fire and fluid, and then, walk-ing through the vineyards, I had seen it thus, the whole universe, quietly there in the mind of man, motion-less and dark and lost, waiting for man, for the thought of man, and I felt the stirring of inanimate sub-stance in the earth, and in myself like the swift growth of the summer, life emerging from time, the germ of man springing from the rock and the fire and the fluid to the face of man, and to the form, to the motion and the thought, suddenly in the emptiness, the thought of man, stirring there. And I was man, and this was the truth I had brought out of the emptiness, walking alone through the vineyards.

I had seen the universe, quietly in the emptiness, secret, and I had re-vealed it to itself, giving it meaning and grace and the truth that could come only from the thought and energy of man, and the truth was man, myself, moment after moment, and man, century after century, and man, and the face of God in man, and the sound of the laughter of man in the vastness of the secret, and the sound of his weeping in the darkness of it, and the truth was myself and I was man.

LOOK HOMEWARD, ANGEL
Thomas Wolfe

[The relation between a child's world of sense experience and his emotional development is traced in *Look Homeward, Angel* through successive phases in the growth of Eugene Gant. Especially interesting here is the illustration of Adler's theory of the child's feeling of inferiority in the presence of adults on whom he is physically dependent. The acute perceptual faculties for which Thomas Wolfe is noted are apparent in the overpowering sense impressions of the boy Eugene. The intense sensuous life of his early childhood becomes fused with his imaginative life in the realm of books as the eight-year-old identifies himself with various romantic heroes. The images from his reading in turn stimulate Eugene's emotions. His sexual impulses are given expression alternately in the boyish obscenities for which he is punished and the extravagant fantasies in which he imagines himself the lover of his teacher.]

Such was the state of history when Eugene entered the theatre of human events in 1900.

We would give willingly some more extended account of the world his life touched during the first few years, showing, in all its perspectives and implications, the meaning of life as seen from the floor, or from the crib, but these impressions are suppressed when they might be told, not through any fault of intelligence, but through lack of muscular control, the powers of articulation, and because of the recurring waves of loneliness, weariness, depression, aberration, and utter blankness which war against the order in a man's mind until he is three or four years old.

Lying darkly in his crib, washed, powdered, and fed, he thought quietly of many things before he dropped off to sleep—the interminable sleep that obliterated time for him, and that gave him a sense of having missed forever a day of sparkling life. At these moments, he was heartsick with weary horror as he thought of the discomfort, weakness, dumbness, the infinite misunderstanding he would have to endure before he gained even physical freedom. He grew sick as he thought of the weary distance before him, the lack of co-ordination of the centres of control, the undisciplined and rowdy bladder, the helpless exhibition he was forced to give in the company of his sniggering, pawing brothers and sisters, dried, cleaned, revolved before them.

He was in agony because he was poverty-stricken in symbols: his mind was caught in a net because he had no words to work with. He had not even names for the objects around him: he probably defined them for himself by some jargon, reinforced by some mangling of the speech that roared about him, to which he listened intently day after day, realizing that his first escape must come through language. He indicated as

From *Look Homeward, Angel* by Thomas Wolfe. Reprinted by permission of Charles Scribner's Sons.

quickly as he could his ravenous hunger for pictures and print: sometimes they brought him great books profusely illustrated, and he bribed them desperately by cooing, shrieking with delight, making extravagant faces, and doing all the other things they understood in him. He wondered savagely how they would feel if they knew what he really thought: at other times he had to laugh at them and at their whole preposterous comedy of errors as they pranced around for his amusement, waggled their heads at him, tickled him roughly, making him squeal violently against his will. The situation was at once profoundly annoying and comic: as he sat in the middle of the floor and watched them enter, seeing the face of each transformed by a foolish leer, and hearing their voices become absurd and sentimental whenever they addressed him, speaking to him words which he did not yet understand, but which he saw they were mangling in the preposterous hope of rendering intelligible that which has been previously mutilated, he had to laugh at the fools, in spite of his vexation.

And left alone to sleep within a shuttered room, with the thick sunlight printed in bars upon the floor, unfathomable loneliness and sadness crept through him: he saw his life down the solemn vista of a forest aisle, and he knew he would always be the sad one: caged in that little round of skull, imprisoned in that beating and most secret heart, his life must always walk down lonely passages. Lost. He understood that men were forever strangers to one another, that no one ever comes really to know any one, that imprisoned in the dark womb of our mother, we come to life without having seen her face, that we are given to her arms a stranger, and

that, caught in that insoluble prison of being, we escape it never, no matter what arms may clasp us, what mouth may kiss us, what heart may warm us. Never, never, never, never, never.

He saw that the great figures that came and went about him, the huge leering heads that bent hideously into his crib, the great voices that rolled incoherently above him, had for one another not much greater understanding than they had for him: that even their speech, their entire fluidity and ease of movement were but meagre communicants of their thought or feeling, and served often not to promote understanding, but to deepen and widen strife, bitterness, and prejudice.

His brain went black with terror. He saw himself an inarticulate stranger, an amusing little clown, to be dandled and nursed by these enormous and remote figures. He had been sent from one mystery into another: somewhere within or without his consciousness he heard a great bell ringing faintly, as if it sounded undersea, and as he listened, the ghost of memory walked through his mind, and for a moment he felt that he had almost recovered what he had lost.

Sometimes, pulling himself abreast the high walls of his crib, he glanced down dizzily at the patterns of the carpet far below; the world swam in and out of his mind like a tide, now printing its whole sharp picture for an instant, again ebbing out dimly and sleepily, while he pieced the puzzle of sensation together bit by bit, seeing only the dancing fire-sheen on the poker, hearing then the elfin clucking of the sun-warm hens, somewhere beyond in a distant and enchanted world. Again, he heard their morning-wakeful crowing clear and loud, suddenly becoming a substantial and alert citizen of life; or, going and coming in alternate waves of fantasy and fact, he heard the loud, faery thunder of Daisy's parlor music. Years later, he heard it again, a door opened in his brain: she told him it was Paderewski's 'Minuet.'

His crib was a great woven basket, well mattressed and pillowed within; as he grew stronger, he was able to perform extraordinary acrobatics in it, tumbling, making a hoop of his body, and drawing himself easily and strongly erect: with patient effort he could worm over the side on to the floor. There, he would crawl on the vast design of the carpet, his eyes intent upon great wooden blocks piled chaotically on the floor. They had belonged to his brother Luke: all the letters of the alphabet, in bright multi-colored carving, were engraved upon them.

Holding them clumsily in his tiny hands, he studied for hours the symbols of speech, knowing that he had here the stones of the temple of language, and striving desperately to find the key that would draw order and intelligence from this anarchy. Great voices soared far above him, vast shapes came and went, lifting him to dizzy heights, depositing him with exhaustless strength. The bell rang under the sea.

One day when the opulent Southern Spring had richly unfolded, when the spongy black earth of the yard was covered with sudden, tender grass, and wet blossoms, the great cherry tree seethed slowly with a massive gem of amber sap, and the cherries hung ripening in prodigal clusters, Gant took him from his basket in the sun on the high front porch, and went with him around the house by the lily beds, taking him back under

trees singing with hidden birds, to the far end of the lot.

Here the earth was unshaded, dry, clotted by the plough. Eugene knew by the stillness that it was Sunday: against the high wire fence there was the heavy smell of hot dock-weed. On the other side, Swain's cow was wrenching the cool coarse grass, lifting her head from time to time, and singing in her strong deep voice her Sunday exuberance. In the warm washed air, Eugene heard with absolute clearness all the brisk backyard sounds of the neighborhood, he became acutely aware of the whole scene, and as Swain's cow sang out again, he felt the flooded gates in him swing open. He answered 'Moo!' phrasing the sound timidly but perfectly, and repeating it confidently in a moment when the cow answered.

Gant's delight was boundless. He turned and raced back toward the house at the full stride of his legs. And as he went, he nuzzled his stiff mustache into Eugene's tender neck, mooing industriously and always getting an answer.

'Lord a' mercy!' cried Eliza, looking from the kitchen window as he raced down the yard with breakneck strides. 'He'll kill that child yet.'

And as he rushed up the kitchen steps—all the house, save the upper side was off the ground—she came out on the little latticed veranda, her hands floury, her nose stove-red.

'Why, what on earth are you doing, Mr. Gant?'

'Moo-o-o! He said "Moo-o-o!" Yes, he did!' Gant spoke to Eugene rather than to Eliza.

Eugene answered him immediately: he felt it was all rather silly, and he saw he would be kept busy imitating Swain's cow for several days, but he was tremendously excited, nevertheless, feeling now that the wall had been breached.

Eliza was likewise thrilled, but her way of showing it was to turn back to the stove, hiding her pleasure, and saying: 'I'll vow, Mr. Gant. I never saw such an idiot with a child.'

Later, Eugene lay wakefully in his basket on the sitting-room floor, watching the smoking dishes go by in the eager hands of the combined family, for Eliza at this time cooked magnificently, and a Sunday dinner was something to remember. For two hours since their return from church, the little boys had been prowling hungrily around the kitchen: Ben, frowning proudly, kept his dignity outside the screen, making excursions frequently through the house to watch the progress of cookery; Grover came in and watched with frank interest until he was driven out; Luke, his broad humorous little face split by a wide exultant smile, rushed through the house, squealing exultantly:

'Weenie, weedie, weeky,
Weenie, weedie, weeky,
Weenie, weedie, weeky,
Wee, Wee, Wee.'

He had heard Daisy and Josephine Brown doing Caesar together, and his chant was his own interpretation of Caesar's brief boast: 'Veni, Vidi, Vici.'

As Eugene lay in his crib, he heard through the open door the dining-room clatter, the shrill excitement of the boys, the clangor of steel and knife as Gant prepared to carve the roast, the repetition of the morning's great event told over and over without variation, but with increasing zest.

'Soon,' he thought, as the heavy food fragrance floated in to him, 'I shall be in there with them.' And he thought lusciously of mysterious and succulent food.

All through the afternoon upon the veranda Gant told the story, summoning the neighbors and calling upon Eugene to perform—Eugene heard clearly all that was said that day: he was not able to answer, but he saw now that speech was imminent.

Thus, later, he saw the first two years of his life in brilliant and isolated flashes. His second Christmas he remembered vaguely as a period of great festivity: it accustomed him to the third when it came. With the miraculous habitude children acquire, it seemed that he had known Christmas forever.

He was conscious of sunlight, rain, the leaping fire, his crib, the grim jail of winter: the second Spring, one warm day, he saw Daisy go off to school up the hill: it was the end of the noon recess, she had been home for lunch. She went to Miss Ford's School for Girls; it was a red brick residence on the corner at the top of the steep hill: he watched her join Eleanor Duncan just below. Her hair was braided in two long hanks down her back: she was demure, shy, maidenly, a timid and blushing girl; but he feared her attentions to him, for she bathed him furiously, wreaking whatever was explosive and violent beneath her placidity upon his hide. She really scrubbed him almost raw. He howled piteously. As she climbed the hill, he remembered her. He saw she was the same person . . .

Eugene was loose now in the limitless meadows of sensation: his sensory equipment was so complete that at the moment of perception of a single thing, the whole background of color, warmth, odor, sound, taste established itself, so that later, the breath of hot dandelion brought back the grass-warm banks of Spring, a day, a place, the rustling of young leaves, or the page of a book, the thin exotic smell of tangerine, the wintry bite of great apples; or, as with Gulliver's Travels, a bright windy day in March, the spurting moments of warmth, the drip and reek of the earth-thaw, the feel of the fire.

He had won his first release from the fences of home—he was not quite six, when, of his own insistence, he went to school. Eliza did not want him to go, but his only close companion, Max Isaacs, a year his senior, was going, and there was in his heart a constricting terror that he would be left alone again. She told him he could not go: she felt, somehow, that school began the slow, the final loosening of the cords that held them together, but as she saw him slide craftily out the gate one morning in September and run at top speed to the corner where the other little boy was waiting, she did nothing to bring him back. Something taut snapped in her: she remembered his furtive backward glance, and she wept. And she did not weep for herself, but for him: the hour after his birth she had looked in his dark eyes and had seen something that would brood there eternally, she knew, unfathomable wells of remote and intangible loneliness: she knew that in her dark and sorrowful womb a stranger had come to life, fed by the lost communications of eternity, his own ghost, haunter of his own house, lonely to himself and to the world. O lost.

Busy with the ache of their own growing-pains, his brothers and sisters had little time for him: he was almost six years younger than Luke, the youngest of them, but they exerted over him the occasional small cruel-ties, petty tormentings by elder children of a younger, interested and excited by the brief screaming insanity of his temper, when, goaded and taunted from some deep dream, he would seize a carving knife and pursue them, or batter his head against the walls.

They felt that he was 'queer'—the other boys preached the smug cowardice of the child-herd, defending themselves, when their persecutions were discovered, by saying they would make a 'real boy' of him. But ·there grew up in him a deep affection for Ben who stalked occasionally and softly through the house, guarding even then with scowling eyes, and surly speech, the secret life. Ben was a stranger: some deep instinct drew him to his child-brother, a portion of his small earnings as a paper carrier he spent in gifts and amusement for Eugene, admonishing him sullenly, cuffing him occasionally, but defending him before the others.

Gant, as he watched his brooding face set for hours before a fire-lit book of pictures, concluded that the boy liked books, more vaguely, that he would make a lawyer of him, send him into politics, see him elected to the governorship, the Senate, the presidency. And he unfolded to him time after time all the rude American legendry of the country boys who became great men because they were country boys, poor boys, and hard-working farm boys. But Eliza thought of him as a scholar, a learned man, a professor, and with that convenient after-thought that annoyed Gant so deeply, but by which she firmly convinced herself, she saw in this book-brooder the fruit of her own deliberate design.

'I read every moment I could get the chance the summer before he was born,' she said. And then, with a complacent and confidential smile which, Gant knew, always preceded some reference to her family, she said: 'I tell you what: it may all come out in the Third Generation.'

'The Third Generation be Goddamned!' answered Gant furiously.

'Now, I want to tell you,' she went on thoughtfully, speaking with her forefinger, 'folks have always said that his grandfather would have made a fine scholar if—'

'Merciful God!' said Gant, getting up suddenly and striding about the room with an ironical laugh. 'I might have known that it would come to this! You may be sure,' he exclaimed in high excitement, wetting his thumb briefly on his tongue, 'that if there's any credit to be given I won't get it. Not from you! You'd rather die than admit it! No, but I'll tell you what you will do! You'll brag about that miserable old freak who never did a hard day's work in his life.'

'Now, I wouldn't be so sure of that if I were you,' Eliza began, her lips working rapidly.

'Jesus God!' he cried, flinging about the room with his customary indifference to reasoned debate. 'Jesus God! What a travesty! A travesty on Nature! Hell hath no fury like a woman scorned!' he exclaimed, indefinitely but violently, and then as he strode about, he gave way to loud, bitter, forced laughter.

Thus, pent in his dark soul, Eugene sat brooding on a fire-lit book, a stranger in a noisy inn. The gates of his life were closing him in from their knowledge, a vast aerial world of phantasy was erecting its fuming and insubstantial fabric. He steeped his soul in streaming imagery, rifling the book-shelves for pictures and finding there such treasures as *With Stanley in Africa,* rich in the mystery of the jungle, alive with combat, black battle, the hurled spear, vast snake-rooted forests, thatched villages, gold and ivory; or Stoddard's Lectures, on whose slick heavy pages were stamped the most-visited scenes of Europe and Asia; a Book of Wonder, with enchanting drawings of all the marvels of the age—Santos Dumont in his balloon, liquid air poured from a kettle, all the navies of the earth lifted two feet from the water by an ounce of radium (Sir William Crookes), the building of the Eiffel Tower, the Flatiron Building, the stick-steered automobile, the submarine. After the earthquake in San Francisco there was a book describing it, its cheap green cover lurid with crumbling towers, shaken spires, toppling many-storied houses plunging into the splitting flame-jawed earth. And there was another called *Palaces of Sin,* or *The Devil in Society,* purporting to be the work of a pious millionaire, who had drained his vast fortune in exposing the painted sores that blemish the spotless-seeming hide of great position, and there were enticing pictures showing the author walking in a silk hat down a street full of magnificent palaces of sin.

Out of this strange jumbled gallery of pictures the pieced-out world was expanding under the brooding power of his imagination: the lost dark angels of the Doré "Milton" swooped into cavernous Hell beyond this upper earth of soaring or toppling spires, machine wonder, maced and mailed romance. And, as he thought of his future liberation into this epic world, where all the color of life blazed brightest far away from home, his heart flooded his face with lakes of blood.

He had heard already the ringing of remote church bells over a countryside on Sunday night; had listened to the earth steeped in the brooding symphony of dark, and the million-noted little night things; and he had heard thus the far retreating wail of a whistle in a distant valley, and faint thunder on the rails; and he felt the infinite depth and width of the golden world in the brief seductions of a thousand multiplex and mixed mysterious odors and sensations, weaving, with a blinding interplay and aural-explosions, one into the other.

He remembered yet the East India Tea House at the Fair, the sandalwood, the turbans, and the robes, the cool interior and the smell of India tea; and he had felt now the nostalgic thrill of dew-wet mornings in Spring, the cherry scent, the cool clarion earth, the wet loaminess of the garden, the pungent breakfast smells and the floating snow of blossoms. He knew the inchoate sharp excitement of hot dandelions in young Spring grass at noon; the smell of cellars, cobwebs, and built-on secret earth; in July, of watermelons bedded in sweet hay, inside a farmer's covered wagon; of cantaloupe and crated peaches; and the scent of orange rind, bitter-sweet, before a fire of coals. He knew the good male smell of his father's sitting-room; of the smooth worn leather sofa, with the gaping horse-hair rent; of the blistered varnished wood upon the hearth; of the heated calf-skin bindings; of the flat moist plug of apple tobacco, stuck with a red flag; of wood-smoke and burnt leaves in October; of the brown tired autumn earth; of honey-suckle at night; of warm nasturtiums; of a clean ruddy farmer who comes weekly with printed butter, eggs and milk; of fat limp underdone bacon and of cof-fee; of a bakery-oven in the wind; of large deep-hued string-beans smoking-hot and seasoned well with salt and butter; of a room of old pine boards in which books and carpets have been stored, long closed; of Concord grapes in their long white baskets.

Yes, and the exciting smell of chalk and varnished desks; the smell of heavy bread-sandwiches of cold fried meat and butter; the smell of new leather in a saddler's shop, or of a warm leather chair; of honey and of unground coffee; of barrelled sweet-pickles and cheese and all the fragrant compost of the grocer's; the smell of stored apples in the cellar, and of orchard-apple smells, of pressed-cider pulp; of pears ripening on a sunny shelf, and of ripe cherries stewing with sugar on hot stoves before preserving; the smell of whittled wood, of all young lumber, of sawdust and shavings; of peaches stuck with cloves and pickled in brandy; of pine-sap, and green pine-needles; of a horse's pared hoof; of chestnuts roasting, of bowls of nuts and raisins; of hot cracklin, and of young roast pork; of butter and cinnamon melting on hot candied yams.

Yes, and of the rank slow river, and of tomatoes rotten on the vine; the smell of rain-wet plums and boiling quinces; of rotten lily-pads; and of foul weeds rotting in green marsh scum; and the exquisite smell of the South, clean but funky, like a big woman; of soaking trees and the earth after heavy rain.

Yes, and the smell of hot daisy-fields in the morning; of melted puddling-iron in a foundry; the winter smell of horse-warm stables and smoking dung; of old oak and walnut; and the butcher's smell of meat, of strong slaughtered lamb, plump gouty liver, ground pasty sausages, and red beef; and of brown sugar melted with slivered bitter chocolate; and of crushed mint leaves, and of a wet lilac bush; of magnolia beneath the heavy moon, of dogwood and laurel; of an old caked pipe and Bourbon rye, aged in kegs of charred oak; the sharp smell of tobacco, of carbolic and nitric acids; the coarse true smell of a dog; of old imprisoned books; and the cool fern-smell near springs; of vanilla in cake-dough; and of cloven ponderous cheeses.

Yes, and of a hardware store, but mostly the good smell of nails; of the developing chemicals in a photographer's dark-room; and the young-life smell of paint and turpentine; of buckwheat batter and black sorghum; and of a negro and his horse, together; of boiling fudge; the brine smell of pickling vats; and the lush undergrowth smell of southern hills; of a slimy oyster-can, of chilled gutted fish; of a hot kitchen negress; of kerosene and linoleum; of sarsaparilla and guavas; and of ripe autumn persimmons; and the smell of the wind and the rain; and of the acrid thunder; of cold starlight, and the brittle-bladed frozen grass; of fog and the misted winter sun; of seed-time, bloom, and mellow dropping harvest.

And now, whetted intemperately by what he had felt, he began, at school, in that fecund romance, the geography, to breathe the mixed odors of the earth, sensing in every squat keg piled on a pier-head a treasure of golden rum, rich port, fat Burgundy; smelling the jungle growth of the tropics, the heavy odor of plantations, the salt-fish smell of harbors, voyaging in the vast, enchanting, but unperplexing world.

Now the innumerable archipelago had been threaded, and he stood, firm-planted, upon the unknown but waiting continent.

He learned to read almost at once, printing the shapes of words immediately with his strong visual memory; but it was weeks later before he learned to write, or even to copy, words. The ragged spume and wrack of fantasy and the lost world still floated from time to time through his clear schoolday morning brain, and although he followed accurately all the other instruction of his teacher, he was walled in his ancient unknowing world when they made letters. The children made their sprawling alphabets below a line of models, but all he accomplished was a line of jagged wavering spear-points on his sheet, which he repeated endlessly and rapturously, unable to see or understand the difference.

'I have learned to write,' he thought.

Then, one day, Max Isaacs looked suddenly, from his exercise, on Eugene's sheet, and saw the jagged line.

'That ain't writin',' said he.

And clubbing his pencil in his warted grimy hand, he scrawled a copy of the exercise across the page. The line of life, that beautiful developing structure of language that he saw flowing from his comrade's pencil, cut the knot in him that all instruction failed to do, and instantly he seized the pencil, and wrote the words in letters fairer and finer than his friend's. And he turned, with a cry in his throat, to the next page, and copied it without hesitation, and the next, the next. They looked at each other a moment with that clear wonder by which children accept miracles, and they never spoke of it again.

'That's writin' now,' said Max. But they kept the mystery caged between them.

Eugene thought of this event later; always he could feel the opening gates in him, the plunge of the tide, the escape; but it happened like this one day at once. Still midget-near the live pelt of the earth, he saw many things that he kept in fearful secret, knowing that revelation would be punished with ridicule. One Saturday in Spring, he stopped with Max Isaacs above a deep pit in Central Avenue where city workmen were patching a broken watermain. The clay walls of their pit were much higher than their heads; behind their huddled backs there was a wide fissure, a window in the earth which opened on some dark subterranean passage. And as the boys looked, they gripped each other suddenly, for past the fissure slid the flat head of an enormous serpent; passed, and was followed by a scaled body as thick as a man's: the monster slid endlessly on into the deep earth and vanished behind the working and unwitting men. Shaken with fear they went away, they talked about it then and later in hushed voices, but they never revealed it.

He fell now easily into the School-Ritual; he choked his breakfast with his brothers every morning, gulped scalding coffee, and rushed off at the ominous warning of the final bell, clutching a hot paper-bag of food, already spattered hungrily with grease blots. He pounded along after his brothers, his heart hammering in his throat with excitement and, as he raced into the hollow at the foot of the Central Avenue hill, grew weak with nervousness, as he heard the bell ringing itself to sleep, jerking the slatting rope about in its dying echoes.

Ben, grinning evilly and scowling, would thrust his hand against the small of his back and rush him screaming, but unable to resist the plunging force behind, up the hill.

In a gasping voice he would sing the morning song, coming in pantingly on the last round of a song the quartered class took up at intervals:

'—Merrily, merrily, merrily, merrily,
Life is but a dream.'

Or, in the frosty Autumn mornings:

'Waken, lords and ladies gay,
On the mountain dawns the day.'

Or the Contest of the West Wind and the South Wind. Or the Miller's Song:

'I envy no man, no, not I,
And no one envies me.'

He read quickly and easily; he spelled accurately. He did well with figures. But he hated the drawing lesson, although the boxes of crayons and paints delighted him. Sometimes the class would go into the woods, returning with specimens of flowers and leaves—the bitten flaming red of the maple, the brown pine comb, the brown oak leaf. These they would paint; or in Spring a spray of cherry-blossom, a tulip. He sat reverently before the authority of the plump woman who first taught him: he was terrified lest he do anything common or mean in her eyes.

The class squirmed: the little boys invented tortures or scrawled obscenities to the little girls. And the wilder and more indolent seized every chance of leaving the room, thus: 'Teacher, may I be excused?' And they would go out into the lavatory, sniggering and dawdling about restlessly.

He could never say it, because it

would reveal to her the shame of nature.

Once, deathly sick, but locked in silence and dumb nausea, he had vomited finally upon his cupped hands.

He feared and hated the recess periods, trembled before the brawling confusion of the mob and the playground, but his pride forbade that he skulk within, or secrete himself away from them. Eliza had allowed his hair to grow long; she wound it around her finger every morning into fat Fauntleroy curls: the agony and humiliation it caused him was horrible, but she was unable or unwilling to understand it, and mouth-pursingly thoughtful and stubborn to all solicitation to cut it. She had the garnered curls of Ben, Grover, and Luke stored in tiny boxes: she wept sometimes when she saw Eugene's, they were the symbol of his babyhood to her, and her sad heart, so keen in marking departures, refused to surrender them. Even when his thick locks had become the luxuriant colony of Harry Tarkinton's lice, she would not cut them: she held his squirming body between her knees twice a day and ploughed his scalp with a fine-toothed comb.

As he made to her his trembling passionate entreaties, she would smile with an affectation of patronizing humor, make a bantering humming noise in her throat, and say: 'Why, say—you can't grow up yet. You're my baby.' Suddenly baffled before the yielding inflexibility of her nature, which could be driven to action only after incessant and maddening prods, Eugene, screaming-mad with helpless fury, would understand the cause of Gant's frenzy.

At school, he was a desperate and hunted little animal. The herd, infallible in its banded instinct, knew at once that a stranger had been thrust into it, and it was merciless at the hunt. As the lunch-time recess came, Eugene, clutching his big grease-stained bag, would rush for the playground pursued by the yelping pack. The leaders, two or three big louts of advanced age and deficient mentality, pressed closely about him, calling out suppliantly, 'You know me, 'Gene. You know me'; and still racing for the far end, he would open his bag and hurl to them one of his big sandwiches, which stayed them for a moment, as they fell upon its possessor and clawed it to fragments, but they were upon him in a moment more with the same yelping insistence, hunting him down into a corner of the fence, and pressing in with outstretched paws and wild entreaty. He would give them what he had, sometimes with a momentary gust of fury, tearing away from a greedy hand half of a sandwich and devouring it. When they saw he had no more to give, they went away.

The great fantasy of Christmas still kept him devout. Gant was his unwearied comrade; night after night in the late autumn and early winter, he would scrawl petitions to Santa Claus, listing interminably the gifts he wanted most, and transmitting each, with perfect trust, to the roaring chimney. As the flame took the paper from his hand and blew its charred ghost away with a howl, Gant would rush with him to the window, point to the stormy northern sky, and say: 'There it goes! Do you see it?'

He saw it. He saw his prayer, winged with the stanch convoying winds, borne northward to the rimed quaint gables of Toyland, into frozen merry Elfland: heard the tiny silver anvil-tones, the deep-lunged laughter of the little men, the stabled cries of aerial reindeer. Gant saw and heard them, too.

He was liberally dowered with bright-painted gimcracks upon Christmas Day; and in his heart he hated those who advocated 'useful' gifts. Gant bought him wagons, sleds, drums, horns—best of all, a small fireman's ladder wagon: it was the wonder, and finally the curse, of the neighborhood. During his unoccupied hours, he lived for months in the cellar with Harry Tarkinton and Max Isaacs: they strung the ladders on wires above the wagon, so that, at a touch, they would fall in accurate stacks. They would pretend to doze in their quarters, as firemen do, would leap to action suddenly, as one of them imitated the warning bell: 'Clang-a-lang-a-lang.' Then, quite beyond reason, Harry and Max yoked in a plunging team, Eugene in the driver's seat, they would leap out through the narrow door, gallop perilously to a neighbor's house, throw up ladders, open windows, effect entries, extinguish imaginary flames, and return oblivious to the shrieking indictment of the housewife.

For months they lived completely in this fantasy, modelling their actions on those of the town's firemen, and on Jannadeau, who was the assistant chief, child-proud over it: they had seen him, at the sound of the alarm, rush like a madman from his window in Gant's shop, leaving the spattered fragments of a watch upon his desk, and arriving at his duty just as the great wagon hurtled at full speed into the Square. The firemen loved to stage the most daring exhibitions before the gaping citizenry: helmeted magnificently, they hung from the wagons in gymnastic postures, one man holding another over rushing space, while number two caught in mid-air the diving heavy body of the Swiss, who deliberately risked his neck as he leaped for the rail. Thus, for one rapturous moment they stood poised triangularly over rocking speed: the spine of the town was chilled ecstatically.

And when the bells broke through the drowning winds at night, his demon rushed into his heart, bursting all cords that held him to the earth, promising his isolation and dominance over sea and land, inhabitation of the dark: he looked down on the whirling disk of dark forest and field, sloped over singing pines upon a huddled town, and carried its grated guarded fires against its own roofs, swerving and pouncing with his haltered storm upon their doomed and flaming walls, howling with thin laughter above their stricken heads and, fiend-voiced, calling down the bullet wind.

Or, holding in fief the storm and the dark and all the black powers of wizardry, to gaze, ghoul-visaged, through a storm-lashed window-pane, briefly planting unutterable horror in grouped and sheltered life; or, no more than a man, but holding, in your more than mortal heart, demoniac ecstasy, to crouch against a lonely storm-swept house, to gaze obliquely through the streaming glass upon a woman, or your enemy, and while still exulting in your victorious dark all-seeing isolation, to feel a touch upon your shoulder, and to look, haunter-haunted, pursuer-pursued, into the green corrupted hell-face of malignant death.

Yes, and a world of bedded women, fair glimmers in the panting darkness, while winds shook the house, and he arrived across the world between the fragrant columns of delight. The great mystery of their bodies groped darkly in him, but he had found there, at the school, instructors to desire—the hair-faced louts of Doubleday. They struck fear and wonder into the hearts of the smaller, gentler boys, for Doubleday was that infested region of the town-grown mountaineers, who lurked viciously through the night, and came at Hallowe'en to break the skulls of other gangs in rock warfare.

There was a boy named Otto Krause, a cheese-nosed, hair-faced, inch-browed German boy, lean and swift in the legs, hoarse-voiced and full of idiot laughter, who showed him the gardens of delight. There was a girl named Bessie Barnes, a black-haired, tall, bold-figured girl of thirteen years who acted as model. Otto Krause was fourteen. Eugene was eight: they were in the third grade. The German boy sat next to him, drew obscenities on his books, and passed his furtive scrawled indecencies across the aisle to Bessie.

And the nymph would answer with a lewd face, and a contemptuous blow against her shapely lifted buttock, a gesture which Otto considered as good as a promise, and which tickled him into hoarse sniggers.

Bessie walked in his brain.

In their furtive moments at school, he and Otto amused each other by drawing obscenities in their geographies, bestowing on the representations of tropical natives sagging breasts and huge organs. And they composed on tiny scraps of paper dirty little rhymes about teachers and principal. Their teacher was a gaunt red-faced spinster, with fierce glaring eyes: Eugene thought always of the soldier and the tinder and the dogs

he had to pass, with eyes like saucers, windmills, the moon. Her name was Miss Groody, and Otto, with the idiot vulgarity of little boys, wrote of her:

'Old Miss Groody
Has Good Toody.'

And Eugene, directing his fire against the principal, a plump, soft, foppish young man whose name was Armstrong, and who wore always a carnation in his coat, which, after whipping an offending boy, he was accustomed to hold delicately between his fingers, sniffing it with sensitive nostrils and lidded eyes, produced in the first rich joy of creation scores of rhymes, all to the discredit of Armstrong, his parentage, and his relations with Miss Groody.

He was obsessed; he spent the entire day now in the composition of poetry—all bawdy variations of a theme. And he could not bring himself to destroy them. His desk was stuffed with tiny crumpled balls of writing: one day, during the geography lesson, the woman caught him. His bones turned to rubber as she bore down on him glaring, and took from the concealing pages of his book the paper on which he had been writing. At recess she cleared his desk, read the sequence, and, with boding quietness, bade him to see the principal after school.

'What does it mean? What do you reckon it means?' he whispered dryly to Otto Krause.

'Oh, you'll ketch it now!' said Otto Krause, laughing hoarsely.

And the class tormented him slily, rubbing their bottoms when they caught his eye, and making grimaces of agony.

He was sick through to his guts. He had a loathing of physical humiliation which was not based on fear, from which he never recovered. The brazen insensitive spirit of the boys he envied but could not imitate: they would howl loudly under punishment, in order to mitigate it, and they were vaingloriously unconcerned ten minutes later. He did not think he could endure being whipped by the fat young man with the flower: at three o'clock, white-faced, he went to the man's office.

Armstrong, slit-eyed and thin lipped, began to swish the cane he held in his hand through the air as Eugene entered. Behind him, smoothed and flatted on his desk, was stacked the damning pile of rhymed insult.

'Did you write these?' he demanded, narrowing his eyes to little points in order to frighten his victim.

'Yes,' said Eugene.

The principal cut the air again with his cane. He had visited Daisy several times, had eaten at Gant's plenteous board. He remembered very well.

'What have I ever done to you, son, that you should feel this way?' he said, with a sudden change to whining magnanimity.

'N-n-nothing,' said Eugene.

'Do you think you'll ever do it again?' said he, becoming ominous again.

'N-no, sir,' Eugene answered, in the ghost of a voice.

'All right,' said God, grandly, throwing away his cane. 'You can go.'

His legs found themselves only when he had reached the playground.

But oh, the brave autumn and the songs they sang; harvest, and the painting of a leaf; and 'half-holiday to-day'; and 'up in the air so high'; and the other one about the train— 'the stations go whistling past'; the

mellow days, the opening gates of desire, the smoky sun, the dropping patter of dead leaves.

'Every little snowflake is different in shape from every other.'

'Good grashus! *All* of them, Miss Pratt?'

'All of the little snowflakes that ever were. Nature never repeats herself.'

'Aw!'

Ben's beard was growing: he had shaved. He tumbled Eugene on the leather sofa, played with him for hours, scraped his stubble chin against the soft face of his brother. Eugene shrieked.

'When you can do that you'll be a man,' said Ben.

And he sang softly, in his thin humming ghost's voice:

'The woodpecker pecked at the school-
    house door,
He pecked and he pecked till his pecker
    got sore.
The woodpecker pecked at the school-
    house bell,
He pecked and he pecked till his pecker
    got well.'

They laughed—Eugene with rocking throatiness, Ben with a quiet snicker. He had aqueous gray eyes and a sallow bumpy skin. His head was shapely, the forehead high and bony. His hair was crisp, maple-brown. Below his perpetual scowl, his face was small, converging to a point: his extraordinarily sensitive mouth smiled briefly, flickeringly, inwardly —like a flash of light along a blade. And he always gave a cuff instead of a caress: he was full of pride and tenderness.

*   *   *

. . . Ah, me! Ah, me! Eugene's heart was filled with joy and sadness

—with sorrow because the book was done. He pulled his clotted handkerchief from his pocket and blew the contents of his loaded heart into it in one mighty, triumphant and ecstatic blast of glory and sentiment. Ah, me! Good old Bruce-Eugene.

Lifted, by his fantasy, into a high interior world, he scored off briefly and entirely all the grimy smudges of life: he existed nobly in a heroic world with lovely and virtuous creatures. He saw himself in exalted circumstances with Bessie Barnes, her pure eyes dim with tears, her sweet lips tremulous with desire: he felt the strong handgrip of Honest Jack, her brother, his truehearted fidelity, the deep eternal locking of their brave souls, as they looked dumbly at each other with misty eyes, and thought of the pact of danger, the shoulder-to-shoulder drive through death and terror which had soldered them silently but implacably.

Eugene wanted the two things all men want: he wanted to be loved, and he wanted to be famous. His fame was chameleon, but its fruit and triumph lay at home, among the people of Altamont. The mountain town had for him enormous authority: with a child's egotism it was for him the centre of the earth, the small but dynamic core of all life. He saw himself winning Napoleonic triumphs in battle, falling, with his fierce picked men, like a thunderbolt upon an enemy's flank, trapping, hemming, and annihilating. He saw himself as the young captain of industry, dominant, victorious, rich; as the great criminal-lawyer bending to his eloquence a charmed court—but always he saw his return from the voyage wearing the great coronal of the world upon his modest brows.

The world was a phantasmal land of faery beyond the misted hem of the hills, a land of great reverberations, of genii-guarded orchards, wine-dark seas, chasmed and fantastical cities from which he would return into this substantial heart of life, his native town, with golden loot.

He quivered deliciously to temptation—he kept his titillated honor secure after subjecting it to the most trying inducements; the groomed beauty of the rich man's wife, publicly humiliated by her brutal husband, defended by Bruce-Eugene, and melting toward him with all the pure ardor of her lonely and womanly heart, pouring the sad measure of her life into his sympathetic ears over the wineglasses of her candled, rich, but intimate table. And as, in the shaded light, she moved yearningly toward him, sheathed plastically in her gown of rich velvet, he would detach gently the round arms that clung about his neck, the firm curved body that stuck gluily to his. Or the blonde princess in the fabulous Balkans, the empress of gabled Toyland, and the Doll Hussars—he would renounce, in a great scene upon the frontiers, her proffered renunciation, drinking eternal farewell on her red mouth, but wedding her to himself and to the citizenship of freedom when revolution had levelled her fortune to his own.

But, steeping himself in ancient myths, where the will and the deed were not thought darkly on, he spent himself, quilted in golden meadows, or in the green light of woods, in pagan love. Oh to be king, and see a fruity wide-hipped Jewess bathing on her roof, and to possess her; or a cragged and castled baron, to execute *le droit de seigneur* upon the choicest of the enfeoffed wives and wenches, in a vast chamber loud with the howling winds and lighted by the mad dancing flames of great logs!

But even more often, the shell of his morality broken to fragments by his desire, he would enact the bawdy fable of schoolboys, and picture himself in hot romance with a handsome teacher. In the fourth grade his teacher was a young, inexperienced, but well-built woman, with carrot-colored hair, and full of reckless laughter.

He saw himself, grown to the age of potency, a strong, heroic, brilliant boy, the one spot of incandescence in a backwoods school attended by snag-toothed children and hair-faced louts. And, as the mellow autumn ripened, her interest in him would intensify, she would 'keep him in' for imaginary offenses, setting him, in a somewhat confused way, to do some task, and gazing at him with steady yearning eyes when she thought he was not looking.

He would pretend to be stumped by the exercise: she would come eagerly and sit beside him, leaning over so that a few fine strands of carrot-colored hair brushed his nostrils, and so that he might feel the firm warmth of her white-waisted arms, and the swell of her tight-skirted thighs. She would explain things to him at great length, guiding his fingers with her own warm, slightly moist hand, when he pretended not to find the place; then she would chide him gently, saying tenderly:

'Why are you such a bad boy?' or softly: 'Do you think you're going to be better after this?'

And he, simulating boyish, inarticu-

late coyness, would say: 'Gosh, Miss Edith, I didn't mean to do nothin.'

Later, as the golden sun was waning redly, and there was nothing in the room but the smell of chalk and the heavy buzz of the old October flies, they would prepare to depart. As he twisted carelessly into his overcoat, she would chide him, call him to her, arrange the lapels and his necktie, and smooth out his tousled hair, saying:

'You're a good-looking boy. I bet all the girls are wild about you.'

He would blush in a maidenly way and she, bitten with curiosity, would press him:

'Come on, now. Who's your girl?'

'I haven't got one, honest, Miss Edith.'

'You don't want one of these silly little girls, Eugene,' she would say, coaxingly. 'You're too good for them—you're a great deal older than your years. You need the understanding a mature woman can give you.'

And they would walk away in the setting sun, skirting the pine-fresh woods, passing along the path red with maple leaves, past great ripening pumpkins in the fields, and under the golden autumnal odor of persimmons.

She would live alone with her mother, an old deaf woman, in a little cottage set back from the road against a shelter of lonely singing pines, with a few grand oaks and maples in the leaf-bedded yard.

Before they came to the house, crossing a field, it would be necessary to go over a stile; he would go over first, helping her down, looking ardently at the graceful curve of her long, deliberately exposed, silk-clad leg.

As the days shortened, they would

come by dark, or under the heavy low-hanging autumnal moon. She would pretend to be frightened as they passed the woods, press in to him and take his arm at imaginary sounds, until one night, crossing the stile, boldly resolved upon an issue, she would pretend difficulty in descending, and he would lift her down in his arms. She would whisper:

'How strong you are, Eugene.' Still holding her, his hand would shift under her knees. And as he lowered her upon the frozen clotted earth, she would kiss him passionately, again and again, pressing him to her, caressing him, and under the frosted persimmon tree fulfilling and yielding herself up to his maiden and unfledged desire.

THE INFLUENCE OF THE FAMILY

His own Parents, he that had father'd him and she that had conceived him in her womb and birth'd him,
They gave this child more of themselves than that,
They gave him afterward every day, they became part of him.

—WALT WHITMAN

THE mental health of the adult is in direct proportion to the sanity and fullness of his early family relationships. Family life constitutes the child's first experience of love or indifference and bears definitely upon his later adjustment to life. The key to the joy or sorrow, success or failure of the adult may often be found in the seemingly half-effaced yet none the less indelible impressions of the child. His first world is that made for him by his parents, and his future world will be conditioned by the feeling of protection and emotional security his home has afforded him. The relation of the parents to each other, their fundamental harmony or their dissension, will in a large measure determine this feeling of security so essential to a balanced emotional development. The child's responses of love, hate, fear, jealousy, cruelty, or tenderness are reflected and repeated in his later feelings toward other individuals and the world in general. If he has been wisely loved, he will expand naturally in self-confidence; if he has been neglected, he may become a restless, bitter individual, forever incapable of facing reality. Too great emotional dependence on his mother may be the cause of a fixation which will limit a boy's ability to shift his affections to another woman in the normal pattern of adult development. His attachment to his father may lead to a feeling of identification with him which, if too long held, will likewise inhibit his emotional development. In the same way a girl's reaction to her father may condition her later responses to members of the opposite sex, making a happy adjustment easy or difficult. The number of brothers and sisters a child has, his position in the family as oldest or youngest, his rivalry with his siblings for parental affection, the favoritism or rejection he experiences, all these factors are of incalculable importance in shaping the growing personality.

THE WAY OF ALL FLESH

Samuel Butler

[There has never been more vehement indictment of parental stupidity than that of Samuel Butler in his novel *The Way of All Flesh*. That much of the material is drawn from Butler's own life, especially his relationship with his father, we know from his statement about his father to his biographer, Henry Festing Jones:

He never liked me, nor I him; from my earliest recollection I can call to mind no time when I did not fear him and dislike him . . . the fact remains that for years and years I have never passed a day without thinking of him many times over as the man who was sure to be against me, and who would be sure to see the bad side rather than the good of everything I said and did.

In the novel the ultimate responsibility for Ernest's years of frustration Butler places squarely upon the selfishness and piety of the boy's father, Theobald, and the blind possessiveness of Christina, his mother. Little wonder that he should interrupt his story of the Pontifexes by the bitter words: 'If a man is to enter the kingdom of Heaven he must do so, not only as a little child, but as a little embryo, or rather as a little zoösperm!' When Christina pried into her son's life, every fresh answer insidiously extracted was as 'the lopping off of a hydra's head' which would give birth to half a dozen more new questions. Ernest was safe from her inquisitions only during her recurrent flights from reality: 'a diadem was set upon her head by the Son of Man himself, amid a host of angels and archangels who looked on with envy and admiration.'

It is probable that Christina's over-possessiveness represented a reaction-formation, or a means by which she kept herself from awareness of her real feeling toward the child—one of rejection.

One of the pious Theobald's interesting defense mechanisms was his habit of cutting little bits out of the Bible and gumming them with exquisite neatness by the side of other little bits. In this way he escaped from the responsibilities of parenthood!

In short, the novel reveals graphically the significance of the relationships within the family in the early years of a child's life; the unconscious penetration of parental discord; the havoc wrought if the child is rejected; and the danger of breeding hostility toward the opposite sex by over protection.]

The birth of his son opened Theobald's eyes to a good deal which he had but faintly realized hitherto. He had had no idea how great a nuisance a baby was. Babies come into the world so suddenly at the end, and up-set everything so terribly when they do come: why cannot they steal in upon us with less of a shock to the domestic system? His wife, too, did not recover rapidly from her confinement; she remained an invalid for

From *The Way of All Flesh* by Samuel Butler, Oxford University Press, London.

months; here was another nuisance and an expensive one, which interfered with the amount which Theobald liked to put by out of his income against, as he said, a rainy day, or to make provision for his family if he should have one. Now he was getting a family, so that it became all the more necessary to put money by, and here was the baby hindering him. Theorists may say what they like about a man's children being a continuation of his own identity, but it will generally be found that those who talk in this way have no children of their own. Practical family men know better.

About twelve months after the birth of Ernest there came a second, also a boy, who was christened Joseph, and in less than twelve months afterwards, a girl, to whom was given the name of Charlotte. A few months before this girl was born Christina paid a visit to the John Pontifexes in London, and, knowing her condition, passed a good deal of time at the Royal Academy exhibition looking at the types of female beauty portrayed by the Academicians, for she had made up her mind that the child this time was to be a girl. Alethea warned her not to do this, but she persisted, and certainly the child turned out plain, but whether the pictures caused this or no I cannot say.

Theobald had never liked children. He had always got away from them as soon as he could, and so had they from him; oh, why, he was inclined to ask himself, could not children be born into the world grown up? If Christina could have given birth to a few full-grown clergymen in priest's orders—of moderate views, but inclining rather to Evangelicalism, with comfortable livings and in all respects facsimiles of Theobald himself—why,

there might have been more sense in it; or if people could buy ready made children at a shop of whatever age and sex they liked, instead of always having to make them at home, and to begin at the beginning with them—that might be better, but as it was he did not like it. He felt as he had felt when he had been required to come and be married to Christina—that he had been going on for a long time quite nicely, and would much rather continue things on their present footing. In the matter of getting married he had been obliged to pretend he liked it; but times were changed, and if he did not like a thing now, he could find a hundred unexceptionable ways of making his dislike apparent.

It might have been better if Theobald in his younger days had kicked more against his father: the fact that he had not done so encouraged him to expect the most implicit obedience from his own children. He could trust himself, he said (and so did Christina), to be more lenient than perhaps his father had been to himself; his danger, he said (and so again did Christina), would be rather in the direction of being too indulgent; he must be on his guard against this, for no duty could be more important than that of teaching a child to obey its parents in all things . . . The first signs of self-will must be carefully looked for, and plucked up by the roots at once before they had time to grow. Theobald picked up this numb serpent of a metaphor and cherished it in his bosom.

Before Ernest could well crawl he was taught to kneel; before he could well speak he was taught to lisp the Lord's Prayer, and the general confession. How was it possible that these things could be taught too early? If his attention flagged or his memory failed him, here was an ill weed which would grow apace, unless it were plucked out immediately, and the only way to pluck it out was to whip him, or shut him up in a cupboard, or dock him of some of the small pleasures of childhood. Before he was three years old he could read, and, after a fashion, write. Before he was four he was learning Latin, and could do rule of three sums.

As for the child himself, he was naturally of an even temper, he doted upon his nurse, on kittens and puppies, and on all things that would do him the kindness of allowing him to be fond of them. He was fond of his mother, too, but as regards his father, he has told me in later life he could remember no feeling but fear and shrinking. Christina did not remonstrate with Theobald concerning the severity of the tasks imposed upon their boy, nor yet as to the continual whippings that were found necessary at lesson times. Indeed, when during any absence of Theobald's the lessons were entrusted to her, she found to her sorrow that it was the only thing to do, and she did it no less effectually than Theobald himself, nevertheless she was fond of her boy, which Theobald never was, and it was long before she could destroy all affection for herself in the mind of her first-born. But she persevered.

*   *   *

Strange! for she believed she doted upon him, and certainly she loved him better than either of her other children. Her version of the matter was that there had never yet been two parents so self-denying and devoted to the highest welfare of their children as Theobald and herself. For Ernest, a very great future—she was certain of it—was in store. This made severity all the more necessary, so that from the first he might have been kept pure from every taint of evil. She could not allow herself the scope for castle building which, we read, was indulged in by every Jewish matron before the appearance of the Messiah, for the Messiah had now come, but there was to be a millennium shortly, certainly not later than 1866, when Ernest would be just about the right age for it, and a modern Elias would be wanted to herald its approach. Heaven would bear her witness that she had never shrunk from the idea of martyrdom for herself and Theobald, nor would she avoid it for her boy, if his life was required of her in her Redeemer's service. Oh, no! If God told her to offer up her first-born, as He had told Abraham, she would take him up to Pigbury Beacon and plunge the—no, that she could not do, but it would be unnecessary—some one else might do that. It was not for nothing that Ernest had been baptized in water from the Jordan . . .

When Ernest was in his second year, Theobald, as I have already said, began to teach him to read; he began to whip him two days after he had begun to teach him.

'It was painful,' as he said to Christina, but it was the only thing to do and it was done. The child was puny, white and sickly, so they sent continually for the doctor who dosed him with calomel and James's powder. All was done in love, anxiety, timidity, stupidity, and impatience. They were stupid in little things; and he that is stupid in little will be stupid also in much.

Presently old Mr. Pontifex died, and then came the revelation of the little alteration he had made in his will simultaneously with his bequest to Ernest. It was rather hard to bear, especially as there was no way of conveying a bit of their minds to the testator now that he could no longer hurt them. As regards the boy himself anyone must see that the bequest would be an unmitigated misfortune to him. To leave him a small independence was perhaps the greatest injury which one could inflict upon a young man. It would cripple his energies, and deaden his desire for active employment. Many a youth was led into evil courses by the knowledge that on arriving at majority he would come into a few thousands. They might surely have been trusted to have their boy's interests at heart, and must be better judges of those interests than he, at twenty-one, could

be expected to be: besides if Jonadab, the son of Rechab's father—or perhaps it might be simpler under the circumstances to say Rechab at once —if Rechab, then, had left handsome legacies to his grandchildren—why Jonadab might not have found those children so easy to deal with, etc. 'My dear,' said Theobald, after having discussed the matter with Christina for the twentieth time, 'my dear, the only thing to guide and console us under misfortunes of this kind is to take refuge in practical work. I will go and pay a visit to Mrs. Thompson.'

On those days Mrs. Thompson would be told that her sins were all washed white, etc., a little sooner and a little more peremptorily than on others . . .

[In the following passage a number of years have passed. Ellen, a maid in the Pontifex household, has been unjustly dismissed. In boyish fondness for one who had always been kind to him, Ernest has run after her to give her his prized watch.]

Then Ernest got into a field by the roadside, flung himself on the grass, and waited under the shadow of a hedge till the carriage should pass on its return from the station and pick him up, for he was dead beat. Thoughts which had already occurred to him with some force now came more strongly before him, and he saw that he had got himself into one mess —or rather into half a dozen messes— the more.

In the first place he should be late for dinner, and this was one of the offences on which Theobald had no mercy. Also he should have to say where he had been, and there was a danger of being found out if he did not speak the truth. Not only this, but sooner or later it must come out that he was no longer possessed of the beautiful watch which his dear aunt had given him—and what, pray,

had he done with it, or how had he lost it? The reader will know very well what he ought to have done. He should have gone straight home, and if questioned should have said, 'I have been running after the carriage to catch our housemaid Ellen, whom I am very fond of; I have given her my watch, my knife and all my pocket-money, so that I have now no pocket-money at all and shall probably ask you for some more sooner than I otherwise might have done, and you will also have to buy me a new knife and a watch.' But then fancy the consternation which such an announcement would have occasioned! Fancy the scowl and flashing eyes of the infuriated Theobald! 'You unprincipled young scoundrel,' he would exclaim, 'do you mean to vilify your own parents by implying that they have dealt harshly by one whose profligacy has disgraced their house?'

Or he might take it with one of those sallies of sarcastic calm, of which he believed himself to be a master.

'Very well, Ernest, very well: I shall say nothing; you can please yourself; you are not yet twenty-one, but pray act as if you were your own master; your poor aunt doubtless gave you the watch that you might fling it away upon the first improper character you came across; I think I can now understand, however, why she did not leave you her money; and, after all, your godfather may just as well have it as the kind of people on whom you would lavish it if it were yours.'

Then his mother would burst into tears and implore him to repent and seek the things belonging to his peace while there was yet time, by falling on his knees to Theobald and assuring him of his unfailing love for him as the kindest and tenderest father in the universe. Ernest could do all this just as well as they could, and now, as he lay on the grass, speeches, some one or other of which was as certain to come as the sun to set, kept running in his head till they confuted the idea of telling the truth by reducing it to an absurdity. Truth might be heroic, but it was not within the range of practical domestic politics.

Having settled then that he was to tell a lie, what lie should he tell? Should he say he had been robbed? He had enough imagination to know that he had not enough imagination to carry out here. Young as he was, his instinct told him that the best liar is he who makes the smallest amount of lying go the longest way—who husbands it too carefully to waste it where it can be dispensed with. The simplest course would be to say that

he had lost the watch, and was late for dinner because he had been looking for it. He had been out for a long walk—he chose the line across the fields that he had actually taken—and the weather being very hot, he had taken off his coat and waistcoat; in carrying them over his arm his watch, his money, and his knife had dropped out of them. He had got nearly home when he found out his loss, and had run back as fast as he could, looking along the line he had followed, till at last he had given it up; seeing the carriage coming back from the station, he had let it pick him up and bring him home.

This covered everything, the running and all; for his face still showed that he must have been running hard; the only question was whether he had been seen about the Rectory by any but the servants for a couple of hours or so before Ellen had gone, and this he was happy to believe was not the case; for he had been out except during his few minutes' interview with the cook. His father had been out in the parish; his mother had certainly not come across him, and his brother and sister had also been out with the governess. He knew he could depend upon the cook and the other servants —the coachman would see to this; on the whole, therefore, both he and the coachman thought the story as proposed by Ernest would meet the requirements of the case.

*　　*　　*

When Ernest got home and sneaked in through the back door, he heard his father's voice in its angriest tones, inquiring whether Master Ernest had already returned. He felt as Jack must have felt in the story of Jack and the Bean Stalk, when from the oven in which he was hidden he heard the ogre ask his wife what young children she had got for his supper. With much courage, and, as the event proved, with not less courage than discretion, he took the bull by the horns, and announced himself as having just come in after having met with a terrible misfortune. Little by little he told his story, and though Theobald stormed somewhat at his 'incredible folly and carelessness,' he got off better than he expected. Theobald and Christina had indeed at first been inclined to connect his absence from dinner with Ellen's dismissal, but on finding it clear, as Theobald said—everything was always clear with Theobald—Ernest had not been in the house all the morning, and could not have known anything of what had happened, he was acquitted on this account for once in a way, without a stain on his character. Perhaps Theobald was in a good temper; he may have seen from the paper that morning that his stocks had been rising; it may have been this or twenty other things, but whatever it was, he did not scold so much as Ernest had expected, and, seeing the boy look exhausted and believing him to be much grieved at the loss of his watch, Theobald actually prescribed a glass of wine after his dinner, which, strange to say, did not choke him, but made him see things more cheerfully than was usual with him.

That night when he said his prayers, he inserted a few paragraphs to the effect that he might not be discovered, and that things might go well with Ellen, but he was anxious and ill at ease. His guilty conscience pointed out to him a score of weak places in his story, through any one of which detection might even yet easily enter. Next day and for many days afterwards he fled when no man

was pursuing, and trembled each time he heard his father's voice calling for him. He had already so many causes of anxiety that he could stand little more, and in spite of all his endeavours to look cheerful, even his mother could tell that something was preying upon his mind. Then the idea returned to her that, after all, her son might not be innocent in the Ellen matter—and this was so interesting that she felt bound to get as near the truth as she could.

'Come here, my poor, pale-faced, heavy-eyed boy,' she said to him one day in her kindest manner; 'come and sit down by me, and we will have a little quiet confidential talk together, will we not?'

The boy went mechanically to the sofa. Whenever his mother wanted what she called a confidential talk with him she always selected the sofa as the most suitable ground on which to open her campaign. All mothers do this; the sofa is to them what the dining-room is to fathers. In the present case the sofa was particularly well adapted for a strategic purpose, being an old-fashioned one with a high back, mattress, bolsters and cushions. Once safely penned into one of its deep corners, it was like a dentist's chair, not too easy to get out of again. Here she could get at him better to pull him about, if this should seem desirable, or if she thought fit to cry she could bury her head in the sofa cushion and abandon herself to an agony of grief which seldom failed of its effect. None of her favourite manoeuvres were so easily adopted in her usual seat, the arm-chair on the right-hand side of the fireplace, and so well did her son know from his mother's tone that this was going to be a sofa conversation that he took his place like a lamb as soon as she began to speak and before she could reach the sofa herself.

'My dearest boy,' began his mother, taking hold of his hand and placing it within her own, 'promise me never to be afraid of either your dear papa or of me; promise me this, my dear, as you love me, promise it to me,' and she kissed him again and again and stroked his hair. But with her other hand she still kept hold of his; she had got him and she meant to keep him.

The lad hung down his head and promised. What else could he do?

'You know there is no one, dear, dear Ernest, who loves you so much as your papa and I do; no one who watches so carefully over your interests, or who is so anxious to enter into all your little joys and troubles as we are; but, my dearest boy, it grieves me to think sometimes that you have not that perfect love for and confidence in us which you ought to have. You know, my darling, that it would be as much our pleasure as our duty to watch over the development of your moral and spiritual nature, but alas! you will not let us see your moral and spiritual nature. At times we are almost inclined to doubt whether you have a moral and spiritual nature at all. Of your inner life, my dear, we know nothing beyond such scraps as we can glean in spite of you, from little things which escape you almost before you know that you have said them.'

The boy winced at this. It made him feel hot and uncomfortable all over. He knew well how careful he ought to be, and yet, do what he could, from time to time his forgetfulness of the part betrayed him into unreserve. His mother saw that he winced, and enjoyed the scratch she had given him. Had she felt less con-

fident of victory she had better have forgone the pleasure of touching as it were the eyes at the end of the snail's horns in order to enjoy seeing the snail draw them in again—but she knew that when she had got him well down into the sofa, and held his hand, she had the enemy almost absolutely at her mercy, and could do pretty much what she liked.

'Papa does not feel,' she continued, 'that you love him with that fullness and unreserve which would prompt you to have no concealment from him, and to tell him everything freely and fearlessly as your most loving earthly friend next only to your Heavenly Father. Perfect love, as we know, casteth out fear: your father loves you perfectly, my darling, but he does not feel as though you loved him perfectly in return. If you fear him it is because you do not love him as he deserves, and I know it sometimes cuts him to the very heart to think that he has earned from you a deeper and more willing sympathy than you display towards him. Oh, Ernest, Ernest, do not grieve one who is so good and noble-hearted by conduct which I can call by no other name than ingratitude.'

Ernest could never stand being spoken to in this way by his mother: for he still believed that she loved him, and that he was fond of her and had a friend in her—up to a certain point. But his mother was beginning to come to the end of her tether; she had played the domestic confidence trick upon him times without number already. Over and over again had she wheedled out of him all she wanted to know, and afterwards got him into the most horrible scrape by telling the whole to Theobald. Ernest had remonstrated more than once upon these occasions, and had pointed out to his mother how disastrous to him his confidences had been, but Christina had always joined issue with him and showed him in the clearest possible manner that in each case she had been right, and that he could not reasonably complain. Generally it was her conscience that forbade her to be silent, and against this there was no appeal, for we are all bound to follow the dictates of our conscience. Ernest used to have to recite a hymn about conscience. It was to the effect that if you did not pay attention to its voice it would soon leave off speaking. 'My mamma's conscience has not left off speaking,' said Ernest to one of his chums at Roughborough; 'it's always jabbering.'

When a boy has once spoken so disrespectfully as this about his mother's conscience it is practically all over between him and her. Ernest through sheer force of habit, of the sofa, and of the return of the associated ideas, was still so moved by the siren's voice as to yearn to sail towards her, and fling himself into her arms, but it would not do; there were other associated ideas that returned also, and the mangled bones of too many murdered confessions were lying whitening round the skirts of his mother's dress, to allow him by any possibility to trust her further. So he hung his head and looked sheepish, but kept his own counsel.

'I see, my dearest,' continued his mother, 'either that I am mistaken, and that there is nothing on your mind, or that you will not unburden yourself to me: but oh, Ernest, tell me at least this much; is there nothing that you repent of, nothing which makes you unhappy in connection with that miserable girl Ellen?'

Ernest's heart failed him. 'I am a dead boy now,' he said to himself. He had not the faintest conception what his mother was driving at, and thought she suspected about the watch; but he held his ground.

I do not believe he was much more of a coward than his neighbours, only he did not know that all sensible people are cowards when they are off their beat, or when they think they are going to be roughly handled. I believe, that if the truth were known, it would be found that even the valiant St. Michael himself tried hard to shirk his famous combat with the dragon; he pretended not to see all sorts of misconduct on the dragon's part; shut his eyes to the eating up of I do not know how many hundreds of men, women and children whom he had promised to protect; allowed himself to be publicly insulted a dozen times over without resenting it; and in the end when even an angel could stand it no longer he shilly-shallied and temporized an unconscionable time before he would fix the day and hour for the encounter. As for the actual combat it was much such another *wurra-wurra* as Mrs. Allaby had had with the young man who had in the end married her eldest daughter, till after a time behold, there was the dragon lying dead, while he was himself alive and not very seriously hurt after all.

'I do not know what you mean, mamma,' exclaimed Ernest anxiously and more or less hurriedly. His mother construed his manner into indignation at being suspected, and being rather frightened herself she turned tail and scuttled off as fast as her tongue could carry her.

'Oh!' she said, 'I see by your tone that you are innocent! Oh! oh! how I thank my heavenly Father for this; may He for his dear Son's sake keep you always pure. Your father, my dear'—(here she spoke hurriedly but gave him a searching look)—'was as pure as a spotless angel when he came to me. Like him, always be self-denying, truly truthful both in word and deed, never forgetful whose son and grandson you are, nor of the name we gave you, of the sacred stream in whose waters your sins were washed out of you through the blood and blessing of Christ,' etc.

But Ernest cut this—I will not say short—but a great deal shorter than it would have been if Christina had had her say out, by extricating himself from his mamma's embrace and showing a clean pair of heels. As he got near the purlieus of the kitchen (where he was more at ease) he heard his father calling for his mother, and again his guilty conscience rose against him. 'He has found all out now,' it cried, 'and he is going to tell mamma—this time I am done for.' But there was nothing in it; his father only wanted the key of the cellaret. Then Ernest slunk off into a coppice of spinney behind the Rectory paddock, and consoled himself with a pipe of tobacco. Here in the wood with the summer sun streaming through the trees and a book and his pipe the boy forgot his cares and had an interval of that rest without which I verily believe his life would have been insupportable . . .

❊

TROTT AND HIS LITTLE SISTER

André Lichtenberger

[The shift in the atmosphere of the home from one of understanding and love to one of harsh words and long silences between his parents presents a real threat to the little boy's security in *Trott and His Little Sister*. No longer does he actively participate in normal play; instead he loses himself in thought and tries desperately to exonerate his parents from blame. With the birth of his little sister (whom he prefers to a baby brother if not to a live turtle) he finds himself still less the center of his universe. He hits upon illness as a means of eliciting parental concern but finally resorts to a simpler form of egocentric behavior.]

Trott is sitting on the sand at the beach. His shovel lies on one side, his pail on the other. Mechanically he scratches the sand with his two hands, looking straight in front of him at nothing in particular. He does not see the little waves come pattering on the sand like soft-footed kittens. He looks into the blue, open-mouthed, his gaze lost in the distance. Trott is serious. Trott is disturbed. Trott is unhappy.

Since when? For several days now, since the day of papa's return, to be exact. Yes, it is extraordinary and hard to believe, but it's so. They had

From *Trott and His Little Sister* by André Lichtenberger. Reprinted by permission of Island Press, Inc., New York City.

been so happy to have him come back, this papa of his. During the three days of waiting, they had been too impatient to keep still, mama and he. And now that he is here and everyone ought to be altogether happy, Trott is sad instead.

Why? He doesn't know exactly himself. It is hard to explain. To begin with, it certainly isn't papa's fault. Papa is always right. You have only to look into his big brown eyes, whose gaze is so straight and so deep, to be sure that he sees everything and that he does everything better than anyone else. And then, he's papa. But one thing is sure and that is that he isn't the same as he was before he went away. He used to laugh and joke and be full of fun. Trott was very small when he sailed away but he remembers that sometimes papa used to play such pranks and say such funny things that mama would have to say to him, 'Pierre, do be serious a minute.' Now papa doesn't romp any more, nor say funny things. His heavy black eyebrows seem almost to have grown blacker and heavier, and his eyes are so bright that you hardly dare look at them. Some people are really afraid of him. Since papa is here, we don't see anything more of Mme. de Bray, Mme. Thilorier, nor of several other ladies; nor of M. Vézy either who used to come almost every day. And mama doesn't pay visits any more. She stays at home and never puts on the dresses with no sleeves to go to balls in the evenings.

She is changed too, his pretty little mama. Trott has never seen her like this. Why, she scarcely ever laughs or talks and never does that little dance with the kick and the song, 'Tararaboom.' All that is over. When papa is there she says very little to him; she lowers her eyes, lets things drop,

breaks them, gets everything mixed. Her movements have become brusque and awkward, like Jip when he is in disgrace. If papa asks her something, she answers very quickly as though the words were hurrying to come out, and yet couldn't quite get through. If by chance she raises her eyes, they have the most curious expression like when you have swallowed some pepper or a drop of cognac or when you are going to cry pretty soon. Even when she is alone with Trott it isn't the way it used to be. She takes him gently on her knee and talks to him tenderly, stroking his hair slowly over and over. And when Trott looks at her he sees that her eyes are full of tears as though she had a great sorrow inside which hurt her very much and could not be contained.

Trott is overwhelmed by all this. What is happening? No one is dead because no one has put on black clothes. No one is sick because the doctor doesn't come. Trott has been good. The weather is fine. The lunches and dinners are always excellent. Then what can it be?

It is so horrible that it makes Trott ill to think about it. Oh, dear, he knows only too well what it is, but he wishes he didn't know. It is too awful. There is no doubt about it. Though it seems perfectly impossible, it is true, it is true!

Trott's papa is angry with his mama.

There! At first Trott wouldn't let himself believe it, but now he has to. Little by little the fact became undeniable. How can it be possible? Papa cannot be wrong. But then can it be that mama . . . ? Has Trott's mama been naughty? It is unheard of for a little boy to ask himself that question. The very thought makes Trott blush. No, mama has not been naughty. That is impossible. Mama is far too good and too nice. And yet, it *is* mama.

Then why is papa angry?

Well, it is pretty hard to understand, but Trott has finally worked it out. Mama liked to go out riding, to put on pretty dresses to go to the balls, to play in the comedies, to listen to music, to laugh and joke with the gentlemen. None of that seems very terrible, does it? Well, when mama or Trott or anyone else talks of these things, why, papa's eyebrows almost come together, and his gaze becomes so heavy that you want to put your hand before your eyes so as not to be crushed; and when he talks, his voice is rough as though his words were put through the grater. Mama turns red, her hands tremble, and her eyes fill with tears. All of a sudden Trott remembers that Mme. de Tréan had looked displeased too when mama was telling her about her pastimes. There are curious things which Trott does not understand. Evidently big people like papa and Mme. de Tréan don't like you to have too good a time. Probably mama is not altogether a big person and she acted like the children who think they can do what they want without being scolded.

The other day, quite without meaning to, Trott heard some dreadful things. Before going into the dining-room, while he was washing his hands at the little basin, he suddenly heard papa's voice, a voice so changed that he hardly recognized it; like the cracking of a whip, and then the rumbling of thunder. He must have been very angry. And he said words which Trott did not understand: 'crowds of hussies and coxcombs—deplorable behavior—anonymous letter—a cardboard husband—cruel surprise

—more than light conduct—old blackguard of a Thilanges—pull his nose—that Vézy fellow'—etc., etc. That was all right for M. Vézy and M. de Thilanges. Trott doesn't like them at all. But those other things. Trott realized they were not for children's ears. He had been so frightened of that heavy voice that he had clapped his hands over his ears so as not to hear it. After a minute he had gone into the dining-room. Papa was walking up and down angrily. Before sitting down at the table mama had gone to the window to look out and had blown her nose hard, yet Trott knew she hadn't a cold. And no one was hungry for lunch.

And since then? Well, since then there is always something. Papa has not lost his temper again but he is not happy. He scarcely talks. He has wrinkles down the middle of his forehead. When he goes walking with Trott he does not tell him stories. And mama acts as though she were ill. You never hear her voice any more. She keeps looking at papa with big, sad eyes which make you want to cry. At table, they let Trott talk as much as he wants, but it's no fun to talk all by yourself. And at times there are long silences as if no one dared to say anything and each one were thinking within himself such sad thoughts that he couldn't give them voice.

Trott is in the depth of despair. He would never have believed that a papa and a mama could be angry with each other. Every time he thinks of it, it hurts so badly, so badly, that he wants to cry for comfort. He glimpses the existence of a crowd of horrid things which he had never suspected before. But since this misfortune he sees them all as if through a sudden little crack. He tries not to look, he shuts his eyes, but, in spite of himself, the horrors approach and lift his eyelids. Oh! When will it finish so that Trott can think of other things, gay, happy things, and no longer see these nightmare figures crawling nearer? It may be that big people have to learn to know them, but surely they don't have to come hurting little children too . . .

It has lasted many days now. Is it going to keep up forever? It is easy to see that mama isn't angry. She would like papa and everybody else to be happy. Well then, why doesn't she ask forgiveness and then it will all be over. The good God always forgives you and papa surely wouldn't be more severe than He. Oh, hurry, hurry! Trott doesn't feel like running any more, nor chattering, nor playing. When he is with mama and papa he can do nothing but study their faces to see if a little gleam of sunshine isn't ready to shine through; and when he is away from them, even when he is playing, he always sees papa's stern forehead with the hard lines down the middle of it and mama's poor mouth which looks so forlorn because it can't smile any more.

'Hurry, M. Trott, there's the dinner bell.'

He has to go. That's too bad because it is nice on the beach. The sun is setting so prettily in a mass of little pink clouds, like soft feather pillows on which it is going to lay its head. After dinner it will all be gone, but now that dinners are such dismal affairs no one lingers over them and perhaps they can go out for a little afterward. For the present Trott will have to look at the somber faces of papa and mama . . . unless . . . by chance . . .

Ah, no! This dinner is going to be just like the others. As soon as he is seated, Trott steals a glance at mama, then at papa. That is enough. Papa seems to be thinking of something tremendously serious, and mama is staring into her plate. They talk about uninteresting things and yet they are glad to see Trott and ask him questions and listen to what he says. But Trott would have liked the old way better when they made him keep still sometimes and it was they who did the talking and laughing. Mama would love to. She tries to say a few pleasant things but they come out with great difficulty. Papa is always serious. His voice is not harsh but it is sad, slow, and very low, and that is almost worse because it seems as though it never again could be laughing and gay.

If it were anyone else who were so stern with his dear little mama, Trott would think he was a bad man, and mama would surely become very angry and would scold him. But she is not angry; she does not scold. Papa must have good reason to be angry; then that would mean that mama . . . Oh! Trott is sick! Oh, dear! Oh, dear! papa and mama just *have* to make it up and be friends; otherwise he can never be happy any more. If papa should go away on another trip before it is all fixed, though, it would be horrible.

Dinner is almost over.

'Mama, it is so nice this evening, don't you want to go out again for a little while?'

Mama asks papa with her eyes. Papa says:

'All right, we can go to the beach and sit down on the sand. It will do us good to get a little air.'

They put on Trott's little sweater. Papa takes his cap and mama wraps a big scarf around her shoulders.

They take a few turns on the beach, then papa and mama sit down on the sand with Trott crouching at their feet. How beautiful the young night is! It is not very dark yet, but the stars are already brightening the sky and the big moon, nearly round, is just rising. Its soft rays spread over everything like caresses and, when they strike the sea, it kindles into light. A silver river gleams on the black waters with here and there a glinting spangle. Over the land come the distant murmurs of sleepy things; the slow lisping of the sea whispers goodnight, and in the skies the stars hurry out so as to keep watch over the drowsy world.

How can anyone be sad or unhappy in the midst of so much loveliness? Trott is forgetting all his troubles and his bad tempers. How that spear of moon dances on the water! It is very beautiful and very joyful; not the kind of joy to make you laugh, but a very nice joy which makes your heart feel warm and soft. The spear seems to be gliding toward Trott, to hesitate, run away, come again, to be playing with him. It comes from up above, from the sky where God is . . . How dark it is! It is really night now, time to go to sleep. They'll be calling Trott in a minute to take him off to bed. Why is that necessary? What earthly good? He would sleep so well here under the ceiling of stars! It is too exquisite a night to stuff yourself inside of four walls. The sand makes a soft bed. Trott stretches out, full length, his feet toward the sea and his head between papa and mama. And now sleep comes sailing over like a great black bird, and his thoughts flutter off like swallows into the sky. Soon there will be nothing. Mama hasn't come to hear Trott's prayers and neither has Jane. He'll have to say them by himself, but he is too sleepy, he can't remember the words. God will forgive him. Oh! But there is one thing he must ask because it is very important. Trott asks it in his mind, he tries to say it, but he can't; he is asleep. And yet God has to hear it, so he makes a huge effort. And suddenly a little voice comes knocking at the hearts of papa and mama, tearing them away from the somber thoughts which beset them.

'Oh, dear good God! I feel so badly because papa is angry with mama. Oh! You know how it hurts! Oh, I pray You, don't let them be angry any more so I won't be frightened of those terrible things. And let me love papa and mama again with my whole whole heart, because You know, dear God, when they are angry I feel so badly and am so frightened and I'm only a little boy. Amen.'

A wide, solemn peace falls from the shining sky. The sea murmurs the lulling refrain of its quiet song. The smile of the hushed earth answers the calm smile of the stars, and Trott's voice echoes like the small, secret, powerful voice which lies in the depths of every heart. Papa bends toward mama. He takes her hand in his. Little by little mama comes nearer and leans her head against his shoulder. She sobs very softly. A few words mount from their hearts to their lips, and forgiveness, confidence, and good will rise and spread enfolding wings like the silken flight of moths.

Trott is in bed. Through a half-opened eye he sees two faces bending over him, close to each other, cheek against cheek. He smiles vaguely and drops back into sleep. To-morrow it will be good to wake up.

*   *   *

Trott has a little sister.

She has taken long enough about coming.

He heard about her first one evening, it is hard to say just when, but it was a long time ago, one of those evenings that warn you that winter is coming. Just when it was the very nicest, all warm and comfortable by the fire near the lighted lamp, mama took Trott on her lap. It was the hour when one feels very tender or thinks things that are a tiny bit scary, as the night falls and masses of shadow fill up the corners of the room. Mama cuddled Trott, kissed him many times, and said to him, 'Trott, would you like to have a little brother?'

Trott was playing with his mother's chain. He thought a moment and then answered, 'No, thanks. If you're getting one to please me, I would much rather you would buy me a live turtle. Because, you see, I would have to lend him my toys and he would break them and make me mad.'

Mama started to laugh. She began to tell him how interesting it would be to have a little brother, to play with, to set a good example. Hm! That means he would have to be good for two. Trott sighs. It is hard enough to be good for one as it is; but for two! That is altogether impossible. Trott explains this to his mother but she only laughs harder than ever.

Papa comes into the room and mama tells him about Trott's fears. There! He is laughing too! It is very strange how grown people laugh sometimes at things that are tremendously serious.

Papa asks Trott, 'Would you like a little sister better?'

Trott gravely examines all phases of the problem. A little sister? Perhaps that would be more fun. Marie de Milly is a very nice girl. Yesterday she brought him an almost whole barley-sugar candy. Yes, Trott likes little girls best. Besides they are not as strong as little boys, and so, if one quarrels . . . Papa and mama are talking together, completely absorbed, when, like a gimlet, Trott's shrill voice pierces their ear drums: 'Well, papa, if it is all the same to you, I should like a little sister best.'

'All right. Don't forget to ask God for one every night.'

And Trott did ask for one every night. Every night? Well perhaps not exactly every. There are nights, you know, when one is so sleepy one does not really know what one does say. So, perhaps on those nights . . . Of course, one said one's prayers, but inside rather than out loud. However, every night that he did not fall asleep too quickly, Trott asked God to send him a little sister. He explained carefully what she should be like. She must be very pretty and very good, not so big as Trott, and she must like meat very much and not care a bit for dessert. Then Trott would give her his meat and eat her dessert himself. Besides she must be called Polycarpe. Polycarpe! This name is very dear to Trott, no one can tell why. Mama got excited when she heard that beautiful name. The little sister's name was to be Lucette. Lucette! What an ugly name! Why, that was a dog's name. Polycarpe is much lovelier. Still, if she is much smaller than Trott and does not like dessert at all . . .

*   *   *

One night Trott returns thoughtful. He is so plunged in meditation that Mme. de Tréan is astonished and questions him. What is the matter? Has he done something naughty, or perhaps he has a little stomach ache?

No, it is not that. Trott finds his voice.

'Madame, I want to know where babies come from. Jane says people find them in cabbages. I have seen a picture where a stork is holding one in his beak. And Bertrand, he's our gardener, has told me that they buy them in the market like little ducks. But I know that isn't true. Tell me, madame, how do they come?'

Mme. de Tréan replies softly, 'It is God who sends them during the night without making any noise and without anyone's seeing them pass by. An angel puts them in the cradle which has been prepared for them. And we must love them and care for them very tenderly because, since up to now they have been in heaven, they are very sad and homesick and cry a great deal.'

Trott considers. How many little children there must be up in heaven waiting to be born! What a lot of noise they must make! Well, those little children must know God. They have just come from seeing him. That is queer. Perhaps the little sister . . . but Jane arrives to take Trott up to bed and interrupts his meditations.

This morning Jane is very gay while dressing Trott. She is so gay that one would hardly know her. 'How queer you seem this morning, Jane.'

Jane laughs and says, 'Do you think so?'

'Jane, what is it? Tell me, oh, please tell me!'

'You have to guess.'

'Someone has found my top! The black horse has run away! It has been raining sugar candy like in the story book about the land of Cockaigne!'

'No, M. Trott . . . well, something we were expecting . . . you know, in the crib.'

'The little sister has come!'

She is here. If Trott is good, he will see her this afternoon. This news makes Trott actually drunk with excitement. At last she is here, the little sister who has been waited for so long! Perhaps he had better bring her a plaything. No, not the mechanical horse, for she might spoil that. The pink doll? She is very ugly. The big clown is too heavy. Oh, well, there are plenty of other toys at mama's.

The morning dragged by very slowly. It is over at last! Trott has had his lunch. He is dressed. He has started. He gambols like a goat the entire way. When he is happy, he needs to laugh with his legs in this way. And today they are laughing like mad, those legs of Trott's. They carry him to the left, to the right, first here, then there. How poky Jane is! She calls to him, telling him to go more slowly. Trott laughs at her, but he is wrong. He falls full length and skins his knee. Jane picks him up, scolds him, brushes him off and takes him by the hand. He calms down.

'Say, Jane, the little sister can't run as fast as I can, can she?'

'No, not quite as fast, M. Trott, you may be sure of that.'

Not quite as fast? Now, that is exactly as it should be. In this way, when they play run and catch, Trott will be able to catch her whenever he wants. He, however, will not let himself be caught except when it suits him. It is wonderful. Only, she mustn't fuss. 'Say, Jane, she will have to be very good, won't she? If she isn't, I'll give her a little punch . . .'

'Try to be good yourself! What kind of a heart must you have to want to hit her already, poor cherub!'

Trott is much offended. That stupid Jane doesn't understand a thing! Naturally he isn't going to hit her right away; it will be later on, after a long, long time, tomorrow, perhaps.

'And try not to make any noise when you go in. Your mama is very tired, and perhaps baby is asleep.'

How tiresome! Trott has such a heap of things to tell his mama. Yesterday he found a very beautiful pink shell. And besides, he has held the bridle of the black horse a long time. Then, too, he will have to tell her he has torn his trousers. Not the new ones, luckily . . . But here is the garden gate already. Trott opens it softly. He is beginning to feel a certain vague disquiet. After all, he does not know her, this little person, and when Jane has pulled the bell, a strange desire seizes him to take heels. How silly! Thérèse, the old cook, is opening the door. She has recognized Trott's voice.

'Well, M. Trott, you are going to see her, that little sister of yours. But don't make any noise. Your mama wants to kiss you first of all. Go up very softly.'

Trott clambers up the stairs. He is more and more disturbed. There is a heavy silence in the house that squeezes his throat. He has to wait in the hall. Jane will see if he can go in to his mama. Trott waits a long time. He is very serious. It must be getting time for tea. But here is papa!

'Papa!'

'Sh—come in to your mama. She is sick. You must only say good afternoon, and then you must go out.'

This is no fun at all. Papa does not look so splendid as he does when he is all dressed up in his navy officer's uniform. Papa is all disorder. His eyes are red, and he is dressed every which way. What an upset just because of that little sister! Trott begins to feel displeased.

Mama's room is almost dark. It smells like a drug store. Mama is in bed, very pale, all white. She looks so tired . . . Yet a little smile touches her lips when Trott approaches. All in a maze he bends over to kiss her, and murmurs mechanically, 'You know, mama, I found a beautiful shell—' but papa interrupts and makes him stop talking and puts him out in the hall into Jane's hands. He finds himself back in daylight again, much bewildered. Now he must go to see the little sister. Oh, well, that will be more fun. One can jump and laugh a bit. But sh—little sister is asleep. The lazy little thing! Trott will soon wake her up . . . But no! 'If you make any noise, M. Trott, you will be sent out immediately.'

Trott promises to be good. He tiptoes along the hall. Jane knocks at a door. The enormous Nounou appears. She smiles and discloses the huge teeth of a cannibal, which greatly impress Trott, and she says to him, 'Papyzleebs.'

Trott stops, dumbfounded. Is she swearing? What is she going to do? No, that's how Alsatians speak. That means that the 'baby sleeps.' Reassured, Trott slips in softly. He turns toward a large pink crib. Nounou pushes the curtains back, Trott bends over, and he sees—!!

He sees a sort of baked apple, all shriveled, very red, with here and there excrescences and holes. It really looks like a very tiny face that someone has sat on and that feels very hot. There are also microscopic hands like those of an old woman, all red and wrinkled. The thing looks old, miserable, dried up! Trott is in consternation.

'Briddypapy!' says the nurse.

Trott lifts his head hesitantly, then he turns his back on the baby who continues to sleep. So that's the little sister!

'Well, M. Trott, what do you think of your little sister?'

'Don't you think, Jane, if we send her back right away, that God would be willing to change her for another baby not quite so ugly?'

Jane becomes very indignant. She overwhelms Trott with reproaches, but he doesn't hear them. He is looking steadily at the little red doll. How ugly she is! Oh, well, Lucette is a pretty enough name for her. Polycarpe would have been much too beautiful. There, she is moving. This is more interesting. They can move then, these little scraps? And even—it looks as if—yes, truly, her eyelids open; two things like round black beans appear, no white; there—her mouth puckers—you must be polite. Trott, a little alarmed, says very low, 'Good morning, Lucette.'

She does not answer. Yes, she does. She is making a face.

'Wa-a-a-a—'

Trott takes a step backward. What kind of conversation is this? He feels his head swim. What, can that voice belong to his little sister! You would think it was the voice of Marie de Milly's doll, which cries when you press its stomach; only this cry is much uglier and louder.

This doll squalls as hard as she can in the voice of a punchinello with a bad cold. Nounou picks her up; she rubs her up and down; she shakes her. Oh, dear kind God, why is she so ugly?

She waves her hands as if she wanted to pull out your eyes and nose. Four miserable hairs stray over a naked pate which wobbles to right and to left. And to think that no one is astonished; that everyone seems to find this quite natural! Is it possible that other babies are like this? To think that that little thing there has come from heaven!

* * *

It is not a bit nice to have a little sister, not the littlest bit! Trott has been back at home for several days now, and everything is wrong. Nothing is the way it used to be. The biggest nuisance of all is to have to go on tiptoe all the time. No running, no shouting, because little sister sleeps from morning till evening. Mama is not sick abed any more, but she is always stretched out on the sofa. You can't play with her, she is always so tired.

Before he went away, Trott had a pretty little bedroom all for himself next to mama's. Now they have expelled him, and put Lucette and her big, fat Nounou in there, while he is simply shoved into a room on the next floor, without even being asked if he wanted to go. As the new bedroom is smaller than the other, they had to leave nearly all his playthings in the closet of the old room, and, as luck will have it, every time he wants one of them, Lucette is asleep and he cannot go in to get it.

It is really a very serious state of affairs. Before Lucette came, Trott was an important personage. The whole household revolved about him. Every act of his, every gesture, was an event. Thérèse, the cook, would give him cookies secretly, and Bertrand, the gardener, would leave the raking to show him birds' nests. Now Thérèse thinks of nothing but making eyes at Lucette, and as soon as that big Nounou appears in the garden Bertrand is at her heels. No one pays any attention at all to Trott. And yet, surely he is much nicer than that little helpless bundle. Little sister is no longer either yellow or red, it is true, but she has the same rather worn-out looking face, the same meaningless arm-wavings, and the same queer grimaces. And when she's not sleeping or crying, she's nursing. She blows out her cheeks, collapses them, blows them out again and collapses them again. She doesn't think of anything else. She's a glutton. And besides, she is dirty. No, no further details. She is very dirty. Enough said. Whereas Trott, he knows how to talk and run; he can turn somersaults, recite verses, and *he* wears trousers that do not need to be changed every hour or so. Isn't that enough to make one cross?

But Trott is not merely cross. There is something else the matter. What can it be? No indeed, he is not jealous of his little sister. He loves her dearly in his own fashion, and he is very kind-hearted. He wants her to be happy and comfortable and does not wish her the slightest harm. Of course Trott isn't jealous. He is merely sad; very, very sad. Perhaps the reason that no one pays attention to him any more is because papa and mama have stopped loving him. Now they have a new child, they do not care about the old one. Trott can understand this, for he himself, as soon as he had been given a new box of leaden soldiers, forsook his old shabby ones. Apparently, it is the same thing with grown-ups. Yes, they have forgotten him entirely. Here is proof. The other evening mama and papa were discussing whether or not to give limewater to the baby. Dinner was announced. They got up and walked into the dining-room, leaving Trott unnoticed. Papa happened to turn around and saw him. 'There, we were forgetting you; hurry up.' Forgetting! Papa said that. They were forgetting Trott! Two or three tears

fell into his soup. No one noticed. They were again deep in discussion over the limewater question.

Great sorrow entered Trott's heart. They did not love him any more. Well, perhaps a little bit, but not as they did before. And when one has been loved to the full, a little is not enough. Trott's heart is very heavy, and he feels somewhat as he did that time he ate too much apple tart.

And today things have gone worse than ever.

This morning he was doing his lessons with Miss, and he was a bit grouchy, so, though usually he is most polite, he said a word that is not very—well, you know. And papa, just coming in, heard him. Trott got no dessert, and they had whipped cream!

After lunch, Trott was in a hurry to stretch his legs. He rushed out of the dining-room, slamming the door behind him. This waked little sister, who began to howl. Mama said, 'That boy is unbearable!'

This evening, coming back from a walk, it was almost dark. That is the time, especially when one's heart is heavy, that one longs for petting. Trott wanted to go to his mother and sit beside her on his little footstool as he always had done, but there in his own place was Lucette in her bassinet, and mama was so absorbed in making faces at her that she hardly took time to give Trott the hastiest little kiss. Trott felt a cold wave go over him and he slipped over to the window and sat there all alone, watching the night descend over the garden.

Finally papa came in. He sat down next to the baby, said to Trott, 'Pouting, my boy?' and began to chat with mama about that little doll who was holding on to his finger. Trott drew farther into his corner, and still blacker melancholy descended upon him. He was sure now, absolutely sure, that no one loved him any longer. Formerly, when he had been naughty, they scolded him a little and then it was all over. They gave him a big kiss, and, really, it was almost nice to have been scolded. Now they scolded him harder, and did not pet him at all. What should he do? And they used to love him so much, so very much. And when he was sick, it seemed as if they loved him even more. Suppose he got sick now . . . perhaps . . .

There's an idea. Baby has been carried out. No one is looking. Papa and mama are talking together softly. With one jump Trott is standing on the seat of his chair. He grasps the back with both hands and gives a good push against the window-frame. The chair falls over with a terrific bang and Trott is thrown to the floor and sent rolling to the center of the room.

Mama utters a piercing cry; papa rushes to Trott, picks him up, and hurriedly looks at his forehead. But mama must have him; she takes possession of him, holds him on her lap, cuddles him, pets him, calls him her dear little awkward boy. Trott cries from joy and pain, for he has a big bump on his forehead.

'How did you come to fall, my poor darling?'

Trott cannot answer. He is crying too hard. Finally he manages, between sobs, 'I—I did it on purpose.'

Papa and mama look at each other in amazement. What can he mean?

Well, boys must never tell lies. Hard as it is, especially when there are so many tears rolling down, Trott explains. He wanted to find out whether his father and mother loved him any more, even the least bit. He knows very well, of course, that they cannot love him, the old child, the way they can little sister who is new, but he thought maybe they still loved him just a little. He wanted to know for sure. And now he is happy, very, very happy, although—and the cataract redoubles in violence.

Mama slips an arm around Trott's neck and wipes his eyes. Papa holds the little hands in his own big ones. Both are smiling, but it is a very special kind of smile, a very tender smile. Music fills Trott's ears, music of soft voices and words, a music that fills his heart as well. And now he is hearing the most wonderful news. It seems that they love him just as much as before; as much, even, as Lucette. Only Lucette is very tiny. She cannot talk. She is not strong and so she has to be cared for all the time, whereas Trott is a big boy. Oh, but they love him just as much, indeed they do. Papa lifts his little boy up in his arms, plants a big kiss on each cheek and asks him, 'Is everything all right now, my man?'

And Trott answers, with eyes still red, but mouth all smiles, 'Oh, yes, but just the same, I'm glad I gave myself that bump.'

SWANN'S WAY

Marcel Proust

[The wily scheming of a child to obtain his desires is memorably portrayed by Proust in this picture of a boy whose obsession for his mother is doubtless one of the causes of his later neuroticism. The child's rivalry with his father for his mother's affection is a conscious one. Unwise parental handling of the situation may have helped to cause the emotional fixation which probably lies at the root of his maladjustments in maturity. Something of this the author foreshadows here in the precocious child's half-realization that, in its effect on his personality, his triumph over his parents may have in it elements of personal defeat.]

I never took my eyes off my mother. I knew that when they were at table I should not be permitted to stay there for the whole of dinner-time, and that Mamma, for fear of annoying my father, would not allow me to give her in public the series of kisses that she would have had in my room. And so I promised myself that in the dining-room, as they began to eat and drink and as I felt the hour approach, I would put beforehand into this kiss, which was bound to be so brief and stealthy in execution, everything that my own efforts could put into it: would look out very carefully first the exact spot on her cheek where I would imprint it, and would so prepare my thoughts that I might be able, thanks to these mental preliminaries, to consecrate the whole of the minute Mamma would allow me to the sensation of her cheek against my lips, as a painter who can have his subject for short sittings only prepares his palette, and from what he remembers and from rough notes does in advance everything which he possibly can do in the sitter's absence. But to-night, before the dinner-bell had sounded, my grandfather said with unconscious cruelty: 'The little man looks tired; he'd better go up to bed. Besides, we are dining late to-night.'

And my father, who was less scrupulous than my grandmother or mother in observing the letter of a treaty, went on: 'Yes; run along; to bed with you.'

I would have kissed Mamma then and there, but at that moment the dinner-bell rang.

'No, no, leave your mother alone. You've said good night quite enough. These exhibitions are absurd. Go on upstairs.'

And so I must set forth without viaticum; must climb each step of the staircase 'against my heart,' as the saying is, climbing in opposition to my heart's desire, which was to return to my mother, since she had not, by her kiss, given my heart leave to accompany me forth. That hateful staircase, up which I always passed with such dismay, gave out a smell of varnish which had to some extent absorbed, made definite and fixed the special quality of sorrow that I felt

From *Swann's Way* by Marcel Proust. Reprinted by permission of Random House, Inc.

each evening, and made it perhaps even more cruel to my sensibility because, when it assumed this olfactory guise, my intellect was powerless to resist it. When we have gone to sleep with a maddening toothache and are conscious of it only as a little girl whom we attempt, time after time, to pull out of the water, or as a line of Molière which we repeat incessantly to ourselves, it is a great relief to wake up, so that our intelligence can disentangle the idea of toothache from any artificial semblance of heroism or rhythmic cadence. It was the precise converse of this relief which I felt when my anguish at having to go up to my room invaded my consciousness in a manner infinitely more rapid, instantaneous almost, a manner at once insidious and brutal as I breathed in —a far more poisonous thing than any moral penetration—the peculiar smell of the varnish upon that staircase.

Once in my room I had to stop every loophole, to close the shutters, to dig my own grave as I turned down the bedclothes, to wrap myself in the shroud of my nightshirt. But before burying myself in the iron bed which had been placed there because, on summer nights, I was too hot among the rep curtains of the four-poster, I was stirred to revolt, and attempted the desperate stratagem of a condemned prisoner. I wrote to my mother begging her to come upstairs for an important reason which I could not put in writing. My fear was that Françoise, my aunt's cook who used to be put in charge of me when I was at Combray, might refuse to take my note. I had a suspicion that, in her eyes, to carry a message to my mother when there was a stranger in the room would appear flatly inconceivable, just as it would be for the doorkeeper of a theatre to hand a letter to an actor upon the stage. For things which might or might not be done she possessed a code at once imperious, abundant, subtle, and uncompromising on points themselves imperceptible or irrelevant, which gave it a resemblance to those ancient laws which combine such cruel ordinances as the massacre of infants at the breast with prohibitions, of exaggerated refinement, against 'seething the kid in his mother's milk,' or 'eating of the sinew which is upon the hollow of the thigh.' This code, if one could judge it by the sudden obstinacy which she would put into her refusal to carry out certain of our instructions, seemed to have foreseen such social complications and refinements of fashion as nothing in Françoise's surroundings or in her career as a servant in a village household could have put into her head; and we were obliged to assume that there was latent in her some past existence in the ancient history of France, noble and little understood, just as there is in those manufacturing towns where old mansions still testify to their former courtly days, and chemical workers toil among delicately sculptured scenes of the Miracle of Theophilus or the Quatre Fils Aymon.

In this particular instance, the article of her code which made it highly improbable that—barring an outbreak of fire—Françoise would go down and disturb Mamma when M. Swann was there for so unimportant a person as myself was one embodying the respect she shewed not only for the family (as for the dead, for the clergy, or for royalty), but also for the stranger within our gates; a respect which I should perhaps have found touching in a book, but which never failed to irritate me on her lips, because of the solemn and gentle tones in which she would utter it, and which irritated me more than usual this evening when the sacred character in which she invested the dinner-party might have the effect of making her decline to disturb its ceremonial. But to give myself one chance of success I lied without hesitation, telling her that it was not in the least myself who had wanted to write to Mamma, but Mamma who, on saying good night to me, had begged me not to forget to send her an answer about something she had asked me to find, and that she would certainly be very angry if this note were not taken to her. I think that Françoise disbelieved me, for, like those primitive men whose senses were so much keener than our own, she could immediately detect, by signs imperceptible by the rest of us, the truth or falsehood of anything that we might wish to conceal from her. She studied the envelope for five minutes as though an examination of the paper itself and the look of my handwriting could enlighten her as to the nature of the contents, or tell her to which article of her code she ought to refer the matter. Then she went out with an air of resignation which seemed to imply: 'What a dreadful thing for parents to have a child like this!'

A moment later she returned to say that they were still at the ice stage and that it was impossible for the butler to deliver the note at once, in front of everybody; but that when the finger-bowls were put round he would find a way of slipping it into Mamma's hand. At once my anxiety subsided; it was now no longer (as it had been a moment ago) until to-morrow that I had lost my mother, for my little line was going—to annoy her, no doubt, and doubly so because this contrivance would make

me ridiculous in Swann's eyes—but was going all the same to admit me, invisibly and by stealth, into the same room as herself, was going to whisper from me into her ear; for that forbidden and unfriendly dining-room, where but a moment ago the ice itself—with burned nuts in it—and the finger-bowls seemed to me to be concealing pleasures that were mischievous and of a mortal sadness because Mamma was tasting of them and I was far away, had opened its doors to me and, like a ripe fruit which bursts through its skin, was going to pour out into my intoxicated heart the gushing sweetness of Mamma's attention while she was reading what I had written. Now I was no longer separated from her; the barriers were down; an exquisite thread was binding us. Besides, that was not all, for surely Mamma would come.

As for the agony through which I had just passed, I imagined that Swann would have laughed heartily at it if he had read my letter and had guessed its purpose; whereas, on the contrary, as I was to learn in due course, a similar anguish had been the bane of his life for many years, and no one perhaps could have understood my feelings at that moment so well as himself; to him, that anguish which lies in knowing that the creature one adores is in some place of enjoyment where oneself is not and cannot follow—to him that anguish came through Love, to which it is in a sense predestined, by which it must be equipped and adapted; but when, as had befallen me, such an anguish possesses one's soul before Love has yet entered into one's life, then it must drift, awaiting Love's coming, vague and free, without precise attachment, at the disposal of one sentiment to-day, of another to-morrow, of filial piety or affection for a comrade. And the joy with which I first bound myself apprentice, when Françoise returned to tell me that my letter would be delivered, Swann, too, had known well that false joy which a friend can give us, or some relative of the woman we love, when on his arrival at the house or theatre where she is to be found, for some ball or party or 'first-night' at which he is to meet her, he sees us wandering outside, desperately awaiting some opportunity of communicating with her. He recognises us, greets us familiarly, and asks what we are doing there. And when we invent a story of having some urgent message to give to his relative or friend, he assures us that nothing could be more simple, takes us in at the door, and promises to send her down to us in five minutes. How much we love him—as at that moment I loved Françoise—the good-natured intermediary who by a single word has made supportable, human, almost propitious the inconceivable, infernal scene of gaiety in the thick of which we had been imagining swarms of enemies, perverse and seductive, beguiling away from us, even making laugh at us, the woman whom we love. If we are to judge of them by him, this relative who has accosted us and who is himself an initiate in those cruel mysteries, then the other guests cannot be so very demoniacal. Those inaccessible and torturing hours into which she had gone to taste of unknown pleasures—behold, a breach in the wall, and we are through it. Behold, one of the moments whose series will go to make up their sum, a moment as genuine as the rest, if not actually more important to ourself because our mistress is more intensely a part of it; we picture it to ourselves,

we possess it, we intervene upon it, almost we have created it: namely, the moment in which he goes to tell her that we are waiting there below. And very probably the other moments of the party will not be essentially different, will contain nothing else so exquisite ₒr so well able to make us suffer, since this kind friend has assured us that 'Of course, she will be delighted to come down! It will be far more amusing for her to talk to you than to be bored up there.' Alas! Swann had learned by experience that the good intentions of a third party are powerless to control a woman who is annoyed to find herself pursued even into a ball-room by a man whom she does not love. Too often, the kind friend comes down again alone.

My mother did not appear, but with no attempt to safe-guard my self-respect (which depended upon her keeping up the fiction that she had asked me to let her know the result of my search for something or other) made Françoise tell me, in so many words 'There is no answer'—words I have so often, since then, heard the hall-porters in 'mansions' and the flunkeys in gambling-clubs and the like, repeat to some poor girl, who replies in bewilderment: 'What! he's said nothing? It's not possible. You did give him my letter, didn't you? Very well, I shall wait a little longer.' And just as she invariably protests that she does not need the extra gas which the porter offers to light for her, and sits on there, hearing nothing further, except an occasional remark on the weather which the porter exchanges with a messenger whom he will send off suddenly, when he notices the time, to put some customer's wine on the ice; so, having declined Françoise's offer to make me some tea or to stay beside me, I let her go off again to the servants' hall, and lay down and shut my eyes, and tried not to hear the voices of my family who were drinking their coffee in the garden.

But after a few seconds I realised that, by writing that line to Mamma, by approaching—at the risk of making her angry—so near to her that I felt I could reach out and grasp the moment in which I should see her again, I had cut myself off from the possibility of going to sleep until I actually had seen her, and my heart began to beat more and more painfully as I increased my agitation by ordering myself to keep calm and to acquiesce in my ill-fortune. Then, suddenly, my anxiety subsided, a feeling of intense happiness coursed through me, as when a strong medicine begins to take effect and one's pain vanishes: I had formed a resolution to abandon all attempts to go to sleep without seeing Mamma, and had decided to kiss her at all costs, even with the certainty of being in disgrace with her for long afterwards, when she herself came up to bed. The tranquillity which followed my anguish made me extremely alert, no less than my sense of expectation, my thirst for and my fear of danger.

Noiselessly I opened the window and sat down on the foot of my bed; hardly daring to move in case they should hear me from below. Things outside seemed also fixed in mute expectation, so as not to disturb the moonlight which, duplicating each of them and throwing it back by the extension, forwards, of a shadow denser and more concrete than its substance, had made the whole landscape seem at once thinner and longer, like a map which, after being folded up, is spread out upon the ground. What had to

move—a leaf of the chestnut-tree, for instance—moved. But its minute shuddering, complete, finished to the least detail and with utmost delicacy of gesture, made no discord with the rest of the scene, and yet was not merged in it, remaining clearly outlined. Exposed upon this surface of silence, which absorbed nothing from them, the most distant sounds, those which must have come from gardens at the far end of the town, could be distinguished with such exact 'finish' that the impression they gave of coming from a distance seemed due only to their 'pianissimo' execution, like those movements on muted strings so well performed by the orchestra of the Conservatoire that, although one does not lose a single note, one thinks all the same that they are being played somewhere outside, a long way from the concert hall, so that all the old subscribers, and my grandmother's sisters too, when Swann had given them his seats, used to strain their ears as if they had caught the distant approach of an army on the march, which had not yet rounded the corner of the Rue de Trévise.

I was well aware that I had placed myself in a position than which none could be counted upon to involve me in graver consequences at my parents' hands; consequences far graver, indeed, than a stranger would have imagined, and such as (he would have thought) could follow only some really shameful fault. But in the system of education which they had given me faults were not classified in the same order as in that of other children, and I had been taught to place at the head of the list (doubtless because there was no other class of faults from which I needed to be more carefully protected) those in which I can now distinguish the common feature that one succumbs to them by yielding to a nervous impulse. But such words as these last had never been uttered in my hearing; no one had yet accounted for my temptations in a way which might have led me to believe that there was some excuse for my giving in to them, or that I was actually incapable of holding out against them. Yet I could easily recognise this class of transgressions by the anguish of mind which preceded, as well as by the rigour of the punishment which followed them; and I knew that what I had just done was in the same category as certain other sins for which I had been severely chastised, though infinitely more serious than they. When I went out to meet my mother as she herself came up to bed, and when she saw that I had remained up so as to say good night to her again in the passage, I should not be allowed to stay in the house a day longer, I should be packed off to school next morning; so much was certain. Very good: had I been obliged, the next moment, to hurl myself out of the window, I should still have preferred such a fate. For what I wanted now was Mamma, and to say good night to her. I had gone too far along the road which led to the realisation of this desire to be able to retrace my steps.

I could hear my parents' footsteps as they went with Swann; and, when the rattle of the gate assured me that he had really gone, I crept to the window. Mamma was asking my father if he had thought the lobster good, and whether M. Swann had had some more of the coffee-and-pistachio ice. 'I thought it rather so-so,' she was saying; 'next time we shall have to try another flavour.

'I can't tell you,' said my great-aunt, 'what a change I find in Swann. He is quite antiquated!' She had grown so accustomed to seeing Swann always in the same stage of adolescence that it was a shock to her to find him suddenly less young than the age she still attributed to him. And the others too were beginning to remark in Swann that abnormal, excessive, scandalous senescence, met only in a celibate, in one of that class for whom it seems that the great day which knows no morrow must be longer than for other men, since for such a one it is void of promise, and from its dawn the moments steadily accumulate without any subsequent partition among his offspring.

'I fancy he has a lot of trouble with that wretched wife of his, who "lives" with a certain Monsieur de Charlus, as all Combray knows. It's the talk of the town.'

My mother observed that, in spite of this, he had looked much less unhappy of late. 'And he doesn't nearly so often do that trick of his, so like his father, of wiping his eyes and passing his hand across his forehead. I think myself that in his heart of hearts he doesn't love his wife any more.'

'Why, of course he doesn't,' answered my grandfather. 'He wrote me a letter about it, ages ago, to which I took care to pay no attention, but it left no doubt as to his feelings, let alone his love for his wife. Hullo! you two; you never thanked him for the Asti!' he went on, turning to his sisters-in-law.

'What! we never thanked him? I think, between you and me, that I put it to him quite neatly,' replied my aunt Flora.

'Yes, you managed it very well; I admired you for it,' said my aunt Celine.

'But you did it very prettily, too,'

'Yes; I liked my expression about "nice neighbours." '

'What! Do you call that thanking him?' shouted my grandfather. 'I heard that all right, but devil take me if I guessed it was meant for Swann. You may be quite sure he never noticed it.'

'Come, come; Swann is not a fool. I am positive he appreciated the compliment. You didn't expect me to tell him the number of bottles, or to guess what he paid for them.'

My father and mother were left alone and sat down for a moment; then my father said: 'Well, shall we go up to bed?'

'As you wish, dear, though I don't feel in the least like sleeping. I don't know why; it can't be the coffee-ice—it wasn't strong enough to keep me awake like this. But I see a light in the servants' hall: poor Françoise has been sitting up for me, so I will get her to unhook me while you go and undress.'

My mother opened the latticed door which led from the hall to the staircase. Presently I heard her coming upstairs to close her window. I went quietly into the passage; my heart was beating so violently that I could hardly move, but at least it was throbbing no longer with anxiety, but with terror and with joy. I saw in the well of the stair a light coming upwards, from Mamma's candle. Then I saw Mamma herself: I threw myself upon her. For an instant she looked at me in astonishment, not realising what could have happened. Then her face assumed an expression of anger. She said not a single word to me; and, for that matter, I used to go for days on end without being spoken to, for far less offences than this. A single word from Mamma would have been an admission that

further intercourse with me was within the bounds of possibility, and that might perhaps have appeared to me more terrible still, as indicating that, with such a punishment as was in store for me, mere silence, and even anger, were relatively puerile.

A word from her then would have implied the false calm in which one converses with a servant to whom one has just decided to give notice; the kiss one bestows on a son who is being packed off to enlist, which would have been denied him if it had merely been a matter of being angry with him for a few days. But she heard my father coming from the dressing-room, where he had gone to take off his clothes, and, to avoid the 'scene' which he would make if he saw me, she said, in a voice half-stifled by her anger: 'Run away at once. Don't let your father see you standing there like a crazy jane!'

But I begged her again to 'Come and say good night to me!' terrified as I saw the light from my father's candle already creeping up the wall, but also making use of his approach as a means of blackmail, in the hope that my mother, not wishing him to find me there, as find me he must if she continued to hold out, would give in to me, and say: 'Go back to your room. I will come.'

Too late: my father was upon us. Instinctively I murmured, though no one heard me, 'I am done for!'

I was not, however. My father used constantly to refuse to let me do things which were quite clearly allowed by the more liberal charters granted me by my mother and grandmother, because he paid no heed to 'Principles,' and because in his sight there were no such things as 'Rights of Man.' For some quite irrelevant reason, or for no reason at all, he would at the last moment prevent me from taking some particular walk, one so regular and so consecrated to my use that to deprive me of it was a clear breach of faith; or again, as he had done this evening, long before the appointed hour he would snap out: 'Run along up to bed now; no excuses!' But then again, simply because he was devoid of principles (in my grandmother's sense), so he could not, properly speaking, be called inexorable. He looked at me for a moment with an air of annoyance and surprise, and then when Mamma had told him, not without some embarrassment, what had happened, said to her: 'Go along with him, then; you said just now that you didn't feel like sleep, so stay in his room for a little. I don't need anything.'

'But, dear,' my mother answered timidly, 'whether or not I feel like sleep is not the point; we must not make the child accustomed . . .'

'There's no question of making him accustomed,' said my father, with a shrug of the shoulders; 'you can see quite well that the child is unhappy. After all, we aren't gaolers. You'll end by making him ill, and a lot of good that will do. There are two beds in his room; tell Françoise to make up the big one for you, and stay beside him for the rest of the night. I'm off to bed, anyhow; I'm not nervous like you. Good night.'

It was impossible for me to thank my father; what he called my sentimentality would have exasperated him. I stood there, not daring to move; he was still confronting us, an immense figure in his white nightshirt, crowned with the pink and violet scarf of Indian cashmere in which, since he had begun to suffer from neuralgia, he used to tie up his head, standing like Abraham in the engraving after Benozzo Gozzoli which M. Swann had given me, telling Sarah that she must tear herself away from Isaac. Many years have passed since that night. The wall of the staircase, up which I had watched the light of his candle gradually climb, was long ago demolished. And in myself, too, many things have perished which, I imagined, would last for ever, and new structures have arisen, giving birth to new sorrows and new joys which in those days I could not have foreseen, just as now the old are difficult of comprehension. It is a long time, too, since my father has been able to tell Mamma to 'Go with the child.' Never again will such hours be possible for me. But of late I have been increasingly able to catch, if I listen attentively, the sound of the sobs which I had the strength to control in my father's presence, and which broke out only when I found myself alone with Mamma. Actually, their echo has never ceased: it is only because life is now growing more and more quiet round about me that I hear them afresh, like those convent bells which are so effectively drowned during the day by the noises of the streets that one would suppose them to have been stopped for ever, until they sound out again through the silent evening air.

Mamma spent that night in my room: when I had just committed a sin so deadly that I was waiting to be banished from the household, my parents gave me a far greater concession than I should ever have won as the reward of a good action. Even at the moment when it manifested itself in this crowning mercy, my father's conduct towards me was still somewhat arbitrary, and regardless of my deserts, as was characteristic of him and due to the fact that his actions were generally dictated by chance expediencies rather than based on any formal plan. And perhaps even what I called his strictness, when he sent me off to bed, deserved that title less, really, than my mother's or grandmother's attitude, for his nature, which in some respects differed more than theirs from my own, had probably prevented him from guessing, until then, how wretched I was every evening, a thing which my mother and grandmother knew well; but they loved me enough to be unwilling to spare me that suffering, which they hoped to teach me to overcome, so as to reduce my nervous sensibility and to strengthen my will. As for my father, whose affection for me was of another kind, I doubt if he would have shewn so much courage, for as soon as he had grasped the fact that I was unhappy he had said to my mother: 'Go and comfort him.'

Mamma stayed all night in my room, and it seemed that she did not wish to mar by recrimination those hours, so different from anything that I had had a right to expect; for when Françoise (who guessed that something extraordinary must have happened when she saw Mamma sitting by my side, holding my hand and letting me cry unchecked) said to her: 'But, Madame, what is little Master crying for?' she replied: 'Why, Françoise, he doesn't know himself: it is his nerves. Make up the big bed for me quickly and then go off to your own.' And thus for the first time my unhappiness was regarded no longer as a fault for which I must be punished, but as an involuntary evil which had been officially recognised, a nervous condition for which I was in no way responsible: I had the consolation that I need no longer mingle apprehensive scruples with the bitter-

ness of my tears; I could weep henceforward without sin. I felt no small degree of pride, either, in Françoise's presence at this return to humane conditions which, not an hour after Mamma had refused to come up to my room and had sent the snubbing message that I was to go to sleep, raised me to the dignity of a grown-up person, brought me of a sudden to a sort of puberty of sorrow, to emancipation from tears. I ought then to have been happy; I was not. It struck me that my mother had just made a first concession which must have been painful to her, that it was a first step down from the ideal she had formed for me, and that for the first time she, with all her courage, had to confess herself beaten. It struck me that if I had just scored a victory it was over her; that I had succeeded, as sickness or sorrow or age might have succeeded, in relaxing her will, in altering her judgment; that this evening opened a new era, must remain a black date in the calendar. And if I had dared now, I should have said to Mamma: 'No, I don't want you; you mustn't sleep here.' But I was conscious of the practical wisdom, of what would be called nowadays the realism with which she tempered the ardent idealism of my grandmother's nature, and I knew that now the mischief was done she would prefer to let me enjoy the soothing pleasure of her company, and not to disturb my father again. Certainly my mother's beautiful features seemed to shine again with youth that evening, as she sat gently holding my hands and trying to check my tears; but just for that reason, it seemed to me that this should not have happened; her anger would have been less difficult to endure than this new kindness which my childhood had not known; I felt that I had with an impious and secret finger traced a first wrinkle upon her soul and made the first white hair shew upon her head. This thought redoubled my sobs, and then I saw that Mamma, who had never allowed herself to go to any length of tenderness with me, was suddenly overcome by my tears and had to struggle to keep back her own. Then, as she saw that I had noticed this, she said to me, with a smile: 'Why, my little buttercup, my little canary-boy, he's going to make Mamma as silly as himself if this goes on. Look, since you can't sleep, and Mamma can't either, we mustn't go on in this stupid way; we must do something; I'll get one of your books.' But I had none there. 'Would you like me to get out the books now that your grandmother is going to give you for your birthday? Just think it over first, and don't be disappointed if there is nothing new for you then.'

❋

TO THE LIGHTHOUSE
Virginia Woolf

[In *To the Lighthouse* Virginia Woolf has made a penetrating psychological study of a family group, developing her portrait largely through a controlled stream of consciousness technique which takes us intimately into the thoughts of the interacting personalities. In these two passages we see how the dominant father arouses feelings of intense hatred in his small son because he intrudes upon the mother-son relationship with his insistent demands upon his wife's emotions. We recognize in Professor Ramsay a neurotic personality who, under guise of a quest for reality in his metaphysical studies, escapes from facing the reality of himself and his relations to others. In the renewed expressions of wifely devotion, in the implicit obedience of his children and the admiration of a group of disciples, he finds compensation for his feelings of personal inadequacy and defeat.

In the later passage the boy is seventeen, the mother long dead, and the father has ordered a voyage to the lighthouse, which in this novel is both objective reality and symbol. The relation between past and present in the emotional life of the boy becomes clear to him as the earlier moment of antagonism to his father returns to his consciousness and he understands something of its significance in the development of his personality.]

But what had happened?

Some one had blundered.

Starting from her musing she gave meaning to words which she had held meaningless in her mind for a long stretch of time. 'Some one had blundered—' Fixing her short-sighted eyes upon her husband, who was now bearing down upon her, she gazed steadily until his closeness revealed

From *To the Lighthouse* by Virginia Woolf. By permission of Harcourt, Brace and Co.

to her (the jingle mated itself in her head) that something had happened, some one had blundered. But she could not for the life of her think what.

He shivered; he quivered. All his vanity, all his satisfaction in his own splendour, riding fell as a thunderbolt, fierce as a hawk at the head of his men through the valley of death, had been shattered, destroyed. Stormed at by shot and shell, boldly we rode and well, flashed through the valley of death, volleyed and thundered—straight into Lily Briscoe and William Bankes. He quivered; he shivered.

Not for the world would she have spoken to him, realising, from the familiar signs, his eyes averted, and some curious gathering together of his person, as if he wrapped himself about and needed privacy into which to regain his equilibrium, that he was outraged and anguished. She stroked James's head; she transferred to him what she felt for her husband, and, as she watched him chalk yellow the white dress shirt of a gentleman in the Army and Navy Stores catalogue, thought what a delight it would be to her should he turn out a great artist; and why should he not? He had a splendid forehead. Then, looking up, as her husband passed her once more, she was relieved to find that the ruin was veiled; domesticity triumphed; custom crooned its soothing rhythm, so that when stopping deliberately, as his turn came round again, at the window he bent quizzically and whimsically to tickle James's bare calf with a sprig of something, she twitted him for having dispatched 'that poor young man,' Charles Tansley. Tansley had had to go in and write his dissertation, he said.

'James will have to write *his* dissertation one of these days,' he added ironically, flicking his sprig.

Hating his father, James brushed away the tickling spray with which in a manner peculiar to him, compound of severity and humour, he teased his youngest son's bare leg.

She was trying to get these tiresome stockings finished to send to Sorley's little boy tomorrow, said Mrs. Ramsay.

There wasn't the slightest possible chance that they could go to the Lighthouse tomorrow, Mr. Ramsay snapped out irascibly.

How did he know? she asked. The wind often changed.

The extraordinary irrationality of her remark, the folly of women's minds enraged him. He had ridden through the valley of death, been shattered and shivered; and now, she flew in the face of facts, made his children hope what was utterly out of the question, in effect, told lies. He stamped his foot on the stone step. 'Damn you,' he said. But what had she said? Simply that it might be fine tomorrow. So it might.

Not with the barometer falling and the wind due west.

To pursue truth with such astonishing lack of consideration for other people's feelings, to rend the thin veils of civilisation so wantonly, so brutally, was to her so horrible an outrage of human decency that, without replying, dazed and blinded, she bent her head as if to let the pelt of jagged hail, the drench of dirty water, bespatter her unrebuked. There was nothing to be said.

He stood by her in silence. Very humbly, at length, he said that he would step over and ask the Coastguards if she liked.

There was nobody whom she reverenced as she reverenced him.

She was quite ready to take his word for it, she said. Only then they need not cut sandwiches—that was all. They came to her, naturally, since she was a woman, all day long with this and that; one wanting this, another that; the children were growing up; she often felt she was nothing but a sponge sopped full of emotions. Then he said, Damn you. He said, It must rain. He said, It won't rain; and instantly a Heaven of security opened before her. There was nobody she reverenced more. She was not good enough to tie his shoe strings, she felt.

Already ashamed of that petulance, of that gesticulation of the hands when charging at the head of his troops, Mr. Ramsay rather sheepishly prodded his son's bare legs once more, and then, as if he had her leave for it, with a movement which oddly reminded his wife of the great sea lion at the Zoo tumbling backwards after swallowing his fish and walloping off so that the water in the tank washes from side to side, he dived into the evening air which, already thinner, was taking the substance from leaves and hedges but, as if in return, restoring to roses and pinks a lustre which they had not had by day.

'Some one had blundered,' he said again, striding off, up and down the terrace.

But how extraordinarily his note had changed! It was like the cuckoo; 'in June he gets out of tune'; as if he were trying over, tentatively seeking, some phrase for a new mood, and having only this at hand, used it, cracked though it was. But it sounded ridiculous—'Some one had blundered'—said like that, almost as a question, without any conviction, melodiously. Mrs. Ramsay could not help smiling, and soon, sure enough, walking up and

down, he hummed it, dropped it, fell silent.

He was safe, he was restored to his privacy. He stopped to light his pipe, looked once at his wife and son in the window, and as one raises one's eyes from a page in an express train and sees a farm, a tree, a cluster of cottages as an illustration, a confirmation of something on the printed page to which one returns, fortified, and satisfied, so without his distinguishing either his son or his wife, the sight of them fortified him and satisfied him and consecrated his effort to arrive at a perfectly clear understanding of the problem which now engaged the energies of his splendid mind.

It was a splendid mind. For if thought is like the keyboard of a piano, divided into so many notes, or like the alphabet is ranged in twenty-six letters all in order, then his splendid mind had no sort of difficulty in running over those letters one by one, firmly and accurately, until it had reached, say, the letter Q. He reached Q. Very few people in the whole of England ever reach Q. Here, stopping for one moment by the stone urn which held the geraniums, he saw, but now far, far away, like children picking up shells, divinely innocent and occupied with little trifles at their feet and somehow entirely defenceless against a doom which he perceived, his wife and son, together, in the window. They needed his protection; he gave it them. But after Q? What comes next? After Q there are a number of letters the last of which is scarcely visible to mortal eyes, but glimmers red in the distance. Z is only reached once by one man in a generation. Still, if he could reach R it would be something. Here at least was Q. He dug his heels in at Q. Q he was sure of. Q he could demonstrate. If Q then is Q—R— Here he knocked his pipe out, with two or three resonant taps on the handle of the urn, and proceeded. 'Then R . . .' He braced himself. He clenched himself.

Qualities that would have saved a ship's company exposed on a broiling sea with six biscuits and a flask of water—endurance and justice, fore-sight, devotion, skill, came to his help. R is then—what is R?

A shutter, like the leathern eyelid of a lizard, flickered over the intensity of his gaze and obscured the letter R. In that flash of darkness he heard people saying—he was a failure—that R was beyond him. He would never reach R. On to R, once more. R—

Qualities that in a desolate expedi-tion across the icy solitudes of the Polar region would have made him the leader, the guide, the counsellor, whose temper, neither sanguine nor despondent, surveys with equanimity what is to be and faces it, came to his help again. R—

The lizard's eye flickered once more. The veins on his forehead bulged. The geranium in the urn became startlingly visible and, displayed among its leaves, he could see, with-out wishing it, that old, that obvious distinction between the two classes of men; on the one hand the steady goers of superhuman strength who, plodding and persevering, repeat the whole alphabet in order, twenty-six letters in all, from start to finish; on the other the gifted, the inspired who, miraculously, lump all the letters to-gether in one flash—the way of genius. He had not genius; he laid no claim to that: but he had, or might have had, the power to repeat every letter of the alphabet from A to Z accu-rately in order. Meanwhile, he stuck at Q. On, then, on to R.

Feelings that would not have dis-graced a leader who, now that the snow has begun to fall and the moun-tain top is covered in mist, knows that he must lay himself down and die before morning comes, stole upon him, paling the colour of his eyes, giving him, even in the two minutes of his turn on the terrace, the bleached look of withered old age. Yet he would not die lying down; he would find some crag of rock, and there, his eyes fixed on the storm, trying to the end to pierce the dark-ness, he would die standing. He would never reach R.

He stood stock-still, by the urn, with the geranium flowing over it. How many men in a thousand mil-lion, he asked himself, reach Z after all? Surely the leader of a forlorn hope may ask himself that, and an-swer, without treachery to the expedi-tion behind him, 'One perhaps.' One in a generation. Is he to be blamed then if he is not that one? provided he has toiled honestly, given to the best of his power, and till he has no more left to give? And his fame lasts how long? It is permissible even for a dying hero to think before he dies how men will speak of him hereafter. His fame lasts perhaps two thousand years. And what are two thousand years? (asked Mr. Ramsay ironically, staring at the hedge). What, indeed, if you look from a mountain top down the long wastes of the ages? The very stone one kicks with one's boot will outlast Shakespeare. His own little light would shine, not very brightly, for a year or two, and would then be merged in some bigger light, and that in a bigger still. (He looked into the hedge, into the intricacy of the twigs.) Who then could blame the leader of that forlorn party which after all has climbed high enough to see the waste of the years and the perishing of stars, if before death stiffens his limbs beyond the power of movement he does a little consciously raise his numbed fingers to his brow, and square his shoulders, so that when the search party comes they will find him dead at his post, the fine figure of a soldier? Mr. Ramsay squared his shoulders and stood very upright by the urn.

Who shall blame him, if, so standing for a moment, he dwells upon fame, upon search parties, upon cairns raised by grateful followers over his bones? Finally, who shall blame the leader of the doomed expedition, if, having adventured to the uttermost, and used his strength wholly to the last ounce and fallen asleep not much caring if he wakes or not, he now perceives by some pricking in his toes that he lives, and does not on the whole object to live, but requires sympathy, and whisky, and some one to tell the story of his suffering to at once? Who shall blame him? Who will not secretly rejoice when the hero puts his armour off, and halts by the window and gazes at his wife and son, who, very distant at first, gradually come closer and closer, till lips and book and head are clearly before him, though still lovely and unfamiliar from the intensity of his isolation and the waste of ages and the perishing of the stars, and finally putting his pipe in his pocket and bending his magnificent head before her—who will blame him if he does homage to the beauty of the world?

*   *   *

But his son hated him. He hated him for coming up to them, for stopping and looking down on them; he hated him for interrupting them; he hated him for the exaltation and sublimity of his gestures; for the magnificence of his head; for his exactingness and egotism (for there he stood, commanding them to attend to him); but most of all he hated the twang and twitter of his father's emotion which, vibrating round them, disturbed the perfect simplicity and good sense of his relations with his mother. By looking fixedly at the page, he hoped to make him move on; by pointing his finger at a word, he hoped to recall his mother's attention, which, he knew angrily, wavered instantly his father stopped. But, no. Nothing would make Mr. Ramsay move on. There he stood, demanding sympathy.

Mrs. Ramsay, who had been sitting loosely, folding her son in her arm, braced herself, and, half turning, seemed to raise herself with an effort, and at once to pour erect into the air a rain of energy, a column of spray, looking at the same time animated and alive as if all her energies were being fused into force, burning and illuminating (quietly though she sat, taking up her stocking again), and into this delicious fecundity, this fountain and spray of life, the fatal sterility of the male plunged itself, like a beak of brass, barren and bare. He wanted sympathy. He was a failure, he said. Mrs. Ramsay flashed her needles. Mr. Ramsay repeated, never taking his eyes from her face, that he was a failure. She blew the words back at him. 'Charles Tansley . . .' she said. But he must have more than that. It was sympathy he wanted, to be assured of his genius, first of all, and then to be taken within the circle of life, warmed and soothed, to have his senses restored to him, his barrenness made fertile, and all the rooms of the house made full of life—the drawing-room; behind the drawing-room the kitchen; above the kitchen the bedrooms; and beyond them the nurseries; they must be furnished, they must be filled with life.

Charles Tansley thought him the greatest metaphysician of the time, he said. But he must have more than that. He must have sympathy. He must be assured that he too lived in the heart of life; was needed; not here only, but all over the world. Flashing her needles, confident, upright, she created drawing-room and kitchen, set them all aglow; bade him take his ease there, go in and out, enjoy himself. She laughed, she knitted. Standing between her knees, very stiff, James felt all her strength flaring up to be drunk and quenched by the beak of brass, the arid scimitar of the male, which smote mercilessly, again and again, demanding sympathy.

He was a failure, he repeated. Well, look then, feel then. Flashing her needles, glancing round about her, out of the window, into the room, at James himself, she assured him, beyond a shadow of a doubt, by her laugh, her poise, her competence (as a nurse carrying a light across a dark room assures a fractious child), that it was real; the house was full; the garden blowing. If he put implicit faith in her, nothing should hurt him; however deep he buried himself or climbed high, not for a second should he find himself without her. So boasting of her capacity to surround and protect, there was scarcely a shell of herself left for her to know herself by; all was so lavished and spent; and James, as he stood stiff between her knees, felt her rise in a rosy-flowered fruit tree laid with leaves and dancing boughs into which the beak of brass, the arid scimitar of his father,

the egotistical man, plunged and smote, demanding sympathy.

Filled with her words, like a child who drops off satisfied, he said, at last, looking at her with humble gratitude, restored, renewed, that he would take a turn; he would watch the children playing cricket. He went.

Immediately, Mrs. Ramsay seemed to fold herself together, one petal closed in another, and the whole fabric fell in exhaustion upon itself, so that she had only strength enough to move her finger, in exquisite abandonment to exhaustion, across the page of Grimm's fairy story, while there throbbed through her, like the pulse in a spring which has expanded to its full width and now gently ceases to beat, the rapture of successful creation.

Every throb of this pulse seemed, as he walked away, to enclose her and her husband, and to give to each that solace which two different notes, one high, one low, struck together, seem to give each other as they combine. Yet, as the resonance died, and she turned to the Fairy Tale again, Mrs. Ramsay felt not only exhausted in body (afterwards, not at the time, she always felt this) but also there tinged her physical fatigue some faintly disagreeable sensation with another origin. Not that, as she read aloud the story of the Fisherman's Wife, she knew precisely what it came from; nor did she let herself put into words her dissatisfaction when she realised, at the turn of the page when she stopped and heard dully, ominously, a wave fall, how it came from this: she did not like, even for a second, to feel finer than her husband; and further, could not bear not being entirely sure, when she spoke to him, of the truth of what she said. Universities and people wanting him, lectures and books and their being of the highest importance—all that she did not doubt for a moment; but it was their relation, and his coming to her like that, openly, so that any one could see, that discomposed her; for then people said he depended on her, when they must know that of the two he was infinitely the more important, and what she gave the world, in comparison with what he gave, negligible. But then again, it was the other thing too—not being able to tell him the truth, being afraid, for instance, about the greenhouse roof and the expense it would be, fifty pounds perhaps, to mend it; and then about his books, to be afraid that he might guess, what she a little suspected, that his last book was not quite his best book (she gathered that from William Bankes); and then to hide small daily things, and the children seeing it, and the burden it laid on them—all this diminished the entire joy, the pure joy, of the two notes sounding together, and let the sound die on her ear now with a dismal flatness.

A shadow was on the page; she looked up. It was Augustus Carmichael shuffling past, precisely now, at the very moment when it was painful to be reminded of the inadequacy of human relationships, that the most perfect was flawed, and could not bear the examination which, loving her husband, with her instinct for truth, she turned upon it; when it was painful to feel herself convicted of unworthiness, and impeded in her proper function by these lies, these exaggerations—it was at this moment when she was fretted thus ignobly in the wake of her exaltation, that Mr. Carmichael shuffled past, in his yellow slippers, and some demon in her made it necessary for her to call out, as he passed,

'Going indoors, Mr. Carmichael?'

* * *

They don't feel a thing there, Cam thought, looking at the shore, which, rising and falling, became steadily more distant and more peaceful. Her hand cut a trail in the sea, as her mind made the green swirls and streaks into patterns and, numbed and shrouded, wandered in imagination in that underworld of waters where the pearls stuck in clusters to white sprays, where in the green light a change came over one's entire mind and one's body shone half transparent enveloped in a green cloak.

Then the eddy slackened round her hand. The rush of water ceased; the world became full of little creaking and squeaking sounds. One heard the waves breaking and flapping against the side of the boat as if they were anchored in harbour. Everything became very close to one. For the sail, upon which James had his eyes fixed until it had become to him like a person whom he knew, sagged entirely; there they came to a stop, flapping about waiting for a breeze, the hot sun, miles from shore, miles from the Lighthouse. Everything in the whole world seemed to stand still. The Lighthouse became immovable, and the line of the distant shore became fixed. The sun grew hotter and everybody seemed to come very close together and to feel each other's presence, which they had almost forgotten. Macalister's fishing line went plumb down into the sea. But Mr. Ramsay went on reading with his legs curled under him.

He was reading a little shiny book with covers mottled like a plover's egg. Now and again, as they hung about in that horrid calm, he turned a page. And James felt that each page was turned with a peculiar gesture aimed at him: now assertively, now commandingly; now with the intention of making people pity him; and all the time, as his father read and turned one after another of those little pages, James kept dreading the moment when he would look up and speak sharply to him about something or other. Why were they lagging about here? he would demand, or something quite unreasonable like that. And if he does, James thought, then I shall take a knife and strike him to the heart.

He had always kept this old symbol of taking a knife and striking his father to the heart. Only now, as he grew older, and sat staring at his father in an impotent rage, it was not him, that old man reading, whom he wanted to kill, but it was the thing that descended on him—without his knowing it perhaps: that fierce sudden black-winged harpy, with its talons and its beak all cold and hard, that struck and struck at you (he could feel the beak on his bare legs, where it had struck when he was a child) and then made off, and there he was again, an old man, very sad, reading his book. That he would kill, that he would strike to the heart. Whatever he did— (and he might do anything, he felt, looking at the Lighthouse and the distant shore) whether he was in a business, in a bank, a barrister, a man at the head of some enterprise, that he would fight, that he would track down and stamp out —tyranny, despotism, he called it— making people do what they did not want to do, cutting off their right to speak. How could any of them say, But I won't, when he said, Come to the Lighthouse. Do this. Fetch me

that. The black wings spread, and the hard beak tore. And then next moment, there he sat reading his book; and he might look up—one never knew—quite reasonably. He might talk to the Macalisters. He might be pressing a sovereign into some frozen old woman's hand in the street, James thought, and he might be shouting out at some fisherman's sports; he might be waving his arms in the air with excitement. Or he might sit at the head of the table dead silent from one end of dinner to the other. Yes, thought James, while the boat slapped and dawdled there in the hot sun; there was a waste of snow and rock very lonely and austere; and there he had come to feel, quite often lately, when his father said something or did something which surprised the others, there were two pairs of footprints only; his own and his father's. They alone knew each other. What then was this terror, this hatred? Turning back among the many leaves which the past had folded in him, peering into the heart of that forest where light and shade so chequer each other that all shape is distorted, and one blunders, now with the sun in one's eyes, now with a dark shadow, he sought an image to cool and detach and round off his feeling in a concrete shape. Suppose then that as a child sitting helpless in a perambulator, or on some one's knee, he had seen a waggon crush ignorantly and innocently, some one's foot? Suppose he had seen the foot first, in the grass, smooth, and whole; then the wheel; and the same foot, purple, crushed. But the wheel was innocent. So now, when his father came striding down the passage knocking them up early in the morning to go to the Lighthouse down it came over his foot, over Cam's foot, over anybody's foot. One sat and watched it.

But whose foot was he thinking of, and in what garden did all this happen? For one had settings for these scenes; trees that grew there; flowers; a certain light; a few figures. Everything tended to set itself in a garden where there was none of this gloom. None of this throwing of hands about; people spoke in an ordinary tone of voice. They went in and out all day long. There was an old woman gossiping in the kitchen; and the blinds were sucked in and out by the breeze; all was blowing, all was growing; and over all those plates and bowls and tall brandishing red and yellow flowers a very thin yellow veil would be drawn, like a vine leaf, at night. Things became stiller and darker at night. But the leaf-like veil was so fine, that lights lifted it, voices crinkled it; he could see through it a figure stooping, hear, coming close, going away, some dress rustling, some chain tinkling.

It was in this world that the wheel went over the person's foot. Something, he remembered, stayed and darkened over him; would not move; something flourished up in the air, something arid and sharp descended even there, like a blade, a scimitar, smiting through the leaves and flowers even of that happy world and making it shrivel and fall.

'It will rain,' he remembered his father saying. 'You won't be able to go to the Lighthouse.'

The Lighthouse was then a silvery, misty-looking tower with a yellow eye, that opened suddenly, and softly in the evening. Now—

James looked at the Lighthouse. He could see the white-washed rocks; the tower, stark and straight; he could see that it was barred with black and white; he could see windows in it; he could even see washing spread on the rocks to dry. So that was the Lighthouse, was it?

No, the other was also the Lighthouse. For nothing was simply one thing. The other Lighthouse was true too. It was sometimes hardly to be seen across the bay. In the evening one looked up and saw the eye opening and shutting and the light seemed to reach them in that airy sunny garden where they sat.

But he pulled himself up. Whenever he said 'they' or 'a person,' and then began hearing the rustle of some one coming, the tinkle of some one going, he became extremely sensitive to the presence of whoever might be in the room. It was his father now. The strain was acute. For in one moment if there was no breeze, his father would slap the covers of his book together, and say: 'What's happening now? What are we dawdling about here for, eh?' as, once before he had brought his blade down among them on the terrace and she had gone stiff all over, and if there had been an axe handy, a knife, or anything with a sharp point he would have seized it and struck his father through the heart. She had gone stiff all over, and then, her arm slackening, so that he felt she listened to him no longer, she had risen somehow and gone away and left him there, impotent, ridiculous, sitting on the floor grasping a pair of scissors.

Not a breath of wind blew. The water chuckled and gurgled in the bottom of the boat where three or four mackerel beat their tails up and down in a pool of water not deep enough to cover them. At any moment Mr. Ramsay (he scarcely dared look at him) might rouse himself, shut his book, and say something sharp; but for the moment he was reading, so that James stealthily, as if he were stealing downstairs on bare feet, afraid of waking a watchdog by a creaking board, went on thinking what was she like, where did she go that day? He began following her from room to room and at last they came to a room where in a blue light, as if the reflection came from many china dishes, she talked to somebody; he listened to her talking. She talked to a servant, saying simply whatever came into her head. She alone spoke the truth; to her alone could he speak it. That was the source of her ever-lasting attraction for him, perhaps; she was a person to whom one could say what came into one's head. But all the time he thought of her, he was conscious of his father following his thought, surveying it, making it shiver and falter. At last he ceased to think.

There he sat with his hand on the tiller in the sun, staring at the Lighthouse, powerless to move, powerless to flick off these grains of misery which settled on his mind one after another. A rope seemed to bind him there, and his father had knotted it and he could only escape by taking a knife and plunging it . . . But at that moment the sail swung slowly round, filled slowly out, the boat seemed to shake herself, and then to move off half conscious in her sleep, and then she woke and shot through the waves. The relief was extraordinary. They all seemed to fall away from each other again and to be at their ease and the fishing-lines slanted taut across the side of the boat. But his father did not rouse himself. He only raised his right hand mysteriously high in the air, and let it fall upon his knee again as if he were conducting some secret symphony.

❋

A GOOD WOMAN

Louis Bromfield

[The harm that may be done when a child's first knowledge of sex is associated with punishment and feelings of guilt is well illustrated in *A Good Woman*. Mrs. Downes' interpretation of the children's innocent pleasure in each other's company intensifies Philip's distrust of himself and his emotional dependence on his mother. We do not wonder that later Philip is unhappy in his marriage to a drab lady-missionary, an alliance Mrs. Downes approves because it seems to crown with triumph her sacrificial rearing of a model son for the service of the Lord in Africa. Moreover, she recognizes that Naomi offers her no rivalry in her emotional dominance over Philip's life. Nor are we surprised when, after a severe nervous illness, Philip decides he can no longer be a missionary. The sensuous beauty of Africa, and the pagan rituals he has witnessed, have called forth repressed emotional responses that make him feel unworthy of his calling. He returns to his mother, to disgrace her by

From *A Good Woman* by Louis Bromfield. Reprinted by permission of Frederick A. Stokes Company, Inc.

working in a factory and taking up painting on the side. His awakened senses arouse forgotten memories of Mary, now a widow. After an illness in which he is obsessed by strange dreams and hallucinations he finally breaks the bondage to his mother and elopes with Mary—to Africa.]

It was immensely complicated—that antlike world.

For Philip it was no more complicated now than it had been in his childhood, when he had gone his own shy, solitary way. He had been lonely as a child, with the loneliness which all children know at moments when they are bruised and hurt; only with him it seemed always to have been so. It may have been the domination, even the very presence, of a woman so insensitive and crushing as Emma Downes that bruised and hurt him ceaselessly and without consciousness of relief. It was worse, too, when she was your mother and you adored her.

He had been happiest in moments when, escaping from his mother and the slate-colored house, he had gone off to wander through the fields beyond the Town or along the railway tracks among the locomotives. It was the great engines which he liked best, monsters that breathed fire and smoke, or sat still and silent in the cavernous roundhouse, waiting patiently to have bolts tightened, or leaks soldered, so that they might go on with their work. They did not frighten him as they might have frightened some children: they seemed ferocious but friendly, like great ungainly dogs. They terrified him less than Uncle Elmer or the preacher, Mr. Temple. (Mr. Temple was gone now and another younger, more flowery man named Castor had taken his place.)

By some miracle he had been able to keep his secret from his mother and continued, even when he was grown, to wander about for hours among the clanging wheels and screaming whistles during his holidays from the theological seminary. Some childish cunning had made him understand that she must never know of these strange expeditions, lest she forbid them. She was always so terrified lest something happen to him.

In all his childhood he could remember having had only two friends —one of them, McTavish, the undertaker, was kept as much a secret as the friendly locomotives had been; for Philip, even as a child, understood that there was something about the fat, jovial man which Emma detested with a wild, unreasonable fury.

The other was the black-haired, blue-eyed, tomboyish Mary Watts, who lived a dozen blocks away in a more fashionable part of Town where each house had its big stables and its negro coachmen and stable boys. She was older than he by nearly two years, and much stronger: she detested girls as poor weak things who liked starched skirts and dickies of white duck that were instruments of torture to anyone who liked climbing and snowball fights. So she had recruited Philip to play on the tin roof of the carriage shed and build the house high up in the branches of the crabapple tree. He always felt sorry for her because she had no mother, but he saw, too, with a childish clarity, that it was an advantage to be able to do exactly as you pleased, and build the tree-house as high in the air as you liked, far up among the shiny little red apples where it made you thrillingly sick to look over the edge.

But this friendship was throttled suddenly on the day (it was Philip's twelfth birthday) they went to play in the hayloft. They had been digging in the fragrant hay and building tunnels, and feeling suddenly tired and hot, they lay down side by side, near the open door. In the heat, Philip, feeling drowsy, closed his eyes and listened to the whirring of the pigeons that haunted the old stable, happy, contented and pleased in a warm, vague way to be lying there beside his friend Mary, when suddenly he heard his mother's hearty voice, and, opening his eyes, saw her standing at the top of the stairs. He could see that she was angry. She said, 'Philip, come home at once—and you, Mary, go right in to your aunt.. You ought to be ashamed of yourself!'

She swept him off without another word and at home she shut him in the storeroom, where she talked to him for an hour. She told him he had done a shameful thing, that boys who behaved like that got a disease and turned black. She said that he was never to go again to Mary Watts' house or even to speak to her. She told him that because he had no father she must be both father and mother to him, and that she must be able to trust him in the hours when she was forced to be at the bakery earning money to feed and clothe them both.

When she had finished, Philip was trembling, though he did not cry, because men didn't behave like babies. He told her he was sorry and promised never to speak to Mary Watts again.

And then she locked him in for an hour to ponder what she had said. He didn't know what it was he had

done: he only felt shameful and dirty in a way he had never felt before, and terrified by a fear of turning black like those nigger boys who lived in the filthy houses along the creek by the Mills.

When Emma came back to release him from the storeroom prison, she forgave him and, taking him in her arms, kissed and fondled him for a long time, saying, 'And when you're a big boy and grown up, your mother will always be your girl, won't she?'

She seemed so pleasant and so happy, it was almost worth the blind pain to be able to repent and make promises. But he never had the fun of playing again with Mary Watts. He went back to his beloved engines. Sometimes he played ball, and he played well when he chose, for he was a smallish, muscular boy, all nerves, who was good at games; but they never interested him. It was as if he wanted always to be alone. He had had friends, but the friendships had ended quickly, as if he had come to the bottom of them too soon. As a little boy, there was always an odd, quizzical, affectionate look in his eye, and there were times when, dreaming, he would wander away into mazes of thought with a perpetual air of searching for something. He, himself, never knew what it was.

And then at seventeen, taciturn, lonely and confused, he had stumbled upon God. The rest was easy for Emma, especially when Naomi came unexpectedly into their lives. Sometimes, in bitter moments, she had thought of Philip as a symbol of vengeance upon his errant father: she had kept him pure and uncontaminated by the world. She had made of him a model for all the world to observe.

* * *

He came back to consciousness out of a strange country peopled with creatures that might have haunted a Gothic nightmare, creatures who seemed as confused and unreal as the fantastic world on which they moved. Sometimes his mother was present, moving about, oddly enough, against the background of the jungle at Megambo, moving about among the niggers, converting them in wholesale lots. At times she would disappear suddenly, to return almost at once, driving before her with Lady Millicent Wimbrooke's rawhide whip whole troops of natives, dressed completely, even to bonnets and shoes, like the people one saw in Main Street. And then she would feed them at the Peerless Restaurant, which seemed to have been set up intact on the borders of the gloomy forest. Once Lady Wimbrooke appeared herself with her portable-bath and rifle, and shooting about her carelessly, she drove all of them, including Emma, out of the restaurant into Main Street, which appeared miraculously to have sprung up just outside the door. Once outside, he discovered that all of them—Emma herself and the niggers—were walking stark naked in the car-tracks in the middle of the street. He, himself, seemed to be carrying a banner at the head of the parade on which was written in fiery letters, 'Let God look out for himself. We will do the same.' And at the corner he found Mary Conyngham waiting to keep a tryst, and neither he nor she seemed to take any notice of the fact that he was as naked as the day he was born.

And Naomi was there, too, always in the background, only she was not the Naomi he knew, but a large woman with a soft, powerful body, like Swanson's, above which her pale face peered out comically from beneath a sunbonnet woven of reeds. Once or twice he had mistaken her for Swanson playing a joke on him.

At other times he seemed to be back in the Mills, or in Hennessey's saloon, where Emma entered presently and broke all the mirrors; and then all of them were suddenly squeezed out of the doors to find themselves in the jungle, which appeared to have sprung up all about them, impenetrable save for a single path in which was stuck a cast-iron guide-post, reading, 'To the Mills.' The air was filled with the sound of distant thunder, but he could not make out whether it was the distant sound of tom-toms, or the pounding of monstrous steel hammers. Oddly enough, it seemed quite natural, as if the trees, the jungle and the Mills belonged thus together.

And Mary Conyngham was always there. It seemed that she was married to him, and that they had somewhere a family of children which he had never seen and could not find.

Once he witnessed a horrible sight. He saw Emma pursuing the black virgin who had long ago been eaten by the leopards. The virgin, naked, save for her ornaments of copper wire, ran to the lake, and across the water, **skimming the surface like a kingfisher** of ebony, and, as Emma gave chase, she sank like a stone, disappearing beneath the brassy surface without a sound.

For a long time after he returned to life, memories of the dead, nightmarish world clung to him like wisps of the haze that sometimes veiled the lake at Megambo in the wet season. He did not know how long he had been ill, and at times it seemed to him that he had died and was not living at all. His body felt light as air, but when he tried to raise it, it failed him, slipping back in a miserable weakness. And then, bit by bit, as the memories of the delirium faded into space, the hard, barren world about him began to take shape . . . the starched lace curtains at the windows, which Emma kept clean despite all the soot, the worn rocking-chair, the table at the side of the bed crowded with medicines, and, finally, the strange figure of the nurse. And then he understood that Naomi must be somewhere near at hand, and his mother. He had a vague feeling that they must have become old now, and gray, after all the years he had been ill.

It was Emma whom he saw first, and recognized. She came into the darkened room, and stood silently by the side of the bed until, he, conscious that there was someone near him, opened his eyes, and said in a weak voice, 'Is that you, Ma?'

Without answering him, she fell on her knees beside the bed and took his head in her hands, kissing him passionately again and again on his forehead. She wept and said over and over again, 'Philip, my boy! The Lord has given me back my boy!'

There was something frightening in the wildness of her emotion. The nurse, hearing her weeping, came in to warn her that she must be calm, and Philip said weakly, 'It's all right. I understand. She's always been like that.'

Once it would never have occurred to him to speak thus, as if he were detached from her and stood quite apart, protecting her. Protecting Emma! Something had happened to him during that long night of four months' delirium.

When his mother had gained control of herself once more, she sat down by the side of the bed, and, taking his hand, she held it clasped passionately in hers, while she sat looking at him, without once speaking. For some reason, he could not look at her, perhaps because in the intensity of her emotion she was asking from him a response which he could not give. He was ashamed, but it was impossible to pretend. Instead of any longer seeming almost a part of her, he was detached now in a strange, definite fashion. In his weakness, it seemed to him that he was seeing her for the first time and he was ashamed and sorry for her. He knew that before long she, too, would understand that there was a difference, that in some way their relationship had been broken forever. The old Philip was dead, and the new one suddenly pitied her from a great distance, as he pitied Naomi. It was as if the weakness gave him a clairvoyance, a second sight, which illuminated all the confusion of mind that had preceded the long night.

Lying there, with his eyes closed, her passionate cry, 'Philip, my boy!' burned itself into his brain. He was, he knew, unworthy of that consuming love she had for him.

After a long time he heard her asking, 'Philip, are you awake?'

'Yes, Ma.' But he did not open his eyes.

'I have some good news that will delight you.'

What could it be? Perhaps she had arranged his return to Megambo. She would think that was good news.

'It's about Naomi. You're a father now, Philip . . . twice a father, Philip. You've two children. They were twins.'

The knot of perplexity which had been tormenting his brain suddenly cleared away. Of course! That was what he couldn't remember about

Naomi. She had been going to have a baby, and now she had two. Still he did not open his eyes. It was more impossible now than ever. He did not answer her, and presently Emma asked, 'You heard what I said, Philip?'

'Yes, Ma.'

'You're glad, aren't you?'

He answered her weakly, 'Of course . . . why, of course, I'm glad.'

Again there was a long silence. He was ashamed again, because he had been forced to lie, ashamed because he wasn't proud and happy. His mother sat there trying to raise his spirits, and each thing she said only drove them lower. In that curious clarity of mind which seemed to possess his soul, he knew with a kind of horror that he had wanted to waken alone, free, in a new country, where he would never again see Naomi, or his mother, or the lace curtains, or the familiar, worn rocking-chair. That, he saw now, was why he had wanted to die. And now he was back again, tied to them more closely than ever.

At last he said in a low voice, 'It was like Naomi, wasn't it . . . to have twins?'

'What do you mean?'

He hesitated a moment, and then said, 'I don't know . . . I'm tired . . . I don't know.'

Again a silence. Deep inside him something kept urging him to break through all this web which seemed to be closing tighter and tighter around him. The last thought he could remember before slipping into the nightmare returned to him now, and, without knowing why, he uttered it, 'There won't be any more children.'

'Why?' asked Emma. 'What are you trying to say?'

'Because I don't mean to live with Naomi ever again. It's a wicked thing that I've done.'

She began to stroke his forehead, continuing for a long time before she spoke. She was having suddenly to face things—things which she had always known, and pretended not to know. At last she said, 'Why is it a wicked thing to live with your lawful wife?'

The world began to whiz dizzily about his head. Odd flashes of light passed before his closed eyes. It seemed to him that he must speak the truth, if he were ever to open them again without shame.

'Because she's not really my wife . . . she's just like any woman, any stranger . . . I never loved her at all. I can't go on . . . living like that. Can't you see how wicked it is?'

Emma was caught in her own web, by the very holy principles she upheld —that it was wrong to marry someone you did not love. It was this same thing which disturbed her peace of mind about Moses Slade.

'You loved her once, Philip, or you wouldn't have married her.'

'No, I didn't know anything then, Ma.' The color of pain entered his voice. 'Can't you see, Ma? I wasn't alive then. I never loved her, and now it's worse than that.'

The stroking of his forehead suddenly ceased. 'I don't know what you're talking about, Philip . . . We'd better not go on now. You're tired and ill. Everything will be different when you are well again.'

For a second time there came to him a blinding flash of revelation. He saw that she had always been like that: she had always pushed things aside to let them work themselves out. An awful doubt dawned upon him that she was not always right, that sometimes she had made a muddle of everything. A feeling of dizziness swept over him.

'But it will break her heart, Philip,' she was saying. 'She worships you . . . It will break her heart.'

Through a giddy haze he managed to say, 'No . . . I'm so tired . . . Let's not talk any more.' He felt the nightmare stealing back again, and presently he was for some strange reason back at Megambo, sitting under the acacia-tree, and through the hot air came the sound of voices singing, in a minor key:

'Go down to the water, little monkey,
To the life of lives, the beginning of all
  things.'

He thought wildly, 'I've got to get free. I must run . . . I must run.'

Emma, holding his hand, felt the fever slipping back. She heard him saying, 'Go down to the water, little monkey,' which clearly made no sense, and suddenly she sprang up and called Miss Bull, the nurse.

'It's odd,' said Miss Bull, white and frightened, 'when he was so much better. Did anything happen to upset him?'

'No,' said Emma. 'Nothing. We barely talked at all.'

The nurse sent Essie for the doctor, reproaching herself all the while for having allowed Emma to stay so long a time by the bed. But it was almost impossible to refuse when a woman like Mrs. Downes said, 'Surely seeing his mother won't upset him. Why, Miss Bull, we've always been wonderful companions—my boy and I. He never had a father, you see. I was both mother and father to him.' Miss Bull knew what a gallant fight she'd made, for everyone in the Town knew it. A widow, left alone, to bring up her boy. You couldn't be cruel enough to stop her from seeing her own son.

When the doctor came and left again, shaking his head, Emma was frightened, but her fright disappeared once more as the fever receded again toward morning, and when at last she fell asleep, she was thinking, 'He doesn't belong to her, after all. He's never belonged to her. He's still my Philip.' There was in the knowledge a sense of passionate triumph and joy, which wiped out all else—her doubts about Moses Slade, her worry over Philip's future, even the sudden, cold terror that gripped her as she felt the fever stealing back into his thin, transparent hand. He didn't belong to Naomi . . . Why, he almost hated her. He was still her boy . . . And she had defeated Naomi.

In the darkness the tears dampened the pillow. God had not, after all, forsaken her.

SOCIAL AND ECONOMIC PRESSURES

> I see men's judgments are
> A parcel of their fortunes; and things outward
> Do draw the inward quality after them
> To suffer all alike.
> —SHAKESPEARE

EVEN before the child can be aware of it, the larger world of social and economic forces is shaping him. Economic laws determine the status of his family, the kind of home he lives in, the quality of his food and clothing. Social attitudes govern the group acceptance accorded him on the basis of his home surroundings, his father's business, his race, church, and politics. Of many of these factors a child may be unaware until he goes to school. Approval of certain actions, disapproval of others, the need to conform to the demands of other people, all these he has met in his home from his earliest days. Without understanding many of the social taboos he has encountered, he has none the less been molded to some measure of conformity with accepted standards of behavior. Now his horizon suddenly expands beyond the home, and he sees himself and his family in relation to others. Inevitably, tensions will result from his attempts, not always successful, to adjust the ideas of right and wrong he has acquired at home to the new situations he confronts. This process of assimilation—of learning to live in the group, to accept its demands and yet to satisfy the needs of his individual nature—will continue all his life long. On the success of his adjustment to the inner laws of his being and to the pressure of the external world of men and institutions will depend his happiness as an individual and his success as a member of society.

❊

THE NEW DRESS

VIRGINIA WOOLF

[One of the most obvious and seemingly superficial ways in which group opinion affects the individual is in his subservience to fashion and custom. Virginia Woolf's story, *The New Dress,* presents a common experience—the effect on one's personality of the sense of isolation and inferiority that may

Reprinted by permission of *Current History* and *Forum.*

come with the realization of difference from the crowd. Mabel shares her group's attitude toward clothes as symbols of the individual's success. Her fantasies of escape into a world of literary achievement or social service, where clothes will not be important, afford her no real satisfaction, for she has been too completely conditioned by the mores of the superficial society she admires.]

Mabel had her first serious suspicion that something was wrong as she took her cloak off and Mrs. Barnet, while handing her the mirror and touching the brushes and thus drawing her attention, perhaps rather markedly, to all the appliances for tidying and improving hair, complexion, clothes, which existed on the dressing table, confirmed the suspicion—that it was not right, not quite right, which growing stronger as she went upstairs and springing at her with conviction as she greeted Clarissa Dalloway, she went straight to the far end of the room to a shaded corner where a looking-glass hung and looked. No! It was not *right*. And at once the misery which she always tried to hide, the profound dissatisfaction—the sense she had had, ever since she was a child, of being inferior to other people—set upon her, relentlessly, remorselessly, with an intensity which she could not beat off, as she would when she woke at night at home, by reading Borrow or Scott; for oh these men, oh these women, all were thinking—'What's Mabel wearing? What a fright she looks! What a hideous new dress!'—their eyelids flickering as they came up and then their lids shutting rather tight. It was her own appalling inadequacy; her cowardice; her mean, water-sprinkled blood that depressed her. And at once the whole of the room where, for ever so many hours, she had planned with the little dressmaker how it was to go, seemed sor-

did, repulsive; and her own drawing-room so shabby, and herself, going out, puffed up with vanity as she touched the letters on the hall table and said: 'How dull!' to show off—all this now seemed unutterably silly, paltry, and provincial. All this had been absolutely destroyed, shown up, exploded, the moment she came into Mrs. Dalloway's drawing-room.

What she had thought that evening when, sitting over the teacups, Mrs. Dalloway's invitation came, was that, of course, she could not be fashionable. It was absurd to pretend it even —fashion meant cut, meant style, meant thirty guineas at least—but why not be original? Why not be herself, anyhow? And, getting up, she had taken that old fashion book of her mother's, a Paris fashion book of the time of the Empire, and had thought how much prettier, more dignified, and more womanly they were then, and so set herself—oh, it was foolish—trying to be like them, pluming herself in fact, upon being modest and old-fashioned and very charming, giving herself up, no doubt about it, to an orgy of self-love, which deserved to be chastised, and so rigged herself out like this.

But she dared not look in the glass. She could not face the whole horror —the pale yellow, idiotically old-fashioned silk dress with its long skirt and its high sleeves and its waist and all the things that looked so charming in the fashion book, but not on her, not among all these ordinary people. She felt like a dressmaker's dummy standing there, for young people to stick pins into.

'But, my dear, it's perfectly charming!' Rose Shaw said, looking her up and down with that little satirical pucker of the lips which she expected —Rose herself being dressed in the height of fashion, precisely like everybody else, always.

We are all like flies trying to crawl over the edge of the saucer, Mabel thought, and repeated the phrase as if she were crossing herself, as if she were trying to find some spell to annul this pain, to make this agony endurable. Tags of Shakespeare, lines from books she had read ages ago, suddenly came to her when she was in agony, and she repeated them over and over again. 'Flies trying to crawl,' she repeated. If she could say that over often enough, and make herself see the flies, she would become numb, chill, frozen, dumb. Now she could see flies crawling slowly out of a saucer of milk with their wings stuck together; and she strained and strained (standing in front of the looking-glass, listening to Rose Shaw) to make herself see Rose Shaw and all the other people there as flies, trying to hoist themselves out of something, or into something, meager, insignificant, toiling flies. But she could not see them like that, not other people. She saw herself like that—she was a fly, but the others were dragonflies, butterflies, beautiful insects, dancing, fluttering, skimming, while she alone dragged herself up out of the saucer. (Envy and spite, the most detestable of the vices, were her chief faults.)

'I feel like some dowdy, decrepit, horribly dingy old fly,' she said, making Robert Haydon stop just to hear her say that, just to reassure herself by furbishing up a poor weak-kneed phrase and so showing how detached she was, how witty, that she did not feel in the least out of anything. And, of course, Robert Haydon answered something quite polite, quite insincere, which she saw through instantly, and said to herself, directly he went (again from some book), 'Lies, lies, lies!' For a party makes things either much more real, or much less real, she thought; she saw in a flash to the bottom of Robert Haydon's heart; she saw through everything. She saw the truth. *This* was true, this drawing-room, this self, and the other false. Miss Milan's little workroom was really terribly hot, stuffy, sordid. It smelt of clothes and cabbage cooking; and yet, when Miss Milan put the glass in her hand, and she looked at herself with the dress on, finished, an extraordinary bliss shot through her heart. Suffused with light, she sprang into existence. Rid of cares and wrinkles, what she had dreamed of herself was there—a beautiful woman. Just for a second (she had not dared look longer, Miss Milan wanted to know about the length of the skirt), there looked at her, framed in the scrolloping mahogany, a gray-white, mysteriously smiling, charming girl, the core of herself, the soul of herself; and it was not vanity only, not only self-love that made her think it good, tender, and true. Miss Milan said that the skirt could not well be longer; if anything the skirt, said Miss Milan, puckering her forehead, considering with all her wits about her, must be shorter; and she felt, suddenly, honestly, full of love for Miss Milan, much, much fonder of Miss Milan than of any one in the whole world, and could have cried for pity that she should be crawling on the floor with her mouth full of pins, and her face red and her eyes bulging—that one human being should be doing this for another, and she saw them all as human beings merely, and herself going off to her party, and Miss Milan pulling the cover over the canary's cage, or letting him pick a hemp-seed from between her lips, and the thought of it, of this side of human nature and its patience and its endurance and its being content with such miserable, scanty, sordid little pleasures filled her eyes with tears.

And now the whole thing had vanished. The dress, the room, the love, the pity, the scrolloping looking-glass, and the canary's cage—all had vanished, and here she was in a corner of Mrs. Dalloway's drawing-room, suffering tortures, woken wide awake to reality.

But it was all so paltry, weak-blooded, and petty-minded to care so much at her age with two children, to be still so utterly dependent on people's opinions and not have principles or convictions, not to be able to say as other people did, 'There's Shakespeare! There's death! We're all weevils in a captain's biscuit,'—or whatever it was that people did say.

She faced herself straight in the glass; she pecked at her left shoulder; she issued out into the room, as if spears were thrown at her yellow dress from all sides. But instead of looking fierce or tragic, as Rose Shaw would have done—Rose would have looked like Boadicea—she looked foolish and self-conscious, and simpered like a schoolgirl and slouched across the room, positively slinking, as if she were a beaten mongrel, and looked at a picture, an engraving. As if one went to a party to look at a picture! Everybody knew why she did it—it was from shame, from humiliation.

'Now the fly's in the saucer,' she said to herself, 'right in the middle, and can't get out, and the milk,' she thought, rigidly staring at the picture, 'is sticking its wings together.'

'It's so old-fashioned,' she said to Charles Burt, making him stop (which by itself he hated) on his way to talk to some one else.

She meant, or she tried to make herself think that she meant, that it was the picture and not her dress that was old-fashioned. And one word of praise, one word of affection from Charles would have made all the difference to her at the moment. If he had only said, 'Mabel, you're looking charming to-night!' it would have changed her life. But then she ought to have been truthful and direct. Charles said nothing of the kind, of course. He was malice itself. He always saw through one, especially if one were feeling particularly mean, paltry, or feeble-minded.

'Mabel's got a new dress!' he said, and the poor fly was absolutely shoved into the middle of the saucer. Really, he would like her to drown, she believed. He had no heart, no fundamental kindness, only a veneer of friendliness. Miss Milan was much more real, much kinder. If only one could feel that and stick to it, always. 'Why,' she asked herself—replying to Charles much too pertly, letting him see that she was out of temper, or 'ruffled' as he called it ('Rather ruffled?' he said and went on to laugh at her with some woman over there)—'Why,' she asked herself, 'can't I feel one thing always, feel quite sure that Miss Milan is right, and Charles wrong and stick to it, feel sure about the canary and pity and love and not be whipped all around in a second by coming into a room full of people?' It was her odious, weak, vacillating character again, always giving at the critical moment and not being seriously interested in conchology, etymology, botany, archeology, cutting up potatoes and watching them fructify like Mary Dennis, like Violet Searle.

Then Mrs. Holman, seeing her standing there, bore down upon her. Of course a thing like a dress was beneath Mrs. Holman's notice, with her family always tumbling downstairs or having the scarlet fever. Could Mabel tell her if Elmthorpe was ever let for August and September? Oh, it was a conversation that bored her unutterably! It made her furious to be treated like a house agent or messenger boy, to be made use of. Not to have value, that was it, she thought, trying to grasp something hard, something real, while she tried to answer sensibly about the bathroom and the south aspect and the hot water to the top of the house; and all the time she could see little bits of her yellow dress in the round looking-glass which made them all the size of boot-buttons or tadpoles; and it was amazing to think how much humiliation and agony and self-loathing and effort and passionate ups and downs of feeling were contained in a thing the size of a threepenny bit. And what was still odder, this thing, this Mabel Waring, was separate, quite disconnected; and though Mrs. Holman (the black button) was leaning forward and telling her how her eldest boy had strained his heart running, she could see her, too, quite detached in the looking-glass, and it was impossible that the black dot, leaning forward, gesticulating, should make the yellow dot, sitting solitary, self-centred, feel what the black dot was feeling, yet they pretended.

'So impossible to keep boys quiet'— that was the kind of thing one said.

And Mrs. Holman, who could never get enough sympathy and snatched what little there was greedily, as if it were her right (but she deserved much more for there was her little girl who had come down this morning with a swollen knee-joint), took this miserable offering and looked at it suspiciously, grudgingly, as if it were a halfpenny when it ought to have been a pound and put it away in her purse, must put up with it, mean and miserly though it was, times being hard, so very hard; and on she went, creaking, injured Mrs. Holman, about the girl with the swollen joints. Ah, it was tragic, this greed, this clamor of human beings, like a row of cormorants, barking and flapping their wings for sympathy— it was tragic, could one have felt it and not merely pretended to feel it!

But in her yellow dress to-night she could not wring out one drop more; she wanted it all, all for herself. She knew (she kept on looking into the glass, dipping into that dreadfully showing-up blue pool) that she was condemned, despised, left like this in a backwater, because of her being like this a feeble, vacillating creature; and it seemed to her that the yellow dress was a penance which she had deserved, and if she had been dressed like Rose Shaw, in lovely, clinging green with a ruffle of swansdown, she would have deserved that; and she thought that there was no escape for her—none whatever. But it was not her fault altogether, after all. It was being one of a family of ten; never having money enough, always skimping and paring; and her mother carrying great cans, and the linoleum worn on the stair edges, and one sordid little domestic tragedy after another—nothing catastrophic, the sheep farm failing, but not utterly; her eldest brother marrying beneath him but not very much—there was no romance, nothing extreme about them all. They petered out respectably in seaside resorts; every watering-place had one of her aunts even now asleep in some lodging with the front windows not quite facing the sea. That was so like them—they had to squint at things always. And she had done the same—she was just like her aunts. For all her dreams of living in India, married to some hero like Sir Henry Lawrence, some empire builder (still the sight of a native in a turban filled her with romance), she had failed utterly. She had married Hubert, with his safe, permanent underling's job in the Law Courts, and they managed tolerably in a smallish house, without proper maids, and hash when she was alone or just bread and butter, but now and then —Mrs. Holman was off, thinking her the most dried-up, unsympathetic twig she had ever met, absurdly dressed, too, and would tell everyone about Mabel's fantastic appearance—now and then, thought Mabel Waring, left alone on the blue sofa, punching the cushion in order to look occupied, for she would not join Charles Burt and Rose Shaw, chattering like magpies and perhaps laughing at her by the fireplace—now and then, there did come to her delicious moments, reading the other night in bed, for instance, or down by the sea on the sand in the sun, at Easter—let her recall it—a great tuft of pale sand-grass standing all twisted like a shock of spears against the sky, which was blue like a smooth china egg, so firm, so hard, and then the melody of the waves—'Hush, hush,' they said, and the children's shouts paddling—yes, it was a divine moment, and there she lay, she felt, in the hand of the God-

dess who was the world; rather a hard-hearted but very beautiful Goddess, a little lamb on the altar (one did think these silly things, and it didn't matter so long as one never said them). And also with Hubert sometimes she had quite unexpectedly—carving the mutton for Sunday lunch, for no reason, opening a letter, coming into a room—divine moments, when she said to herself (for she would never say this to anybody else), 'This is it. This has happened. This is it!' And the other way about it was equally surprising—that is, when everything was arranged—music, weather, holidays, every reason for happiness was there—then nothing happened at all. One wasn't happy. It was flat, just flat, that was all.

Her wretched self again, no doubt! She had always been a fretful, weak, unsatisfactory mother, a wobbly wife, lolling about in a kind of twilight existence with nothing very clear or very bold or more one thing than another, like all her brothers and sisters, except perhaps Herbert—they were all the same poor water-veined creatures who did nothing. Then in the midst of this creeping, crawling life, suddenly she was on the crest of a wave. That wretched fly—where had she read the story that kept coming into her mind about the fly and the saucer?—struggled out. Yes, she had those moments. But now that she was forty, they might come more and more seldom. By degrees she would cease to struggle any more. But that was deplorable! That was not to be endured! That made her feel ashamed of herself!

She would go to the London Library to-morrow. She would find some wonderful, helpful, astonishing book, quite by chance, a book by a clergyman, by an American no one had ever heard of; or she would walk down the Strand and drop, accidentally, into a hall where a miner was telling about the life in the pit and suddenly she would become a new person. She would be absolutely transformed. She would wear a uniform; she would be called Sister Somebody; she would never give a thought to clothes again. And for ever after she would be perfectly clear about Charles Burt and Miss Milan and this room and that room; and it would be always, day after day, as if she were lying in the sun or carving the mutton. It would be it!

So she got up from the blue sofa, and the yellow button in the looking-glass got up too, and she waved her hand to Charles and Rose to show them she did not depend on them one scrap, and the yellow button moved out of the looking-glass, and all the spears were gathered into her breast as she walked toward Mrs. Dalloway and said, 'Good-night.'

'But it's too early to go,' said Mrs. Dalloway, who was always so charming.

'I'm afraid I must,' said Mabel Waring. 'But,' she added in her weak, wobbly voice which only sounded ridiculous when she tried to strengthen it, 'I have enjoyed myself enormously.'

'I have enjoyed myself,' she said to Mr. Dalloway, whom she met on the stairs.

'Lies, lies, lies!' she said to herself, going downstairs, and 'Right in the saucer!' she said to herself as she thanked Mrs. Barnet for helping her and wrapped herself, round and round and round, in the Chinese cloak she had worn these twenty years.

❋

AN AMERICAN TRAGEDY

Theodore Dreiser

[The most intimate of human emotions and relationships are vulnerable to the pressure of group disapproval. In *An American Tragedy* Dreiser reveals the bewilderment and shame of an adolescent boy in whom the taunts of others serve to confirm a distaste for the street corner evangelism of his parents. Clyde felt what Dreiser calls 'man's yearning to find a likeness in all things.' He saw that neither his father nor his mother was like other people in this fanatical absorption in religion, and he felt deeply humiliated that he must be seen with them. Clyde's sister was untouched by a sense of difference. For her the role of gospel singer afforded an opportunity to attract attention. But Clyde was disturbed when he saw laughing couples speeding by in powerful cars, a spectacle which suggested a life of comfort and beauty from which he was shut out. It was this shame and resentment that later drove him to restless pursuit of material success and social acceptance and ultimately led to the murder of the girl who seemed to stand between him and his goal.]

From *An American Tragedy*, by Theodore Dreiser. By permission of Simon and Schuster, Inc.

Dusk—of a summer night.

And the tall walls of the commercial heart of an American city of perhaps 400,000 inhabitants—such walls as in time may linger as a mere fable.

And up the broad street, now comparatively hushed, a little band of six, —a man of about fifty, short, stout, with bushy hair protruding from under a round black felt hat, a most unimportant-looking person, who carried a small portable organ such as is customarily used by street preachers and singers. And with him a woman perhaps five years his junior, taller, not so broad, but solid of frame and vigorous, very plain in face and dress, and yet not homely, leading with one hand a small boy of seven and in the other carrying a Bible and several hymn books. With these three, but walking independently behind, was a girl of fifteen, a boy of twelve and another girl of nine, all following obediently, but not too enthusiastically, in the wake of the others.

It was hot, yet with a sweet languor about it all.

Crossing at right angles the great thoroughfare on which they walked, was a second canyon-like way, threaded by throngs and vehicles and various lines of cars which clanged their bells and made such progress as they might amid swiftly moving streams of traffic. Yet the little group seemed unconscious of anything save a set purpose to make its way between the contending lines of traffic and pedestrians which flowed by them.

Having reached an intersection this side of the second principal thoroughfare—really just an alley between two tall structures—now quite bare of life of any kind, the man put down the organ, which the woman immediately opened, setting up a music rack upon which she placed a wide flat hymn book. Then handing the Bible to the man, she fell back in line with him, while the twelve-year-old boy put down a small camp-stool in front of the organ. The man—the father, as he chanced to be—looked about him with seeming wide-eyed assurance, and announced, without appearing to care whether he had any auditors or not:

'We will first sing a hymn of praise, so that any who may wish to acknowledge the Lord may join us. Will you oblige, Hester?'

At this the eldest girl, who until now had attempted to appear as unconscious and unaffected as possible, bestowed her rather slim and as yet undeveloped figure upon the camp chair and turned the leaves of the hymn book, pumping the organ while her mother observed:

'I should think it might be nice to sing twenty-seven tonight—"How Sweet the Balm of Jesus' Love."'

By this time various homeward-bound individuals of diverse grades and walks of life, noticing the small group disposing itself in this fashion, hesitated for a moment to eye them askance or paused to ascertain the character of their work. This hesitancy, construed by the man apparently to constitute attention, however mobile, was seized upon by him and he began addressing them as though they were specifically here to hear him.

'Let us all sing twenty-seven, then —"How Sweet the Balm of Jesus' Love."'

At this the young girl began to interpret the melody upon the organ, emitting a thin though correct strain, at the same time joining her rather high soprano with that of her mother, together with the rather dubious baritone of the father. The other children piped weakly along, the boy and girl having taken hymn books from the small pile stacked upon the organ. As they sang, this nondescript and indifferent street audience gazed, held by the peculiarity of such an unimportant-looking family publicly raising its collective voice against the vast skepticism and apathy of life. Some were interested or moved sympathetically by the rather tame and inadequate figure of the girl at the organ, others by the impractical and materially inefficient texture of the father, whose weak blue eyes and rather flabby but poorly-clothed figure bespoke more of failure than anything else. Of the group the mother alone stood out as having that force and determination which, however blind or erroneous, makes for self-preservation, if not success in life. She, more than any of the others, stood up with an ignorant, yet somehow respectable air of conviction. If you had watched her, her hymn book dropped to her side, her glance directed straight before her into space, you would have said: 'Well, here is one who, whatever her defects, probably does what she believes as nearly as possible.' A kind of hard, fighting faith in the wisdom and mercy of that definite overruling and watchful power which she proclaimed, was written in her every feature and gesture.

> 'The love of Jesus saves me whole,
> The love of God my steps control,'

she sang resonantly, if slightly nasally, between the towering walls of adjacent buildings.

The boy moved restlessly from one foot to the other, keeping his eyes down, and for the most part only half singing. A tall and as yet slight figure, surmounted by an interesting head and face—white skin, dark hair—he seemed more keenly observant and decidedly more sensitive than most of the others—appeared indeed to resent and even to suffer from the position in which he found himself. Plainly pagan rather than religious, life interested him, although as yet he was not fully aware of this. All that could be truly said of him now was that there was no definite appeal in all this for him. He was too young, his mind much too responsive to phases of beauty and pleasure which had little, if anything, to do with the remote and cloudy romance which swayed the minds of his mother and father.

Indeed the home life of which this boy found himself a part and the various contacts, material and psychic, which thus far had been his, did not tend to convince him of the reality and force of all that his mother and father seemed so certainly to believe and say. Rather, they seemed more or less troubled in their lives, at least materially. His father was always reading the Bible and speaking in meeting at different places, especially in the 'mission,' which he and his mother conducted not so far from this corner. At the same time, as he understood it, they collected money from various interested or charitably inclined business men here and there who appeared to believe in such philanthropic work. Yet the family was always 'hard up,' never very well clothed, and deprived of many comforts and pleasures which seemed common enough to others. And his father and mother were constantly proclaiming the love and mercy and care of God for him and for all. Plainly there was something wrong somewhere. He could not get it all straight, but still he could not help respecting his mother, a woman whose force and earnestness, as well as her sweetness, appealed to him. Despite much mission work and family cares, she managed to be fairly cheerful, or at least sustaining, often declaring most emphatically, 'God will provide' or 'God will show the way,' especially in times of too great stress about food or clothes. Yet apparently, in spite of this, as he and all the other children could see, God did not show any very clear way, even though there was always an extreme necessity for His favorable intervention in their affairs.

To-night, walking up the great street with his sisters and brother, he wished that they need not do this any more, or at least that he need not be a part of it. Other boys did not do such things, and besides, somehow it seemed shabby and even degrading. On more than one occasion, before he had been taken on the street in this fashion, other boys had called to him and made fun of his father, because he was always publicly emphasizing his religious beliefs or convictions. Thus in one neighborhood in which they had lived, when he was but a child of seven, his father, having always preluded every conversation with 'Praise the Lord,' he heard boys call, 'Here comes old Praise-the-Lord Griffiths.' Or they would call out after him, 'Hey, you're the fellow whose sister plays the organ. Is there anything else she can play?'

'What does he always want to go around saying, "Praise the Lord" for? Other people don't do it.'

It was that old mass yearning for a likeness in all things that troubled them, and him. Neither his father nor his mother was like other people, because they were always making so much of religion, and now at last they were making a business of it.

On this night in this great street with its cars and crowds and tall buildings, he felt ashamed, dragged out of normal life, to be made a show and jest of. The handsome automobiles that sped by, the loitering pedestrians moving off to what interests and comforts he could only surmise; the gay pairs of young people, laughing and jesting and the 'kids' staring, all troubled him with a sense of something different, better, more beautiful than his, or rather their life.

And now units of this vagrant and unstable street throng, which was forever shifting and changing about them, seemed to sense the psychologic error of all this in so far as these children were concerned, for they would nudge one another, the more sophisticated and indifferent lifting an eyebrow and smiling contemptuously, the more sympathetic or experienced commenting on the useless presence of these children.

'I see these people around here nearly every night now—two or three times a week, anyhow,' this from a young clerk who had just met his girl and was escorting her toward a restaurant. 'They're just working some religious dodge or other, I guess.'

'That oldest boy don't wanta be here. He feels outa place, I can see that. It ain't right to make a kid like that come out unless he wants to. He can't understand all this stuff, anyhow.' This from an idler and loafer of about forty, one of those odd hangers-on about the commercial heart of a city, addressing a pausing and seemingly amiable stranger.

'Yeh, I guess that's so,' the other assented, taking in the peculiar cast of the boy's head and face. In view of the uneasy and self-conscious expression upon the face whenever it was lifted, one might have intelligently suggested that it was a little unkind as well as idle to thus publicly force upon a temperament as yet unfitted to absorb their import, religious and psychic services best suited to reflective temperaments of maturer years.

Yet so it was.

As for the remainder of the family, both the youngest girl and boy were too small to really understand much of what it was all about or to care. The eldest girl at the organ appeared not so much to mind, as to enjoy the attention and comment her presence and singing evoked, for more than once, not only strangers, but her mother and father, had assured her that she had an appealing and compelling voice, which was only partially true. It was not a good voice. They did not really understand music. Physically, she was of a pale, emasculate and unimportant structure, with no real mental force or depth, and was easily made to feel that this was an excellent field in which to distinguish herself and attract a little attention. As for the parents, they were determined upon spiritualizing the world as much as possible, and, once the hymn was concluded, the father launched into one of those hackneyed descriptions of the delights of a release, via self-realization of the mercy of God and the love of Christ and the will of God toward sinners, from the burdensome cares of an evil conscience.

'All men are sinners in the light of the Lord,' he declared. 'Unless they repent, unless they accept Christ, His love and forgiveness of them, they can never know the happiness of being spiritually whole and clean. Oh, my friends! If you could but know the peace and content that come with the knowledge, the inward understanding, that Christ lived and died

for you and that He walks with you every day and hour, by light and by dark, at dawn and at dusk, to keep and strengthen you for the tasks and cares of the world that are ever before you. Oh, the snares and pitfalls that beset us all! And then the soothing realization that Christ is ever with us, to counsel, to aid, to hearten, to bind up our wounds and make us whole! Oh, the peace, the satisfaction, the comfort, the glory of that!'

'Amen!' asseverated his wife, and the daughter, Hester, or Esta, as she was called by the family, moved by the need of as much public support as possible for all of them—echoed it after her.

Clyde, the eldest boy, and the two younger children merely gazed at the ground, or occasionally at their father, with a feeling that possibly it was all true and important, yet somehow not as significant or inviting as some of the other things which life held. They heard so much of this, and to their young and eager minds life was made for something more than street and mission hall protestations of this sort.

Finally, after a second hymn and an address by Mrs. Griffiths, during which she took occasion to refer to the mission work jointly conducted by them in a near-by street, and their services to the cause of Christ in general, a third hymn was indulged in, and then some tracts describing the mission rescue work being distributed, such voluntary gifts as were forthcoming were taken up by Asa—the father. The small organ was closed, the camp chair folded up and given to Clyde, the Bible and hymn books picked up by Mrs. Griffiths, and with the organ supported by a leather strap passed over the shoulder of Griffiths, senior, the missionward march was taken up.

During all this time Clyde was saying to himself that he did not wish to do this any more, that he and his parents looked foolish and less than normal—'cheap' was the word he would have used if he could have brought himself to express his full measure of resentment at being compelled to participate in this way—and that he would not do it any more if he could help. What good did it do them to have him along? His life should not be like this. Other boys did not have to do as he did. He meditated now more determinedly than ever a rebellion by which he would rid himself of the need of going out in this way. Let his elder sister go if she chose; she liked it. His younger sister and brother might be too young to care. But he—

'They seemed a little more attentive than usual to-night, I thought,' commented Griffiths to his wife as they walked along, the seductive quality of the summer evening air softening him into a more generous interpretation of the customary indifferent spirit of the passer-by.

'Yes; twenty-seven took tracts to-night as against eighteen on Thursday.'

'The love of Christ must eventually prevail,' comforted the father, as much to hearten himself as his wife. 'The pleasures and cares of the world hold a very great many, but when sorrow overtakes them then some of these seeds will take root.'

'I am sure of it. That is the thought which always keeps me up. Sorrow and the weight of sin eventually bring some of them to see the error of their way.'

They now entered into the narrow side street from which they had emerged, and walking as many as a dozen doors from the corner, entered the door of a yellow single-story wooden building, the large window and the two glass panes in the central door of which had been painted a gray-white. Across both windows and smaller panels in the double door had been painted: 'The Door of Hope. Bethel Independent Mission. Meetings Every Wednesday and Saturday night 8 to 10. Sundays at 11, 3 and 8. Everybody Welcome.' Under this legend on each window were printed the words: 'God is Love,' and below this again, in smaller type: 'How Long Since You Wrote to Mother?'

The small company entered the yellow unprepossessing door and disappeared.

❈

PERSONAL HISTORY

Vincent Sheean

[The desire for identification with a certain group often prompts us to feelings and actions which as individuals we may vehemently condemn. Vincent Sheean shows how group pressure impelled him to share attitudes of prejudice which were alien to him and for which he despised himself. This passage from his autobiography makes us see that it is not only the victim of prejudice who suffers. Intolerance may be even more humiliating and corrosive in its effects on the personality of the individual who becomes its agent.]

The social system of the undergraduate world in which I lived was the villain of the piece. No teacher could have compelled full attention from a mind preoccupied with elaborate details of social relationship. The University of Chicago, one of the largest and richest institutions of learning in the world, was partly inhabited by a couple of thousand young nincompoops whose ambition in life was to get into the right fraternity or club, go to the right parties, and get elected to something or other. The frivolous two thousand—the undergraduate body, the 'campus'—may have been a minority, for the University contained a great many solitary workers in both the undergraduate and graduate fields; but the minority thought itself a majority, thought itself, in fact, the whole of the University. And it was to the frivolous two thousand that I belonged.

Chicago was by no means the worst American university in this respect— it was supposed, on the contrary, to be one of the best; but even at Chicago 'campus activities' were the most serious part of life. Freshmen chose, on the advice of their elders, which of these 'activities' to pursue throughout the four years. Some 'went out for the *Maroon*' (i.e., worked for the college's daily newspaper), some 'for the team' (i.e., football), some for other organized athletics, and some for 'class politics.' Rare and wonderful freshmen 'went out for' everything at once.

There were hierarchies in the *Daily Maroon,* in the Dramatic Club, which made productions every two or three months, and in the Blackfriars. This last was an association of undergraduates interested in producing an operetta (original, more or less) in the spring of every year with men in all the parts. Freshmen were graduated through the successive steps in all these organizations until the survivors, by natural selection and incredibly hard work, stood out in their senior year, immortal: the editor of the *Maroon,* the president of the Dramatic Club, the abbot (and other officials) of Blackfriars. Football and track athletics had their four-year plans as well, but they were not my line of country, and I knew little about them.

Organized 'activities,' as occupation for the energies of youth, could have done no harm if they had not been supplemented, and to some extent even controlled, by a social life of singular ferocity. The women undergraduates had a number of clubs to which all the 'nice' girls were supposed to belong. Four or five of these clubs were 'good' and the rest 'bad.' Their goodness and badness were absolute, past, present and future, and could not be called into question. They had no houses or rooms of their own, but they maintained a rigid solidarity and succeeded in imposing upon the undergraduate society a tone of intricate, overweening snobbery.

The men were grouped in Greek-letter fraternities with houses for residence. Half a dozen of these were 'good' and the rest 'bad'; but their goodness and badness were not quite so irremediable as the similar qualifications among the women's clubs. The fraternities were national organizations, with chapters in most of the American universities, and it was well known that the same fraternity might be 'good' at the University of California and 'bad' at Yale. The salutary effect of this consideration was supported by the fact that the men did not seem to have the same high degree of social cruelty as the women. Men often joined a fraternity because their brothers or fathers had belonged to it, because they had friends in it, because they liked some one person in it, or even because its house or its food or its heating system appealed to them. Such homely, sensible reasons weighed little with the women. All of them, true to the great tradition of American womanhood, took the very 'best' club to which they could possibly be elected, and the logic of their behavior kept their club system rigid throughout my four years at the University.

My experience with the fraternity system was a weird one. It was in no way typical, but it exhibited some of the cannibalistic character of the institution and the intensity with which its importance was felt among the undergraduates. I entered the University ignorant of even the names of the Greek-letter societies. On my first or second day I was asked to lunch at a fraternity house and went. On the next day I discovered that that godlike creature, the editor of the *Maroon*, was a member of this very fraternity. When, on about the fourth day, I was asked to pledge myself to join it, I accepted at once.

Followed what has since appeared to be a grand tragi-comic episode. I moved into the fraternity house, where lived the friends, ready-made, among whom I was supposed to pass four years. My room-mate was Alan Le May, a dour, dark and silent freshman with a sharp intelligence. He afterwards took to making vast sums of money by writing about the wild and woolly West, but at the time he was more concerned with such effete Eastern matters as French composition and English literature. There were a number of other brothers-in-the-bond who loomed particularly large. Above them all, in a kind of hazy splendor like that which crowns a high mountain in the sun, there dwelt the supreme god, A. B., the editor of the *Maroon*. He was kind to me, suggested books to read, talked to me about the scraps of verse I used to write. I never saw anybody afterwards who possessed quite his Olympian quality, and two or three kings, with a pope and a president thrown in, could not possibly have awed me so much in later days as he awed me then. In all, I was happy in that life; but it was not prolonged.

On the day of our initiation into the fraternity, three months after the taking of the pledge, a girl asked me to cut my classes and take a long walk with her. She was a pretty girl, a freshman, whom I had met in the office of the *Daily Maroon* and with whom I was conducting a shy and tentative flirtation. It was bitter cold that day; she was wrapped in furs, and I decidedly was not; but we walked for many hours through the snowy streets, down to Jackson Park with its trees hung in ice, and out to the wintry lake. After we had been chattering about ordinary things for ten or fifteen minutes she suddenly opened up on me.

'I've been talking to various people around the *Maroon* about you,' she said. 'We all think you're a pretty good freshman. You might amount to something if you had any sense. I don't think you know what you're doing. I realize it's none of my business, but I've made up my mind to talk to you about it before it's too late.'

This meant nothing to me, and I said so.

'Oh, don't pretend that you don't understand,' she said. 'It's that damned fraternity. You can't possibly belong to it and make anything at all out of your college life. You'll be miserable in another year, when you know where you are. No girl will go out with you—no nice girl, that is. And you're barred from everything that makes college life what it is. Of course, I know you're not Jewish, but everybody doesn't realize that, and I think it's a terrible shame.'

In my entire life I had never heard a more surprising series of statements.

'But what are you talking about, anyway?' I asked. 'Why on earth should anybody think I was Jewish?'

'Because you belong to a Jewish fraternity,' she said.

Ensued a ludicrous, painful, silly and melancholy conversation. In the course of it I made acquaintance with (a) the social system of the University of Chicago; (b) the Jewish problem; (c) the way of the world; (d) my own colossal ignorance. Incredible though it seemed afterwards, I had never known a Jew in my life and had no idea that there were so many of them growing there under my eyes. I had only the romantic and provincial notions about Jews: thought of them as bearded old gentlemen with magic powers and vast stores of gold. Except for Rebecca in *Ivanhoe*, I had

never made the acquaintance of a *young* Jew even in literature. I suppose I must have thought they had sprung full grown into the Middle Ages and thence vanished into the oblivion of eastern Europe. At any rate, the fact was that I had never thought of the Jews as a possibility in the here and now: my contemporaries in America, in Chicago. To Lucy, my pretty little girl-friend—a wise little girl indeed, striding along in her muskrat coat—I must have seemed an imbecile. At first she refused to believe that this was new to me.

'You're sixteen years old,' she scolded. 'You've got a fair amount of brains. My God, boy, do you mean to tell me you don't know a Jew when you see one? Look at them, idiot; look at them. They have noses, hair, eyes, features, mouths, all different from anybody else. Can you honestly tell me you didn't know that —— was a Jew?'

And then the melancholy catalogue began. One by one we ran through the list of every member of my fraternity. They were all, it seemed, Jews.[1] So were half the freshmen, male and female, on the *Daily Maroon*. The last name, the one I dreaded to pronounce, was that of the godlike senior, the editor of the *Maroon*. And he too, as Lucy proved by a merciless analysis of his name and appearance, was certainly Jewish.

After this I walked along for a long time in silence. Lucy kept on talking, but I scarcely heard what she said. I was trying to realize that I had been living for nearly three months in a houseful of Jews and had never known it. I was shocked, humiliated,

[1] They weren't, but this was a detail I did not know for years. The undergraduate body called it a 'Jewish fraternity' because it contained Jews; and among the supposed Jews were a good many Gentiles.

and angry, not because my fraternity brothers were Jewish, but because I had not known about it. The shock would have been the same if they had all turned out to be Swedenborgians, or Spaniards, or vegetarians, or believers in the transmigration of souls. It made them a special caste, a marked and unvariable species, to which I could not possibly belong. To have failed to recognize a quality so singular was also a proof of abysmal ignorance on my part. I was naïf and provincial, of course, but I had never realized to what a degree. In the end I had recourse to the expedient we all come to at one time or another—I refused to believe the truth.

'Well, Lucy,' I said combatively, 'I don't believe a single thing you say, but let's just suppose for a minute that it's true. Then what? What's the difference? What possible harm can it do me to belong to a Jewish fraternity?'

She began a recital that horrified me. It horrified me more afterwards, as I came to know that the state of affairs described was by no means peculiar to the University of Chicago or to university life. The Jews, it seemed, could not possibly go to the 'nice' parties in college. They could not be elected to any class office, or to office in any club, or to any fraternity except the two they had themselves organized; they could not dance with whom they pleased or go out with the girls they wanted to go out with; they could not even walk across the quadrangles with a 'nice' girl if she could possibly escape. And so on. The picture was painted with violence, but it was true, as I was to learn before long. Hitler himself could not have invented a more savage and degrading system of anti-Semitism than that worked out by

those little monsters, the undergraduates. The system had been operating all around me from the day I entered college, and I had never seen it. As Lucy explained, my position was peculiar. I was a non-Jewish freshman pledged to a Jewish fraternity. My own brothers-in-the-bond would naturally not explain these things to me, said she, and nobody else had the courage to do so.

It took another period of painful argument to convince me that such prejudices and restrictions existed. Having, finally, accepted them as true on Lucy's testimony, I then asked why they should apply to me.

'After all,' I argued, 'I've got the map of Ireland in my face. Not to speak of my name. How on earth could anybody think I was Jewish?'

'It doesn't make any difference,' she said. 'You belong to a Jewish fraternity. That's enough. Lots of Jews take Irish names, and lots of Jews don't look especially Jewish. You'll be marked as a Jew, all right, if you go on into the fraternity. Take my word for it: I know.'

After hours of explaining, exhorting and laying down the law, Lucy brought forth the suggestion to which all this had been a preparation. It was that I should break my pledge to the fraternity, spend two or three months living in a 'dormitory' (i.e., a college hall) , and then, in the spring, join one of the better Gentile fraternities.

I repudiated the notion with vehemence. What? Leave the place I liked best in the whole University? Abandon my friends? Desert the roommate who was the only person I knew foolish enough, and amiable enough, to sit up arguing with me until two or three in the morning? Above all, forsake the precincts hallowed by the presence of that saint, that prince of the world, the editor of the *Maroon?* Impossible!

And on that note the afternoon ended. We had walked from early afternoon until dark; we had ploughed through snow and shivered on the icy lake front; I had been more thoroughly upset than ever before in my seventeen years. Lucy entered the gates of Foster Hall without knowing whether her effort had been in vain or not, and I went on home to the fraternity house, which seemed to have been invested, between lunch and dinner, with mystery.

It is difficult to make out just what my idea of a Jew was. It seems probable that the word had no significance at all, except the dubious significance given it in the romances I had spent my childhood reading. But it must have set up some kind of reverberation in my mind, because all my friends began to seem a little mysterious to me from the moment I thought they were Jewish. The ideas that Jews are a terrifying people, that they deal in dark magic, that they belong to an especially gifted and especially tragic race, are scattered so widely through all the literature of Christian Europe that we take them in unconsciously, more or less as we absorb air and moisture, without troubling to notice the process. Unconscious anti-Semitism was here, as in larger issues, what made the problem so extraordinarily difficult. I was not knowingly anti-Jewish; I had never knowingly spoken to a Jew or thought about the Jewish problem; and yet the accumulated prejudices of two thousand years had so subtly and insensibly poisoned my mind that it came as a shock to hear that my particular friends, the most admired of my acquaintance, were Jews.

Such shocks are absorbed by time. Along with other oddments of superstition, the origins of which we cannot always trace, there disappears the notion that the Jews are a sinister race, gifted in the black arts or banded together in sorcery; we learn that when they are treated like anybody else they do not greatly differ from anybody else. But to dispel these ancestral fancies, clinging like vague vapours in the mind, we require the light and air of experience. And it was precisely experience that was most conspicuously lacking in the equipment of the freshman who ploughed through the snow that night, going home, for the first time in his life, with a Problem.

'Lemmy!' I said, coming into my room, 'I've got to talk to you. Do you think that A. B. is Jewish?'

'Of course,' he said. 'What's the matter?'

I told him as much as I could of the afternoon's discoveries, but there was little time. The dinner bell was ringing, and freshmen could not be late.

'It's all true enough,' he said. 'I've known it all the time. Haven't you?'

His glum face was glummer than ever; he frowned intently, scratched his close-cropped black head.

'After dinner,' he said, 'we can lock the door and talk it out. Let's eat.'

Lemmy completed the education Lucy had begun. After dinner, a nervous meal under the circumstances, we made for our room at once to 'study.' With the door locked we sat there and talked in the quiet voices of conspirators. He had learned, from his father probably, a great deal about the world we lived in.

Our fraternity, he told me, had been founded to include (and perhaps to reconcile) Jews and non-Jews; it had only succeeded in getting itself labeled as wholly Jewish; and a national convention the year before had restricted its membership in future to Gentiles. (I remember my feeling of relief when I learned that he too was a Gentile; I was never to be sure whether anybody else in the house was or not.)

Like Lucy a few hours earlier, Lemmy found my ignorance hard to believe. He said, patiently enough, that everybody knew these things; that the difference between Jews and Gentiles was as obvious as that between men and women, and that it would never occur to anybody to state it. He further corroborated everything Lucy had told me about the opprobrium, the ridicule, the complicated varieties of discrimination and prejudice, to which any Gentile who belonged to a Jewish fraternity would have to submit throughout four years in college. He had known all this when he was pledged, he said; and he had still taken the pledge because (in his humility) he supposed the 'bid' to join a fraternity to be a rare thing, and a Jewish fraternity to be better than none. He agreed that no house could be pleasanter than ours, no friends more satisfactory; but he was convinced that remaining in the fraternity meant accepting a kind of permanent ostracism from the life of the Gentile part of the undergraduate body.

We agreed, in a high state of hysterical agitation, to do 'something.' But that 'something' could not be long delayed. The informal initiation into the fraternity would take place in an hour, and the following day we were to take the solemn, irrevocable oaths of the formal initiation. We were still in turmoil when a solemn knock on our door summoned us to the ordeal.

'Informal initiation' into a fraternity was supposed to be a test for the courage or endurance of the freshman candidate for membership. The candidate was stripped naked and led, blindfolded, into a room where the elders of the fraternity exercised their strength and wits in an attempt to try his nerve. Actually no candidate, however poltroonishly he behaved during the tests, was ever refused admission to the brotherhood, and the 'informal initiation' was therefore merely an excuse for some rather rudimentary fun. The ordeal by fire, the ordeal by water, and a dozen other curious relics of savagery were brought into play, ostensibly to prove that a boy of sixteen or seventeen was made of the right stuff to be a brother in the bond.

I went into the initiation in a state of nerves that might have made the simplest trial difficult for me. Fortunately it worked the opposite way. No matter what the brothers had done I doubt if I should have cried out or betrayed my mortal terror. The only thing I can remember saying is a sudden and involuntary 'What's that?' when the brand of the fraternity's initial letter was put on my arm and I felt the searing of the flesh. That brand remained ever afterwards, faint but quite clear, to remind me of the fantastic episode of which it was a part.

My initiation was short and easy. In five minutes it was all over and I heard A. B.'s kindly voice saying, 'All right, Jim, you can go back to your room.' Trembling with relief, I raced down the corridor to my own place and got into my clothes. Lemmy was already there, dressing. The house was quiet with our door closed, but occasionally the loud laughter of the upper classmen came through from the continuing initiation. Lemmy sat on the edge of the bed and looked glum.

'We can pack a bag,' he said, 'and go to Aurora after everybody is asleep. We'll have to jump out the window. But that is only if you've made up your mind. You've got to make up your mind. If you want to do it, I'll stick.'

We agreed on the plan of escape. We both felt that it would be impossible to face the assembled brethren, headed by A. B., and tell them our decision. They could easily overwhelm us with arguments; and tomorrow, after the formal oaths of allegiance, it would be too late.

It was most unpleasant, after this, to receive congratulations on having passed through the horseplay initiation 'successfully.' I suppose we both felt like the lowest of traitors; I know I did. But the congratulations were over in half an hour; the whole house went to sleep; at some time after midnight, with the precautions and terrors of an elopement, we dropped a bag out the window and jumped after it. From the narrow garden side of the house it was a quick scramble to the street, to a taxicab, to the train. We arrived in the middle of the night at the house of Lemmy's astonished parents in Aurora and remained there for the next two days. It was Lemmy who wrote to the fraternity to explain what we had done.

On the following afternoon A. B. arrived to talk to us. In that painful interview, all the arguments were brought forth in their unrelieved ugliness. Lemmy and A. B. did most of the talking. In the end A. B. said that since our decision was not to be changed, he would accept it, and that it would make no difference to either

of us on the *Daily Maroon*. In a state of suicidal gloom, all three of us then returned on the afternoon train to Chicago and to the University.

A. B. seemed to me, then and afterwards, the most admirable person I knew in Chicago. He could not have been more than twenty, but he was invested (in my eyes at least) with the wisdom of the ages. He had apparently founded great hopes for the fraternity on both of us, and our desertion was a blow to him; but he had a sense of justice. He could see that there was something to be said on our side, and having accepted the monstrous situation he made the best of it. During the rest of the year, A. B. seemed to be little changed, and in the spring, when the freshmen were weeded out for the next step in the *Daily Maroon's* hierarchy, it was A. B. who made me night editor for the following year. I never took the job; my exploits in the democratic army, followed by three months out of college, kept me from going on in the scheme that was to lead (in A. B.'s plan) to the editorship-in-chief. But anybody who knows the fierce antagonisms and merciless injustice of the fraternity system can see that in treating a renegade so fairly A. B. was showing a character rare among undergraduates. There may have been other fraternity men with enough maturity of mind to rise above the system, but I never knew one.

The next three months were, for Lemmy and me, a taste of thoroughgoing ostracism from the normal 'campus.' In the fraternity system the offense of 'pledge stealing' (i.e., inducing a freshman pledged to one fraternity to break his pledge in order to join another) was rigidly condemned. Consequently nobody in any other fraternity would talk to us. The offense of 'pledge breaking' was regarded as equally heinous by our former brothers in the bond, and not one of them except A. B. ever spoke to us again. It was a curious and painful experience to pass them on the campus, as we did a dozen times every morning. After a few experiences we learned to look the other way, but the effort was not pleasant. We were, for the winter term, 'barbs' (i.e., 'barbarians,' since 'all who are not Greeks are barbarians'). But we were in a far worse position than other 'barbs,' because they, for the most part, cared nothing about the ordinary undergraduates, led their own lives, and had their own friends. We had none.

'Barbarians' included most of the Jewish students, who were a majority of the total enrolled; the 'grinds' and 'Christers' among the Christian students; and a few notably 'queer' ones who were too violently unlike the average to be desirable recruits to the campus life. Glenway Wescott, descending upon the University from a Wisconsin farm, frightened most of his classmates with his waving yellow hair and his floating black cape and his weirdly literary manner of speech. Elizabeth Roberts, austere and diligent, serious with a terrifying concentration, never showed the slightest interest in the frivolities of the ordinary undergraduates. These and other eccentrics came to be almost my only acquaintances in the University during that term of ostracism from the gaieties of the campus. They were (God save us all!) the 'Poetry Club.'

The Poetry Club had been formed early in the winter of my freshman year by professorial advocates of an intellectual life for undergraduates. It had started as a prize competition for student poetry. The prize was the sum of $25. I had sent in two bits of verse, neither of them much good, and had thereafter concealed my temerity from everybody, even from A. B. The prize was awarded to a senior whose name I forget, a medical student; but it was explained in the *Daily Maroon* that this had required two ballots, since on the first it was found that three undergraduates had tied for first place. The three were the aforesaid medical student, Glenway Wescott, and myself. The medical student got the $25 and we got the Poetry Club.

We used to meet solemnly in little padded drawing rooms in Ida Noyes Hall and discuss the productions of our colleagues. Glenway always had a sheaf of immortal poetry somewhere about him, which he was ready to read out at the drop of a hat. His poetry was exceedingly 'modern,' without rhyme or metre or capital letters or punctuation, and very often (to my untutored ear) without sense either. But I was conscious enough of my shortcomings to realize that this was probably my fault, not his; and I sat through many a long reading of which I could make neither head nor tail. His modern verse was eclipsed in modernity and incomprehensibility by that of a senior who was president of the Poetry Club. Indeed, the whole club was excessively modern, and it would have taken more courage than I possessed to affront its contemporary ears with such a deplorable throwback as a sonnet. And since, at that time, I was writing sonnets by the dozen, my contribution to the poetic feast was nil.

We used to enjoy, in our first year, a flattering amount of attention from literary personages not in the University. We were thought, for some reason, to be 'promising,' and consequently Miss Harriet Monroe, Mr. Carl Sandburg, and other notables from the Chicago *cénacle*, condescended to visit us and read us their own verse. Thus I formed the belief that all poets loved reading aloud and traveled about with reams of unpublished poetry in their pockets.

The solemnity of our gatherings at the Poetry Club would have stunned T. S. Eliot himself. It was sometimes difficult for me to keep from snickering, particularly when the young poets were carried away by the excitement of reading their own productions. More than once the president had to reprove me for undue levity in comment. No doubt the whole thing was funny, but not perhaps so uproariously funny as it seemed to me at seventeen. The whole fraternity-and-campus-collegiate side of me crinkled with hostile, unreasoning laughter at the sight of Glenway declaiming his impassioned verses, his yellow mane thrown back and his childish face uplifted. His later development into a sincere and sensitive artist would have seemed incredible to me then, if anybody had been so rash as to predict it.

The barbarians, the grinds, and the highbrows learned much more than I did at the University. Scornful of the 'campus life' that preoccupied the rest of us, they grew into intellectual maturity more rapidly than their fellows, and their interest in general ideas was aroused before most of us knew what an idea was. They knew nothing of the fraternities or clubs, went to no 'parties,' and ignored the existence of football. It might have been a good thing if I had remained one of them. But I was afflicted by a dichotomy that has never left me: I could not avoid trying to make the best of two worlds. The term of ostracism to which Lemmy and I had been submitted by interfraternity rules came to an end in the spring, and I soon forgot all about the Poetry Club in the excitement of readmission to the other, the average, world of the undergraduates.

No freshman who had broken his pledge to one fraternity could be 'rushed' for another for three months. But when the period of suspension ended, at Easter, a change came over the complexion of things. People who had avoided me like the plague all through the winter suddenly started asking me to lunch. In two or three weeks after the ending of the ban I had been pledged again to another fraternity—this time to a Gentile one, which I believe had been exceedingly 'good' and was afterwards 'good' again. At the precise moment of my admission it was not one of the most brilliant of the undergraduate houses, but it did contain two or three freshmen who were to be among my best and most lasting friends in Chicago. Lemmy—who was off to the wars that summer—joined me in it the following year.

But I was never what is called a 'good fraternity man.' After the bizarre introduction I had had to the system, it was impossible for me to take it with the literal seriousness it required of its adherents. The adolescent sentimentality that was supposed to be lavished upon the fraternity and the brothers in the bond had been pretty well burned out by my unorthodox experience. It was hard to get up enthusiasm for songs, rituals, and ceremonies when I knew they were being gone through in a couple of dozen other fraternity houses at the same time and by almost exactly the same people. Uniformity —the true uniformity of the good American undergraduate, who talked the same language and wore the same clothes and did exactly the same things as every other undergraduate —was not really accessible to me. It fascinated me for a long time, and I attempted for two years to achieve it; but the effort was useless and soon began to appear uninteresting as well. After about a year in the house (the new house) I moved away from it, to a college hall, and for the rest of my time in the University I lived alone, like a 'barb,' with the single difference that I did have a fraternity to go to when I pleased. The brothers did not like this attitude and said so more than once, but by the time I had been two years in the college I knew that the heavens would not fall if I went my own way, and their protests did not disturb me.

Christmas of 1920 was my last in the University. My mother was very ill; early in January, 1921, she died. The disaster would probably have made college life unbearable in any case, but there was also the question of money. There had been little enough before; there was none now. January passed in unrelieved gloom. I returned to Chicago lonely and helpless. There was a job for me (thanks to a friend) as a reporter on the Chicago *Daily News,* but I must have been phenomenally stupid at it, for I lasted only two or three weeks. When I received my congé I did, almost without thinking, something that had probably been floating about in the undergrowth of my mind for weeks or months. I walked out of the *Daily News* office, down to the old Dearborn Street station, and onto a train for New York—without luggage and with very little money. For hour after hour I sat at a train window and stared out through tears and dirt. It was a fairly typical departure, to be

worked out during the next ten years into a system of going away. *Fuir, là-bas fuir,* could serve as a kind of epigraph for my youth, for it was spent in flight.

I was not to see Chicago again except on two short visits years later, in a world altogether different from that of the University. Those brief visits were sufficient to show me, in retrospect, how narrow my experience had been. For example, there were in Chicago some of the finest collections of modern pictures in the world: I never saw one of them while I was in the University. The Chicago Symphony Orchestra had a long season of concerts and was one of the best ensembles to be found in the United States: but the only concerts I heard in college were a few of the few (four or five a year) given in the University chapel. There were buildings, clubs, interiors, examples of modern art and architecture, and a thousand varieties of life to be seen in the lusty, sprawling, vulgar and vigorous town: I had seen only one. For the whole of my three years and a half beside Lake Michigan I was walled up in a world self-contained, self-governing and self-sufficient, the world of the college undergraduates. Ten years later I could not even remember my way about Chicago, and had to walk all the way to the lake front every time I wanted to distinguish north from south. So much for the people who believed that a university could not lead its own life in a great city! Youth, at least my variety of ignorant youth, built its own walls very high, and no city was powerful enough to batter them down.

Within those walls what, after all, had I learned? What did I take away from the pseudo-Gothic sanctuary of my pseudo-education? Not much. I had some vague idea of history and philosophy, a bowing acquaintance with English and French literature. I had learned a good deal about snobbery, cruelty, prejudice, injustice and stupidity. I had acquired half a dozen friends—perhaps. I had learned how to dance the fox trot.

It is stupefying to remember how little else I carried from Chicago with me. I spent the next ten years learning the course of events in the world from 1917 to 1921, approaching them as one approaches the course of events in the Renaissance or the Middle Ages. I was a freshman when the Bolshevik Revolution took place, and I am certain that I did not even read the accounts of it that appeared in the Chicago newspapers. The Treaty of Versailles, the defeat and collapse of Woodrow Wilson, the crash of monarchies all through Europe, the revolution in Turkey and the whole bestirring of assorted nationalisms, Wilson's legacy to the world, were duly recorded in history while I went to class dances and wrote songs for Blackfriars. The bourgeois system insulated all its children as much as possible from a knowledge of the processes of human development, and in my case it succeeded admirably in its purpose. Few Hottentots or South Sea Islanders could be less prepared for life in the great world than I was at twenty-one. As I sat in that filthy day coach on the train to New York (filthy with a concentrated filth known only to American day coaches) I was the least respectable of passengers: my ticket went one way only, and I had no baggage of any kind.

✳

WIFE OF THE HERO

Sally Benson

[The need for the approval of our own group is an impelling one, often conditioning our choice of friend or lover. When this need comes in conflict with more primitive impulses we may call into play the various defenses that Libby employs in Sally Benson's *Wife of the Hero*. We thus protect ourselves from facing an unwelcome reality. From the first, Libby's feeling for Joe, who is so different from her family and friends, has had about it a good deal of the element of fantasy. In imagination she identifies herself with strong women who have made their husbands successful and admired. When she is forced to make a decision, the behavior pattern of her family and friends dominates her actions. Her treatment of Joe reveals unconscious elements of both sadism and masochism. Interesting too is her rationalization of her action as a subtle way of disillusioning her lover and thus sparing his feelings.]

I

The trouble was, Libby told herself, she had talked **too much** about him to her family, and now they were curious, quite naturally, and wanted to see him. But there had been so much

From *People Are Fascinating* by Sally Benson. By permission of Covici-Friede, Inc., 1936.

to explain about him; why he never came out to Pelham to see her, not even on Sundays; why she had met him in town for dinner, and then took the train home by herself afterwards. Her mother thought this all very odd, so Libby had tried to explain him and, as her own thoughts were so vague and excited, she had made a separate picture of him for her mother and father and Jeanie that wasn't true at all. But the picture suited them, as she knew it would, because it was a picture with which they were familiar.

She had made him exceptionally fine for Jeanie who was seventeen and still expected the finest.

'What's he like?' Jeanie had asked.

'What's *who* like?'

'Oh, this Mr. X. that you keep seeing and that you're so mysterious about.'

'Well,' Libby had said as a picture of him that would suit Jeanie began to form in her mind, 'he's not like anybody you ever saw, exactly. He's —well—he's simply swell.'

'I know. But what's he *like?*' Jeanie had asked again. 'Is he like Gene Raymond, or Clark Gable, or who?'

Jeanie was very definite about people. They had to look like somebody or almost like somebody. Somebody handsome, or famous, or interesting. Men, to Jeanie, who couldn't be classified as, 'He's sort of like Dick Powell,' or 'He's Bing Crosby's double,' just didn't exist. Even though, for a while, during the early part of the summer, she had devoted a few evenings to a young man who wore glasses and had no redeeming features that the family could see. But Jeanie had insisted that he danced like Fred Astaire and, as the floor of the country club was always so crowded that you couldn't tell how anyone was danc-

ing, no one had been able to prove she was wrong.

So Libby told her, 'Well, you see, he's studying to be a doctor. Not a doctor, exactly, though. He's going to do all sorts of work with microbes and things. Like Arrowsmith.'

'Oh,' Jeanie had exclaimed, terribly impressed. 'You're lucky. Someone like Ronald Colman around all the time! Libby, you've *got* to marry him and go to the tropics and everything. Not that I want *you* to die like the girl in *Arrowsmith,* but think how grand it would be to live down there in those funny places and have your husband be like a sort of god to those people. And I can visit you and, maybe, meet someone like him myself. Libby, you can be a hero's wife! I bet you never thought you'd be a hero's wife!'

Libby thought of Arrowsmith, too, and of Arrowsmith's wife in the movies being brave and waiting for him, to the accompaniment of the kind of music that did things to you and lifted you up to places that were spacious and light.

Then Jeanie had said, 'Of course, he's grand-looking and everything, too, isn't he, Libby? I mean, he's not one of those funny little men you see with brief cases?'

And Libby had denied this emphatically, although for a moment her heart had sunk. But she was in a haze, those days, and as long as she could keep her inner picture of Joe intact, she was willing to present him to her world in any way that would please them. He was too short, she knew, and when she walked with him she bent her knees a little so that never, by any possible chance, would he be aware of it. As to whether or not he was good-looking, she couldn't have honestly said. From the moment she had been introduced to him on a Fifth Avenue bus by Marjory Scott, a rather dreadful girl she had gone to school with, she had had such a feeling of excitement about him that it was as though he were out of focus in her sight. Marjory Scott had got off the bus and Libby had sat with him all the way to Forty-second Street, and then he had walked over to Grand Central with her. Riding back to Pelham, it seemed to her that she had never said so much to anyone in so short a time, although later when she tried to piece together what she had said, it didn't sound so unusual. And when he asked her to have dinner with him the next night, his invitation and her acceptance had seemed weighted with a sort of insistence.

After that, everything between them had been wonderful; the little place they went for dinner; the talks they had; and the things he told her about himself. His whole life, as he told it, became Romance for Libby; about how hard he had worked, about his father's poor little farm in Indiana, about running away from home, about his working his way through an obscure little college, and not even belonging to a fraternity. He couldn't drive a car, he said, he'd never owned one, nor did he play any games because he hadn't had time for them. She thought of him as some sort of bright light that had found its way up from depths of darkness she didn't know existed. She was terribly in love with him and she became fiercely partisan for him in hundreds of small, absurd ways. She began to despise the boys she knew at home because they had everything and thought nothing of it—the tanned young men who drove up to her house in cars and blew the horns peremptorily, to see if she were home. She felt that she, herself, was too comfortable, and she became aware of money and of how much things cost, and she began to ask for very little and to be ashamed of extravagances. She wouldn't let Joe ride home on the train with her, the fare was too much, and at dinner she said she wasn't hungry and ordered the cheapest thing on the menu. At night she lay awake thinking, and sometimes, when she thought of the things he had told her, she cried.

She was like a stone wall between him and her family. She was careful to give them no cause to be amused at anything about him. And to do this, she had lied desperately. She had told Jeanie that he was a Princeton man of a year before the time of any of Jeanie's young men; she told her mother that he lived in a sort of studio near Gramercy Park, because she knew that One Hundred and Seventy-eight Street was beyond her mother's comprehension; she told her father that she couldn't possibly ask him out for golf on Sundays because he was taking all sorts of summer classes and was studying terribly hard. She said that his father was dead, which was true, but that he had been a mining engineer some place out West; she said that the reason she met him in town always was because he knew so many interesting people and that it was such fun to sit around and really talk instead of chasing around to night clubs and roof gardens dancing. She won Jeanie over to him completely; her father said that he sounded like an up and coming young man; but her mother was still uneasy and unconvinced.

II

As for herself, Libby was strong in her feeling that she had discovered something that would never come to her again in her lifetime. But it was a feeling she couldn't expose to anyone else just yet. So for over six weeks she battled for Joe with lies to her family, and then the terrible moment came. She had known all along that it was coming, but she had hoped for more time.

It happened one evening just as she was leaving the house to catch the train for New York, where he was to meet her for dinner. As she passed the door to the living room, she knew instantly that her mother and father had been talking about her, and she wished there was some way that she could be out of the house and on her way to the station before her mother called her. But there wasn't.

'Libby,' her mother said. 'Come here. I want to speak to you a minute.'

'I'm late,' she answered. 'I'll miss my train.'

'You have a few minutes,' her mother said. 'I won't keep you long, Libby. Your father and I have been talking about this young man you keep meeting in New York. And we both feel, your father and I, that you should ask him to the house so that we can meet him. I don't like the idea of your being constantly in the company of a young man we've never seen. I don't doubt he is all you say he is, but you're young and your judgments aren't formed yet, and I really must insist you ask him here. This Sunday.'

'But, mother,' she said, 'I told you. It's awfully hard for him to get away. He's terribly busy and everything. I explained all that.'

'Libby,' her mother said, 'you are talking like a foolish child. No young man is so busy that he can't spare a few hours to come this short way to meet your parents. I don't like it, I tell you. I don't like it at all. And if you won't ask him, then I must forbid your meeting him in New York.'

'Oh, mother, please!' she begged. But she knew it was no use.

Usually on the train she sat in a happy daze, a queer feeling of anticipation in the pit of her stomach that got better as the train went into the tunnel after it passed One Hundred and Twenty-fifth Street. But this evening she was miserable with the sensation that she was facing something she was powerless to handle. She began to wish, for the first time, that Joe was different, that he dressed a little better, that his manner was not quite so brusque, that he wasn't always so terribly on the defensive, that his indignation over things was more subdued. She thought of her father, and supposed that Joe would despise a man like her father, despise him for his golf and his detective stories. And she tried to picture Joe and her father sitting on the porch of the country club having a drink together and talking. Joe would be quiet and polite in a frozen sort of way, sitting there in his blue suit, his good one, and her father, after a few hearty attempts to talk to him in the manner he always used toward young men, would give up and dismiss him as being queerer than Dick's hatband.

What would Jeanie say when she saw him? She would begin to talk a lot and hand him her line. She would overwhelm him with her silliest talk to cover her own confusion. Afterwards, she would be lovely to Libby about him, saying, 'He's terribly nice. Really he is. He must be awfully bright.' But . .

Her family would be too polite to question him much, but Jeanie was sure to ask him about Princeton, and one by one the lies she had told about him would be exposed. If she could only look ahead and be sure of his greatness! How did women like Leora Arrowsmith and Margaret Clive *know* that their husbands were going to be great men? Did they just love them, not caring? Did they have to explain them to their families? She felt she would like to be insured against humiliation and defeat. But how could she say to Joe, 'Look, I will love you and marry you and be faithful to you, if you will guarantee me greatness and immortality. I will stand funny little restaurants, dreary apartments, and clothes that aren't right, if you will promise me that some day I will be pictured against a great background with the sound of a symphony orchestra.'

III

He was waiting for her in the restaurant and when she saw him sitting at their table in the corner, she saw him for an instant through Jeanie's eyes. 'That funny looking little man!' and she felt a rush of indignation toward him.

Then, 'Hello,' she said.

He only half rose, she noticed, and he made no effort to help her with her coat. Perversely, she made a chore of slipping out of its full sleeves and arranging it on the back of her chair. Then she looked around the little restaurant, at the corrugated tin ceiling, at the pink paper roses on a trellis by the window, at the tiled floor, and her glance stripped the place of glamour. She wondered what her mother would say if she could see it, her mother who always stopped at the Plaza and who understood that sometimes whimsical young people ate at Schrafft's.

'How are all the Pelham ladies today in their hats and their pastel shades?' he asked.

It was the worst thing he could have said.

'They look all right,' she answered defensively. 'What's the matter with them?'

He looked at the menu and then, curiously, across the table at her. She looked back at him steadily and let her gaze fall to his hands and to his nails that were too short and looked as though he bit them.

'Some of them are sweet,' she said.

It seemed to her that he decided with almost indecent interest what he was going to eat. He was always hungry, too hungry, and she resented feeling that perhaps these dinners with her were the best ones he knew. She suddenly thought of the way he had of pushing his plate back when he had finished eating.

'It was perfect in the country today,' she told him. 'I very nearly called you to tell you I wouldn't be in.'

'Oh,' he said. 'Why didn't you?'

'Well, it wasn't *vital*. It was just so heavenly, and I knew New York would be hot and sticky and dreadful. *You* know.'

'It would have been all right,' he said, 'if you didn't want to come in.'

'Don't be silly,' she said. 'We all went to Rye for a swim, and Douglas Collins was there. I haven't seen him in ages. He was all scratched up. He'd smashed his car, and he was terribly funny about it. He's perfectly crazy. He doesn't care about anything.'

She shook her head amusedly over Douglas Collins. Across the table beside Joe's water glass, she noticed an envelope stuffed with papers and she knew that he had brought something to show her.

'Did I ever tell you about the time we all went to Coney Island all the way from Pelham in a taxi? I don't know what made us, except that it seemed like a good idea at the time. Anyway, we took this terrible old cab and the driver's name was Cecil something. Imagine a taxi driver being named Cecil! None of the windows would open and Douglas put his hand through one and smashed the glass. It was funny.'

Joe's head was bent too close to his plate as he ate. 'Why can't he talk to me?' she thought indignantly. 'Why can't he talk in just a silly sort of way? He's waiting for me to be quiet so he can begin telling me about himself again.'

She gave a suppressed little yawn. 'Do you know, I think I'm *sleepy*! Or maybe it's because this place is hot. I was telling Jeanie about this place and she *adored* it. Once this boy took Jeanie just for fun to a little Rumanian place on Second Avenue and she was thrilled!' She nodded toward the trellis. 'I told her about the roses,' she said. And laughed.

'Did you tell her about me?'

'Oh,' she said. 'Jeanie loves hearing about you. You fascinate her.'

She pushed her food about the plate with her fork. It was a veal cutlet covered thickly with tomato sauce. 'I'm not hungry,' she told him. 'I don't know how you can eat in this weather.'

'I didn't have any lunch,' he said.

'We ate on the beach. A lot of terrible things.'

'Look, Libby,' Joe said. 'I want to tell you something. I have a chance to do some tutoring. This fellow is no darned good, but his old man is dead set on having him be a doctor,

and I thought I'd talk it over with you and see if you minded.'

'See if I *minded?*' she repeated. 'Why should I mind? I mean, if you can get this job, I suppose you have to.'

'Well, you see, I'll be tutoring in the evenings mostly. I won't be able to see you much.'

'Life is real, life is earnest,' she said. She leaned back in her chair and looked at him. 'I used to have a funny teacher. And every time I did anything half-way decent, he used to say it was very commendable. So I think what you're going to do is very commendable.'

She took a sip of her water, but the water was warm and the glass felt greasy. 'Now then,' she said. 'Tell me about it.'

But he was silent for so long that she began to talk again and her voice sounded unpleasant to her. 'Jeanie and I have been deviling mother to take us somewhere. Of course, we're having loads of fun, but I think every once in a while anybody's apt to get restless. We thought it would be fun to just get in the car and start off somewhere. Maybe Canada or some place like that.'

It seemed to her that she talked on and on. She told him about the youngest Owen boy getting tight at the Club and waking up the next morning on the fifth tee; she told him about the Harrises who had only been married four months and were getting a divorce, and that 'Nina Harris is no fool, though, she's going to ask for plenty of alimony and she'll get it, too'; she told him about middle-aged Harvey Lyon who had simply walked out on his wife, but 'you couldn't blame him much. She was this perfect *mouse,* and he'd stood her for fifteen years'; she told him that the Marsdens had had another baby and 'weren't they foolish? Because they're posted at the club even'; she told him that Jeanie didn't want to go back to the same school and had threatened to get herself kicked out if her mother made her go. Her talk was a cruel caricature of the sort of talk she had heard all her life.

But it gave her a queer sense of exhilaration and for a while she enjoyed listening to herself and watching Joe's face. She remembered a book she had read once about a woman who had deliberately disillusioned the man she was in love with for his own good, and it made her feel hard and unnatural.

IV

Outside the restaurant, standing in the street, Joe asked, 'What would you like to do? Would you like to see a movie or something?'

It was the first time he had suggested doing anything. Usually, they sat and talked, or, rather, he talked and she listened until it was time for her train to leave. There was something about his asking her what she wanted to do that made her collapse completely. 'I don't know,' she said. 'I think I'm tired. I think I want to go home.'

They started walking toward the subway. 'Joe,' she asked, 'may we take a taxi?'

In the taxi, they sat far apart, Joe, with his face set, looking out the window. If he would only, she thought, take my hand or kiss me now, everything would be all right. I could tell him then. I could tell him what I've done.

At the station, after he paid the driver, she touched his arm. 'Joe,' she said, 'don't come any farther with me. I'm going to get a magazine or something. And I want to call up this girl I know. I promised her I would.'

He stood there looking miserably at her. 'Libby,' he asked. 'What's the matter?'

She looked back at him brightly. 'Why, nothing,' she told him, her voice surprised and puzzled.

'Well, I'll telephone you. Shall I?'

But she could only keep on looking at him brightly, and touch his hand before she walked away. Once, going down the steps, she almost turned and ran back, but she hurried on until she was seated in the train and it was too late. It was quite a while before the train pulled out, and she sat there in the dark hot station wanting to cry.

I've done something terrible, she thought. What kind of a girl am I? What will ever happen to me now? Nothing fine can ever happen to me now. How are heroes' wives made?

❋

DRY SEPTEMBER

William Faulkner

[The power of prejudice to arouse irrational action is forcefully illustrated in *Dry September*. In McLendon, the leader of the lynching group,

From *These Thirteen*, by William Faulkner, copyright, 1931. Reprinted by permission of Random House, Inc.

one detects a sexual basis for the sadistic impulses which seem to be prompted by his thought of a Negro raping a white woman. His irresponsible hysteria is transferred to the crowd, who lynch their apparently innocent victim in the name of racial honor. The terrible irony of the situation is the more evident because we recognize in the neurotic middle-aged woman who has made the accusation an individual whose feelings of sexual inadequacy and failure have driven her to this means of attracting attention and re-establishing herself in the eyes of the villagers as a desirable woman.]

Through the bloody September twilight, aftermath of sixty-two rainless days, it had gone like a fire in dry grass—the rumor, the story, whatever it was. Something about Miss Minnie Cooper and a negro. Attacked, insulted, frightened: none of them, gathered in the barbershop on that Saturday evening where the ceiling fan stirred, without freshening it, the vitiated air, sending back upon them, in recurrent surges of stale pomade and lotion, their own stale breath and odors, knew exactly what had happened.

'Except it wasn't Will Mayes,' a barber said. He was a man of middle age; a thin, sand-colored man with a mild face, who was shaving a client. 'I know Will Mayes. He's a good nigger. And I know Miss Minnie Cooper, too.'

'What do you know about her?' a second barber said.

'Who is she?' the client said. 'A girl?'

'No,' the barber said. 'She's about forty, I reckon. She ain't married. That's why I don't believe—'

'Believe hell!' a hulking youth in a sweat-stained silk shirt said. 'Won't you take a white woman's word before a nigger's?'

'I don't believe Will Mayes did it,' the barber said. 'I know Will Mayes.'

'Maybe you know who did it, then. Maybe you already got him out of town, you damn nigger-lover.'

'I don't believe anybody did anything. I don't believe anything happened. I leave it to you fellows if them ladies that gets old without getting married don't have notions that a man can't—'

'Then you're a hell of a white man,' the client said. He moved under the cloth. The youth had sprung to his feet.

'You don't?' he said. 'Do you accuse a white woman of telling a lie?'

The barber held the razor poised above the half-risen client. He did not look around.

'It's this durn weather,' another said. 'It's enough to make any man do anything. Even to her.'

Nobody laughed. The barber said in his mild, stubborn tone: 'I ain't accusing nobody of nothing. I just know and you fellows know how a woman that never—'

'You damn nigger-lover!' the youth said.

'Shut up, Butch,' another said. 'We'll get the facts in plenty of time to act.'

'Who is? Who's getting them?' the youth said. 'Facts, hell! I—'

'You're a fine white man,' the client said. 'Ain't you?' In his frothy beard he looked like a desert-rat in the moving pictures. 'You tell them, Jack,' he said to the youth. 'If they ain't any white men in this town, you can count on me, even if I ain't only a drummer and a stranger.'

'That's right, boys,' the barber said. 'Find out the truth first. I know Will Mayes.'

'Well, by God!' the youth shouted. 'To think that a white man in this town—'

'Shut up, Butch,' the second speaker said. 'We got plenty of time.'

The client sat up. He looked at the speaker. 'Do you claim that anything excuses a nigger attacking a white woman? Do you mean to tell me that you're a white man and you'll stand for it? You better go back North where you come from. The South don't want your kind here.'

'North what?' the second said. 'I was born and raised in this town.'

'Well, by God!' the youth said. He looked about with a strained, baffled gaze, as if he was trying to remember what it was he wanted to say or to do. He drew his sleeve across his sweating face. 'Damn if I'm going to let a white woman—'

'You tell them, Jack,' the drummer said. 'By God, if they—'

The screen-door crashed open. A man stood in the floor, his feet apart and his heavy-set body poised easily. His white shirt was open at the throat; he wore a felt hat. His hot, bold glance swept the group. His name was Plunkett. He had commanded troops at the front in France and had been decorated for valor.

'Well,' he said, 'are you going to sit there and let a black son rape a white woman on the streets of Jefferson?'

Butch sprang up again. The silk of his shirt clung flat to his heavy shoulders. At each armpit was a dark half-moon. 'That's what I been telling them! That's what I—'

'Did it really happen?' a third said. 'This ain't the first man-scare she ever had, like Hawkshaw says. Wasn't there something about a man on the kitchen roof, watching her undress, about a year ago?'

'What?' the client said. 'What's that?' The barber had been slowly forcing him back into the chair; he arrested himself reclining, his head lifted, the barber still pressing him down.

Plunkett whirled on the third speaker. 'Happen? What the hell difference does it make? Are you going to let the black sons get away with it until one really does it?'

'That's what I'm telling them!' Butch shouted. He cursed, long and steady, pointless.

'Here, here,' a fourth said. 'Not so loud. Don't talk so loud.'

'Sure,' Plunkett said; 'no talking necessary at all. I've done my talking. Who's with me?' He poised on the balls of his feet, roving his gaze.

The barber held the client's face down, the razor poised. 'Find out the facts first, boys. I know Willy Mayes. It wasn't him. Let's get the sheriff and do this thing right.'

Plunkett whirled upon him his furious, rigid face. The barber did not look away. They looked like men of different races. The other barbers had ceased also above their prone clients. 'You mean to tell me,' Plunkett said, 'that you'd take a nigger's word before a white woman's? Why, you damn nigger-loving—'

The third rose and grasped Plunkett's arm; he too had been a soldier. 'Now, now! Let's figure this thing out. Who knows anything about what really happened?'

'Figure out hell!' Plunkett jerked his arm free. 'All that're with me get up from there. The ones that ain't—' He roved his gaze, dragging his sleeve across his face.

Three men rose. The client in the

chair sat up. 'Here,' he said, jerking at the cloth around his neck; 'get this rag off me. I'm with him. I don't live here, but, by God, if our mothers and wives and sisters—' He smeared the cloth over his face and flung it to the floor. Plunkett stood in the floor and cursed the others. Another rose and moved toward him. The remainder sat uncomfortably, not looking at one another, then one by one they rose and joined him.

The barber picked the cloth from the floor. He began to fold it neatly. 'Boys, don't do that. Will Mayes never done it. I know.'

'Come on,' Plunkett said. He whirled. From his hip pocket protruded the butt of a heavy automatic pistol. They went out. The screen-door crashed behind them reverberant in the dead air.

The barber wiped the razor carefully and swiftly, and put it away, and ran to the rear, and took his hat from the wall. 'I'll be back soon as I can,' he said to the other barbers. 'I can't let—' He went out, running. The two other barbers followed him to the door and caught it on the rebound, leaning out and looking up the street after him. The air was flat and dead. It had a metallic taste at the base of the tongue.

'What can he do?' the first said. The second one was saying 'Jees Christ, Jees Christ' under his breath. 'I'd just as lief be Will Mayes as Hawk, if he gets Plunkett riled.'

'Jees Christ, Jees Christ,' the second whispered.

'You reckon he really done it to her?' the first said.

II

She was thirty-eight or thirty-nine. She lived in a small frame house with her invalid mother and a thin, sal-low, unflagging aunt, where each morning, between ten and eleven, she would appear on the porch in a lace-trimmed boudoir cap, to sit swinging in the porch swing until noon. After dinner she lay down for a while, until the afternoon began to cool. Then, in one of the three or four new voile dresses which she had each summer, she would go down-town to spend the afternoon in the stores with the other ladies, where they would handle the goods and haggle over prices in cold, immediate voices, without any intention of buying.

She was of comfortable people—not the best in Jefferson, but good people enough—and she was still on the slender side of ordinary-looking, with a bright, faintly haggard manner and dress. When she was young she had had a slender, nervous body and a sort of hard vivacity which had enabled her to ride for the time upon the crest of the town's social life as exemplified by the high-school party and church-social period of her contemporaries while still children enough to be un-class-conscious.

She was the last to realize that she was losing ground; that those among whom she had been a little brighter and louder flame than any other were beginning to learn the pleasure of snobbery—male—and retaliation—female. That was when her face began to wear that bright, haggard look. She still carried it to parties on shadowy porticos and summer lawns, like a mask or a flag, with that bafflement and furious repudiation of truth in her eyes. One evening at a party she heard a boy and two girls, all schoolmates, talking. She never accepted another invitation.

She watched the girls with whom she had grown up as they married and got houses and children, but no man ever called on her steadily until the children of the other girls had been calling her 'aunty' for several years, the while their mothers told them in bright voices about how popular Minnie had been as a girl. Then the town began to see her driving on Sunday afternoons with the cashier in the bank. He was a widower of about forty—a high-colored man, smelling always faintly of the barber-shop or of whiskey. He owned the first automobile in town, a red run-about; Minnie had the first motoring bonnet and veil the town ever saw. Then the town began to say: 'Poor Minnie!' 'But she is old enough to take care of herself,' others said. That was when she first asked her schoolmates that the children call her 'cousin' instead of 'aunty.'

It was twelve years now since she had been relegated into adultery by public opinion, and eight years since the cashier had gone to a Memphis bank, returning for one day each Christmas, which he spent at an annual bachelors' party in a hunting-club on the river. From behind their curtains the neighbors would see him pass, and during the across-the-street Christmas-day visiting they would tell her about him, about how well he looked, and how they heard that he was prospering in the city, watching with bright, secret eyes her haggard, bright face. Usually by that hour there would be the scent of whiskey on her breath. It was supplied her by a youth, a clerk at the soda-fountain: 'Sure; I buy it for the old gal. I reckon she's entitled to a little fun.'

Her mother kept to her room altogether now; the gaunt aunt ran the house. Against that background Minnie's bright dresses, her idle and empty days, had a quality of furious unreality. She went out in the evenings only with women now, neighbors, to the moving pictures. Each afternoon she dressed in one of the new dresses and went down-town alone, where her young cousins were already strolling in the late afternoons with their delicate, silken heads and thin, awkward arms and conscious hips, clinging to one another or shrieking and giggling with paired boys in the soda-fountain when she passed and went on along the serried stores, in the doors of which sitting and lounging men did not even follow her with their eyes any more.

III

The barber went swiftly up the street where the sparse lights, insect-swirled, glared in rigid and violent suspension in the lifeless air. The day had died in a pall of dust; above the darkened square, shrouded by the spent dust, the sky was clear as the inside of a brass bell. Below the east was a rumor of the twice-waxed moon.

When he overtook them Plunkett and three others were getting into a car parked in an alley. Plunkett stooped his thick head, peering out beneath the top. 'Changed your mind, did you?' he said. 'Damn good thing; by God, tomorrow when this town hears about how you talked to-night—'

'Now, now,' the other ex-soldier said. 'Hawkshaw's all right. Come on, Hawk; jump in!'

'Will Mayes never done it, boys,' the barber said. 'If anybody done it. Why, you all know well as I do there ain't any town where they got better niggers than us. And you know how a lady will kind of think things about men when there ain't any reason to, and Miss Minnie anyway—'

'Sure, sure,' the soldier said. 'We're

just going to talk to him a little; that's all.'

'Talk hell!' Butch said. 'When we're done with the—'

'Shut up, for God's sake!' the soldier said. 'Do you want everybody in town—'

'Tell them, by God!' Plunkett said. 'Tell every one of the sons that'll let a white woman—'

'Let's go; let's go: here's the other car.' The second car slid squealing out of a cloud of dust at the alley-mouth. Plunkett started his car and backed out and took the lead. Dust lay like fog in the street. The street lights hung nimbused as in water. They drove on out of town.

A rutted lane turned at right angles. Dust hung above it too, and above all the land. The dark bulk of the ice-plant, where the negro Mayes was night-watchman, rose against the sky. 'Better stop here, hadn't we?' the soldier said. Plunkett did not reply. He hurled the car up and slammed to a stop, the headlights glaring on the blank wall.

'Listen here, boys,' the barber said; 'if he's here, don't that prove he never done it? Don't it? If it was him, he would run. Don't you see he would?' The second car came up and stopped. Plunkett got down; Butch sprang down beside him. 'Listen, boys,' the barber said.

'Cut the lights off!' Plunkett said. The breathless darkness rushed down. There was no sound in it save their lungs as they sought air in the parched dust in which for two months they had lived; then the diminishing crunch of Plunkett's and Butch's feet, and a moment later Plunkett's voice:

'Will! . . . Will!'

Below the east the wan hemorrhage of the moon increased. It heaved above the ridge, silvering the air, the dust, so that they seemed to breathe, live, in a bowl of molten lead. There was no sound of night-bird nor insect, no sound save their breathing and a faint ticking of contracting metal about the cars. Where their bodies touched one another they seemed to sweat dryly, for no more moisture came. 'Christ!' a voice said; 'let's get out of here.'

But they didn't move until vague noises began to grow out of the darkness ahead; then they got out and waited tensely in the breathless dark. There was another sound: a blow, a hissing expulsion of breath and Plunkett cursing in undertone. They stood a moment longer, then they ran forward. They ran in a stumbling clump, as though they were fleeing something. 'Kill him, kill the son!' a voice whispered. Plunkett flung them back.

'Not here,' he said. 'Get him into the car.' They hauled the negro up. 'Kill him, kill the black son!' the voice murmured. They dragged the negro to the car. The barber had waited beside the car. He could feel himself sweating and he knew he was going to be sick at the stomach.

'What is it, captains?' the negro said. 'I ain't done nothing. 'Fore God, Mr. John.' Someone produced handcuffs. They worked busily about him as though he were a post, quiet, intent, getting in one another's way. He submitted to the handcuffs, looking swiftly and constantly from dim face to face. 'Who's here, captains?' he said, leaning to peer into the faces until they could feel his breath and smell his sweaty reek. He spoke a name or two. 'What you-all say I done, Mr. John?'

Plunkett jerked the car-door open. 'Get in!' he said.

The negro did not move. 'What

you-all going to do with me, Mr. John? I ain't done nothing. White folks, captains, I ain't done nothing: I swear 'fore God.' He called another name.

'Get in!' Plunkett said. He struck the negro. The others expelled their breath in a dry hissing and struck him with random blows, and he whirled and cursed them, and swept his manacled hands across their faces and slashed the barber upon the mouth, and the barber struck him also. 'Get him in there,' Plunkett said. They pushed at him. He ceased struggling and got in, and sat quietly as the others took their places. He sat between the barber and the soldier, drawing his limbs in so as not to touch them, his eyes going swiftly and constantly from face to face. Butch clung to the running-board. The car moved on. The barber nursed his mouth in his handkerchief.

'What's the matter, Hawk?' the soldier said.

'Nothing,' the barber said. They regained the high road and turned away from town. The second car dropped back out of the dust. They went on, gaining speed; the final fringe of houses dropped behind.

'Goddam, he stinks!' the soldier said.

'We'll fix that,' the man in front beside Plunkett said. On the running-board Butch cursed into the hot rush of air. The barber leaned suddenly forward and touched Plunkett's shoulder.

'Let me out, John.'

'Jump out, nigger-lover,' Plunkett said without turning his head. He drove swiftly. Behind them the sourceless lights of the second car glared in the dust. Presently Plunkett turned into a narrow road. It too was rutted in disuse. It led back to an old brick-

kiln—a series of reddish mounds and weed-and-vine-choked vats without bottom. It had been used for pasture once, until one day the owner missed one of his mules. Although he prodded carefully in the vats with a long pole, he could not even find the bottom of them.

'John,' the barber said.

'Jump out, then,' Plunkett said, hurling the car along the ruts. Beside the barber the negro spoke:

'Mr. Henry.'

The barber sat forward. The narrow tunnel of the road rushed up and past. Their motion was like an extinct furnace blast: cooler, but utterly dead. The car bounded from rut to rut.

'Mr. Henry,' the negro said.

The barber began to tug furiously at the door. 'Look out, there!' the soldier said, but he had already kicked the door open and swung onto the running-board. The soldier leaned across the negro and grasped at him, but he had already jumped. The car went on without checking speed.

The impetus hurled him crashing, through dust-sheathed weeds, into the ditch. Dust puffed about him, and in a thin, vicious crackling of sapless stems he lay choking and retching until the second car passed and died away. Then he rose and limped on until he reached the high road and turned toward town, brushing at his clothes with his hands. The moon was higher, riding high and clear of the dust at last, and after a while the town began to glare beneath the dust. He went on, limping. Presently he heard the cars and the glow of them grew in the dust behind him and he left the road and crouched again in the weeds until they passed. Plunkett's car came last now. There were four people in it and Butch was not on the running-board.

They went on; the dust swallowed them; the glare and the sound died away. The dust of them hung for a while, but soon the eternal dust absorbed it again. The barber climbed back onto the road and limped on toward town.

IV

As she dressed after supper, on that Saturday evening, her own flesh felt like fever. Her hands trembled among the hooks and eyes, and her eyes had a feverish look, and her hair swirled crisp and crackling under the comb. While she was still dressing, the friends called for her and sat while she donned her sheerest underthings and stockings and a new voile dress. 'Do you feel strong enough to go out?' they said, their eyes bright too, with a dark glitter. 'When you have had time to get over the shock, you must tell us what happened. What he said and did; everything.'

In the leafed darkness, as they walked toward the square, she began to breathe deeply, something like a swimmer preparing to dive, until she ceased trembling, the four of them walking slowly because of the terrible heat and out of solicitude for her. But as they neared the square she began to tremble again, walking with her head up, her hands clinched at her sides, their voices about her murmurous, also with that feverish, glittering quality of their eyes.

They entered the square, she in the center of the group, fragile in her fresh dress. She was trembling worse. She walked slower and slower, as children eat ice-cream, her head up and her eyes bright in the haggard banner of her face, passing the hotel and the coatless drummers in chairs along

the curb looking around at her: 'That's the one: see? The one in pink in the middle.' 'Is that her? What did they do with the nigger? Did they—?' 'Sure. He's all right.' 'All right, is he?' 'Sure. He went on a little trip.' Then the drug-store, where even the young men lounging in the doorway tipped their hats and followed with their eyes the motion of her hips and legs when she passed.

They went on, passing the lifted hats of the gentlemen, the suddenly ceased voices, protective, deferent. 'Do you see?' the friends said. Their voices sounded like long hovering sighs of hissing exultation. 'There's not a negro on the square. Not one.'

They reached the picture-show. It was like a miniature fairyland with its lighted lobby and colored lithographs of life caught in its terrible and beautiful mutations. Her lips began to tingle. In the dark, when the picture began, it would be all right; she could hold back the laughing so it would not waste away so fast and so soon. So she hurried on before the turning faces, the undertones of low astonishment, and they took their accustomed places where she could see the aisle against the silver glare and the young men and girls coming in two and two against it.

The lights flicked away; the screen glowed silver, and soon life began to unfold, beautiful and passionate and sad, while still the young men and girls entered, scented and sibilant in the half-dark, their paired backs in silhouette delicate and sleek, their slim, quick bodies awkward, divinely young, while beyond them the silver dream accumulated, inevitably on and on. She began to laugh. In trying to suppress it, it made more noise than ever; heads began to turn. Still laughing, her friends raised her and led her out, and she stood at the curb, laughing on a high, sustained note, until the taxi came up and they helped her in.

They removed the pink voile and the sheer underthings, and the stockings, and put her to bed, and cracked ice for her temples, and sent for the doctor. He was hard to locate, so they ministered to her with hushed ejaculations, renewing the ice and fanning her. While the ice was fresh and cold she stopped laughing and lay still for a time, moaning only a little. But soon the laughing welled again and her voice rose screaming.

'Shhhhhhhhhh! Shhhhhhhhhhh!' they said, freshening the ice-pack, smoothing her hair, examining it for gray; 'poor girl!' Then to one another: 'Do you suppose anything really happened?' their eyes darkly aglitter, secret and passionate. 'Shhhhhhhhhh! Poor girl! Poor Minnie!'

V

It was midnight when Plunkett drove up to his neat new house. It was trim and fresh as a bird-cage and almost as small, with its clean green-and-white paint. He locked the car and mounted the porch and entered. His wife rose from a chair beside the reading-lamp. Plunkett stopped in the floor and stared at her until she looked down.

'Look at that clock!' he said, lifting his arm, pointing. She stood before him, her face lowered, a magazine in her hands. Her face was pale, strained, and weary-looking. 'Haven't I told you about sitting up like this, waiting to see when I come in?'

'John!' she said. She laid the magazine down. Poised on the balls of his feet, he glared at her with his hot eyes, his sweating face.

'Didn't I tell you?' He went toward her. She looked up then. He caught her shoulder. She stood passive, looking at him.

'Don't, John. I couldn't sleep . . . The heat; something. Please, John. You're hurting me.'

'Didn't I tell you?' He released her and half struck, half flung her across the chair, and she lay there and watched him quietly as he left the room.

He went on through the house, ripping off his shirt, and on the dark, screened porch at the rear he stood and mopped his head and shoulders with the shirt and flung it away. He took the pistol from his hip and laid it on the table beside the bed, and sat on the bed and removed his shoes, and rose and slipped his trousers off. He was sweating again already, and he stooped and hunted furiously for the shirt. At last he found it and wiped his body again, and, with his body pressed against the dusty screen, he stood panting. There was no movement, no sound, not even an insect. The dark world seemed to lie stricken beneath the cold moon and the lidless stars.

JEAN-CHRISTOPHE

ROMAIN ROLLAND

[The problem of the individual caught in an economic system which has no regard for him is not a new one, although the conflicts of the modern world have heightened our consciousness of it. Economic deprivation necessarily leaves an imprint upon the child's personality as well as upon his physical well-being. A sudden recognition of another way of life comes to Jean-Christophe when he sees his mother obsequious to the woman for whom she cooks, and when he himself is taunted by the rich lady's children for wearing their cast-off clothes. This awareness of his own inferior position, enforced by punishment from all sides, drives him to escape into a fantasy world in which the little rich girl, now submissive and pleading, begs him for mercy.]

Jean-Christophe had as yet no idea of the difficulties of life; he knew no other limit to his will than the will of his parents, and that did not stand much in his way, for they let him do pretty much as he pleased. His one idea was to grow up, so as to be able to do as he liked. He had no conception of obstacles standing in the way at every turn, and he had never the least idea but that his parents were completely their own masters. It was a shock to his whole being when, for the first time, he perceived that among men there are those who command, and those who are commanded, and that his own people were not of the first class; it was the first crisis of his life.

It happened one afternoon. His mother had dressed him in his cleanest clothes, old clothes given to her which Louisa's ingenuity and patience had turned to account. He went to find her, as they had agreed, at the house in which she was working. He was abashed at the idea of entering alone. A footman was swaggering in the porch; he stopped the boy, and asked him patronizingly what he wanted. Jean-Christophe blushed, and murmured that he had come to see 'Frau Krafft'—as he had been told to say.

'Frau Krafft? What do you want with Frau Krafft?' asked the footman, ironically emphasizing the word *Frau*. 'Your mother? Go down there. You will find Louisa in the kitchen at the end of the passage.'

He went, growing redder and redder. He was ashamed to hear his mother called familiarly *Louisa*. He was humiliated; he would have liked to run away down to his dear river, and the shelter of the brushwood where he used to tell himself stories.

In the kitchen he came upon a number of other servants, who greeted him with noisy exclamations. At the back, near the stove, his mother smiled at him with tender embarrassment. He ran to her, and clung to her skirts. She was wearing a white apron, and holding a wooden spoon. She made him more unhappy by trying to raise his chin so as to look in his face, and to make him hold out his

From *Jean-Christophe* by Romain Rolland. By permission of Henry Holt and Co., Inc.

hand to everybody there and say good-day to them. He would not; he turned to the wall and hid his face in his arms. Then gradually he gained courage, and peeped out of his hiding-place with merry bright eyes, which hid again every time any one looked at him. He stole looks at the people there. His mother looked busy and important, and he did not know her like that; she went from one saucepan to another, tasting, giving advice, in a sure voice, explaining recipes, and the cook of the house listened respectfully. The boy's heart swelled with pride as he saw how much his mother was appreciated, and the great part that she played in this splendid room, adorned with magnificent objects of gold and silver.

Suddenly conversation ceased. The door opened. A lady entered with a rustling of the stuffs she was wearing. She cast a suspicious look about her. She was no longer young, and yet she was wearing a light dress with wide sleeves. She caught up her dress in her hand, so as not to brush against anything. It did not prevent her going to the stove and looking at the dishes, and even tasting them. When she raised her hand a little, her sleeve fell back, and her arm was bare to the elbow. Jean-Christophe thought this ugly and improper. How dryly and abruptly she spoke to Louisa! And how humbly Louisa replied! Jean-Christophe hated it. He hid away in his corner, so as not to be observed, but it was no use. The lady asked who the little boy might be. Louisa fetched him and presented him; she held his hands to prevent his hiding his face. And, though he wanted to break away and flee, Jean-Christophe felt instinctively that this time he must not resist. The lady looked at the boy's scared face, and at first she gave him a kindly, motherly smile. But then she resumed her patronizing air, and asked him about his behavior, and his piety, and put questions to him, to which he did not reply. She looked to see how his clothes fitted him, and Louisa eagerly declared that they were magnificent. She pulled down his waistcoat to remove the creases. Jean-Christophe wanted to cry, it fitted so tightly. He did not understand why his mother was giving thanks.

The lady took him by the hand and said that she would take him to her own children. Jean-Christophe cast a look of despair at his mother; but she smiled at the mistress so eagerly that he saw that there was nothing to hope for from her, and he followed his guide like a sheep that is led to the slaughter.

They came to a garden, where two cross-looking children, a boy and a girl, about the same age as Jean-Christophe, were apparently sulky with each other. Jean-Christophe's advent created a diversion. They came up to examine the new arrival. Jean-Christophe, left with the children by the lady, stood stock-still in a pathway, not daring to raise his eyes. The two others stood motionless a short distance away, and looked him up and down, nudged each other, and tittered. Finally, they made up their minds. They asked him who he was, whence he came, and what his father did. Jean-Christophe, turned to stone, made no reply; he was terrified almost to the point of tears, especially of the little girl, who had fair hair in plaits, a short skirt, and bare legs.

They began to play. Just as Jean-Christophe was beginning to be a little happier, the little boy stopped dead in front of him, and touching his coat, said:

'Hullo! That's mine!'

Jean-Christophe did not understand. Furious at this assertion that his coat belonged to some one else, he shook his head violently in denial.

'I know it all right,' said the boy. 'It's my old blue waistcoat. There's a spot on it.'

And he put his finger on the spot. Then, going on with his inspection, he examined Jean-Christophe's feet, and asked what his mended-up shoes were made of. Jean-Christophe grew crimson. The little girl pouted and whispered to her brother—Jean-Christophe heard it—that it was a little poor boy. Jean-Christophe resented the word. He thought he would succeed in combating the insulting opinions, as he stammered in a choking voice that he was the son of Melchior Krafft, and that his mother was Louisa the cook. It seemed to him that this title was as good as any other, and he was right. But the two children, interested in the news, did not seem to esteem him any the more for it. On the contrary, they took on a patronizing tone. They asked him what he was going to be—a cook or a coachman. Jean-Christophe revolted. He felt an iciness steal into his heart.

Encouraged by his silence, the two rich children, who had conceived for the little poor boy one of those cruel and unreasoning antipathies which children have, tried various amusing ways of tormenting him. The little girl especially was implacable. She observed that Jean-Christophe could hardly run, because his clothes were so tight, and she conceived the subtle idea of making him jump. They made an obstacle of little seats, and insisted on Jean-Christophe clearing it. The wretched child dared not say what it was that prevented his jumping. He gathered himself together, hurled himself through the air, and measured his length on the ground. They roared with laughter at him. He had to try again. Tears in his eyes, he made a desperate attempt, and this time succeeded in jumping. That did not satisfy his tormentors, who decided that the obstacle was not high enough, and they built it up until it became a regular break-neck affair. Jean-Christophe tried to rebel, and declared that he would not jump. Then the little girl called him a coward, and said that he was afraid. Jean-Christophe could not stand that, and, knowing that he must fall, he jumped, and fell. His feet caught in the obstacle; the whole thing toppled over with him. He grazed his hands and almost broke his head, and, as a crowning misfortune, his trousers tore at the knees and elsewhere. He was sick with shame; he heard the two children dancing with delight round him; he suffered horribly. He felt that they despised and hated him. Why? Why? He would gladly have died! There is no more cruel suffering than that of a child who discovers for the first time the wickedness of others; he believes then that he is persecuted by the whole world, and there is nothing to support him; there is nothing then—nothing! . . . Jean-Christophe tried to get up; the little boy pushed him down again; the little girl kicked him. He tried again, and they both jumped on him, and sat on his back and pressed his face down into the ground. Then rage seized him—it was too much. His hands were bruised, his fine coat was torn—a catastrophe for him!—shame, pain, revolt against the injustice of it, so many misfortunes all at once, plunged him in blind fury. He rose to his hands and knees, shook himself like a dog, and rolled his tormentors over; and when they returned to the assault he butted at them, head down, bowled over the little girl, and, with one blow of his fist, knocked the boy into the middle of a flower-bed.

They howled. The children ran into the house with piercing cries. Doors slammed, and cries of anger were heard. The lady ran out as quickly as her long dress would let her. Jean-Christophe saw her coming, and made no attempt to escape. He was terrified at what he had done; it was a thing unheard of, a crime; but he regretted nothing. He waited. He was lost. So much the better! He was reduced to despair.

The lady pounced on him. He felt her beat him. He heard her talking in a furious voice, a flood of words; but he could distinguish nothing. His little enemies had come back to see his shame, and screamed shrilly. There were servants—a babel of voices. To complete his downfall, Louisa, who had been summoned, appeared, and, instead of defending him, she began to scold him—she, too, without knowing anything—and bade him beg pardon. He refused angrily. She shook him, and dragged him by the hand to the lady and the children, and bade him go on his knees. But he stamped and roared, and bit his mother's hand. Finally, he escaped among the servants, who laughed.

He went away, his heart beating furiously, his face burning with anger and the slaps which he had received. He tried not to think, and he hurried along because he did not want to cry in the street. He wanted to be at home, so as to be able to find the comfort of tears. He choked; the blood beat in his head; he was at bursting-point.

Finally, he arrived; he ran up the old black staircase to his usual nook in the bay of a window above the river; he hurled himself into it breathlessly, and then there came a flood of tears. He did not know exactly why he was crying, but he had to cry; and when the first flood of them was done, he wept again because he wanted, with a sort of rage, to make himself suffer, as if he could in this way punish the others as well as himself. Then he thought that his father must be coming home, and that his mother would tell him everything, and that his own miseries were by no means at an end. He resolved on flight, no matter whither, never to return.

Just as he was going downstairs, he bumped into his father, who was coming up.

'What are you doing, boy? Where are you going?' asked Melchior.

He did not reply.

'You are up to some folly. What have you done?'

The boy began to cry and Melchior to shout, vying with each other until they heard Louisa hurriedly coming up the stairs. She arrived, still upset. She began with violent reproach and further chastisement, in which Melchior joined as soon as he understood—and probably before—with blows that would have felled an ox. Both shouted; the boy roared. They ended by argument. All the time that he was beating his son, Melchior maintained that he was right, and that this was the sort of thing that one came by, by going out to service with people who thought they could do everything because they had money; and as she beat the child, Louisa shouted that her husband was a brute, that she would never let him touch the boy, and that he had really hurt him. Jean-Christophe was, in fact, bleeding a little from the nose, but he hardly gave a thought to it, and he was not in the least thankful to his mother for stopping it with a wet cloth, since she went on scolding him. In the end they pushed him away in a dark closet, and shut him up without any supper.

He heard them shouting at each other, and he did not know which of them he detested most. He thought it must be his mother, for he had never expected any such wickedness from her. All the misfortunes of the day overwhelmed him: all that he had suffered—the injustice of the children, the injustice of the lady, the injustice of his parents, and—this he felt like an open wound, without quite knowing why—the degradation of his parents, of whom he was so proud, before these evil and contemptible people. Such cowardice, of which for the first time he had become vaguely conscious, seemed ignoble to him. Everything was upset for him—his admiration for his own people, the religious respect with which they inspired him, his confidence in life, the simple need that he had of loving others and of being loved, his moral faith, blind but absolute. It was a complete cataclysm. He was crushed by brute force, without any means of defending himself or of ever again escaping. He choked. He thought himself on the point of death. All his body stiffened in desperate revolt. He beat with fists, feet, head, against the wall, howled, was seized with convulsions, and fell to the floor, hurting himself against the furniture.

His parents, running up, took him in their arms. They vied with each other now as to who should be the

more tender with him. His mother undressed him, carried him to his bed, and sat by him and remained with him until he was calmer. But he did not yield one inch. He forgave her nothing, and pretended to be asleep to get rid of her. His mother seemed to him bad and cowardly. He had no suspicion of all the suffering that she had to go through in order to live and give a living to her family, and of what she had borne in taking sides against him.

After he had exhausted to the last drop the incredible store of tears that is in the eyes of a child, he felt somewhat comforted. He was tired and worn out, but his nerves were too much on stretch for him to sleep. The visions that had been with him floated before him in his semi-stupor. Especially he saw again the little girl with her bright eyes and her turned-up, disdainful little nose, her hair hanging down to her shoulders, her bare legs and her childish, affected way of talking. He trembled, as it seemed to him that he could hear her voice. He remembered how stupid he had been with her, and he conceived a savage hatred for her. He did not pardon her for having brought him low, and was consumed with the desire to humiliate her and to make her weep. He sought means of doing this, but found none. There was no sign of her ever caring about him. But by way of consoling himself he supposed that everything was as he wished it to be. He supposed that he had become very powerful and famous, and decided that she was in love with him. Then he began to tell himself one of those absurd stories which in the end he would regard as more than reality.

She was dying of love, but he spurned her. When he passed before her house she watched him pass, hiding behind the curtains, and he knew that she watched him, but he pretended to take no notice, and talked gaily. Even he left the country, and journeyed far to add to her anguish. He did great things. Here he introduced into his narrative fragments chosen from his grandfather's heroic tales, and all this time she was falling ill of grief. Her mother, that proud dame, came to beg of him: 'My poor child is dying. I beg you to come!' He went. She was in her bed. She could not speak, but she took his hands and kissed them and wept.

Then he looked at her with marvelous kindness and tenderness. He bade her recover, and consented to let her love him. At this point of the story, when he amused himself by drawing out the coming together by repeating their gestures and words several times, sleep overcame him, and he slept and was consoled.

But when he opened his eyes it was day, and it no longer shone so lightly or so carelessly as its predecessor. There was a great change in the world. Jean-Christophe now knew the meaning of injustice.

✳

HOMECOMING

Floyd Dell

[When a child goes to school the feeling of security that his home should give him becomes dependent also on the recognition and approval of a larger group. For little Floyd Dell the sudden realization that his family were 'poor people' was a shocking experience, for he had unconsciously absorbed middle-class ideas of respectability and the feeling that poverty means personal failure. His tendencies toward introversion became intensified. Withdrawing from people and things, he found solace in the world of fantasy and reading. For the father whom he had admired he now felt silent scorn. He came to rely on his mother beyond the normal period of childish dependence. It was not until later, in adolescence, that he again discovered his father as one whose wisdom was to be admired and his example imitated.]

Fool's Paradise

. . . Anthony Dell, in 1872, was one of Barry's thriving young business men. He could look forward to building himself a fine house; and Kate Dell, with her first son in her arms, could look forward to sending him to college to become a lawyer or doctor. They were securely, as it seemed, members of the class which was, in Pike County, and perhaps all through America, called 'respectable.' 'Respectability,' in Pike County, meant the appearance and presumption of belonging to the class of those who lived by their superior brains, preferably upon profits, interest or rent, rather than unambitiously and stupidly by manual labor. There was an elaborate code of dress and of manners which connoted 'respectability.'

From *Homecoming* by Floyd Dell. By permission of Farrar and Rinehart, 1933.

Then came the panic of 1873 . . . I do not know when the butcher-shop of Dell & Preston ceased its struggle to exist. But by the time I was born it had been long a thing of the past, which served only to give the family in its own estimation the needed status of middle-class 'respectability.' I can remember, when I was first able to walk so far, being taken down to a butcher-shop where my father was employed—that was when we still had a hired girl, and before my brother's pigeons were sold. Later, my father was a foreman in the woolen mills; I remember, when he came home, rushing to have the proud privilege of pulling off his felt boots—being Papa's bootjack. One winter one of my big brothers worked in the woolen mills, too, and the other went to Quincy to look for work. Both of them had dropped out of school, because they didn't like to wear patched clothes.

The family was, in fact, losing its hold upon the golden ladder. But all the more it clung to its 'respectable' status. The condition of being a work-ingman was one which a recently prosperous business man must not admit, except as a temporary piece of bad luck. My father's age, of course, was against him; in his fifties now, he stood no chance of getting back—not much chance, even, of competing with younger men for available jobs.

The older children were adjusting themselves to the situation as well as they could. They got jobs, any jobs they could get, and held them until they were fired. The first jobs from which they were not fired, furnished them their trades for the rest of their lives. That was the method of vocational choice by which one of my big brothers, a sensitive artist, with a love of drawing, became a harness-maker; and the other, who was good at figures, a sash-and-door factory employee, running a saw which presently took off a thumb.

But here was a new baby, myself. A mother in her forties, seeing her hopes for the older children blasted by harsh circumstances, would center new fond hopes upon this golden-haired blue-eyed boy. And, early in childhood, there were ways, perhaps not as infallible as those now in vogue, of recognizing the intelligence of children. Quickness in understand-ing, quickness in learning, memory, vocabulary, these and other things were noted; and they spelled to an Irish mother a future 'scholar,' from whom wonderful things might be expected.

She was a nice Irish mother, small and slender and physically frail, sweet and gentle, patient and lovable. She had given her little son many beauti-ful gifts—love, and tenderness, and devotion, lullaby music and poetry, stories about real and imaginary peo-ple and places. The beauty of flowers and skies was first shown to me by her pointing finger. She taught me to un-derstand words, and to speak them, and no little bit of childish progress was too small for her to notice and re-ward with praise. Queen of the mys-terious universe in which I was a helpless stranger, she did not laugh at my clumsy blunders; she took me by the hand and led me into the uni-verse to be its prince. For me there always would be, in almost every re-gion of beauty and knowledge, the sweet ghostly presence of my mother, who first guided me in those realms, kindling my eyes to see and my ears to hear, blessing my infant under-standing with smiling looks of ap-proval. And from her too I had the mysterious knowledge of Right and

Wrong; she gave me a Conscience to govern my most imperious impulses, a phantom of herself to be with me always, closer than blood and breath. She was the Lawgiver. I learned from her the sense of *ought*. If I followed obscure unruly impulses, if I were selfish, greedy, lazy, quarrelsome, afraid, unwilling, then I was afflicted with her sorrowful eyes, not to be endured. My shame was a worse punishment than any outward one that could be inflicted. I *had* to be all that she expected of me.

I was—and all this is up to the winter after my sixth birthday—an arrogant, eager, friendly, confident, innocently bumptious little boy. I had been trained in the manual of arms by my father, and I had a soldierly bearing. But I was vastly talkative, and profoundly impressed by the Fourth of July speeches I had heard in the Square. I was going to be a lawyer. My mother had heard that Ann Arbor was the best college to study law in, and so I was going there. When I got to be a lawyer, I was going to make Fourth of July speeches from the band-stand in the Square. And then I was going to be President of the United States. I had asked my mother if I could be, and she had said that I could if I worked hard and studied and got the most votes. I was going to be a Republican President, of course. All this was clear and certain in my mind. My mother was encouraging to my ambitions, though not so definitely set on the Presidency as I was. She said, 'You're going to be Somebody, all right.' My Presidential ambition was somehow mixed up with my admiration for my father, whose political discourses I had listened to with profound respect, and with whom I had been privileged to go to hear patriotic orations in the Square.

One morning, as I was looking at a story-book, I discovered that I could read. The words of the story, of course, I knew by heart; but I found now that I knew each word separately, and the realization of it almost took my breath away. It was true! In my excitement, I screamed, 'Mamma! Mamma!' and she came running from the kitchen, her arms white with flour. 'I can read!' I cried. Hardly less excited than I, she sat down with me, and I demonstrated this new magical power. She kissed me fondly and said, 'You shall go to school this fall!' I was not yet five, but I would be in June.

It may have been some time in summer, when I was being taken for a walk in my white starched kilts by my big sister, that some ladies stopped and said to her, 'What beautiful curls your brother has.' My mother was proud of them; she should have been, for she made them herself, by twisting my hair around her finger and stiffening it with the white of an egg. I was proud of them, too. So when one of the inquiring ladies went on to ask, 'Does his hair curl that way naturally?' I spoke up for myself. 'Yes'm,' I said, 'and my mother fixes it with white-of-egg.' From their smiles, and my sister's scornful jerk on my arm, I knew that I had said the wrong thing, and felt ashamed . . . In the respectable world into which I was growing up, there were all sorts of things that must not be said even though they were true, and other things that must be said whether they were true or not; but it takes a little boy time to learn that code.

At school the first day, I was so bumptious as to be a nuisance. I corrected the teacher, told her she must say 'Fire!' and not 'Shoot!' when putting us through our military drill. I made moustaches on my face, which pleased everybody but the teacher; and when told to wash my face, I clumsily spilled the water from the wash-basin on to the floor. Sent to the janitor for a mop, it took me an hour to find him, but at last I came back triumphantly with the mop over my shoulder. When everybody laughed, the teacher said, 'Floyd, you have caused us a great deal of trouble today.' That grieved me, for I felt toward my teacher the same emotions of loyalty and obedience that I felt toward my mother. I wanted to be a good little boy.

At recesses, I began to be tormented by a big bully who would snatch my cap and run away with it, and then offer it to me, but throw it away, and get it before I could. I was in misery, for at that time my cap was a part of me, which I had to follow about and try to rescue. My sister once slapped the big boy's face and got my cap for me, but she could not be watching over her baby brother all the time. I endured these torments for weeks, and then, one morning, coming upon the boy around the corner of the building, I sprang at him in a fit of rage and tears, hitting and kicking. I knocked out one of his front teeth, and he ran away, spitting blood, with me after him, not yet glutted with revenge. After that I was never afraid to fight, and did not hesitate to attack bigger boys, though I always got licked. If I knocked my opponent down, I would chivalrously wait till he got up; but if he got me down, he would sit on my chest and pound my head against the sidewalk. But fighting was something I did only in rage or pride, never for fun;

dare-base and other games where swiftness counted more than strength were my favorites. It was in the schoolroom, however, that I felt that I was cock-of-the-walk. And my teacher, when she found that I wasn't trying to be obstreperous, but just didn't know any better, gave me her approval. I learned everything easily, and had a prodigious memory, my only fault being absent-mindedness.

It was not considered necessary to tell me anything about the financial status of the family. I was not able to make comparative observations in school, because I was sent there immaculately dressed. And I knew that my mother regarded some of the children in the neighborhood as not nice enough for me to play with. I thought we were just a little bit more 're-spectable' than other people. I did not realize that in the currency of 'respectability' a father who used to have a butcher shop was not quite on a par with a father who was cashier of the bank. My father spoke famil-iarly of the Mayor and other city dignitaries. And, as I understood it, his membership in the G.A.R. made him one of what I felt to be the aris-tocracy of the nation—certainly on Decoration Day he was treated as such. So I had no idea that we were not the very flower of Barry 're-spectability.' There undoubtedly were plenty of things that might have en-lightened me about our financial condition. But there was a deceptive parental softening and evasion of harsh facts for my benefit. A child, in their opinion, should be protected from unpleasant things. And the parental gloss marvelously protected me from the facts that were before my eyes . . .

So, next year, I didn't know there was a Panic. The shutting down of the Barry woolen mills was in my young mind, as in my father's talk, a political and not an economic tragedy. Grover Cleveland was to blame for it all. He was a Democratic President, and that was why he did it. Governor Altgeld was a Democrat, too—that was why he pardoned the Haymarket Anarchists. I wondered why Democrats were allowed to exist.

* * *

(Memories of childhood are strange things. The obscurity of the past opens upon a little lighted space—a scene, unconnected with anything else. One must figure out when it happened. There may be anomalies in the scene, which need explanation. Sometimes the scenes are tiny fragments only. Again they are long dramas. Having once been remembered, they can be lived through again in every moment, with a detailed experiencing of movement and sensation and thought. One can start the scene in one's mind and see it all through again. Exactly so it was— clearer in memory than something that happened yesterday, though it was forty years ago. And, oddly enough, if there is some detail skipped over, lost out of the memory picture, no repetition of the remembering process will supply it—the gap is always there.)

That fall, before it was discovered that the soles of both my shoes were worn clear through, I still went to Sunday school. And one time the Sunday-school superintendent made a speech to all the classes. He said that these were hard times, and that many poor children weren't getting enough to eat. It was the first that I had heard about it. He asked everybody to bring some food for the poor chil-

dren next Sunday. I felt very sorry for the poor children.

Also, little envelopes were distributed to all the classes. Each little boy and girl was to bring money for the poor, next Sunday. The pretty Sunday-school teacher explained that we were to write our names, or have our parents write them, up in the left-hand corner of the little envelopes . . . I told my mother when I came home. And my mother gave me, the next Sunday, a small bag of potatoes to carry to Sunday school. I supposed the poor children's mothers would make potato soup out of them . . . Potato soup was good. My father, who was quite a joker, would always say, as if he were surprised, 'Ah! I see we have some nourishing potato soup today!' It was so good that we had it every day. My father was at home all day long and every day, now; and I liked that, even if he was grumpy as he sat reading Grant's 'Memoirs.' I had my parents all to myself, too; the others were away. My oldest brother was in Quincy, and memory does not reveal where the others were: perhaps with relatives in the country.

Taking my small bag of potatoes to Sunday school, I looked around for the poor children; I was disappointed not to see them. I had heard about poor children in stories. But I was told just to put my contribution with the others on the big table in the side room.

I had brought with me the little yellow envelope, with some money in it for the poor children. My mother had put the money in it and sealed it up. She wouldn't tell me how much money she had put in it, but it felt like several dimes. Only she wouldn't let me write my name on the envelope. I had learned to write my name, and I was proud of being able to do it. But my mother said firmly, *no,* I must *not* write my name on the envelope; she didn't tell me why. On the way to Sunday school I had pressed the envelope against the coins until I could tell what they were; they weren't dimes but pennies.

When I handed in my envelope, my Sunday-school teacher noticed that my name wasn't on it, and she gave me a pencil; I could write my own name, she said. So I did. But I was confused because my mother had said not to; and when I came home, I confessed what I had done. She looked distressed. 'I told you not to!' she said. But she didn't explain why . . .

I didn't go back to school that fall. My mother said it was because I was sick. I did have a cold the week that school opened; I had been playing in the gutters and had got my feet wet, because there were holes in my shoes. My father cut insoles out of cardboard, and I wore those in my shoes. As long as I had to stay in the house anyway, they were all right.

I stayed cooped up in the house, without any companionship. We didn't take a Sunday paper any more, but the Barry Adage came every week in the mails; and though I did not read small print, I could see the Santa Clauses and holly wreaths in the advertisements.

There was a calendar in the kitchen. The red days were Sundays and holidays; and that red 25 was Christmas. (It was on a Monday, and the two red figures would come right together in 1893; but this represents research in the World Almanac, not memory.) I knew when Sunday was, because I could look out of the window and see the neighbor's children, all dressed up, going to Sunday school. I knew just when Christmas was going to be.

But there was something queer! My father and mother didn't say a word about Christmas. And once, when I spoke of it, there was a strange, embarrassed silence; so I didn't say anything more about it. But I wondered, and was troubled. Why didn't they say anything about it? Was what I had said I wanted (memory refuses to supply that detail) too expensive?

I wasn't arrogant and talkative now. I was silent and frightened. What was the matter? Why didn't my father and mother say anything about Christmas? As the day approached, my chest grew tighter with anxiety.

Now it was the day before Christmas. I couldn't be mistaken. But not a word about it from my father and mother. I waited in painful bewilderment all day. I had supper with them, and was allowed to sit up for an hour. I was waiting for them to say something. 'It's time for you to go to bed,' my mother said gently. I *had* to say something.

'This is Christmas Eve, isn't it?' I asked, as if I didn't know.

My father and mother looked at one another. Then my mother looked away. Her face was pale and stony. My father cleared his throat, and his face took on a joking look. He pretended he hadn't known it was Christmas Eve, because he hadn't been reading the papers. He said he would go downtown and find out.

My mother got up and walked out of the room. I didn't want my father to have to keep on being funny about it, so I got up and went to bed. I went by myself without having a light. I undressed in the dark and crawled into bed.

I was numb. As if I had been hit by something. It was hard to breathe. I ached all through. I was stunned—with finding out the truth.

My body knew before my mind quite did. In a minute, when I could think, my mind would know. And as the pain in my body ebbed, the pain in my mind began. I *knew*. I couldn't put it into words yet. But I knew why I had taken only a little bag of potatoes to Sunday school that fall. I knew why I hadn't gone to school that fall—why I hadn't any new shoes—why we had been living on potato soup all winter. All these things, and others, many others, fitted themselves together in my mind and meant something.

Then the words came into my mind and I whispered them into the darkness:

'*We're poor!*'

That was it. I was one of those poor children I had been sorry for, when I heard about them in Sunday school. My mother hadn't told me. My father was out of work, and we hadn't any money. That was why there wasn't going to be any Christmas at our house.

Then I remembered something that made me squirm with shame—a boast. (Memory will not yield this up. Had I said to some Nice little boy, 'I'm going to be President of the United States'? Or to a Nice little girl: 'I'll marry you when I grow up'? It was some boast as horribly shameful to remember.)

'*We're poor!*' There in bed in the dark, I whispered it over and over to myself. I was making myself get used to it. (Or—just torturing myself, as one presses the tongue against a sore tooth? No, memory says not like that —but to keep myself from ever being such a fool again: suffering now, to keep this awful thing from ever happening again. Memory is clear on that; it was more like pulling the tooth, to get it over with—never mind the pain, this will be the end!)

It wasn't so bad, now that I knew. I just *hadn't known!* I had thought all sorts of foolish things: that I was going to Ann Arbor—going to be a lawyer—going to make speeches in the Square, going to be President. Now I knew better.

I had wanted (something) for Christmas. I didn't want it, now. I didn't want anything.

I lay there in the dark, feeling the cold emotion of renunciation. (The tendrils of desire unfold their clasp on the outer world of objects, withdraw, shrivel up. Wishes shrivel up, turn black, die. It is like that.)

It hurt. But nothing would ever hurt again. I would never let myself want anything again.

I lay there stretched out straight and still in the dark, my fists clenched hard upon Nothing . . .

In the morning it had been like a nightmare that is not clearly remembered—that one wishes to forget. Though I hadn't hung up any stocking, there was one hanging at the foot of my bed. A bag of popcorn, and a lead pencil, for me. They had done the best they could, now they realized that I knew about Christmas. But they needn't have thought they had to. I didn't want anything.

Child Stoic

It was, I think, right after this Christmas-Eve renunciation of all the good things of life that I fell sick, with a long and severe and wretched sickness centering in my stomach. Memory brings back a bedquilt world, with the vast squares of the coverlet stretching endlessly before me. Yellow lamplight, shapes of people going to and fro. Whispers. Medicine bottles on a chair at the head of my bed. The flower-pattern in the wall-paper. Cracks in the ceiling, and stains that made grotesque pictures. Nausea. 'Try to keep something down, darling.' Dreams of geometrical Space that widened out towards infinity, and myself in the middle, smaller and smaller—waking in fright just before I became Nothing . . .

From this I emerged to play quietly around the house, sitting preferably with my toys and picture books.

My father, as I remember, had a job hauling dirt for a road which the county was building. In the spring we moved to a cheaper house on the edge of a gully. It was only part of a house; the people that owned it lived in the other part.

I cannot remember very much about that house, nor the life we lived there for a year and a half. It is covered with a kind of darkness, through which there are only a few peep-holes. I see my father sitting in the big arm chair by the window, reading Grant's 'Memoirs.' I see my brother—the one who is still at home —coming back to my mother after he has given her his pay-envelope, and asking to 'borrow' another quarter this week; and the way she is torn between her wanting to give him money to spend and her knowledge of the unpaid grocery bill. And the attic—I remember something about that, though that is all mixed up with dreams and fantasy.

It was remarked that my sickness had changed me, as sicknesses often do change children. I was quieter, more polite, more even-tempered.

And I never teased for pennies to spend. I was a window-shopper.

The center of interest in the town through which I passed on my way to and from school was the grassy Square and the streets on each side with their row of shops and stores. I would loiter on the way home and look at everything. In the Square itself the boys played marbles and spun tops, and in the noon hour groups of idlers stood about talking and telling stories, with a fringe of boys for an audience. The bandstand in the Square had an upper story, with no steps or ladder reaching up there; but somehow, as I knew, big boys got up there and lay reading 'dime novels,' which really cost a nickel, and were forbidden literature. This escape from the world of people fascinated me, and may have had something to do with my attic fantasies, which presently began. I walked slowly about the Square, making a side trip around the corner to stand at the door of the blacksmith shop, and watch the red-hot horseshoes being dropped sizzling into a bucket of water, and smell the pungent odor of seared hoofs and hear the music of hammer on anvil. Back on the Square, I would loiter in front of the stationery store window, studying its changing display of 'Diamond Dick' and 'Nick Carter' and 'Frank Merriwell' novels, on the covers of which some new and exciting episode was displayed in picture every week. There was nothing wrong in looking at these novels; it was only wrong to read them, which I had no wish to do. Then I would press my nose against the glass of other shop-windows, looking at knives, tops, marbles, kites, toys. My fingers, however, did not itch to play with these things; I was content to look at them.

I was particularly fascinated by the display of tools of all sorts in the windows of the hardware store; but so far was I from wishing to use any of these tools that when, much later, at the age of twelve, I first held the familiar tools of carpentry in my hands at school, I hardly knew how to handle them. When I was taken into a store full of exciting things, the little-boy tendency to reach out and touch—or grab—was not operative in me. I didn't even pick flowers, when I was out in the woods; I only looked at them. Sight aroused no motor impulses. And this made me seem very well-behaved indeed. But I enjoyed thoroughly the sight of things which, if I had ever wanted to buy them, might have been a painful reminder that I was poor. So long as I didn't want to own or use them, I had a fine time just looking at them. When one is in a Museum, if one is well bred, one does not think of carrying off its treasures. Perhaps it may be regarded as the proper grown-up attitude. But I had it at seven, and never quite got over it. Always there was an invisible plate-glass window separating me from the things I looked at. My hands hung at my sides, and I touched things only with my gaze. Before I found the library, I had begun to take note of the shapes of things, and to draw pictures like those that one of my big brothers drew.

It was the sign, 'Free Public Library,' that attracted me. I went up the stairs and into a room with a counter in front of serried bookshelves, guarded by a grey-haired woman. Against the front windows was a long table covered with magazines. I watched, and people picked them up carelessly and looked through them. That was permitted, then. I sat down and read. For some reason what seems to have interested me most in that first day's reading was a long controversial article in the back of one of these magazines, with diagrams, on the flush-bowl toilet. I had never seen one.

Afterward, I found that books could be taken away. The grey-haired librarian took pains to keep young readers going in the same series, if possible. She started me off with the Elsie books; apparently I was going to have to read them all before I got anything else to read. But luck was with me, and I switched to 'Frank on a Gunboat' before my budding literary enthusiasm was blighted. I liked Frank. He carried me into the war my father had fought in. 'Damn the torpedoes!' cried Farragut, and in a rain of shot and shell we swept past the rebel batteries to victory . . . Then there were the bound volumes of 'St. Nicholas.' And, intermixed with these, were 'grown-up' books. My father usually had plenty of time to read now, too. When one would finish a book the other would begin it. I remember that when I was ten we both read, and were impressed but puzzled by, a book which opened most promisingly with the words: ' "Dead for a ducat, dead!" cried Dick' . . . a book which turned out not to be an adventure story but a description of Utopia. My father read, and I tried hard to read, Dickens and Thackeray; I could not go them—an incapacity which has been permanent. But we both read and enjoyed deeply Defoe's 'Captain Jacques,' and a book which I was to read over and over at intervals for many years, Hugo's 'Les Misérables.'—Not at seven years old, but soon afterward; years pass quickly in public libraries, and one may grow as old as Rip Van

Winkle in that enchanted cave, while remaining a child in the outside world.

I spent all the time I could at the public library, preferring its peace rather than the environment of a home where there was always some painful reminder of our poverty.

In school, where there was always time left over after the studying of lessons, but where outside books were forbidden, drawing was a solace. To the general rule of my not asking for money to buy anything, there was one exception—drawing and writing materials, a modest want which it did not strain our family poverty to supply. Picture-making, like writing, was an intermittent and never abandoned pleasure. If I had chanced to become a painter, I should, looking back, have thought pictorial art my obviously destined career, for I should have been able to trace from my earliest imitations of my big brother's pictures a fairly continuous practice of drawing. But, as I sat on the couch with a drawing-board on my lap, I had no intention or wish or hope to become an artist. I was just being an artist, without thinking of anything except the picture I was drawing. And so it was with writing.

A curtain was drifting down, fold upon fold, in my mind, shutting out the past. I did not remember what I was like when I was a little boy, except that I had been sick a good deal. And there were some pigeons—my brother's pigeons (I had called them 'doves')—sold before I had half seen enough of them. And there had been Corbett the cat. And a hired girl named Sack Sheets . . .

Somewhere in the oblivion of childhood was hidden an ambition. I had now no notion of what it had been. I had no plans of going to any college, or of practicing any profession when I grew up. I had no plans for the future at all. I never thought about the future.

There were some children to play with, in our new neighborhood, in spite of my mother being so particular about my playing with nice children. There was a little boy whose father worked in the bank; I liked him until he asked me distastefully, 'Why do you smell the way you do?' I answered, 'I guess it's because I eat potato soup so often'—and after that I avoided him. There was a nice little girl, with whom I walked to school every day for a week or so—a dark-eyed, quiet little girl. But when I was gently teased about my 'little sweetheart,' I stopped. Having a sweetheart meant, I knew, buying candy for her; and I had no money to buy candy with.

There was a little boy that year who bought some candy and shared it with me as we were walking to school; a few days later, he asked me when I was going to 'treat back.' I went to my mother in shame, hating to ask her for money, and resolved never to go into that trap again. With her nickel I bought some candy, gave the other boy half, and grimly ate my own half. Next time I would know better.

I had no real friends, no chums, no one I trusted or let myself care for.

Yellow Curls

I still wore my long yellow curls. The sight of me coming home from the public library, my head with its cluster of yellow curls bent over a book which I read as I walked, and another book tightly clasped under my arm, was commented upon. My mother loved those curls, and would *not* have them cut.

Mothers do things like that to their pet little boys. But little boys do not have to stand for it. There are always scissors around a house. Three or four snips, and the curls are gone. Why, I have to ask myself, did I let my mother make a Little Lord Fauntleroy of me?

The reason was that I did not care what anyone else thought about those curls that my mother wanted me to wear. I had no admired boy chums whose opinions I could have respected or whose appearance I could wish to imitate. My brothers were young men of voting age and older; they were like uncles. The one who was at home did protest about my curls; and so did my father. But my mother liked them, and I preferred to please her. Curls are, for that matter, pretty—as on mediæval page-boy in a picture or play. They may be inconvenient, but I did not find them so. I fought my fist-fights in them without feeling any incongruity. The importance of a hair-cut is wholly a symbolic one. There was in me at that time no identification with the masculine world such as would make me wish to look 'like a boy.'

And for such a boy one would be inclined to predict trouble. The question would arise, how is he going to become masculine enough in his attitudes, to hold a job, or accept a responsible relationship to the other sex? The whole problem of ultimate success in love and work comes up.

That is a considerably more important question for this boy than the question of whether he will ever become a writer or not. So let us pursue it.

* * *

But first, how has it happened that a child stoic has turned into Little Lord Fauntleroy? A stoic is one who no longer expects anything good. But in whom has he placed his naive and boundless trust? In whom can a child place his trust, but in his all-powerful, heroic, wonderful, beneficent father? And when he finds that he is not a prince but a pauper, he is cruelly disillusioned in his father. He has, in fact, lost the god-like, all-powerful father of his childhood, as if by death; this jobless workingman who sits around the house trying to maintain authority over growing children who are supporting the family, is no such personage as the father that the boy lost one Christmas Eve. Who he is, and what the boy can do about him, remains to be seen. But evidently he can be, at present, no model, no hero, no masculine influence in his son's boyhood, no guide along the pathway of life, no evoker of ambition.

There remains the Mother. A little, bent, ailing, tireless woman, she is yet, within her own realm, an all-powerful Goddess. And her own realm is not just the kitchen where she bends over the hot cook-stove, or the table, where she sits anxiously on the edge of her chair so as to be ready to jump up and serve her husband and children. Her realm, for her youngest son certainly, is the Ideal Universe . . . Before I could see very much of the wide world myself, it was already there in my mind, a far-flung world taken on trust from her teaching lips, a world that extended in Time as well as in mere Space. It grew in my mind, that Ideal Universe, until it was infinitely vaster than the small world which my young body inhabited, the small world of which I could learn something for myself by my five senses. The Picture of the World in my mind stretched out further than my swift little legs could ever run, on and on past the furthest hills that my young eyes could see—out, out beyond the familiar house and yard, the half-explored neighborhood, the partly-glimpsed small town, out past Pike County itself, into America, an America come to by my pioneer ancestors as a free country, a country to be proud of, with Washington and Lincoln to reverence, a flag to cherish as a soldier's son; out, out to a world beyond that, the older world from which Columbus came, with knights and heroes in it, Greece and Rome to remember, China and Africa to civilize and explore. This firm clear sketch that my mother drew for me, after being gradually disentangled from the other pretend-world of giants and fairies and dragons, was presently being filled in at school by women like my mother, beautiful and wise and good and firm and kind—at least some of them were. And always before I came to anything as I went further and further into the world, before I could hear it, see it, smell it, touch it, taste it, I had it already in my mind, in its place among other things, explained and understood in advance. Books were taking up the work; the Ideal Universe grew every day larger, brighter, more orderly, more understandable, more complete.

And all this Ideal Universe, her gift to me, was filled with a sense of *ought* and *must*—her laws, which I must obey. Whom should I trust, if not her? Whose opinion or taste or authority could I rank above hers? Not my father's, not my brothers' or sister's, not the neighbors'. If she wanted me to wear curls, that was surely little enough to do for her.

There was no possibility of my being anything else but a 'mamma's boy.'

So that was how the fiercely cold child-stoic that crept into my mind upon Christmas Eve had turned me into Little Lord Fauntleroy. He had given me the strength never to want anything that a father could give, lest I be disappointed. But he had no power to shield me from the inexorable radiance of a mother's love.

And the question is: who can supply other influences which will keep a good mother's love from turning her helpless son into a perfect sissy?

'He ought to have boys of his own age to play with.' Well, I did; and in their company I escaped for moments from my mother's world of *ought* and *must*. It was a relief, too. In the play world of my own age-group, in activities that were real and imaginary both at once, I experienced the joys of being rather than the joys of understanding. This world of play was not orderly; it had none of the qualities that reigned in my Ideal Universe. Yet it was not real freedom; for the play world was subject to criticism and punishment from my Ideal Universe; the delicious green apples of the play world gave (not always, but sometimes) the bellyaches which righteously belonged to them in my Ideal Universe, my Moral Universe; the water in the pond, so cool and exciting to splash around in naked, did (as I had been told it would) drown one of my schoolmates. I myself could never be one who habitually and recklessly lived in this small world of joyous experience; but sometimes I did make, then and later, brief excursions into its anarchic freedom, knowing that it would serve me right if I got my neck broken in forbidden climbs, my hands blown off by gunpowder ex-

periments, my good name irretrievably lost in some small-boy gang-
theft, marvelously ingenious, of apples or candy—and, at the time, being
quite indifferent to any price I might
have to pay for my anarchic self-in-
dulgence. Afterward it always seemed
a miracle that I had come off scot-
free. And, though the universe of actuality had not punished me, I did
not go unpunished. The Ideal Universe in my mind had power to punish me, even if mere reality had been
so disorderly and lacking in justice as
to neglect to do it. I could vividly
imagine all the things that *might*
have happened, that *should* have
happened, and suffer from those.

Though I never quite lost touch
with this realm of lawless fact, I was
much more at home in the Ideal Universe; and from its inexorable *oughts*
and *musts* I found a safer refuge in
that permitted realm of imaginary
experience, the reading of stories.
These, too, gave a kind of freedom
from *ought* and *must;* they had the
wild charm of lawlessness, yet in-
curred no blame; unless they were in
paper covers with colored pictures on
them.

Playmates were not the answer to
the problem which I did not know
existed: how to gain some moral freedom from the overwhelming domination of a good mother's love. But
there was at least the possibility of
an inch of freedom being gained,
through the intervention of that Ideal
Universe which she had built up in
my mind. By the just laws which eternally reigned there and judged all
things, she must herself be judged.

She was, as I have said, always particular about whom I played with,
and I sought to understand her dis-
criminations. Politeness, neatness and
lack of profanity seemed to be the
chief points in her social decisions.
But one Sunday I found a nice little
colored boy out in front of the house,
who was very polite, and quite neat,
and used no bad words: moreover, he
had a pocket full of colored chalks
with which pictures could be drawn
on the sidewalk. Nevertheless, my
mother called me back into the house.
I could not understand why, and demanded fretfully, 'He's a nice boy,
isn't he, Mamma?' My mother looked
embarrassed and ashamed, and did
not reply.

This ashamed silence of hers somehow threatened the moral fabric of
my universe. From the window I
could see the little colored boy, after
waiting a while, gather up his chalks,
turn his back on the house, and
slowly walk away. 'Why, Mamma?
Why can't I play with him?' No answer. At least, she had the grace to be
ashamed.

She did not know that at school
I had kept the laws of her Ideal Universe which she was playing fast and
loose with. There, at a double desk,
I had sat with a little colored boy,
whom the other boys didn't want to
sit with . . . How did my teacher
know that I did not regard girls or
Negro boys as my inferiors? Anyway,
she was right. I took seriously the
story about my father having fought
and suffered in the war to set free
the slaves.

It is horribly painful for a child to
judge a parent; but it has to be done.
Once the trial is over, the reluctant
verdict is forgotten, a free pardon
wipes it off the records. One seems
not to know, but one acts as if one
did know. I did know something,
scarcely to be put in words. It was
the only way in which my mother
ever did fail to be entirely consistent
with the just and beautiful ideals

which she taught me—in this one thing, of timidly and ashamedly attaching importance to 'what people might think'; she tried to keep up all the pretenses of prosperous respectability, that a little boy couldn't help knowing were false. And when a loving son found her out, he could only become an unwilling conspirator in her pretenses. She was, in part, human; not absolutely perfect. It was an inch of freedom gained for a little boy fast tied to her apron strings.

My father grew sick of the sight of those girlish curls on his son, and took me over to the barber shop. The curls were snipped off. My father said with satisfaction that I looked like a boy at last. He put the curls in his pocket. When I came home and showed my shorn head to my mother, she cried. My father took the curls from his pocket and gave them to her. She put them away in a little tin box with the baby dresses of her dead child.

*   *   *

Money vs. Heroism

My mother went the next summer to visit relatives back in Pike County; and being proud of her tall son, she took me along to show me off.

Out in the country, at the house of my uncle and aunt where we spent the first week in July, there was a pretty girl-cousin, Lela, about my age or a little older. On the Fourth, we were all loaded into the surrey and taken to the county-seat, I think it was, to enjoy the celebration. My mother took me aside beforehand and gave me a quarter. 'Treat your cousin Lela to some ice-cream,' she said.

Black misery descended upon me. A thing like that might seem easy, but it wasn't. I had had no practice in that sort of thing. I had never had any money. I had never learned how to treat.

The life of a stoic does not fit one to meet an emergency like this. But for my mother's sake I would have to do this thing. I tried to figure it out. You had to say something to the girl, first. I knew the sort of thing that was said, and I tried over several verbal formulas in my mind. 'Shall we have some ice-cream?' But I didn't think I could say that. 'Come on, let's get some ice-cream'—that was better. But it had to be said naturally. I knew that any other boy would be able to say it naturally. But I was afraid I couldn't. My tongue became paralyzed at the very thought of saying it. Perhaps I could lead up to it in some roundabout way . . . But all the things I thought of saying seemed to lead away from ice-cream, not toward it.

Meanwhile I wasn't saying anything. I was sitting there in the surrey beside my pretty cousin Lela, silent and helpless and scared. My mother was expecting me to behave like the manly little boy that I seemed. She had given me her fond approval as a little boy who never spent any money; but now, when she wanted to show me off, I was supposed to act as if I were accustomed to carrying quarters in my pocket and spending them on girls!

We arrived at the Square in town, and the others began to climb down from the surrey. Now was the time to say something to Lela about ice-cream. But I couldn't speak. I sat there, white and helpless. Lela got down. Everybody got down, except me. I couldn't move.

I am told that at this point I impressed people with my cool, self-sufficient airs. Nobody knew I was a helpless child. Nobody gave me a shove and told me what to do. 'Don't you want to see the races?' asked my uncle. I said 'No,' evidently in a way that settled the matter. They all went away, leaving me alone.

But they would come back. And then what would I do? Nothing. I couldn't do anything. The battle was lost. I despised myself. I hated the quarter in my pocket. I wished—and wished truly, and for the only time in my life—that I could die.

I should have liked to die trying to stop a runaway horse, and saving Lela's life. I could be a hero if I had a chance. (And I haven't the slightest doubt I would have jumped at the chance.) But any kind of death—any kind at all—would be better than this.

It went on all day.

I had time, again and again, to say those words, 'Let's have some ice-cream.' But I couldn't.

I just sat there, stonily, in frozen despair.

The icy child-stoic that had crept into my brain that Christmas Eve was stronger than anything else in me. And it seemed that nothing outside myself could shake his power. I was in his grip.

When we got back to the farm late that afternoon, the hateful quarter was still in my pocket. I gave it back to my mother. 'Here!' I said bitterly, and put it into her hand.

* * *

Now it happened that out in the country I met the Socialist farmer who had given my father that book on the Co-operative Commonwealth. He was a gentle and intellectual man with a white beard. He was respected in Pike County for having found natural gas on his farm and lighted his barns and henhouses with it; though at the same time, as a Socialist, he was regarded by solid Republican farmers (with their farms mortgaged up to the hilt) as an impractical visionary. I talked with him about the book he had lent my father; he was pleased that I had read it, and he listened without condescension to my Republican criticisms and answered them thoughtfully, which was very flattering. In the course of our discussion he remarked that Socialism was not a matter of economics only, but of a different kind of life, based upon service for the common good and not on money. 'It is the kind of world a poet would want to live in,' he said, looking at me. 'Or a hero,' he added. I had no reason to think of myself as a poet, and would have blushed at being caught thinking of myself as a hero. But his words impressed me. And when I went home I re-read the book and thought better of it. At the same time I became aware of Markham's poem, 'The Man with the Hoe,' which had made a great stir in America the year before. I soon knew the lines by heart: 'Plundered, profaned, and disinherited' . . .

This is not especially the story of my political opinions or of my intellectual development, but rather of my quest for life, liberty and happiness. It seems to me that I was engaged at this time in a desperate search for grounds of emotional reconciliation with my father. I was certainly badly in need of some inward strength to save me from another such frightful experience as I had just had in my helplessness. The connection of Socialism with these needs is not apparent, I know. But it happened to answer these needs in certain ways, and that is why I tell about it.

When we had moved to Quincy, the first thing that one of my new schoolmates said to me was, 'My father is a doctor—what's yours?' I evaded answering, and told my mother about it. She said: 'Tell them that your father is a retired butcher.' I couldn't tell them that. I wanted to tell them to go to hell.

That next fall, in school, suddenly and with little outward reason, I wrote a poem—the second I had ever written. Again the lines poured out easily, rhymes and all. It was on the subject of Lincoln, the martyr President. But underneath that (I am quite sure), I was praising and excusing my father. Heroism was enough; the hero did not have to be a good business man. What if my father had not supported his family in respectable style? I could be proud of him! That, certainly, was how I suddenly felt. American respectability had taken my father away from me. Socialism was giving me a chance to get him back.

And I had him back, not only in a poem, but, already that summer, in fact. In a rather silly but very satisfying way, it happened. As my father sat reading his Sunday paper, I began—strange behavior in so dignified a boy—to tickle his ear with a broomstraw. He thought it was a fly, and brushed at it. I kept it up until he turned and saw me. Even then I did not stop, but persisted in this silly trick until—'You seem to want a spanking,' he said, 'so I'll give it to you!'—and he did. I burst out laughing. I was happy.

He seemed to understand, for he invited me to go fishing with him. I dug the worms, and we started. On the way to the creek we passed the 'Last Chance' saloon, and my father went in for a glass of beer, telling me that I might come in and have a glass of soda-pop if I liked.

But I was embarrassed, and stood waiting for him outside.

At that moment when I decided to stay outside, I was my mother's little boy.

But some new self within me made me feel ashamed. I wished I had gone in with him.

And after our fishing was done, on the way back, when we stopped there again, I marched in proudly and happily at his side. And when my soda-pop was served me in a bottle with a straw, I insisted on having it in a glass. I shyly pushed the glass along the bar till it touched my father's, and then drank deep.

* * *

In a moment I will tell what kind of father it was that I got back. But first I must say a little more about my Socialism, and what it had to do with my feelings about my father.

In search of further information, I tried to read a small digest of the Marxian theory, which I found at the public library, but it was too algebraic for my comprehension. However, I proceeded to read several books, beginning with Kennan's, and including something of Kropotkin's, on the Nihilist movement in Russia, and I became happily at home in those scenes of heroic conspiratorial effort on behalf of human liberty. Also I read an interesting Populist novel by Ignatius Donnelly, the author of the 'Atlantis' book, giving an imaginative account of an American revolution, one not accomplished by votes but by a violent and bloody uprising against a ruthless Napoleonic dictator. From these it is possible that

I got a more realistic notion of revolution than I would have had from current Socialist Party propaganda, which was at that time very peacefully Parliamentarian. At all events, this revolutionary literature provided for me an imaginative world in which considerations of respectability and manners did not count, and in which heroism was conceived as being directed to the creation of a better world rather than to setting the wedding bells to ringing. What this Nihilist literature did for me was to put an end to any hold of respectability upon my conscience. And at the same time it lifted from my shoulders a frightful burden of obligation which I owed to my mother—the obligation of doing or being something by which she should be enabled to sit on a cushion in the parlor. The rest of the burden of my obligation to her was at least more bearable. And by lifting this burden from myself, I kept it lifted, in my own mind, from my father—who was thus no longer, by any relapse into an earlier attitude, to be regarded as morally culpable in having failed to maintain her and us in respectable comfort. I had no right to expect my father to be anything but what he was.

Now about my father. I listened to his war-stories again for the first time since my very earliest childhood. One story which I now enjoyed immensely (and still do), was the one about how, as a staff orderly attached to the hospital at camp, he thought he was going to be left behind when his company was being shipped to the front. He appealed to the General, whom he found seated behind a mahogany desk in an office building. The General told Private Dell that he would have to obey orders, and Private Dell disgustedly spat tobacco juice on the General's carpet. The outraged General fined him a month's pay, and Private Dell, as he related the story, said: 'You might as well make it a million dollars, General—I'll never pay it!' And he galloped his horse to the boat, and, while Company K cheered, rode on board just as the gangplank was lifted. And he didn't pay that fine, either, for, when he was reported dead, the fine was crossed from the rolls; 'otherwise,' he said, 'I'd have sued the government!' Among his war memories was the remark of Colonel Clodd, whose orderly he was: 'Banty, you'll either be shot for general insubordination, or promoted for extraordinary and useless daring, and I don't care which!' Around Vicksburg (if his son remembers rightly) he had the chance to earn a commission by enlisting a company of Negroes; he enlisted them at the point of a carbine, very successfully; but then, while he awaited his commission, he was put in charge of them while they built a road for the artillery in the marshy ground along the river; he got tired of that, told the colonel he'd be damned if he'd be a nigger overseer, and was sent back to the company. After the war, released from the rebel prison, he swam half way across the Mississippi, but then got to thinking about the alligators, and climbed into the rowboat that was following along.

And this belligerent and adventurous father of mine was happier now, I think, when he was out of his home town, in a strange city, where he did not have to uphold his respectability as a formerly prosperous business man. He was in his sixties, now; he dyed his hair and moustache, and demanded a job—and sometimes got one.

The fact that he could not get work as a butcher never ceased to puzzle him, for he knew himself to be a better butcher than any of the young snips he saw behind the marble counters in Quincy. He did get a job as a bartender, but he had to hold it by stealth, for the fraternal insurance society to which he belonged virtuously forbade such employment, and he dared not lose the insurance upon which he had kept up his payments for so long. That job was ended by a dispute with the bartender. He was reduced for the most part to washing dishes at home.

He was less aldermanic now in appearance than he had once been—much less imposing than I remembered him as being in my childhood. He had something of jauntiness in his manner, and carried his small plump body with the vestiges of a military pride. His tongue was sharp, and his eyes bright; his cheeks were jolly, his jaw stubborn. He was now amusingly militant in his economic adventures; if he was an unwanted old man who always got fired, he managed to get some fun out of it, and not merely humiliation, as before.

One of his job-losing stories in Quincy, much enjoyed by our whole family at the supper table, was about the glucose factory. He had managed to get a job there nailing up boxes packed with cans of corn-syrup. He had held it a week and a half when the superintendent happened to stroll through the packing-room. The superintendent was young and English; it is possible that my father may have been misled by a Ha'va'd accent, but the superintendent was English in his story. The superintendent had stopped to watch my father nail up a box, and then had said: 'You'll have to work faster than that, my man!' My father, in telling the story, reproduced the broad English *a* in 'faster,' and emphasized the preposterous phrase, 'my man'; and anyone who heard it understood why we had fought two wars with England. Of course my father had ignored him and had gone on working. And then the young fool actually kicked him! or at least touched my father's kneeling body with the toe of his shoe. 'Do you heah me?' he had asked.

My father, who had in his time defied a General, rose. In front of him was a container marked in large letters, 'Sulphuric Acid.' My father stooped, ladled out a dipperful of the liquid, and turned to the superintendent.

'Do you know what this is?' he demanded fiercely.

'Why, it's sulphuric acid!' said the superintendent, looking frightened.

'Then get down on your knees, you dog,' said my father, 'or I'll throw this right in your damned insolent face. And be quick about it!'

'And,' my father would say, telling the story at the supper table, 'he got down on his knees. And then—everybody in the room was looking, and didn't know what to make of it— then I put the dipper up to my mouth and drank it down. It was nothing but drinking water. And damn if that Englishman didn't just crawl out on his hands and knees.'

He was a perfectly grand father for a boy to have.

EMOTIONAL CONFLICTS

I hate and love—the why I cannot tell,
But by my tortures know the fact too well.

—CATULLUS

OUR emotions are the inner forces that move us—the powerful drives of anger, fear, and love, with their infinitely complex variations of jealousy, pity, anxiety, tenderness, and innumerable other feelings that manage to keep us in a stirred-up state much of the time. Convenient though it would be, one cannot fit into sharply differentiated categories anything so complex as human emotions. To say that here is an individual whose reactions are wholly emotional, another whose responses are totally rational, is to ignore the truth that behavior may be measured only in relation to the functioning of the entire organism. One's emotions cannot be divorced from the whole of his life. They are inextricably interwoven with drives of self-preservation, sex-expression, and food-getting—in short, with the individual's fundamental human needs. While physical characteristics may exercise considerable influence upon one's emotional reactions, as has already been suggested, one's behavior may be modified by learned adaptations to one's environment. Since the sex drive is given its direction in the early years of the child's life, one important key to emotional behavior lies in the attitudes and inter-relationships within the family. And because self-preservation and food-getting are primary drives of every human being, the social and economic structure of society cannot be overlooked in attaching responsibility for man's actions.

While psychologists generally agree that love, fear, and anger are the primary emotions, so conditioned are these drives by other aspects of the personality that one never finds them manifested in what might be called a pure or unadulterated state. In his earliest years the child discovers that certain of his desires are acceded to, others are denied. Early expressions of rage—the anger of the infant whose physical needs or desires meet some obstacle, the aggressive impulses revealed by the older child in his play—are overt emotional expressions. As he grows, the individual learns to control or divert his emotional energy—perhaps to use biting words instead of blows when his desires are thwarted, when his activities in work or play are interfered with, or when some social situation arises which makes him appear ridiculous or inferior. If he finds no acceptable outlet for his feelings of rage and frustration, they may become destructive, turned either in upon himself or outward upon society.

Our fears are probably largely learned, the result of our physical and social conditioning. In a great variety of forms and in varying degrees of intensity, they complicate life for us, driving us to many responses, from the simple reaction of running away to elaborate rationalizations of our conduct. Since most fears are learned, they may also be eliminated through understanding and facing them—a need vital to the development of a healthy personality.

The emotion of love continually drives one to seek an object upon which it may be expended. We have noted how the child's first experience of love in the home may determine his subsequent emotional patterns. Not only his relation to his parents as the first objects of his affection, but his awareness of their relation to each other will indelibly affect his attitudes. He has been a witness, not always a conscious one, to their relationship, sensing their happiness or their misery. As he grows older, more and more he observes the lives of those outside of the family circle. He learns what is regarded as socially acceptable, what is merely expedient, what is criminal. His primary drives thus become subservient to repressive forces. Unconsciously his impulses will be modified to conform with the dictates of his conscience or the mandates of society. Or by the process of sublimation, his emotion may be directed away from its primitive objectives to socially approved goals in friendship, devotion to the arts, achievement in work of social usefulness, love of man, of country, or of God.

On the other hand, the emotion of love may encounter obstacles which result in repression rather than in overt or sublimated expression. It may become entangled with feelings of hate or fear.

❅

OTHELLO

WILLIAM SHAKESPEARE

[An ambivalent attitude is clearly revealed in *Othello*. At the moment Othello protests that he will not be governed by his emotions but rather by his reason—'I'll see before I doubt; when I doubt, prove; and, on the proof, there is no more but this,—away at once with love or jealousy!'—he is taken in by Iago's diabolical machinations. He cannot separate his love of Desdemona from his hate of her, nor can he summon his intellect to temper his passion. He is making what the psychologist Rivers calls the protopathic response to a stimulus, one in which the separation of the emotional and cognitive aspects of the personality induces an all or nothing response.]

Enter OTHELLO *and* IAGO *(at a distance)*.

EMILIA. Madam, here comes my lord.

CASSIO. Madam, I'll take my leave.

DESDEMONA. Why, stay, and hear me speak.

CASSIO. Madam, not now; I am very ill at ease,
Unfit for mine own purposes.

DESDEMONA. Well, do your discretion.

(*Exit* CASSIO.

IAGO. Ha! I like not that.

OTHELLO. What dost thou say?

IAGO. Nothing, my lord: or if—I know not what.

OTHELLO. Was not that Cassio parted from my wife?

IAGO. Cassio, my lord? No, sure, I cannot think it
That he would steal away so guilty-like,
Seeing you coming.

OTHELLO. I do believe 'twas he.

DESDEMONA. How now, my lord!
I have been talking with a suitor here,
A man that languishes in your displeasure.

OTHELLO. Who is't you mean?

DESDEMONA. Why, your lieutenant, Cassio. Good my lord,
If I have any grace or power to move you,
His present reconciliation take;
For if he be not one that truly loves you,
That errs in ignorance and not in cunning,
I have no judgment in an honest face.
I prithee call him back.

OTHELLO. Went he hence now?

DESDEMONA. Ay, sooth; so humbled,
That he hath left part of his grief with me,
To suffer with him. Good love, call him back.

OTHELLO. Not now, sweet Desdemona; some other time.

DESDEMONA. But shall't be shortly?

OTHELLO. The sooner, sweet, for you.

DESDEMONA. Shall't be to-night at supper?

OTHELLO. No, not to-night.

DESDEMONA. To-morrow dinner then?

OTHELLO. I shall not dine at home;
I meet the captains at the citadel.

DESDEMONA. Why then, to-morrow night; or Tuesday morn;
On Tuesday noon, or night; on Wednesday morn:
I prithee name the time, but let it not
Exceed three days: in faith, he's penitent;
And yet his trespass, in our common reason,—
Save that they say, the wars must make examples
Out of their best,—is not almost a fault
To incur a private check. When shall he come?
Tell me, Othello: I wonder in my soul,
What you could ask me that I should deny,
Or stand so mammering on. What! Michael Cassio,
That came a wooing with you, and so many a time,
When I have spoke of you dispraisingly,
Hath ta'en your part; to have so much to do
To bring him in! Trust me, I could do much,—

OTHELLO. Prithee, no more; let him come when he will;
I will deny thee nothing.

DESDEMONA. Why, this is not a boon;
'Tis as I should entreat you wear your gloves,
Or feed on nourishing dishes, or keep you warm,
Or sue to you to do a peculiar profit
To your own person; nay, when I have a suit
Wherein I mean to touch your love indeed,
It shall be full of poise and difficult weight,
And fearful to be granted.

OTHELLO. I will deny thee nothing:
Whereon, I do beseech thee, grant me this,
To leave me but a little to myself.

DESDEMONA. Shall I deny you? no: farewell, my lord.

OTHELLO. Farewell, my Desdemona: I'll come to thee straight.

DESDEMONA. Emilia, come. Be as your fancies teach you:
Whate'er you be, I am obedient.

(*Exit with* EMILIA.

OTHELLO. Excellent wretch! Perdition **catch my soul**

But I do love thee! and when I love thee
not,
Chaos is come again.

IAGO. My noble lord,—

OTHELLO.   What dost thou say, Iago?

IAGO. Did Michael Cassio, when you
woo'd my lady,
Know of your love?

OTHELLO. He did, from first to last: why
dost thou ask?

IAGO. But for a satisfaction of my
thought;
No further harm.

OTHELLO.   Why of thy thought, Iago?

IAGO. I did not think he had been acquainted with her.

OTHELLO. O! yes; and went between us
very oft.

IAGO. Indeed!

OTHELLO. Indeed! ay, indeed; discern'st
thou aught in that?
Is he not honest?

IAGO. Honest, my lord?

OTHELLO.   Honest! ay, honest.

IAGO. My lord, for aught I know.

OTHELLO. What dost thou think?

IAGO.   Think, my lord!

OTHELLO.   Think, my lord!
By heaven, he echoes me,
As if there were some monster in his
thought
Too hideous to be shown. Thou dost
mean something:
I heard thee say but now, thou lik'dst
not that,
When Cassio left my wife; what didst
not like?
And when I told thee he was of my
counsel
In my whole course of wooing, thou
criedst, 'Indeed!'
And didst contract and purse thy brow
together,
As if thou then hadst shut up in thy
brain
Some horrible conceit. If thou dost love
me,
Show me thy thought.

IAGO. My lord, you know I love you.

OTHELLO.   I think thou dost;
And, for I know thou art full of love
and honesty,

And weigh'st thy words before thou
giv'st them breath,
Therefore these stops of thine fright me
the more;
For such things in a false disloyal knave
Are tricks of custom, but in a man that's
just
They are close delations, working from
the heart
That passion cannot rule.

IAGO.   For Michael Cassio,
I dare be sworn I think that he is honest.

OTHELLO. I think so too.

IAGO.   Men should be what they seem;
Or those that be not, would they might
seem none!

OTHELLO. Certain, men should be what
they seem.

IAGO. Why then, I think Cassio's an honest man.

OTHELLO. Nay, yet there's more in this.
I pray thee, speak to me as to thy think-
ings,
As thou dost ruminate, and give thy
worst of thoughts
The worst of words.

IAGO.   Good my lord, pardon me;
Though I am bound to every act of duty.
I am not bound to that all slaves are free
to.
Utter my thoughts? Why, say they are
vile and false;
As where's that palace whereinto foul
things
Sometimes intrude not? who has a breast
so pure
But some uncleanly apprehensions
Keep leets and law-days, and in session
sit
With meditations lawful?

OTHELLO. Thou dost conspire against
thy friend, Iago,
If thou but think'st him wrong'd, and
mak'st his ear
A stranger to thy thoughts.

IAGO.   I do beseech you,
Though I perchance am vicious in my
guess,—
As, I confess, it is my nature's plague
To spy into abuses, and oft my jealousy
Shapes faults that are not,—that your
wisdom yet,
From one that so imperfectly conceits,

Would take no notice, nor build yourself
 a trouble
Out of his scattering and unsure observ-
 ance.
It were not for your quiet nor your good,
Nor for my manhood, honesty, or wis-
 dom,
To let you know my thoughts.
 OTHELLO.   What dost thou mean?
 IAGO. Good name in man and woman,
  dear my lord,
Is the immediate jewel of their souls:
Who steals my purse steals trash; 'tis
 something, nothing;
'Twas mine, 'tis his, and has been slave
 to thousands;
But he that filches from me my good
 name
Robs me of that which not enriches him,
And makes me poor indeed.
 OTHELLO. By heaven, I'll know thy
  thoughts.
 IAGO. You cannot, if my heart were in
  your hand;
Nor shall not, whilst 'tis in my custody.
 OTHELLO. Ha!
 IAGO. O! beware, my lord, of jealousy;
It is the green-ey'd monster which doth
 mock
The meat it feeds on; that cuckold lives
 in bliss
Who, certain of his fate, loves not his
 wronger;
But, O! what damned minutes tells he
 o'er
Who dotes, yet doubts; suspects, yet
 strongly loves!
 OTHELLO. O misery!
 IAGO. Poor and content is rich, and rich
  enough,
But riches fineless is as poor as winter
To him that ever fears he shall be poor.
Good heaven, the souls of all my tribe
 defend
From jealousy.
 OTHELLO. Why, why is this?
Think'st thou I'd make a life of jealousy,
To follow still the changes of the moon
With fresh suspicions? No; to be once
 in doubt
Is once to be resolv'd. Exchange me for a
 goat

When I shall turn the business of my soul
To such exsufflicate and blown surmises,
Matching thy inference. 'Tis not to make
 me jealous
To say my wife is fair, feeds well, loves
 company,
Is free of speech, sings, plays, and dances
 well;
Where virtue is, these are more virtu-
 ous:
Nor from mine own weak merits will I
 draw
The smallest fear, or doubt of her revolt;
For she had eyes, and chose me. No, Iago;
I'll see before I doubt; when I doubt,
 prove;
And, on the proof, there is no more but
 this,
Away at once with love or jealousy!
 IAGO. I am glad of it; for now I shall
  have reason
To show the love and duty that I bear
 you
With franker spirit; therefore, as I am
 bound,
Receive it from me; I speak not yet of
 proof.
Look to your wife; observe her well with
 Cassio;
Wear your eye thus, not jealous nor se-
 cure;
I would not have your free and noble
 nature
Out of self-bounty be abus'd; look to't;
I know our country disposition well;
In Venice they do let heaven see the
 pranks
They dare not show their husbands; their
 best conscience
Is not to leave't undone, but keep't un-
 known.
 OTHELLO. Dost thou say so?
 IAGO. She did deceive her father, mar-
  rying you:
And when she seem'd to shake and fear
 your looks,
She lov'd them most.
 OTHELLO.   And so she did.
 IAGO.   Why, go to, then;
She that so young could give out such a
 seeming,
To seel her father's eyes up close as oak,

He thought 'twas witchcraft; but I am much to blame;
I humbly do beseech you of your pardon
For too much loving you.

OTHELLO. I am bound to thee for ever.

IAGO. I see, this hath a little dash'd your spirits.

OTHELLO. Not a jot, not a jot.

IAGO. I' faith, I fear it has.
I hope you will consider what is spoke
Comes from my love. But, I do see you're mov'd;
I am to pray you not to strain my speech
To grosser issues nor to larger reach
Than to suspicion.

OTHELLO. I will not.

IAGO. Should you do so, my lord,
My speech should fall into such vile success
As my thoughts aim not at. Cassio's my worthy friend—
My lord, I see you're mov'd.

OTHELLO. No, not much mov'd;
I do not think but Desdemona's honest.

IAGO. Long live she so! and long live you to think so!

OTHELLO. And, yet, how nature erring from itself,—

IAGO. Ay, there's the point: as, to be bold with you,
Not to affect many proposed matches
Of her own clime, complexion, and degree,
Whereto, we see, in all things nature tends;
Foh! one may smell in such, a will most rank,
Foul disproportion, thoughts unnatural.
But pardon me; I do not in position
Distinctly speak of her, though I may fear
Her will, recoiling to her better judgment,
May fall to match you with her country forms
And happily repent.

OTHELLO. Farewell, farewell;
If more thou dost perceive, let me know more;
Set on thy wife to observe. Leave me, Iago.

IAGO. My lord, I take my leave. (*Going.*

OTHELLO. Why did I marry? This honest creature, doubtless,
Sees and knows more, much more, than he unfolds.

IAGO. (*Returning.*) My lord, I would I might entreat your honour
To scan this thing no further; leave it to time.
Although 'tis fit that Cassio have his place,
For, sure he fills it up with great ability,
Yet, if you please to hold him off awhile,
You shall by that perceive him and his means:
Note if your lady strain his entertainment
With any strong or vehement importunity;
Much will be seen in that. In the mean time,
Let me be thought too busy in my fears,
As worthy cause I have to fear I am,
And hold her free, I do beseech your honour.

OTHELLO. Fear not my government.

IAGO. I once more take my leave. (*Exit.*

OTHELLO. This fellow's of exceeding honesty,
And knows all qualities, with a learned spirit,
Of human dealings; if I do prove her haggard,
Though that her jesses were my dear heart-strings,
I'd whistle her off and let her down the wind,
To prey at fortune. Haply, for I am black,
And have not those soft parts of conversation
That chamberers have, or, for I am declin'd
Into the vale of years—yet that's not much—
She's gone, I am abus'd; and my relief
Must be to loathe her. O curse of marriage!
That we can call these delicate creatures ours,
And not their appetites. I had rather be a toad,
And live upon the vapour of a dungeon,
Than keep a corner in the thing I love

For others' uses. Yet, 'tis the plague of
   great ones;
Prerogativ'd are they less than the base;
'Tis destiny unshunnable, like death:
Even then this forked plague is fated to
   us
When we do quicken.
                     Look! where she comes.
If she be false, O! then heaven mocks
   itself.
I'll not believe it.
   Re-enter DESDEMONA *and* EMILIA
   DESDEMONA.   How now, my dear
   Othello!
Your dinner and the generous islanders
By you invited, do attend your presence.
   OTHELLO. I am to blame.
   DESDEMONA.   Why do you speak so
   faintly?
Are you not well?
   OTHELLO. I have a pain upon my fore-
   head here.
   DESDEMONA. Faith, that's with watching;
   'twill away again:
Let me but bind it hard, within this
   hour
It will be well.
   OTHELLO.   Your napkin is too little:
                  (*She drops her handkerchief.*
Let it alone. Come, I'll go in with you.
   DESDEMONA. I am very sorry that you
   are not well.
              (*Exeunt* OTHELLO *and* DESDEMONA.
   EMILIA. I am glad I have found this
   napkin;
This was her first remembrance from
   the Moor;
My wayward husband hath a hundred
   times
Woo'd me to steal it, but she so loves
   the token,
For he conjur'd her she should ever keep
   it,
That she reserves it evermore about her
To kiss and talk to. I'll have the work
   ta'en out,
And give't Iago:
What he will do with it heaven knows,
   not I;
I nothing but to please his fantasy.
              Enter IAGO
   IAGO. How now! what do you here
   alone?

EMILIA. Do you not chide; I have a
   thing for you.
IAGO. A thing for me? It is a common
   thing—
EMILIA. Ha!
IAGO. To have a foolish wife.
EMILIA. O! is that all? What will you
   give me now
For that same handkerchief?
IAGO.   What handkerchief?
EMILIA. What handkerchief!
Why, that the Moor first gave to Des-
   demona:
That which so often you did bid me
   steal.
IAGO. Hast stol'n it from her?
EMILIA. No, faith; she let it drop by
   negligence,
And, to the advantage, I, being there,
   took't up.
Look, here it is.
IAGO.   A good wench; give it me.
EMILIA. What will you do with't, that
   you have been so earnest
To have me filch it?
IAGO. Why, what's that to you?
                        (*Snatches it.*
EMILIA. If it be not for some purpose
   of import
Give't me again; poor lady! she'll run
   mad
When she shall lack it.
IAGO. Be not acknown on't; I have use
   for it.
Go, leave me.   (*Exit* EMILIA.
I will in Cassio's lodging lose this napkin,
And let him find it; trifles light as air
Are to the jealous confirmations strong
As proofs of holy writ; this may do
   something.
The Moor already changes with my
   poison:
Dangerous conceits are in their natures
   poisons,
Which at the first are scarce found to dis-
   taste,
But with a little act upon the blood,
Burn like the mines of sulphur. I did
   say so:
Look! where he comes!
              Enter OTHELLO.
         Not poppy, nor mandragora,
Nor all the drowsy syrups of the world,

Shall ever medicine thee to that sweet
  sleep
Which thou owedst yesterday.

    OTHELLO.   Ha! Ha! false to me?

    IAGO. Why, how now, general! no more
  of that.

    OTHELLO. Avaunt! be gone! thou hast
  set me on the rack;
I swear 'tis better to be much abus'd
Than but to know't a little.

    IAGO.   How now, my lord!

    OTHELLO. What sense had I of her stol'n
  hours of lust?
I saw't not, thought it not, it harm'd not
  me;
I slept the next night well, was free and
  merry;
I found not Cassio's kisses on her lips;
He that is robb'd, not wanting what is
  stol'n,
Let him not know't and he's not robb'd
  at all.

    IAGO. I am sorry to hear this.

    OTHELLO. I had been happy, if the gen-
  eral camp,
Pioneers and all, had tasted her sweet
  body,
So I had nothing known. O! now, for
  ever
Farewell the tranquil mind; farewell
  content!
Farewell the plumed troop and the big
  wars
That make ambition virtue! O, farewell!
Farewell the neighing steed, and the shrill
  trump,
The spirit-stirring drum, the ear-piercing
  fife,
The royal banner, and all quality,
Pride, pomp, and circumstance of glorious
  war!
And, O you mortal engines, whose rude
  throats
The immortal Jove's dread clamours
  counterfeit,
Farewell! Othello's occupation's gone!

    IAGO. Is it possible, my lord?

    OTHELLO. Villain, be sure thou prove
  my love a whore,
Be sure of it; give me the ocular proof;
Or, by the worth of mine eternal soul,

Thou hadst been better have been born
  a dog
Than answer my wak'd wrath.

    IAGO.   Is't come to this?

    OTHELLO. Make me to see't; or, at least,
  so prove it,
That the probation bear no hinge nor
  loop
To hang a doubt on; or woe upon thy
  life!

    IAGO. My noble lord,—

    OTHELLO. If thou dost slander her and
  torture me,
Never pray more; abandon all remorse;
On horror's head horrors accumulate;
Do deeds to make heaven weep, all earth
  amaz'd;
For nothing canst thou to damnation add
Greater than that.

    IAGO.   O grace! O heaven forgive me!
Are you a man! have you a soul or sense?
God be wi' you; take mine office. O
  wretched fool!
That liv'st to make thine honesty a vice.
O monstrous world! Take note, take note,
  O world!
To be direct and honest is not safe.
I thank you for this profit, and, from
  hence
I'll love no friend, sith love breeds such
  offence.

    OTHELLO. Nay, stay; thou shouldst be
  honest.

    IAGO. I should be wise; for honesty's a
  fool,
And loses that it works for.

    OTHELLO.   By the world,
I think my wife be honest and think she
  is not;
I think that thou art just and think thou
  art not.
I'll have some proof. Her name, that was
  as fresh
As Dian's visage, is now begrim'd and
  black
As mine own face. If there be cords or
  knives,
Poison or fire or suffocating streams,
I'll not endure it. Would I were satisfied!

    IAGO. I see, sir, you are eaten up with
  passion.
I do repent me that I put it to you.

You would be satisfied?

OTHELLO. Would! nay, I will.

IAGO. And may; but how? how satisfied, my lord?

Would you, the supervisor, grossly gape on;

Behold her tupp'd?

OTHELLO. Death and damnation! O!

IAGO. It were a tedious difficulty, I think,

To bring them to that prospect; damn them then,

If ever mortal eyes do see them bolster

More than their own! What then? how then?

What shall I say? Where's satisfaction?

It is impossible you should see this,

Were they as prime as goats, as hot as monkeys,

As salt as wolves in pride, and fools as gross

As ignorance made drunk; but yet, I say,

If imputation, and strong circumstances,

Which lead directly to the door of truth,

Will give you satisfaction, you may have it.

OTHELLO. Give me a living reason she's disloyal.

IAGO. I do not like the office;

But, sith I am enter'd in this cause so far,

Prick'd to't by foolish honesty and love,

I will go on. I lay with Cassio lately;

And, being troubled with a raging tooth,

I could not sleep.

There are a kind of men so loose of soul

That in their sleeps will mutter their affairs;

One of this kind is Cassio.

In sleep I heard him say, 'Sweet Desdemona,

Let us be wary, let us hide our loves!'

And then, sir, would he gripe and wring my hand,

Cry, 'O, sweet creature!' and then kiss me hard,

As if he pluck'd up kisses by the roots,

That grew upon my lips; then laid his leg

Over my thigh, and sigh'd, and kiss'd; and then

Cried, 'Cursed fate, that gave thee to the Moor!'

OTHELLO. O monstrous! monstrous!

IAGO. Nay, this was but his dream.

OTHELLO. But this denoted a foregone conclusion:

'Tis a shrewd doubt, though it be but a dream.

IAGO. And this may help to thicken other proofs

That do demonstrate thinly.

OTHELLO. I'll tear her all to pieces.

IAGO. Nay, but be wise; yet we see nothing done;

She may be honest yet. Tell me but this:

Have you not sometimes seen a handkerchief

Spotted with strawberries in your wife's hand?

OTHELLO. I gave her such a one; 'twas my first gift.

IAGO. I know not that; but such a handkerchief—

I am sure it was your wife's—did I to-day

See Cassio wipe his beard with.

OTHELLO. If it be that,—

IAGO. If it be that, or any that was hers,

It speaks against her with the other proofs.

OTHELLO. O! that the slave had forty thousand lives;

One is too poor, too weak for my revenge.

Now do I see 'tis true. Look here, Iago;

All my fond love thus do I blow to heaven:

'Tis gone.

Arise, black vengeance, from the hollow hell!

Yield up, O love! thy crown and hearted throne

To tyrannous hate. Swell, bosom, with thy fraught,

For 'tis of aspics' tongues!

IAGO. Yet be content.

OTHELLO. O! blood, blood, blood!

IAGO. Patience, I say; your mind, perhaps, may change.

OTHELLO. Never, Iago. Like to the Pontic sea,

Whose icy current and compulsive course

Ne'er feels retiring ebb, but keeps due on

To the Propontic and the Hellespont,
Even so my bloody thoughts, with vio-
   lent pace,
Shall ne'er look back, ne'er ebb to humble
   love,
Till that a capable and wide revenge
Swallow them up.   (*Kneels.*
        Now, by yond marble heaven,
In the due reverence of a sacred vow
I here engage my words.
   IAGO.   Do not rise yet. (*Kneels.*
Witness, you ever-burning lights above!
You elements that clip us round about!
Witness, that here Iago doth give up
The execution of his wit, hands, heart,
To wrong'd Othello's service! Let him
   command,
And to obey shall be in me remorse,
What bloody business ever.   (*They rise.*

OTHELLO.   I greet thy love,
Not with vain thanks, but with accept-
   ance bounteous,
And will upon the instant put thee to't:
Within these three days let me hear thee
   say
That Cassio's not alive.
   IAGO. My friend is dead; 'tis done at
   your request;
But let her live.
   OTHELLO. Damn her, lewd minx! O,
   damn her!
Come, go with me apart; I will with-
   draw
To furnish me with some swift means of
   death
For the fair devil. Now art thou my
   lieutenant.
   IAGO. I am your own for ever. (*Exeunt.*

❋

THE RETURN OF THE NATIVE
THOMAS HARDY

[Like Othello, Eustacia, in Hardy's *The Return of the Native,* is incapable of moderation in love. She would be loved to madness or she would walk alone. Although her mind tells her it was unwise to recall Wildeve, she is defenseless in her all-consuming passion. Interwoven with her love and inseparable from it is her need to assert her power over the life of one bound to her emotionally.]

Eustacia stepped upon the bank.
'Yes?' she said, and held her breath.
Thereupon the contour of a man became dimly visible against the low-reaching sky over the valley, beyond the outer margin of the pool. He came round it and leapt upon the bank beside her. A low laugh escaped her—the third utterance which the girl had indulged in to-night. The first, when she stood upon Rainbarrow, had expressed anxiety; the sec-ond, on the ridge, had expressed impatience; the present was one of triumphant pleasure. She let her joyous eyes rest upon him without speaking, as upon some wondrous thing she had created out of chaos.

'I have come,' said the man, who was Wildeve. 'You give me no peace. Why do you not leave me alone? I have seen your bonfire all the evening.' The words were not without emotion, and retained their level tone

From *The Return of the Native* by Thomas Hardy. By permission of Harper and Brothers.

as if by a careful equipoise between imminent extremes.

At this unexpectedly repressing manner in her lover the girl seemed to repress herself also. 'Of course you have seen my fire,' she answered with languid calmness, artificially maintained. 'Why shouldn't I have a bonfire on the Fifth of November, like other denizens of the heath?'

'I knew it was meant for me.'

'How did you know it? I have had no word with you since you—you chose her, and walked about with her, and deserted me entirely, as if I had never been yours body and soul so irretrievably!'

'Eustacia! could I forget that last autumn at this same day of the month and at this same place you lighted exactly such a fire as a signal for me to come and see you? Why should there have been a bonfire again by Captain Vye's house if not for the same purpose?'

'Yes, yes—I own it,' she cried under her breath, with a drowsy fervour of manner and tone which was quite peculiar to her. 'Don't begin speaking to me as you did, Damon; you will drive me to say words I would not wish to say to you. I had given you up, and resolved not to think of you any more; and then I heard the news, and I came out and got the fire ready because I thought that you had been faithful to me.'

'What have you heard to make you think that?' said Wildeve, astonished.

'That you did not marry her!' she murmured exultingly. 'And I knew it was because you loved me best, and couldn't do it . . . Damon, you have been cruel to me to go away, and I have said I would never forgive you. I do not think I can forgive you entirely, even now—it is too much for a

woman of any spirit to quite overlook.'

'If I had known you wished to call me up here only to reproach me, I wouldn't have come.'

'But I don't mind it, and I do forgive you now that you have not married her, and have come back to me!'

'Who told you that I had not married her?'

'My grandfather. He took a long walk to-day, and as he was coming home he overtook some person who told him of a broken-off wedding: he thought it might be yours; and I knew it was.'

'Does anybody else know?'

'I suppose not. Now, Damon, do you see why I lit my signal fire? You did not think I would have lit it if I had imagined you to have become the husband of this woman. It is insulting my pride to suppose that.'

Wildeve was silent: it was evident that he had supposed as much.

'Did you indeed think I believed you were married?' she again demanded earnestly. 'Then you wronged me; and upon my life and heart I can hardly bear to recognize that you have such ill thoughts of me! Damon, you are not worthy of me: I see it, and yet I love you. Never mind: let it go—I must bear your mean opinion as best I may . . . It is true, is it not,' she added, with ill-concealed anxiety, on his making no demonstration, 'that you could not bring yourself to give me up, and are still going to love me best of all?'

'Yes; or why should I have come?' he said touchily. 'Not that fidelity will be any great merit in me after your kind speech about my unworthiness, which should have been said by myself if by anybody, and comes with an ill grace from you. However, the curse of inflammability is upon me, and I must live under it, and take any snub from a woman. It has brought me down from engineering to innkeeping: what lower stage it has in store for me I have yet to learn.' He continued to look upon her gloomily.

She seized the moment, and throwing back the shawl so that the firelight shone full upon her face and throat, said with a smile, 'Have you seen anything better than that in your travels?'

Eustacia was not one to commit herself to such a position without good ground. He said quietly, 'No.'

'Not even on the shoulders of Thomasin?'

'Thomasin is a pleasing and innocent woman.'

'That's nothing to do with it,' she cried with quick passionateness. 'We will leave her out; there are only you and me now to think of.' After a long look at him she resumed with the old quiescent warmth: 'Must I go on weakly confessing to you things a woman ought to conceal; and own that no words can express how gloomy I have been because of that dreadful belief I held till two hours ago—that you had quite deserted me?'

'I am sorry I caused you that pain.'

'But perhaps it is not wholly because of you that I get gloomy,' she archly added. 'It is in my nature to feel like that. It was born in my blood, I suppose.'

'Hypochondriasis.'

'Or else it was coming into this wild heath. I was happy enough at Budmouth. O the times, O the days at Budmouth! But Egdon will be brighter again now.'

'I hope it will,' said Wildeve moodily. 'Do you know the consequence of this recall to me, my old

darling? I shall come to see you again as before, at Rainbarrow.'

'Of course you will.'

'And yet I declare that until I got here to-night I intended, after this one good-bye, never to meet you again.'

'I don't thank you for that,' she said, turning away, while indignation spread through her like subterranean heat. 'You may come again to Rainbarrow if you like, but you won't see me; and you may call, but I shall not listen; and you may tempt me, but I won't give myself to you any more.'

'You have said as much before, sweet; but such natures as yours don't so easily adhere to their words. Neither, for the matter of that, do such natures as mine.

'This is the pleasure I have won by my trouble,' she whispered bitterly. 'Why did I try to recall you? Damon, a strange warring takes place in my mind occasionally. I think when I become calm after your woundings, "Do I embrace a cloud of common fog after all?" You are a chameleon, and now you are at your worst colour. Go home, or I shall hate you!'

He looked absently towards Rainbarrow while one might have counted twenty, and said, as if he did not much mind all this, 'Yes, I will go home. Do you mean to see me again?'

'If you own to me that the wedding is broken off because you love me best.'

'I don't think it would be good policy,' said Wildeve, smiling. 'You would get to know the extent of your power too clearly.'

'But tell me!'

'You know.'

'Where is she now?'

'I don't know. I prefer not to speak of her to you. I have not yet married her: I have come in obedience to your call. That is enough.'

'I merely lit that fire because I was dull, and thought I would get a little excitement by calling you up and triumphing over you as the Witch of Endor called up Samuel. I determined you should come; and you have come! I have shown my power. A mile and half hither, and a mile and half back again to your home—three miles in the dark for me. Have I not shown my power?'

He shook his head at her. 'I know you too well, my Eustacia; I know you too well. There isn't a note in you which I don't know; and that hot little bosom couldn't play such a cold-blooded trick to save its life. I saw a woman on Rainbarrow at dusk looking down towards my house. I think I drew out you before you drew out me.'

The revived embers of an old passion glowed clearly in Wildeve now; and he leant forward as if about to put his face towards her cheek.

'O no,' she said, intractably moving to the other side of the decayed fire. 'What did you mean by that?'

'Perhaps I may kiss your hand?'

'No, you may not.'

'Then I may shake your hand?'

'No.'

'Then I wish you good-night without caring for either. Good-bye, good-bye.'

She returned no answer, and with the bow of a dancing-master he vanished on the other side of the pool as he had come.

Eustacia sighed: it was no fragile maiden sigh, but a sigh which shook her like a shiver. Whenever a flash of reason darted like an electric light upon her lover—as it sometimes would—and showed his imperfections, she shivered thus. But it was over in a second, and she loved on. She knew that he trifled with her; but she loved on. She scattered the half-burnt brands, went indoors immediately, and up to her bedroom without a light. Amid the rustles which denoted her to be undressing in the darkness other heavy breaths frequently came; and the same kind of shudder occasionally moved through her when, ten minutes later, she lay on her bed asleep.

✳

JEAN-CHRISTOPHE

Romain Rolland

[The intensely emotional friendship of Jean-Christophe and Otto illustrates a phase of early adolescent experience. The investing of the loved one with the attributes of perfection, the romantic illusions, the extravagant delight in the new-found intimacy, the tempestuous quarrels, jealousies, and reconciliations are a part of the emotional turbulence through which many young people must pass before progressing to a relationship with one of the opposite sex. It is natural that after the waning of this friendship Jean-Christophe should turn to Minna, not sure at first whether he loves her or

From *Jean-Christophe* by Romain Rolland. By permission of Henry Holt and Co., Inc.

her mother. He is fascinated by the new world of gentle refinements and playful grace they represent. Minna, too, is entranced by this strange, talented boy until the half idyllic first love of these two young people, with its only vaguely understood sensuousness, is broken by the harsh intrusion of the worldly social standards represented by the mother.]

One Sunday when Jean-Christophe had been invited by his *Musik Direktor* to dine at the little country house which Tobias Pfeiffer owned an hour's journey from the town, he took the Rhine steamboat. On deck he sat next to a boy about his own age, who eagerly made room for him. Jean-Christophe paid no attention, but after a moment, feeling that his neighbor had never taken his eyes off him, he turned and looked at him. He looked frankly what he was—a hobbledehoy—though he made great efforts to seem grown up. He was dressed with ostentatious care—flannel suit, light gloves, white shoes, and a pale blue tie—and he carried a little stick in his hand. He looked at Jean-Christophe out of the corner of his eye without turning his head, with his neck stiff, like a hen; and when Jean-Christophe looked at him he blushed up to his ears, took a newspaper from his pocket, and pretended to be absorbed in it, and to look important over it. But a few minutes later he dashed to pick up Jean-Christophe's hat, which had fallen. Jean-Christophe, surprised at such politeness, looked once more at the boy, and once more he blushed. Jean-Christophe thanked him curtly, for he did not like such obsequious eagerness, and he hated to be fussed with. All the same, he was flattered by it.

Soon it passed from his thoughts; his attention was occupied by the view. It was long since he had been able to escape from the town, and so he had keen pleasure in the wind that beat against his face, in the sound of the water against the boat, in the great stretch of water and the changing spectacle presented by the banks —bluffs gray and dull, willow-trees half under water, pale vines, legendary rocks, towns crowned with Gothic towers and factory chimneys belching black smoke. And as he was in ecstasy over it all, his neighbor in a choking voice timidly imparted a few historic facts concerning the ruins that they saw, cleverly restored and covered with ivy. He seemed to be lecturing to himself. Jean-Christophe, roused to interest, plied him with questions. The other replied eagerly, glad to display his knowledge, and with every sentence he addressed himself directly to Jean-Christophe, calling him 'Herr Hof Violinist.'

'You know me, then?' said Jean-Christophe.

'Oh, yes,' said the boy, with a simple admiration that tickled Jean-Christophe's vanity.

They talked. The boy had often seen Jean-Christophe at concerts, and his imagination had been touched by everything that he had heard about him. He did not say so to Jean-Christophe, but Jean-Christophe felt it, and was pleasantly surprised by it. He was not used to being spoken to in this tone of eager respect. He went on questioning his neighbor about the history of the country through which they were passing. The other set out all the knowledge that he had, and Jean-Christophe admired his learning. But that was only the peg on which their conversation hung. What interested them was the making of each other's acquaintance. They dared not frankly approach the subject; they returned to it again and again with awkward questions. Finally they plunged, and Jean-Christophe learned that his new friend was called Otto Diener, and was the son of a rich merchant in the town. It appeared, naturally, that they had friends in common, and little by little their tongues were loosed. They were talking eagerly when the boat arrived at the town at which Jean-Christophe was to get out. Otto got out, too. That surprised them, and Jean-Christophe proposed that they should take a walk together until dinner-time. They struck out across the fields. Jean-Christophe had taken Otto's arm familiarly, and was telling him his plans as if he had known him from his birth. He had been so much deprived of the society of children of his own age that he found an inexpressible joy in being with this boy, so learned and well brought up, who was in sympathy with him.

Time passed, and Jean-Christophe took no count of it. Diener, proud of the confidence which the young musician showed him, dared not point out that the dinner-hour had rung. At last he thought that he must remind him of it, but Jean-Christophe, who had begun the ascent of a hill in the woods, declared that they must go to the top, and when they reached it he lay down on the grass as though he meant to spend the day there. After a quarter of an hour Diener, seeing that he seemed to have no intention of moving, hazarded again:

'And your dinner?'

Jean-Christophe, lying at full length, with his hands behind his head, said quietly:

'Tssh!'

Then he looked at Otto, saw his scared look, and began to laugh.

'It is too good here,' he explained. 'I shan't go. Let them wait for me!'

He half rose.

'Are you in a hurry? No? Do you know what we'll do? We'll dine together. I know of an inn.'

Diener would have had many objections to make—not that any one was waiting for him, but because it was hard for him to come to any sudden decision, whatever it might be. He was methodical, and needed to be prepared beforehand. But Jean-Christophe's question was put in such a tone as allowed of no refusal. He let himself be dragged off, and they began to talk again.

At the inn their eagerness died down. Both were occupied with the question as to who should give the dinner, and each within himself made it a point of honor to give it—Diener because he was the richer, Jean-Christophe because he was the poorer. They made no direct reference to the matter, but Diener made great efforts to assert his right by the tone of authority which he tried to take as he asked for the menu. Jean-Christophe understood what he was at and turned the tables on him by ordering other dishes of a rare kind. He wanted to show that he was as much at his ease as anybody, and when Diener tried again by endeavoring to take upon himself the choice of wine, Jean-Christophe crushed him with a look, and ordered a bottle of one of the most expensive vintages they had in the inn.

When they found themselves seated before a considerable repast, they were abashed by it. They could find nothing to say, ate mincingly, and were awkward and constrained in their movements. They became conscious suddenly that they were strangers, and they watched each other. They made vain efforts to revive conversation; it dropped immediately. Their first half-hour was a time of fearful boredom. Fortunately, the meat and drink soon had an effect on them, and they looked at each other more confidently. Jean-Christophe especially, who was not used to such good things, became extraordinarily loquacious. He told of the difficulties of his life, and Otto, breaking through his reserve, confessed that he also was not happy. He was weak and timid, and his schoolfellows put upon him. They laughed at him, and could not forgive him for despising their vulgar manners. They played all sorts of tricks on him. Jean-Christophe clenched his fists, and said they had better not try it in his presence. Otto also was misunderstood by his family. Jean-Christophe knew the unhappiness of that, and they commiserated each other on their common misfortunes. Diener's parents wanted him to become a merchant, and to step into his father's place, but he wanted to be a poet. He would be a poet, even though he had to fly the town, like Schiller, and brave poverty! (His father's fortune would all come to him, and it was considerable.) He confessed blushingly that he had already written verses on the sadness of life, but he could not bring himself to recite them, in spite of Jean-Christophe's entreaties. But in the end he did give two or three of them, dithering with emotion. Jean-Christophe thought them admirable. They exchanged plans. Later on they would work together; they would write dramas and song-cycles. They admired each other. Besides his reputation as a musician, Jean-Christophe's strength and bold ways made an impression on Otto, and Jean-Christophe was sensible of Otto's elegance and distinguished manners—everything in this world is relative—and of his ease of manner—that ease of manner which he looked and longed for.

Made drowsy by their meal, with their elbows on the table, they talked and listened to each other with softness in their eyes. The afternoon drew on; they had to go. Otto made a last attempt to procure the bill, but Jean-Christophe nailed him to his seat with an angry look which made it impossible for him to insist. Jean-Christophe was only uneasy on one point—that he might be asked for more than he had. He would have given his watch and everything that he had about him rather than admit it to Otto. But he was not called on to go so far. He had to spend on the dinner almost the whole of his month's money. They went down the hill again. The shades of evening were beginning to fall over the pine-woods. Their tops were still bathed in rosy light; they swung slowly with a surging sound. The carpet of purple pine-needles deadened the sound of their footsteps. They said no word. Jean-Christophe felt a strange sweet sadness welling through his heart. He was happy; he wished to talk, but was weighted down with his sweet sorrow. He stopped for a moment, and so did Otto. All was silence. Flies buzzed high above them in a ray of sunlight; a rotten branch fell. Jean-Christophe took Otto's hand, and in a trembling voice said:

'Will you be my friend?'

Otto murmured:

'Yes.'

They shook hands; their hearts

beat; they dared hardly look at each other.

After a moment they walked on. They were a few paces away from each other, and they dared say no more until they were out of the woods. They were fearful of each other, and of their strange emotion. They walked very fast, and never stopped until they had issued from the shadow of the trees; then they took courage again, and joined hands. They marveled at the limpid evening falling, and they talked disconnectedly.

On the boat, sitting at the bows in the brilliant twilight, they tried to talk of trivial matters, but they gave no heed to what they were saying. They were lost in their own happiness and weariness. They felt no need to talk, or to hold hands, or even to look at each other; they were near each other.

When they were near their journey's end they agreed to meet on the following Sunday. Jean-Christophe took Otto to his door. Under the light of the gas they timidly smiled and murmured *au revoir*. They were glad to part, so wearied were they by the tension at which they had been living for those hours and by the pain it cost them to break the silence with a single word.

Jean-Christophe returned alone in the night. His heart was singing: 'I have a friend! I have a friend!' He saw nothing, he heard nothing, he thought of nothing else.

He was very sleepy, and fell asleep as soon as he reached his room; but he was awakened twice or thrice during the night, as by some fixed idea. He repeated, 'I have a friend,' and went to sleep again at once.

Next morning it seemed to be all a dream. To test the reality of it, he tried to recall the smallest details of the day. He was absorbed by this occupation while he was giving his lessons, and even during the afternoon he was so absent during the orchestra rehearsal that when he left he could hardly remember what he had been playing.

When he returned home he found a letter waiting for him. He had no need to ask himself whence it came. He ran and shut himself up in his room to read it. It was written on pale blue paper in a labored, long, uncertain hand, with very correct flourishes:

'DEAR HERR JEAN-CHRISTOPHE—dare I say HONORED FRIEND?—

'I am thinking much of our doings yesterday, and I do thank you tremendously for your kindness to me. I am so grateful for all that you have done, and for your kind words, and the delightful walk and excellent dinner! I am only worried that you should have spent so much money on it. What a lovely day! Do you not think there was something providential in that strange meeting? It seems to me that it was Fate decreed that we should meet. How glad I shall be to see you again on Sunday! I hope you will not have had too much unpleasantness for having missed the *Hof Musik Direktor's* dinner. I should be so sorry if you had any trouble because of me.

'Dear Herr Jean-Christophe, I am always

'Your very devoted servant and friend,

'OTTO DIENER.

'P.S.—On Sunday please do not call for me at home. It would be better, if you will, for us to meet at the *Schloss Garten*.'

Jean-Christophe read the letter with tears in his eyes. He kissed it; he laughed aloud; he jumped about on his bed. Then he ran to the table and took pen in hand to reply at once. He could not wait a moment.

But he was not used to writing. He could not express what was swelling in his heart; he dug into the paper with his pen, and blackened his fingers with ink; he stamped impatiently. At last, by dint of putting out his tongue and making five or six drafts, he succeeded in writing in malformed letters, which flew out in all directions, and with terrific mistakes in spelling:

'My Soul,—

'How dare you speak of gratitude, because I love you? Have I not told you how sad I was and lonely before I knew you? Your friendship is the greatest of blessings. Yesterday I was happy, happy! —for the first time in my life. I weep for joy as I read your letter. Yes, my beloved, there is no doubt that it was Fate brought us together. Fate wishes that we should be friends to do great things. Friends! The lovely word! Can it be that at last I have a friend? Oh! you will never leave me? You will be faithful to me? Always! always! . . . How beautiful it will be to grow up together, to work together, to bring together—I my musical whimsies, and all the crazy things that go chasing through my mind; you your intelligence and amazing learning! How much you know! I have never met a man so clever as you. There are moments when I am uneasy. I seem to be unworthy of your friendship. You are so noble and so accomplished, and I am so grateful to you for loving so coarse a creature as myself! . . . But no! I have just said, let there be no talk of gratitude. In friendship there is no obligation nor benefaction! I would not accept any benefaction! We are equal, since we love. How impatient I am to see you! I will not call for you at home, since you do not wish it— although, to tell the truth, I do not understand all these precautions—but you are the wiser; you are surely right . . .

'One word only! No more talk of money. I hate money—the word and the thing itself. If I am not rich, I am yet rich enough to give to my friend, and it is my joy to give all I can for him. Would not you do the same? And if I needed it, would you not be the first to give me all your fortune? But that shall never be! I have sound fists and a sound head, and I shall always be able to earn the bread that I eat. Till Sunday! Dear God, a whole week without seeing you! And for two days I have not seen you! How have I been able to live so long without you?

'The conductor tried to grumble, but do not bother about it any more than I do. What are others to me? I care nothing what they think or what they may ever think of me. Only you matter. Love me well, my soul; love me as I love you! I cannot tell how much I love you. I am yours, yours, yours, from the tips of my fingers to the apple of my eye.

'Yours always,
'Jean-Christophe.'

Jean-Christophe was devoured with impatience for the rest of the week. He would go out of his way, and make long turns to pass by Otto's house. Not that he counted on seeing him, but the sight of the house was enough to make him grow pale and red with emotion. On the Thursday he could bear it no longer, and sent a second letter even more high-flown than the first. Otto answered it sentimentally.

Sunday came at length, and Otto was punctually at the meeting-place. But Jean-Christophe had been there for an hour, waiting impatiently for the walk. He began to imagine dreadfully that Otto would not come. He trembled lest Otto should be ill, for he did not suppose for a moment that Otto might break his word. He whispered over and over again, 'Dear God, let him come—let him come!' and he struck at the pebbles in the avenue with his stick, saying to himself that if he missed three times Otto would not come, but if he hit them Otto would appear at once. In spite of his care and the easiness of the test, he had just missed three times when he saw Otto coming at his easy, deliberate pace; for Otto was above all things correct, even when he was most moved. Jean-Christophe ran to him, and with his throat dry wished him 'Good-day!' Otto replied, 'Good-day!' and they found that they had nothing more to say to each other, except that the weather was fine and that it was five or six minutes past ten, or it might be ten past, because the castle clock was always slow.

They went to the station, and went by rail to a neighboring place which was a favorite excursion from the town. On the way they exchanged not more than ten words. They tried to make up for it by eloquent looks, but they were no more successful. In vain did they try to tell each other what friends they were; their eyes would say nothing at all. They were just play-acting. Jean-Christophe saw that, and was humiliated. He did not understand how he could not express or even feel all that had filled his heart an hour before. Otto did not, perhaps, so exactly take stock of their failure, because he was less sincere, and examined himself with more circumspection, but he was just as disappointed. The truth is that the boys had, during their week of separation, blown out their feelings to such a diapason that it was impossible for them to keep them actually at that pitch, and when they met again their first impression must of necessity be false. They had to break away from it, but they could not bring themselves to agree to it.

All day they wandered in the country without ever breaking through the awkwardness and constraint that were upon them. It was a holiday. The inns and woods were filled with a rabble of excursionists—little *bourgeois* families who made a great noise and ate everywhere. That added to their ill-humor. They attributed to the poor people the impossibility of again finding the carelessness of their first walk. But they talked, they took great pains to find subjects of conversation; they were afraid of finding that they had nothing to say to each other. Otto displayed his school-learning; Jean-Christophe entered into technical explanations of musical compositions and violin-playing. They oppressed each other; they crushed each other by talking; and they never stopped talking, trembling lest they should, for then there opened before them abysses of silence which horrified them. Otto came near to weeping, and Jean-Christophe was near leaving him and running away as hard as he could, he was so bored and ashamed.

Only an hour before they had to take the train again did they thaw. In the depths of the woods a dog was barking; he was hunting on his own account. Jean-Christophe proposed that they should hide by his path to try and see his quarry. They ran into the midst of the thicket. The dog came near them, and then went away again. They went to right and left, went forward and doubled. The barking grew louder: the dog was choking with impatience in his lust for slaughter. He came near once more. Jean-Christophe and Otto, lying on the dead leaves in the rut of a path, waited and held their breath. The barking stopped; the dog had lost the scent. They heard his yap once again in the distance; then silence came upon the woods. Not a sound, only the mysterious hum of millions of creatures, insects, and creeping things, moving unceasingly, destroying the forest—the measured breathing of death, which never stops. The boys listened, they did not stir. Just when they got up, disappointed, and said, 'It is all over; he will not come!' a little hare plunged out of the thicket. He came straight upon them. They saw him at the same moment, and gave a cry of joy. The hare turned in his tracks and jumped aside. They saw him dash into the brushwood head over heels. The stirring of the rumpled leaves vanished away like a ripple on the face of waters. Although they were sorry for having cried out, the adventure filled them with joy. They rocked with laughter as they thought of the hare's terrified leap, and Jean-Christophe imitated grotesquely. Otto did the same. Then they chased each other. Otto was the hare, Jean-Christophe the dog. They plunged through woods and meadows, dashing through hedges and leaping ditches. A peasant shouted at them, because they had rushed over a field of rye. They did not stop to hear him. Jean-Christophe imitated the hoarse barking of the dog to such perfection that Otto laughed until he cried. At last they rolled down a slope, shouting like mad things. When they could not utter another sound they sat up and looked at each other, with tears of laughter in their eyes. They were quite happy and pleased with themselves. They were no longer trying to play the heroic friend; they were frankly what they were—two boys.

They came back arm-in-arm, singing senseless songs, and yet, when they were on the point of returning to the town, they thought they had better resume their pose, and under the last tree of the woods they carved their initials intertwined. But then good temper had the better of their sentimentality, and in the train they shouted with laughter whenever they looked at each other. They parted assuring each other that they had had a 'hugely delightful' [*kolossal entzückend*] day, and that conviction gained with them when they were alone once more.

They resumed their work of construction more patient and ingenious even than that of the bees, for of a few mediocre scraps of memory they fashioned a marvelous image of themselves and their friendship. After having idealized each other during the week, they met again on the Sunday, and in spite of the discrepancy between the truth and their illusion, they got used to not noticing it and to twisting things to fit in with their desires.

They were proud of being friends. The very contrast of their natures brought them together. Jean-Christophe knew nothing so beautiful as Otto. His fine hands, his lovely hair, his fresh complexion, his shy speech, the politeness of his manners, and his scrupulous care of his appearance delighted him. Otto was subjugated by Jean-Christophe's brimming strength and independence. Accustomed by age-old inheritance to religious respect for all authority, he took a fearful joy in the company of a comrade in whose nature was so little reverence for the established order of things. He had a little voluptuous thrill of terror whenever he heard him decry every reputation in the town, and even mimic the Grand Duke himself. Jean-Christophe knew the fascination that he exercised over his friend, and used to exaggerate his aggressive temper. Like some old revolutionary, he hewed away at social conventions and the laws of the State. Otto would listen, scandalized and delighted. He used timidly to try and join in, but he was always careful to look round to see if any one could hear.

Jean-Christophe never failed, when they walked together, to leap the fences of a field whenever he saw a board forbidding it, or he would pick fruit over the walls of private grounds. Otto was in terror lest they should be discovered. But such feelings had for him an exquisite savor, and in the evening, when he had returned, he would think himself a hero. He admired Jean-Christophe fearfully. His instinct of obedience found a satisfying quality in a friendship in which he had only to acquiesce in the will of his friend. Jean-Christophe never put him to the trouble of coming to a decision. He decided everything, decreed the doings of the day, decreed even the ordering of life, making plans, which admitted of no discussion, for Otto's future, just as he did for his own family. Otto fell in with them, though he was a little put aback by hearing Jean-Christophe dispose of his fortune for the building later on of a theater of his own contriving. But, intimidated by his friend's imperious tones, he did not protest, being convinced also by his friend's conviction that the money amassed by *Commerzienrath* Oscar Diener could be put to no nobler use. Jean-Christophe never for a moment had any idea that he might be violating Otto's will. He was instinctively a despot, and never imagined that his friend's wishes might be different from his own. Had Otto expressed a desire different from his own, he would not have hesitated to sacrifice his own personal preference. He would have sacrificed even

more for him. He was consumed by the desire to run some risk for him. He wished passionately that there might appear some opportunity of putting his friendship to the test. When they were out walking he used to hope that they might meet some danger, so that he might fling himself forward to face it. He would have loved to die for Otto. Meanwhile, he watched over him with a restless solicitude, gave him his hand in awkward places, as though he were a girl. He was afraid that he might be tired, afraid that he might be hot, afraid that he might be cold. When they sat down under a tree he took off his coat to put it about his friend's shoulders; when they walked he carried his cloak. He would have carried Otto himself. He used to devour him with his eyes like a lover, and, to tell the truth, he was in love.

He did not know it, not knowing yet what love was. But sometimes, when they were together, he was overtaken by a strange unease—the same that had choked him on that first day of their friendship in the pine-woods —and the blood would rush to his face and set his cheeks aflame. He was afraid. By an instinctive unanimity the two boys used furtively to separate and run away from each other, and one would lag behind on the road. They would pretend to be busy looking for black-berries in the hedges, and they did not know what it was that so perturbed them.

But it was in their letters especially that their feelings flew high. They were not then in any danger of being contradicted by facts, and nothing could check their illusions or intimidate them. They wrote to each other two or three times a week in a passionately lyric style. They hardly ever spoke of real happenings or common things; they raised great problems in an apocalyptic manner, which passed imperceptibly from enthusiasm to despair. They called each other, 'My blessing, my hope, my beloved, my Self.' They made a fearful hash of the word 'Soul.' They painted in tragic colors the sadness of their lot, and were desolate at having brought into the existence of their friend the sorrows of their existence.

'I am sorry, my love,' wrote Jean-Christophe, 'for the pain which I bring you. I cannot bear that you should suffer. It must not be. *I will not have it.*' (He underlined the words with a stroke of the pen that dug into the paper.) 'If you suffer, where shall I find strength to live? I have no happiness but in you. Oh, be happy! I will gladly take all the burden of sorrow upon myself! Think of me! Love me! I have such great need of being loved. From your love there comes to me a warmth which gives me life. If you knew how I shiver! There is winter and a biting wind in my heart. I embrace your soul.'

'My thought kisses yours,' replied Otto.

'I take your face in my hands,' was Jean-Christophe's answer, 'and what I have not done and will not do with my lips I do with all my being. I kiss you as I love you, Prudence!'

Otto pretended to doubt him.

'Do you love me as much as I love you?'

'O God,' wrote Jean-Christophe, 'not as much, but ten, a hundred, a thousand times more! What! Do you not feel it? What would you have me do to stir your heart?'

'What a lovely friendship is ours!' sighed Otto. 'Was there ever its like in history? It is sweet and fresh as a dream. If only it does not pass away! If you were to cease to love me!'

'How stupid you are, my beloved!' replied Jean-Christophe. 'Forgive me, but your weakling fear enrages me. How can you ask whether I shall cease to love you! For me to live is to love you. Death is powerless against my love. You yourself could do nothing if you wished to destroy it. Even if you betray me, even if you rent my heart, I should die with a blessing upon you for the love with which you fill me. Once for all, then, do not be uneasy, and vex me no more with these cowardly doubts!'

But a week later it was he who wrote:

'It is three days now since I heard a word fall from your lips. I tremble. Would you forget me? My blood freezes at the thought . . . Yes, doubtless . . . The other day only I saw your coldness towards me. You love me no longer! You are thinking of leaving me! . . . Listen! If you forget me, if you ever betray me, I will kill you like a dog!'

'You do me wrong, my dear heart,' groaned Otto. 'You draw tears from me. I do not deserve this. But you can do as you will. You have such rights over me that, if you were to break my soul, there would always be a spark left to live and love you always!'

'Heavenly powers!' cried Jean-Christophe. 'I have made my friend weep! . . . Heap insults on me, beat me, trample me underfoot! I am a wretch! I do not deserve your love!'

One day, as he was returning from a lesson, Jean-Christophe saw Otto in the street with a boy of his own age. They were laughing and talking familiarly. Jean-Christophe went pale, and followed them with his eyes until they had disappeared round the corner of the street. They had not seen him. He went home. It was as though a cloud had passed over the sun; all was dark.

When they met on the following Sunday, Jean-Christophe said nothing at first; but after they had been walking for half an hour he said in a choking voice:

'I saw you on Wednesday in the *Königgasse.*'

'Ah!' said Otto.

And he blushed.

Jean-Christophe went on:

'You were not alone.'

'No,' said Otto; 'I was with some one.'

Jean-Christophe swallowed down his spittle and asked in a voice which he strove to make careless:

'Who was it?'

'My cousin Franz.'

'Ah!' said Jean-Christophe; and after a moment: 'You have never said anything about him to me.'

'He lives at Rheinbach.'

'Do you see him often?'

'He comes here sometimes.'

'And you, do you go and stay with him?'

'Sometimes.'

'Ah!' said Jean-Christophe again.

Otto, who was not sorry to turn the conversation, pointed out a bird who was pecking at a tree. They talked of other things. Ten minutes later Jean-Christophe broke out again:

'Are you friends with him?'

'With whom?' asked Otto.

(He knew perfectly who was meant.)

'With your cousin.'

'Yes. Why?'

'Oh, nothing!'

Otto did not like his cousin much, for he used to bother him with bad jokes; but a strange malign instinct made him add a few moments later:

'He is very nice.'

'Who?' asked Jean-Christophe.

(He knew quite well who was meant.)

'Franz.'

Otto waited for Jean-Christophe to say something, but he seemed not to have heard. He was cutting a switch from a hazel-tree. Otto went on:

'He is amusing. He has all sorts of stories.'

Jean-Christophe whistled carelessly.

Otto renewed the attack:

'And he is so clever . . . and distinguished! . . .'

Jean-Christophe shrugged his shoulders as though to say:

'What interest can this person have for me?'

And as Otto, piqued, began to go on, he brutally cut him short, and pointed out a spot to which to run.

They did not touch on the subject again the whole afternoon, but they were frigid, affecting an exaggerated politeness which was unusual for them, especially for Jean-Christophe. The words stuck in his throat. At last he could contain himself no longer, and in the middle of the road he turned to Otto, who was lagging five yards behind. He took him fiercely by the hands, and let loose upon him:

'Listen, Otto! I will not let you be so friendly with Franz, because . . . because you are my friend, and I will not let you love any one more than me! I will not! You see, you are everything to me! You cannot . . . you must not! . . . If I lost you, there would be nothing left but death. I do not know what I should do. I should kill myself; I should kill you! No, forgive me! . . .'

Tears fell from his eyes.

Otto, moved and frightened by the sincerity of such grief, growling out threats, made haste to swear that he did not and never would love anybody so much as Jean-Christophe, that Franz was nothing to him, and that he would not see him again if Jean-Christophe wished it. Jean-Christophe drank in his words, and his heart took new life. He laughed and breathed heavily; he thanked Otto effusively. He was ashamed of having made such a scene, but he was relieved of a great weight. They stood face to face and looked at each other, not moving, and holding hands. They were very happy and very much embarrassed. They became silent; then they began to talk again, and found their old gaiety. They felt more at one than ever.

But it was not the last scene of the kind. Now that Otto felt his power over Jean-Christophe, he was tempted to abuse it. He knew his sore spot, and was irresistibly tempted to place his finger on it. Not that he had any pleasure in Jean-Christophe's anger; on the contrary, it made him unhappy—but he felt his power by making Jean-Christophe suffer. He was not bad; he had the soul of a girl.

In spite of his promises, he continued to appear arm in arm with Franz or some other comrade. They made a great noise between them, and he used to laugh in an affected way. When Jean-Christophe reproached him with it, he used to titter and pretend not to take him seriously, until, seeing Jean-Christophe's eyes change and his lips tremble with anger, he would change his tone, and fearfully promise not to do it again, and the next day he would do it. Jean-Christophe would write him furious letters, in which he called him:

'Scoundrel! Let me never hear of you again! I do not know you! May the devil take you and all dogs of your kidney!'

* * *

In spite of their disagreement it was impossible for them to do without each other. They had many faults; they were both egoists. But their egoism was naive; it knew not the self-seeking of maturity which makes it so repulsive; it knew not itself even; it was almost lovable, and did not prevent them from sincerely loving each other! Young Otto used to weep on his pillow as he told himself stories of romantic devotion of which he was the hero; he used to invent pathetic adventures, in which he was strong, valiant, intrepid, and protected Jean-Christophe, whom he used to imagine that he adored. Jean-Christophe never saw or heard anything beautiful or strange without thinking: 'If only Otto were here!' He carried the image of his friend into his whole life, and that image used to be transfigured, and become so gentle that, in spite of all that he knew about Otto, it used to intoxicate him. Certain words of Otto's which he used to remember long after they were spoken, and to embellish by the way, used to make him tremble with emotion. They imitated each other. Otto aped Jean-Christophe's manners, gestures, and writing. Jean-Christophe was sometimes irritated by the shadow which repeated every word that he said and dished up his thoughts as though they were its own. But he did not see that he himself was imitating Otto, and copying his way of dressing, walking, and pronouncing certain words. They were under a fascination. They were infused one in the other; their hearts were overflowing with tenderness. They trickled over with it on every side like a fountain. Each imagined that his friend was the cause of it. They did not know that it was the waking of their adolescence.

* * *

One misty morning in March, when little flakes of snow were flying, like feathers, in the gray air, they were in the studio. It was hardly daylight. Minna was arguing, as usual, about a false note that she had struck, and pretending that it 'was written so.' Although he knew perfectly well that she was lying, Jean-Christophe bent over the book to look at the passage in question closely. Her hand was on the rack, and she did not move it. His lips were near her hand. He tried to read and could not; he was looking at something else—a thing soft, transparent, like the petals of a flower. Suddenly he did not know what he was thinking of—he pressed his lips as hard as he could on the little hand.

They were both dumbfounded by it. He flung backwards; she withdrew her hand—both blushing. They said no word; they did not look at each other. After a moment of confused silence she began to play again; she was very uneasy: her bosom rose and fell as though she were under some weight: she struck wrong note after wrong note. He did not notice it: he was more uneasy than she. His temples throbbed; he heard nothing; he knew not what she was playing; and, to break the silence, he made a few random remarks in a choking voice. He thought that he was forever lost in Minna's opinion. He was confounded by what he had done, thought it stupid and rude. The lesson-hour over, he left Minna without looking at her, and even forgot to say good-bye. She did not mind. She had

no thought now of deeming Jean-Christophe ill-mannered; and if she made so many mistakes in playing, it was because all the time she was watching him out of the corner of her eye with astonishment and curiosity, and—for the first time—sympathy.

When she was left alone, instead of going to look for her mother as usual, she shut herself up in her room and examined this extraordinary event. She sat with her face in her hands in front of the mirror. Her eyes seemed to her soft and gleaming. She bit gently at her lip in the effort of thinking. And as she looked complacently at her pretty face, she visualized the scene, and blushed and smiled. At dinner she was animated and merry. She refused to go out at once, and stayed in the drawing-room for part of the afternoon; she had some work in her hand, and did not make ten stitches without a mistake, but what did that matter! In a corner of the room, with her back turned to her mother, she smiled; or, under a sudden impulse to let herself go, she pranced about the room and sang at the top of her voice. Frau von Kerich started and called her mad. Minna flung her arms round her neck, shaking with laughter, and hugged and kissed her.

In the evening, when she went to her room, it was a long time before she went to bed. She went on looking at herself in the mirror, trying to remember, and having thought all through the day of the same thing— thinking of nothing. She undressed slowly; she stopped every moment, sitting on the bed, trying to remember what Jean-Christophe was like. It was a Jean-Christophe of fantasy who appeared, and now he did not seem nearly so uncouth to her. She went to bed and put out the light. Ten minutes later the scene of the morning rushed back into her mind, and she burst out laughing. Her mother got up softly and opened the door, thinking that, against orders, she was reading in bed. She found Minna lying quietly in her bed, with her eyes wide open in the dim candlelight.

'What is it?' she asked. 'What is amusing you?'

'Nothing,' said Minna gravely. 'I was thinking.'

'You are very lucky to find your own company so amusing. But go to sleep.'

'Yes, mama,' replied Minna meekly. Inside herself she was grumbling: 'Go away! Do go away!' until the door was closed, and she could go on enjoying her dreams. She fell into a sweet drowsiness. When she was nearly asleep, she leaped for joy:

'He loves me . . . What happiness! How good of him to love me! . . . How I love him!'

She kissed her pillow and went fast asleep.

When next they were together Jean-Christophe was surprised at Minna's amiability. She gave him 'Good-day,' and asked him how he was in a very soft voice; she sat at the piano, looking wise and modest; she was an angel of docility. There were none of her naughty schoolgirl's tricks, but she listened religiously to Jean-Christophe's remarks, acknowledged that they were right, gave little timid cries herself when she made a mistake and set herself to be more accurate. Jean-Christophe could not understand it. In a very short time she made astounding progress. Not only did she play better, but with musical feeling. Little as he was given to flattery, he had to pay her a compliment. She blushed with pleasure,

and thanked him for it with a look tearful with gratitude. She took pains with her toilet for him; she wore ribbons of an exquisite shade; she gave Jean-Christophe little smiles and soft glances, which he disliked, for they irritated him, and moved him to the depths of his soul. And now it was she who made conversation, but there was nothing childish in what she said; she talked gravely, and quoted the poets in a pedantic and pretentious way. He hardly ever replied; he was ill at ease. This new Minna that he did not know astonished and disquieted him.

Always she watched him. She was waiting . . . For what? . . . Did she know herself? . . . She was waiting for him to do it again. He took good care not to, for he was convinced that he had behaved like a clod; he seemed never to give a thought to it. She grew restless, and one day when he was sitting quietly at a respectful distance from her dangerous little paws, she was seized with impatience; with a movement so quick that she had no time to think of it, she herself thrust her little hand against his lips. He was staggered by it, then furious and ashamed. But none the less he kissed it very passionately. Her naïve effrontery enraged him; he was on the point of leaving her there and then.

But he could not. He was entrapped. Whirling thoughts rushed in his mind; he could make nothing of them. Like mists ascending from a valley they rose from the depths of his heart. He wandered hither and thither at random through his mist of love, and whatever he did, he did but turn round and round an obscure fixed idea, a Desire unknown, terrible and fascinating as a flame to an insect. It was the sudden eruption of the blind forces of Nature.

They passed through a period of waiting. They watched each other, desired each other, were fearful of each other. They were uneasy. But they did not for that desist from their little hostilities and sulkinesses; only there were no more familiarities between them; they were silent. Each was busy constructing their love in silence.

Love has curious retroactive effects. As soon as Jean-Christophe discovered that he loved Minna, he discovered at the same time that he had always loved her. For three months they had been seeing each other almost every day without ever suspecting the existence of their love. But from the day when he did actually love her, he was absolutely convinced that he had loved her from all eternity.

It was a good thing for him to have discovered at last *whom* he loved. He had loved for so long without knowing whom! It was a sort of relief to him, like a sick man, who, suffering from a general illness, vague and enervating, sees it become definite in sharp pain in some portion of his body. Nothing is more wearing than love without a definite object; it eats away and saps the strength like a fever. A known passion leads the mind to excess; that is exhausting, but at least one knows why. It is an excess; it is not a wasting away. Anything rather than emptiness.

Although Minna had given Jean-Christophe good reason to believe that she was not indifferent to him, he did not fail to torture himself with the idea that she despised him. They had never had any very clear idea of each other, but this idea had never been more confused and false than it was now; it consisted of a series of strange fantasies which could never be made to agree, for they passed from one extreme to the other, endowing each other in turn with faults and charms which they did not possess—charms when they were parted, faults when they were together. In either case they were wide of the mark.

They did not know themselves what they desired. For Jean-Christophe his love took shape as that thirst for tenderness, imperious, absolute, demanding reciprocation, which had burned in him since childhood, which he demanded from others, and wished to impose on them by will or force. Sometimes this despotic desire of full sacrifice of himself and others —especially others, perhaps—was mingled with gusts of a brutal and obscure desire, which set him whirling, and he did not understand it. Minna, curious above all things, and delighted to have a romance, tried to extract as much pleasure as possible from it for her vanity and sentimentality; she tricked herself wholeheartedly as to what she was feeling. A great part of their love was purely literary. They fed on the books they had read, and were forever ascribing to themselves feelings which they did not possess.

But the moment was to come when all these little lies and small egoisms were to vanish away before the divine light of love. A day, an hour, a few seconds of eternity . . . And it was so unexpected! . . .

One evening they were alone talking. The room was growing dark. Their conversation took a serious turn. They talked of the infinite, of Life, and Death. It made a larger frame for their passion. Minna complained of her loneliness, which led naturally to Jean-Christophe's answer that she was not so lonely as she thought.

'No,' she said, shaking her head. 'That is only words. Every one lives for himself; no one is interested in you; nobody loves you.'

Silence.

'And I?' said Jean-Christophe suddenly, pale with emotion.

Impulsive Minna jumped to her feet, and took his hands.

The door opened. They flung apart. Frau von Kerich entered. Jean-Christophe buried himself in a book, which he held upside down. Minna bent over her work, and pricked her finger with her needle.

They were not alone together for the rest of the evening, and they were afraid of being left. When Frau von Kerich got up to look for something in the next room, Minna, not usually obliging, ran to fetch it for her, and Jean-Christophe took advantage of her absence to take his leave without saying good-night to her.

Next day they met again, impatient to resume their interrupted conversation. They did not succeed. Yet circumstances were favorable to them. They went a walk with Frau von Kerich, and had plenty of opportunity for talking as much as they liked. But Jean-Christophe could not speak, and he was so unhappy that he stayed as far away as possible from Minna. And she pretended not to notice his discourtesy; but she was piqued by it, and showed it. When Jean-Christophe did at last contrive to utter a few words, she listened icily; he had hardly the courage to finish his sentence. They were coming to the end of the walk. Time was flying. And he was wretched at not having been able to make use of it.

A week passed. They thought they had mistaken their feeling for each other. They were not sure but that they had dreamed the scene of that evening. Minna was resentful against Jean-Christophe. Jean-Christophe was afraid of meeting her alone. They were colder to each other than ever.

A day came when it had rained all morning and part of the afternoon. They had stayed in the house without speaking, reading, yawning, looking out of the window; they were bored and cross. About four o'clock the sky cleared. They ran into the garden. They leaned their elbows on the terrace wall, and looked down at the lawns sloping to the river. The earth was streaming; a soft mist was ascending to the sun; little raindrops glittered on the grass; the smell of the damp earth and the perfume of the flowers intermingled; around them buzzed a golden swarm of bees. They were side by side, not looking at each other; they could not bring themselves to break the silence. A bee came up and clung awkwardly to a clump of wistaria heavy with rain, and sent a shower of water down on them. They both laughed, and at once they felt that they were no longer cross at each other, and were friends again. But still they did not look at each other. Suddenly, without turning her head, she took his hand, and said:

'Come!'

She led him quickly to the little labyrinth with its box-bordered paths, which was in the middle of the grove. They climbed up the slope, slipping on the soaking ground, and the wet trees shook out their branches over them. Near the top she stopped to breathe.

'Wait . . . wait . . .' she said in a low voice, trying to take breath.

He looked at her. She was looking away; she was smiling, breathing hard, with her lips parted; her hand was trembling in Jean-Christophe's. They felt the blood throbbing in their linked hands and their trembling fingers. Around them all was silent. The pale shoots of the trees were quivering in the sun; a gentle rain dropped from the leaves with silvery sounds, and in the sky were the shrill cries of swallows.

She turned her head towards him; it was a lightning flash. She flung her arms about his neck; he flung himself into her arms.

'Minna! Minna! My darling! . . .'

'I love you, Jean-Christophe! I love you!'

They sat on a wet wooden seat. They were filled with love, sweet, profound, absurd. Everything else had vanished. No more egoism, no more vanity, no more reservation. Love, love—that is what their laughing, tearful eyes were saying. The cold coquette of a girl, the proud boy, were devoured with the need of self-sacrifice, of giving, of suffering, of dying for each other. They did not know each other; they were not the same; everything was changed; their hearts, their faces, their eyes, gave out a radiance of the most touching kindness and tenderness. Moments of purity, of self-denial, of absolute giving of themselves, which through life will never return!

After a desperate murmuring of words and passionate promises to belong to each other forever, after kisses and incoherent words of delight, they saw that it was late, and they ran back hand in hand, almost falling in the narrow paths, bumping into trees, feeling nothing, blind and drunk with the joy of it.

When he left her he did not go home; he could not have gone to sleep. He left the town, and walked over the fields; he walked blindly through the night. The air was fresh, the country dark and deserted. A screech-owl hooted shrilly. Jean-Christophe went on like a sleep-walker. The little lights of the town quivered on the plain, and the stars in the dark sky. He sat on a wall by the road and suddenly burst into tears. He did not know why. He was too happy, and the excess of his joy was compounded of sadness and delight; there was in it thankfulness for his happiness, pity for those who were not happy, a melancholy and sweet feeling of the frailty of things, the mad joy of living. He wept for delight, and slept in the midst of his tears. When he awoke dawn was peeping. White mists floated over the river, and veiled the town, where Minna, worn out, was sleeping, while in her heart was the light of her smile of happiness.

They contrived to meet again in the garden next morning and told their love once more, but now the divine unconsciousness of it all was gone. She was a little playing the part of the girl in love, and he, though more sincere, was also playing a part. They talked of what their life should be. He regretted his poverty and humble estate. She affected to be generous, and enjoyed her generosity. She said that she cared nothing for money. That was true, for she knew nothing about it, having never known the lack of it. He promised that he would become a great artist; that she thought fine and amusing, like a novel. She thought it her duty to behave really like a woman in love. She read poetry; she was sentimental. He was touched by the infection. He took pains with his dress; he was absurd; he set a guard upon his speech;

he was pretentious. Frau von Kerich watched him and laughed, and asked herself what could have made him so stupid.

But they had moments of marvelous poetry, and these would suddenly burst upon them out of dull days, like sunshine through a mist. A look, a gesture, a meaningless word, and they were bathed in happiness; they had their good-byes in the evening on the dimly-lighted stairs, and their eyes would seek each other, divine each other through the half darkness, and the thrill of their hands as they touched, the trembling in their voices, all those little nothings that fed their memory at night, as they slept so lightly that the chiming of each hour would awake them, and their hearts would sing 'I am loved,' like the murmuring of a stream.

They discovered the charm of things. Spring smiled with a marvelous sweetness. The heavens were brilliant, the air was soft, as they had never been before. All the town—the red roofs, the old walls, the cobbled streets—showed with a kindly charm that moved Jean-Christophe. At night, when everybody was asleep, Minna would get up from her bed, and stand by the window, drowsy and feverish. And in the afternoon, when he was not there, she would sit in a swing, and dream, with a book on her knees, her eyes half closed, sleepy and lazily happy, mind and body hovering in the spring air. She would spend hours at the piano, with a patience exasperating to others, going over and over again scales and passages which made her turn pale and cold with emotion. She would weep when she heard Schumann's music. She felt full of pity and kindness for all creatures, and so did he. They would give money stealthily to poor people whom they met in the street, and would then exchange glances of compassion; they were happy in their kindness.

To tell the truth, they were kind only by fits and starts. Minna suddenly discovered how sad was the humble life of devotion of old Frida, who had been a servant in the house since her mother's childhood, and at once she ran and hugged her, to the great astonishment of the good old creature, who was busy mending the linen in the kitchen. But that did not keep her from speaking harshly to her a few hours later, when Frida did not come at once on the sound of the bell. And Jean-Christophe, who was consumed with love for all humanity, and would turn aside so as not to crush an insect, was entirely indifferent to his own family. By a strange reaction he was colder and more curt with them the more affectionate he was to all other creatures; he hardly gave thought to them; he spoke abruptly to them, and found no interest in seeing them. Both in Jean-Christophe and Minna their kindness was only a surfeit of tenderness which overflowed at intervals to the benefit of the first comer. Except for these overflowings they were more egoistic than ever, for their minds were filled only with one thought, and everything was brought back to that.

How much of Jean-Christophe's life was filled with the girl's face! What emotion was in him when he saw her white frock in the distance, when he was looking for her in the garden; when at the theater, sitting a few yards away from their empty places, he heard the door of their box open, and the mocking voice that he knew so well; when in some outside conversation the dear name of Kerich cropped up! He would go pale and blush; for a moment or two he would see and hear nothing. And then there would be a rush of blood over all his body, the assault of unknown forces.

The little German girl, naïve and sensual, had odd little tricks. She would place her ring on a little pile of flour, and he would have to get it again and again with his teeth without whitening his nose. Or she would pass a thread through a biscuit, and put one end of it in her mouth and one in his and then they had to nibble the thread to see who could get to the biscuit first. Their faces would come together; they would feel each other's breathing; their lips would touch, and they would laugh forcedly, while their hands would turn to ice. Jean-Christophe would feel a desire to bite, to hurt; she would fling back, and she would go on laughing forcedly. They would turn away, pretend indifference, and steal glances at each other.

These disturbing games had a disquieting attraction for them; they wanted to play them, and yet avoided them. Jean-Christophe was fearful of them, and preferred even the constraint of the meetings when Frau von Kerich or some one else was present. No outside presence could break in upon the converse of their loving hearts; constraint only made their love sweeter and more intense. Every-

thing gained infinitely in value; a word, a movement of the lips, a glance were enough to make the rich new treasure of their inner life shine through the dull veil of ordinary existence. They alone could see it, or so they thought, and smiled, happy in their little mysteries. Their words were no more than those of a drawing-room conversation about trivial matters; to them they were an unending song of love. They read the most fleeting changes in their faces and voices as in an open book; they could have read as well with their eyes closed, for they had only to listen to their hearts to hear in them the echo of the heart of the beloved. They were full of confidence in life, in happiness, in themselves. Their hopes were boundless. They loved, they were loved, happy, without a shadow, without a doubt, without a fear of the future. Wonderful serenity of those days of spring! Not a cloud in the sky. A faith so fresh that it seems that nothing can ever tarnish it. A joy so abounding that nothing can ever exhaust it. Are they living? Are they dreaming? Doubtless they are dreaming. There is nothing in common between life and their dream— nothing, except in that moment of magic: they are but a dream themselves; their being has melted away at the touch of love.

HELEN, I LOVE YOU

James T. Farrell

[A boy just emerging from the gang stage to awareness of girls and the beginnings of romantic interest in one of them is vividly presented in *Helen, I Love You*. Dan is a typical extrovert, but under pressure of his adolescent consciousness of sex he indulges in conquering-hero fantasies and tender moods of reminiscence. These, however, never dominate him but are subordinated to boyish bluster and release of emotional energy in physical activity.]

'You got a goofy look,' Dick Buckford said.

'Yeh,' Dan said.

The two boys stood in front of one of the small gray-stone houses in the 5700 block on Indiana Avenue, glaring at each other.

Dan didn't know what to say. He glanced aside at the hopeless, rainy autumn day. His eyes roved over the damp street, the withered grass and mud by the sidewalk across the street, the three-story apartment buildings, and at the sky which dumped down top-heavily behind the buildings.

'Yeah, you're goofy! You're goofy!' Dick sneered.

'Then so are you,' Dan countered.

'Am I?' Dick challenged.

'Yes!' Dan answered with determination.

'Am I goofy?'

'If you say I am, then you're a goof, too!'

Dan hoped nothing would happen. He knew how, if he lost a fight when he was still new in the neighborhood, everybody would start taking picks on him, bullying him, making a dope out of him, and kidding him all the time because he had been licked. He hoped that he wouldn't be forced into a fight with Dick, who was about ten pounds heavier than he was. But he pretended that he was fighting Dick, beating hell out of him. He pretended that he slugged Dick in the face, and saw the blood spurt from his big nose. He slugged Dick, until Dick was bloody and winded and said quits, and a crowd of guys and girls watching the fight cheered and said that Dan was certainly a fine fighter, and then he pretended that Helen Scanlan came up to him and told him she was so glad.

But he'd already had his chance with her. She had seemed to like him, but he'd been too damn bashful. Once, he could have held her hand and kissed her, and they could have gone over to the park, and kissed some more, if he only hadn't been so bashful. She had even said that she liked him.

They were standing right in front of the parlor window of the Scanlan house. He thought again of himself slamming Dick around, with Helen in the window watching him. Red-haired Helen Scanlan, he loved her. He said to himself:

Helen, I love you!

'Why don't you pull in your ears? Huh?' said Dick.

'Aw, freeze your teeth and give

your tongue a sleigh-ride,' Dan said.

He wished Dick would go away, because he wanted to walk around alone, and maybe go over to the park, where it would be all quiet except for the wind, and where the leaves would be wet and yellow, and it would be easy to think of Helen. He could walk around, and think and be a little happy-sad, and think about Helen. And here was Dick before him, and Dick was supposed to be one of the best scrappers in the neighborhood, and he seemed to want to pick a fight, and right here, too, outside of Helen's window. And maybe Dick would win, with Helen there to watch it all.

Dan wanted Dick to go away. He told himself that he loved Helen. He told himself that he was awfully in love with curly, red-haired Helen. He remembered last summer, when he had peddled bills for half a dollar, putting them in mail boxes all over the neighborhood. The day after, they had gone riding on the tail-gate of hump-backed George's grocery wagon, and it had been fun, himself and Helen sitting there on the back of the wagon, holding hands as they bounced through the alleys, and while they waited for George to deliver his orders. And he had spent all his money on her. He told himself that he loved her.

He remembered how, after riding on the wagon, he had gone home, and they had bawled him out because he had worn the soles on his shoes out delivering the bills, and then had gone and spent the money so foolishly, with nothing to show for it. There had been a big scrap, and he had answered them back, and got so sore that he had bawled like a cry-baby. Afterwards, he'd sat in the parlor, crying and cursing, because he was sore. He'd had such a swell time that afternoon, too. And the family just hadn't understood it at all. And then Helen had come around, because all the kids in the neighborhood used to come around to his front steps at night to play and talk. Somebody had called to tell him she was there. He hadn't known what he was doing, and he'd answered that he didn't care if she was there or not.

After that Helen hadn't paid any attention to him.

He told himself:

Helen, I love you!

II

'If I was as goofy as you, I'd do something about it,' Dick said.

'Yeh. Well, I ain't got nothing on you.'

'No? Well, look at it, your stockings are falling down. You can't even keep your stockings up,' said Dick.

'Well, you're sniffin' and don't even know enough to blow your nose.'

'Don't talk to me like that!' Dick said.

'Well, don't talk to me like that, either!'

'I ain't afraid of you!' Dick said.

'And I ain't afraid of you, either!' said Dan.

'Wanna fight?' asked Dick.

'If you do, I do!' said Dan.

'Well, start something,' said Dick.

'You start something,' said Dan.

'But maybe you won't, because you're yellow,' said Dick.

'No, I ain't, neither. I ain't afraid of you.'

Dick smiled sarcastically at Dan.

'I don't know whether to kiss you or kill you,' he said with exaggerated sweetness.

'Yeh, you heard Red Kelly make that crack, and you're just copying it from him. You ain't funny,' Dan said.

'That's all you know about it! Well, I made it up and Red heard me say it. That's where he got it. How you like that?'

'Tie your bull in somebody else's alley,' Dan said.

Dick tried to out-stare Dan. Dan frowned back at him.

'And today in school, when Sister Cyrilla called on you, you didn't even know enough how to divide fractions. You're goofy,' Dick said.

'Well, if I'm goofy, I don't know what you ain't,' Dan said.

Dan again pretended that they were fighting, and that he was kicking the hell out of Dick with Helen watching. And he remembered how last summer when he had gotten those hats advertising Cracker Jack, he had given one to her. He had felt good that day, because she had worn the hat he gave her. And every night they had all played tin-tin, or run-sheep-run, or chase-one-chase-all, or eeny-meeny-miny-mo. He had just moved around then, and he had thought that it was such a good neighborhood, and now, if Dick went picking a fight with him and beat him, well, he just wouldn't be able to show his face any more and would just about have to sneak down alleys and everything.

But if he beat Dick up and Helen saw him, he would be her hero, and he would be one of the leaders of their gang, and then maybe she would like him again, and twice as much, and everything would be all so swell, just like it was at the end of the stories he sometimes read in the *Saturday Evening Post*.

Last summer, too, he had read *Penrod*, and he had thought of Helen because she was like Marjorie Jones in the book, only more so, and prettier, and nicer, and she had nicer hair, because the book said Marjorie Jones's hair was black, and Helen's was red, and red hair was nicer than black hair.

'One thing I wouldn't be called is yellow,' Dick sneered.

'I ain't yellow,' Dan said.

'I wouldn't be yellow,' Dick said.

'And I wouldn't be a sniffer, and not have enough sense to blow my nose,' said Dan.

'Who's a sniffer?' demanded Dick.

'Well, why don't you blow your nose?'

'Why doncha not be so goofy?' demanded Dick.

'I ain't no goofier than you.'

'If I was as goofy as you, I'd quit living,' Dick said.

'Yeh, and if I was like you, I'd drown myself.'

'You better do it then, because you're goofier than anybody I know,' Dick said.

'Yeh?'

'Yeh!'

'Yeh!'

'And let me tell you, I ain't afraid of nobody like you,' Dick said.

'I ain't, neither. Just start something, and see!'

'I would, only I don't wanna get my hands dirty, picking on a goof. If you wasn't afraid of me, you wouldn't stand there, letting me say you're goofy.'

'Well, I'm here saying you're just as goofy.'

'I couldn't be like you.'

'And I couldn't be as dumb as you,' Dan said.

'You're so goofy, I wouldn't be seen with you.'

'Don't, then!' said Dan.

'I ain't! I was here first!'

'I live on this street.'

'I lived in this neighborhood longer than you,' said Dick.

'I live on this street, and you can beat it if you don't like it.'

'You're so goofy you belong in the Kankakee nut house. Your whole family's goofy. My old man says I shouldn't have nothing to do with you because of all the goofiness in your family.'

'Well, my old man and my uncle don't think nothing of your old man,' Dan said.

'Well, don't let my old man hear them sayin' it, because if he does, he's liable to bat their snoots off,' said Dick.

'Let him try! My old man ain't afraid of nothing!'

'Yeh? Don't never think so. My old man could take your old man on blindfolded.'

'Yeh? My old man could trim your old man with his little finger, and it's cut off,' said Dan.

'Say, if my old man's hands were tied behind his back, and he said "Boo," your old man would take to his heels lickety-split down the streets, afraid.'

'Let him start something and see, then!'

'If he ever does, I'd feel sorry for your old man,' said Dick.

'You don't need to be.'

'My old man's strong, and he says I take after him, and when I grow up, I'll be like him, a lineman climbing telephone poles for the telephone company,' said Dick.

'Yeh?' said Dan.

'Yeh!' said Dick.

'Yeh?' said Dan.

'Baloney,' said Dick.

'Bouswah,' said Dan.

'B.S.,' said Dick.

They sneered toughly at one another.

'That for you!' Dick said, snapping his fingers in Dan's face.

'That for you!' Dan said, screwing up his lips and twitching his nose.

'If this is the street you live on, I won't hang around it no more, because it smells just as bad as you do,' said Dick.

'That's because you're on it.'

'I'm going, because I don't want nobody to know that I'm even acquainted with anyone as goofy as you.'

'Good riddance to bad rubbage,' said Dan.

'If you weren't such a clown, I'd break you with my little finger!' said Dick.

'And I'd blow you over with my breath!' said Dan.

III

Dan watched Dick walk away, without looking back. He sat on the iron fence around the grass plot, feeling good because he had proven to himself that he wasn't afraid of Dick. He said to himself:

Helen, I love you!

He sat.

He sat through slow, oblivious minutes. He arose and decided to take a walk. Wishing that he could see Helen, he strolled down to Fifty-eighth Street, and bought five cents' worth of candy. He returned and sat on the iron fence in front of her house, and for about twenty-five minutes he nibbled at his candy, hoping that she would come along, wondering where she was, wishing he could give her some of his candy. He told himself:

Helen, I love you!

He thought of how he had held her hand that day on the grocery wagon. He imagined her watching him while he cleaned the stuffings out of Dick Buckford.

The day was sad. He wished that it

had some sun. The day wouldn't be sad, though, if she came along and talked to him.

He walked over to Washington Park. It was lonely, and he didn't see anybody in the park. The wind kept beating against the trees and bushes, and sometimes, when he listened closely, it seemed to him like an unhappy person, crying. He walked on and on, wetting his feet, but he didn't care. He stopped to stand by the lagoon. There were small waves on it, and it looked dark, and black, and mean. He said to himself:

Helen, I love you!

He continued gazing at the lagoon. Then, he strolled on.

Yes, if Dick had started something, he would have cleaned the guts out of him. Dick would have rushed him, and he would have biffed Dick, giving him a pretty shiner. Dick would have rushed him again, and he would have biffed Dick a second time, and Dick would have had a bloody nose. He would have stood back and led with a left to the solar plexus, and Dick would have doubled up, and he would have smashed Dick with a right, and Dick would have fallen down with another black eye. Dick would have yelled quits, and Helen, who would have been watching it all, would have yelled for him, and maybe she would have said:

Dan, I want to be your girl!

He walked. He looked all around him at the park stretching away in wet, darkened, dying grass, with shadows falling down over it. The light was going out of the sky, and he said good-bye to Mr. Day. He felt all alone, and thought how nice it would be if he only had someone to talk to. Maybe Helen. Maybe himself and Helen walking in the wet grass. Maybe some man would try to kidnap her. The man would run away with her under his arm crying for help. And he would pick up a rock and fling at the guy, and it would smack the guy in the skull, and he would drop down unconscious, but Helen wouldn't be hurt. And he would rush up, hit the guy with another rock so that he would be out colder than if he had been hit by Ruby Bob Fitzsimmons in his prime. Police would come, and he would have his picture in the papers, and he would be a real hero, and Helen would say to him:

Dan, I love you, and I'll always love you.

He walked. It was almost dark, and the wind sounds seemed worse than the voices of ghosts. He wished he wasn't so all alone. He had strange feelings. He wondered what he ought to do, and it seemed like there were people behind every tree. The park was too lonely to be in, and he decided that he'd better go home. And it was getting to be supper time.

The wind was awfully sad. There wasn't any moon or stars in the sky yet.

He didn't know what he was afraid of, but he was awfully afraid.

And it would have been so nice, and so different, if he was only with Helen. She would be afraid, too, and he would be protecting her.

He started back toward home, thinking what he would have done to Dick if Dick had really started a fight. Yes, sir, he would have made Dick sorry.

Helen, I love you!

❄

THE SEVEN THAT WERE HANGED

Leonid Andreyev

[In Andreyev's *The Seven That Were Hanged* the adult emotion of fear may more readily be isolated from its total emotional context than it can be in more normal situations. This is the fear of one for whom all efforts of self-preservation can be of no avail. It is the fear of a man who is doomed to death, who no longer has any power of choice, who, for a moment 'the incarnation of will, of life, and of force,' is now reduced to a 'lamentable specimen of impotence.']

The Horrible Solitude

Under the same roof and to the same melodious chant of the indifferent hours, separated from Sergey and from Musya by a few empty cells, but as isolated as if he alone had existed in the whole universe, the unhappy Vasily Kashirin was finishing his life in anguish and terror.

Covered with sweat, his shirt adhering to his body, his formerly curly hair now falling in straight locks, he went back and forth in his cell with the jerky and lamentable gait of one suffering atrociously with the toothache. He sat down for a moment, and then began to run again; then he rested his forehead against the wall, stopped, and looked about as if in search of a remedy. He had so changed that one might think that he possessed two different faces, one of which, the younger, had gone nobody knows where, to give place to the second, a terrible face, that seemed to have come from darkness.

Fear had shown itself suddenly to him, and had seized upon his person as an exclusive and sovereign mistress. On the fatal morning, when he was marching to certain death, he had played with it; but that evening, confined in his cell, he had been carried away and lashed by a wave of mad terror. As long as he had gone freely forward to meet danger and death, as long as he had held his fate in his own hands, however terrible it might be, he had appeared tranquil and even joyous, the small amount of shameful and decrepit fear that he had felt having disappeared in a consciousness of infinite liberty, in the firm and audacious affirmation of his intrepid will, leaving no trace behind. With an infernal machine strapped around his waist, he had transformed himself into an instrument of death, he had borrowed from the dynamite its cruel reason and its flashing and homicidal power. In the street, among the busy people preoccupied with their affairs and quickly dodging the tramcars and the cabs, it seemed to him as if he came from another and an unknown world where there was no such thing as death or fear.

Suddenly a brutal, bewildering change had taken place. Vasily no longer went where he wanted to go,

From *The Seven That Were Hanged* by Leonid Andreyev. By permission of Random House, Inc.

but was led where others wanted him to go. He no longer chose his place; they placed him in a stone cage and locked him in, as if he were a thing. He could no longer choose between life and death; they led him to death, certainly and inevitably. He who had been for a moment the incarnation of will, of life, and of force, had become a lamentable specimen of impotence; he was nothing but an animal destined for the slaughter. Whatever he might say, they would not listen; if he started to cry out, they would stuff a rag in his mouth; and, if he even tried to walk, they would take him away and hang him. If he resisted, if he struggled, if he lay down on the ground, they would be stronger than he; they would pick him up, they would tie him, and thus they would carry him to the gallows. And his imagination gave to the men charged with this execution, men like himself, the new, extraordinary, and terrifying aspect of unthinking automata, whom nothing in the world could stop, and who seized a man, overpowered him, hanged him, pulled him by the feet, cut the rope, put the body in a coffin, carried it away, and buried it.

From the first day of his imprisonment, people and life had transformed themselves for him into an unspeakably frightful world filled with mechanical dolls. Almost mad with fear, he tried to fancy to himself that these people had tongues and spoke, but he did not succeed. Their mouths opened, something like a sound came from them; then they separated with movements of their legs, and all was over. He was in the situation of a man who, left alone in a house at night, should see all things become animate, move, and assume over him an unlimited power; sud-

denly the wardrobe, the chair, the sofa, the writing-table would sit in judgment upon him. He would cry out, call for help, beg, and rove from room to room; and the things would speak to each other in their own tongue; and then the wardrobe, the chair, the sofa, and the writing-table would start to hang him, the other things looking on.

In the eyes of Vasily Kashirin, sentenced to be hanged, everything took on a puerile aspect; the cell, the grated door, the striking apparatus of the clock, the fortress with its carefully modelled ceilings, and, above, the mechanical doll equipped with a musket, who walked up and down in the corridor, and the other dolls who frightened him by looking through the grating and handing him his food without a word.

A man had disappeared from the world.

In court the presence of the comrades had brought Kashirin back to himself. Again for a moment he saw people; they were there, judging him, speaking the language of men, listening, and seeming to understand. But, when he saw his mother, he felt clearly, with the terror of a man who is going mad and he knows it, that this old woman in a black neckerchief was a simple mechanical doll. He was astonished at not having suspected it before, and at having awaited this visit as something infinitely sorrowful in its distressing gentleness. While forcing himself to speak, he thought with a shudder: 'My God! But it is a doll! A doll-mother! And yonder is a doll-soldier; at home there is a doll-father, and this is the doll Vasily Kashirin.'

When the mother began to weep, Vasily again saw something human in her, but this disappeared with the first words that she uttered. With curiosity and terror he watched the tears flow from the doll's eyes.

When his fear became intolerable, Vasily Kashirin tried to pray. There remained with him only a bitter, detestable, and enervating rancor against all the religious principles upon which his youth had been nourished, in the house of his father, a large merchant. He had no faith. But one day, in his childhood, he had heard some words that had made an impression upon him and that remained surrounded forever with a gentle poesy: These words were: 'Joy of all the afflicted!'

Sometimes, in painful moments, he whispered, without praying, without even accounting to himself for what he was doing: 'Joy of all the afflicted!' And then he suddenly felt relieved; he had a desire to approach someone who was dear to him and complain gently:

'Our life! . . . but is it really a life? Say, my dear, is it really a life?'

And then suddenly he felt himself ridiculous; he would have liked to bare his breast and ask someone to beat it.

He had spoken to no one, not even to his best comrades, of his 'Joy of all the afflicted!' He seemed to know nothing of it himself, so deeply hidden was it in his soul. And he evoked it rarely, with precaution.

Now that the fear of the unfathomable mystery which was rising before him completely covered him, as the water covers the plants on the bank when the tide is rising, he had a desire to pray. He wanted to fall upon his knees, but was seized with shame before the sentinel; so, with hands clasped upon his breast, he murmured in a low voice:

'Joy of all the afflicted!'

And he repeated with anxiety, in a tone of supplication:

'Joy of all the afflicted, descend into me, sustain me!'

Something moved softly. It seemed to him that a sorrowful and gentle force hovered in the distance and then vanished, without illuminating the shades of the agony. In the steeple the hour struck. The soldier yawned long and repeatedly.

'Joy of all the afflicted! You are silent! And you will say nothing to Vasily Kashirin!'

He wore an imploring smile, and waited. But in his soul there was the same void as around him. Useless and tormenting thoughts came to him; again he saw the lighted candles, the priest in his robe, the holy image painted on the wall, his father bending and straightening up again, praying and kneeling, casting furtive glances at Vasily to see if he too was praying or was simply amusing himself. And Kashirin was in still deeper anguish than before.

Everything disappeared.

His consciousness went out like the dying embers that one scatters on the hearth; it froze, like the body of a man just dead in which the heart is still warm while the hands and feet are already cold.

Vasily had a moment of wild terror when they came into his cell to get him. He did not even suspect that the hour of the execution had arrived; he simply saw the people and took fright, almost like a child.

'I will not do it again! I will not do it again!' he whispered, without being heard; and his lips became icy as he recoiled slowly toward the rear of his cell, just as in childhood he had tried to escape the punishments of his father.

'You will have to go . . .'

They talked, they walked around him, they gave him he knew not what. He closed his eyes, staggered, and began to prepare himself painfully. Undoubtedly he had recovered consciousness; he suddenly asked a cigarette of one of the officials, who amiably extended his cigarette-case.

❆

THE LOCOMOTIVE-GOD

WILLIAM ELLERY LEONARD

[That forgotten fears may later impinge upon the consciousness and bring about seemingly unreasonable phobias and obsessions is attested to in William Ellery Leonard's account of an experience which took place in his second year. His sense of security and eagerness for adventure, his superiority to little Mary, whom he adores, become overshadowed by terror, hysteria, and shame as he is catapulted into a strange world of fascination and fear. The locomotive becomes a God who will devour him alive. Feelings of guilt add to his terror as he conceives of the monster God roaring from heaven to slay him for having disobeyed his mother. His reaction becomes one of physical pain, but the pain does not shut out his fear of ridicule, his fear that Mary will think him a fool. Although this incident remained buried in his unconscious for years, it became the dominant motivating force in his life; it is reflected no less in his poetic creation than in his chronic neurosis which confines him to a restricted area in Madison, Wisconsin.]

I am standing agape on the platform. But I cannot communicate either the world about me or the world within, exactly as it is to me; for my consciousness is still so largely nameless objects and nameless feelings and thoughts. I think largely in terms of things, relations, emotions. My speech must be a blend of childhood's vocabulary and manhood's craftsmanship. But the data, external and internal, are scientifically exact. I am some two hundred and fifty feet from my young mother and her friends. I have been pulling on her skirts, bothering her. She has yielded to my nagging and let me walk up to the further end; for she wants to talk undisturbed with the family doctor about the bright ways and promising future of her little boy. Nurse Tina, the pretty negress in a plaid bodice, and a stocky man, have now let go my hands. I have promised both her and my mother not to go near the tracks. This is my first journey so far from home, since a baby in arms . . . a mile from home into a world more venturous and engrossing than I can ever know twice. How big and brave I am! I had been looking round a little nervously toward my mother three or four times as our steps had increased the distance from her; but my curiosity and courage have conquered. I look back past the length

From *The Locomotive-God* by William Ellery Leonard. Reprinted by permission of D. Appleton-Century Co.

of the long red station to the diminished figure of my mother with her red parasol. There too is little Mary. She is nearly four, I say to myself . . . she is so much bigger, yet not nearly as brave as I . . . she was afraid to come 'way off here with Tina and me. And, besides, her mother was afraid to let her. How wonderful I must seem to her 'way off here! And I hitch up the little black leather belt of my clean white dress (there are blue anchors on the sleeves), and stalk about in the sun for her distant, admiring eyes. And Mary loves me. How proud I am that Mary loves me, more even than that mama does! Though I do not know it, I am already lover and hero . . . the aboriginal masculine of the race.

But I almost forget Mary. For forward and all around me I see so much that astounds: 'way down below right under my legs, beyond a protecting wooden rail, painted blue, lies the gulf of a cross-street that is spanned by the iron railroad bridge. A man drives along in a red-wheeled buggy and disappears marvelously under the bridge, to my right. Across the street, before one comes to the bridge, is an enormous white house, with great shingles, reached by a curving driveway—that is the Quaker Meeting-House, Tina tells me. And on my side of the cross-street, down in a little square of dirt marked by squares of white lines, a boy and girl are knocking balls with a sort of shovel back and forth across a net— how fast the balls fly, and how both the boy and the girl jump around! Still farther down the cross-street from where the man in the buggy came, stands another white house with a steeple; it's facing me, for it's really on Front Street, the street we live on—only our house is far along

the other way. Behind the steeple in the open fields is the pond gleaming in the light with the ice-house on its hither border. Out on the pond is some one in a rowboat . . . 'What is he doing, Tina?' . . . and beyond in the immeasurable distance (of two or three miles) are the long hills of the Blue Ridge that I have never, never seen so long and so blue from our porch or dining-room window. But see, across the track to my right in another field, a big man is batting a ball and several other big men run to snatch it right out of the sky . . . again and again. Over there too is a huge house, round and gray. Tina says it is the gas-tank. We have gas in our house, blue inside the yellow. But more and more it is the track itself that fascinates—those lines that stretch so straight, yet getting narrower and narrower, so very much farther from me than I am from Mary and all the folks . . . right up to the edge of the low blue air where they seem to shoot into the woods. This is to be the Path of the Train. 'Papa is coming from Westfield on the train?' Tina says, 'Yes, from Westfield.' 'When is the train coming, Tina?' The stocky man snaps open his watch and says, 'It's five o'clock.' I know vaguely a train carries people to far away and sometimes back from far away, and I have seen trains going by on the embankment off behind our back yard and the empty lots. But now I shall soon really see one, Tina tells me.

The size of the world, its bombardment of our curiosity, the thrill in new experience and in anticipating new experience, the intense surrender of the self to its sudden universe— these are but the pallid phrases of makeshift analysis for the incommunicable vitality of a consciousness already in richness and complexity beyond either psychologist or poet. The few who have thus relived the birthday of their intellectual passions, the first great hour of their imagination in this world of wonders, will realize with me that nothing in all their experience thereafter is so beyond our ordinary instruments of expression, whether in words, color, or music. Not love, not death. Yet always the nearer we come home to reality the harder to find the word: the politician finds a hundred for his universe, the artist finds one . . . and then hardly. And in the greatest art words are perhaps no longer words at all. Perhaps Dante could give something of the infant's stupendous reality by that sunny tract of rails and water overarched by more than God—I cannot . . . beyond the bald confession that I cannot.

From out of the woods, a far whistle, a puff of far smoke. The Train! On the Path. Beside the interminable row of poles and wires. It moves. Toward us. I beg Tina to let me go—I want to look straight down the Path and see just how IT comes. Yes, I promise not to get too near the rails . . . and the Stocky Man strolls over after me. He stands and lights a cigar, looking idly up the tracks. The Train. Nearer. I can see it sway. The great black, puffing head-part. The length of moving sheds behind it. The chug-a-chug-chug, louder and louder. The almost musical rattle, with humming overtones, of the rails, louder and louder. I lean over to get the view more nearly head-on. The sky is back of it, farther and farther back of it. The Thing lengthens out, swaying this way and that. And it seems to surge up and down. A Train? What *is* a train? Curiosity before the unknown

now suddenly becomes apprehension . . . dread . . . We are human from the start. We do not need to see a man die to know death. Death is born with our birth; the self that craves life shrinks by the very law of life as instinctively from the constriction and blockage of that craving. A little child . . . what should it know of death? All there is to know, O sage of Winander. The Premonition is upon me. I realize with horror what a Train is. It is a gigantic Caterpillar . . . gigantic beyond anything I have ever seen in our garden or Mary's. I am fascinated, rooted to the barren planks, while the Caterpillar roars and wriggles and arches along. The Stocky Man puffs his cigar, Tina is lolling by the blue rail, and calling idly, 'Come back away from the tracks, Ellery,' while curiosity overmasters even my horror at my own realized disobedience; my mother is still talking doubtless with the family doctor, who brought me into the world, about the bright ways and promising future of her little son. But for the little son the universe is the Caterpillar . . . then the jerking angles of the driving-rod and the long boiler-belly make it for one tumultuous instant a tremendous Grasshopper . . . till it towers and lowers and grins in one awful metamorphosis, more grotesque than the most bizarre dreams of Greek mythology, as Something indescribably greater than Caterpillar or Grasshopper. As It roars over the bridge, with the engineer . . . I see again today his face peering out of the cabin window high above me . . . madly pulling the bell-rope, while the clanging fills what just now remained of silence in the world . . . as it roars with thunder and smoke over the bridge, scattering dust and a strewn newspaper, the black circle of the boiler-front swells to the size of the round sky out of which the Thing now seems to have leaped upon me. It sets up conscious reverberations of a picture in Uncle Oliver's insurance office . . . up the same stairs as papa's newspaper office . . . a locomotive on a calendar of Ætna Company which floods my mind . . . even as a generation later a picture on another wall is to set up subconscious reverberations of this Aboriginal Monster. My eyeballs, transfixed in one stare, ache in their sockets. The head-light glass in a square black box above the Black Circle flames with the reflected light of the afternoon sun down there where my mother is. But I am to postpone these realistic deductions for forty-seven years. To me at a little more than two years, the Black Circle flashes a fiercely shaking Face of infinite menace, more hideous and hostile than Gorgon-shield or the squat demon in a Chinese temple, with gaping Jaws, flanked by bulging jowls, to swallow me down, to eat me alive—and the Thing is God. Coetaneous with the Face and maw, a long lank Arm shoots out low down from around the further side of the engine, with an end half-spoon, half-claws, to scoop me up, to ladle me in! (This was a fantastic transfer from the swift vicious thrust of the driving-rod visible on my side.) God roaring from heaven to slay me for having disobeyed my mother and gone so close to the track. Guilt . . . remorse . . . Mary . . . in air above the great puffing smoke-stack, a tumultuous image of Mary's house . . . small hands clapped to eyes. My heart leaps to my throat . . . I think it is coming out of my mouth. 'Al-leady' (i.e., 'I am all ready. Come!') I moan in-side me, summoning the resolution of an absolute despair.

The locomotive sweeps by, and my physical paralysis ends in a sudden leap away. The steam discharges from under the piston-box into the child's anus, with hot pain through his kilt-skirt. 'God kills me here too,' he thinks with a scream out loud, and presses his hand to the pain. I am to feel that pain a generation later . . . for ten years, it will wake me from sleep. His little straw hat with scarlet band whirls off in the blast and roar, as the Stocky Man makes a futile grab. The monstrous boiler on the monstrous wheels rolls by, topped by the clangor and swaying of the bell. If I am dead, I think, how strange that I can still move so fast. It *is* God—God thunders out of the sky . . . I have heard him . . . this is God, I think in my panic . . . for I still think. The Face, that Face. Then the flight. Our house, so safe, but so horribly far, floods my mind. The parlor, with its carpet-designs in red and yellow and its maroon plush chairs, becomes an image so intense and vivid, with feel so protecting and close, that I am bewildered between being there and not there, with a paradoxical interpenetration of experience best comparable perhaps to our dream-states of maturity. The Face, that Face. The distance from my mother and Mary is terrible and hopeless: the proud moment in getting so far has supplied the suggestion for the terror of the immeasurable far-awayness from safety. The flight, down that long, level, narrow highway. And I can't see my mother. The Face, the Face, the Face. A baggage-truck down there has rolled between . . . blockage . . . I am shrieking. The cars keep passing me. I am so small that I see under them, past their tangle of iron rods, to the freight-depot on the other (the left) side of the track. The wheels pound and bump, one after the other, where rail joins rail. The Face. A thought more awful still: This Thing, God or whatever it is, will kill Mary. I must get to Mary. The Face, the Jaws. The end of the station grows nearer. I see a white frame house just beyond the station where the platform ends. The Stocky Man runs after, Tina runs, and a dog races beside me. It is fun for him. I see to my right the awnings on the stores on the street across the way from the station-park. The last car has passed. A slight relief. I stare toward its retreating rear end. My side aches . . . that frightens me too . . . I put my hand on the ache . . . I have lived through all thus far; I can live till I reach mama and Mary, I say to myself. My mother sees me and signals with her red parasol. Relief. But where is Mary? . . . a new despair . . . till she darts out from behind the two mothers and is running toward me. Spiritual relief . . . a little. Then I stumble and flop flat. The dog noses my neck. My anguish will burst from the subconscious, as the university professor overhears himself saying half asleep (i.e., in twilight sleep) the apparently meaningless phrase, 'Aeneas rushing at me,' and 'Aeneas' will be a Freudian pun for 'her knees,' and the informing point will be that he lay there unable to raise his infant head to her face, eyes fixed on her legs bending under her skirts . . . Meantime Tina picks me up, and I sob and shriek my tale of the God-Face in my mother's comforting arms. The talk with the family doctor has been interrupted. 'Now you're all hunky-dory,' says my mother, setting me down beside the baby-carriage of sister. I rush behind the baby-carriage to Mary. She caresses me. I cling with my arms about her, long . . . like a lover . . . a little shy (believe me, or not) lest the mothers see how hard I cling, how that clinging is all the world to me. I feel a sweet comfortableness in my body too . . . And when she starts away at the joyous sight of her father descending from the train, I am jealous and grieved. I lean against my little wagon. Tina gives me an orange to suck. I am getting myself together and thinking matters over. What a fool I am, I think. A Highlander, in costume, stands with his bagpipe against the station wall, laughing. The people on the platform are staring. Rows of heads too from all the car-windows. The world is all eyes. I am the Great Fool. A generation later I will be reading books that say little children don't feel shame, until taught and mistaught; and I will know that, though one needs teaching a plenty to be ashamed of the little naked body that nature gave him, he needs no teaching to be ashamed of lapsing from himself, as Intelligence and Courage.

The train didn't bring papa after all. So we all walk through the station with Mary's folks. They drive off with a span of horses, Mary on the front seat with her bearded papa. She seems almost to pay no more attention to me, and that hurts. She too must think me the Great Fool. Then my mother leads me back to the Engine. A man is oiling the wheel. I am urged to touch them and the cow-catcher. I do . . . gingerly. My mother shows me that it is not really alive, that it has no face, that it has no long arm, that it is not God but a Locomotive. I am trying to convince myself . . . but am still nervous and a little skeptical . . . especially when it starts to move away.

I ask on the walk home, when but a few rods from the station, with my mind full of my little lover riding away behind the turning span of great horses: 'Mama, do you suppose Mary thinks I'm a fool?' She cajoles and chides me: 'You mustn't talk like that.' I brood, deeply troubled. And again as we near our house at last: 'Mama, do you suppose Mary loves me?' . . . My papa arrives in time for supper, after all. Mama is telling him how scared I was, and how I thought the Locomotive was God. I am such a little boy that she thinks I don't understand her big words. But, just as I lift my glass of milk to my mouth, I see for a second the Locomotive-God plunging at me through the hall door. I shriek out. My father's face is troubled, a kindlier face than the years are ever to carve out for his childless son . . . The Face of St. Francis . . . He is very grave, worried about the shock and what it may do to me . . . perhaps (as I am to speculate when I am a dozen years older than my father is now) worried too that the shock may affect my love for the good God whom he loves more now, as a newspaper editor in a small city, than when before my birth he resigned his pastorate in far-off Evanston because he no longer liked the Baptist God. Yet what he and my mother had already told me of the Heavenly Father that thunders and his Power and Love of Good Little Boys was, it seems (I conjecture here), enough for my reconstruction of the Locomotive-God. Sometime the race of man will be wise enough, courageous enough, not to talk about God to little children at all. My mother is crying quietly . . . she is depressed before her hus-

band as having failed in her care of the son—*his* son. The next day he takes me to the station and has me stand and walk about on the spot of my fright. I think how silly I was. Three days later my mother makes an insert in the diary she is keeping in my name . . . she forgot the item at first. What made her forget? Here it is:

Tuesday, the 4th. (June, 1878) I went to the *depot* to meet my papa for the *first* time. I never had been so near to a Locomotive, or 'locomoti' as I call it. I was so frightened when it came rushing along past us that I screamed and mama had to hold me in her arms. My papa did not come home from Westfield on that train and so we had to come away without him, but I have been to the *depot* and seen a *'locomoti and the pattenger cars'* and I have been talking a great deal about it ever since.

The italics are my mother's. Forty-seven years later my mother is to remember only how lovingly she dried my tears. Mary will remember nothing, or at least will fail to answer my letter. My father and Mary's will be dead. But Mary's aged mother will write me verifying the external outlines of the episode as I have recorded it. I am to forget it—in a few months—for forty-odd years. But it is not going to forget me . . . *jamais.*

That afternoon changed my whole life. In recovering my lost years, I have uncovered a hundred dreams dreamed in the years not lost: that afternoon was involved in their pattern. I have uncovered conduct and motives for conduct: that afternoon was in their pattern. Emotions, opinions, scholarly interests, materials in my poems: that afternoon was there too. Long years of unexplained, intermittent nervousness, followed by fifteen years (to date) of a chronic neurosis, with all its accompanying limitations and handicaps: that afternoon was in their pattern. Can ten minutes' time control fifty years? It can. Children's diseases—measles, scarlet fever, infantile paralysis—how parents dread them, for, even if the little lives are saved, they may be maimed, in eyes, ears, or legs, for life. And nurse-maids must not drop or bump them—for a scar is a lifelong misfortune. We must guard their morals and manners too—training them not to tell lies or to spit or to do nasty things in the clothes-closet. But a scare, with a few shrieks and tears, is soon a neighborhood joke. Yet what was this scare of mine? Sex, self-respect, self-confidence, friendliness to the world, the will to roam and the will to know, basic forces for normal manhood, here unfolding with wholesome promise, were abruptly disintegrated in the explosion of complete collapse before the attack of alien and incomprehensible power, to be replaced by terror, guilt, shame, and the cringing need of shelter. In a nervous system, a little more than two years out of the womb. I was born again that day.

JEAN-CHRISTOPHE

Romain Rolland

[A child's fear is graphically presented in an early chapter of *Jean-Christophe.* Although of strong physical constitution, the boy was constantly haunted by the terror of darkness, of strange shapes and images which his imagination conjured up, and of death. The key to an understanding of his fear lies in awareness of the total picture of his environment—the actual hunger that he often experienced, his father's drunkenness and subsequent beating of his son, the taunts of other children, and his mother's lack of understanding.]

Jean-Christophe was impervious to sickness. He had inherited from his father and grandfather their robust constitutions. They were not mollycoddles in that family; well or ill, they never worried, and nothing could bring about any change in the habits of the two Kraffts, father and son. They went out winter and summer, in all weathers, and stayed for hours together out in rain or sun, sometimes bareheaded and with their coats open, from carelessness or bravado, and walked for miles without being tired, and they looked with pity and disdain upon poor Louisa, who never said anything, but had to stop. She would go pale, and her legs would swell, and her heart would thump. Jean-Christophe was not far from sharing the scorn of his mother; he did not understand people being ill. When he fell, or knocked himself, or cut himself, or burned himself, he

From *Jean-Christophe* by Romain Rolland. By permission of Henry Holt and Co., Inc.

did not cry; but he was angry with the thing that had injured him. His father's brutalities and the roughness of his little playmates, the urchins of the street, with whom he used to fight, hardened him. He was not afraid of blows, and more than once he returned home with bleeding nose and bruised forehead. One day he had to be wrenched away, almost suffocated, from one of these fierce tussles in which he had bowled over his adversary, who was savagely banging his head on the ground. That seemed natural enough to him, for he was prepared to do unto others as they did unto himself.

And yet he was afraid of all sorts of things, and although no one knew it—for he was very proud—nothing brought him so much suffering during a part of his childhood as these same terrors. For two or three years especially they gnawed at him like a disease.

He was afraid of the mysterious something that lurks in darkness—evil powers that seemed to lie in wait for his life, the roaring of monsters which fearfully haunt the mind of every child and appear in everything that he sees, the relic perhaps of a form long dead, hallucinations of the first days after emerging from chaos, from the fearful slumber in the mother's womb, from the awakening of the larva from the depths of matter.

He was afraid of the garret door. It opened on to the stairs, and was almost always ajar. When he had to pass it he felt his heart beating; he would spring forward and jump by it without looking. It seemed to him that there was some one or something behind it. When it was closed he heard distinctly something moving behind it. That was not surprising, for there were large rats; but he imagined a monster, with rattling bones, and flesh hanging in rags, a horse's head, horrible and terrifying eyes, shapeless. He did not want to think of it, but did so in spite of himself. With trembling hand he would make sure that the door was locked; but that did not keep him from turning round ten times as he went downstairs.

He was afraid of the night outside. Sometimes he used to stay late with his grandfather, or was sent out in the evening on some errand. Old Krafft lived a little outside the town in the last house on the Cologne road. Between the house and the first lighted windows of the town there was a distance of two or three hundred yards, which seemed three times as long to Jean-Christophe. There were places where the road twisted and it was impossible to see anything. The country was deserted in the evening, the earth grew black, and the sky was awfully pale. When he came out from the hedges that lined the road, and climbed up the slope, he could still see a yellowish gleam on the horizon, but it gave no light, and was more oppressive than the night; it made the darkness only darker; it was a deathly light. The clouds came down almost to earth. The hedges grew enormous and moved. The gaunt trees were like grotesque old men. The sides of the wood were stark white. The darkness moved. There were dwarfs sitting in the ditches, lights in the grass, fearful flying things in the air, shrill cries of insects coming from nowhere. Jean-Christophe was always in anguish, expecting some fearsome or strange putting forth of Nature. He would run, with his heart leaping in his bosom.

When he saw the light in his grandfather's room he would gain confidence. But worst of all was when old Krafft was not at home. That was most terrifying. The old house, lost in the country, frightened the boy even in daylight. He forgot his fears when his grandfather was there, but sometimes the old man would leave him alone, and go out without warning him. Jean-Christophe did not mind that. The room was quiet. Everything in it was familiar and kindly. There was a great white wooden bedstead, by the bedside was a great Bible on a shelf, artificial flowers were on the mantelpiece, with photographs of the old man's two wives and eleven children—and at the bottom of each photograph he had written the date of birth and death—on the walls were framed texts and vile chromolithographs of Mozart and Beethoven. A little piano stood in one corner, a great violoncello in another; rows of books higgledy-piggledy, pipes, and in the window pots of geraniums. It was like being surrounded with friends. The old man could be heard moving about in the next room, and planing or hammering, and talking to himself, calling himself an idiot, or singing in a loud voice, improvising a *potpourri* of scraps of chants and sentimental *Lieder,* warlike marches, and drinking songs. Here was shelter and refuge. Jean-Christophe would sit in the great armchair by the window, with a book on his knees, bending over the pictures and losing himself in them. The day would die down, his eyes would grow weary, and then he would look no more, and fall into vague dreaming. The wheels of a cart would rumble by along the road, a cow would moo in the fields; the bells of the town, weary and sleepy, would ring the evening Angelus. Vague desires, happy presenti-ments, would awake in the heart of the dreaming child.

Suddenly Jean-Christophe would awake, filled with dull uneasiness. He would raise his eyes—night! He would listen—silence! His grandfather had just gone out. He shuddered. He leaned out of the window to try to see him. The road was deserted; things began to take on a threatening aspect. Oh God! If *that* should be coming! What? He could not tell. The fearful thing. The doors were not properly shut. The wooden stairs creaked as under a footstep. The boy leaped up, dragged the armchair, the two chairs and the table, to the most remote corner of the room: he made a barrier of them; the armchair against the wall, a chair to the right, a chair to the left, and the table in front of him. In the middle he planted a pair of steps, and, perched on top with his book and other books, like provisions against a siege, he breathed again, having decided in his childish imagination that the enemy could not pass the barrier—that was not to be allowed.

But the enemy would creep forth, even from his book. Among the old books which the old man had picked up were some with pictures which made a profound impression on the child: they attracted and yet terrified him. There were fantastic visions—temptations of St. Anthony—in which skeletons of birds hung in bottles, and thousands of eggs writhe like worms in disemboweled frogs, and heads walk on feet, and asses play trumpets, and household utensils and corpses of animals walk gravely, wrapped in great cloths, bowing like old ladies. Jean-Christophe was horrified by them, but always returned to them, drawn on by disgust. He would look at them for a long time, and every now and then look furtively about him to see what was stirring in the folds of the curtains. A picture of a flayed man in an anatomy book was still more horrible to him. He trembled as he turned the page when he came to the place where it was in the book. This shapeless medley was grimly etched for him. The creative power inherent in every child's mind filled out the meagerness of the setting of them. He saw no difference between the daubs and the reality. At night they had an even more powerful influence over his dreams than the living things that he saw during the day.

He was afraid to sleep. For several years nightmares poisoned his rest. He wandered in cellars, and through the manhole saw the grinning flayed man entering. He was alone in a room, and he heard a stealthy footstep in the corridor; he hurled himself against the door to close it, and was just in time to hold the handle; but it was turned from the outside; he could not turn the key, his strength left him, and he cried for help. He was with his family, and suddenly their faces changed; they did crazy things. He was reading quietly, and he felt that an invisible being was all *round* him. He tried to fly, but felt himself bound. He tried to cry out, but he was gagged. A loathsome grip was about his neck. He awoke, suffocating, and with his teeth chattering; and he went on trembling long after he was awake; he could not be rid of his agony.

The room in which he slept was a hole without door or windows; an old curtain hung up by a curtain-rod over the entrance was all that separated it from the room of his father and mother. The thick air stifled him. His brother, who slept in the same bed, used to kick him. His head burned, and he was a prey to a sort of hallucination in which all the little troubles of the day reappeared infinitely magnified. In this state of nervous tension, bordering on delirium, the least shock was an agony to him. The creaking of a plank terrified him. His father's breathing took on fantastic proportions. It seemed to be no longer a human breathing, and the monstrous sound was horrible to him; it seemed to him that there must be a beast sleeping there. The night crushed him; it would never end; it must always be so; he was lying there for months and months. He gasped for breath; he half raised himself on his bed, sat up, dried his sweating face with his shirt-sleeve. Sometimes he nudged his brother Rodolphe to wake him up; but Rodolphe moaned, drew away from him the rest of the bedclothes, and went on sleeping.

So he stayed in feverish agony until a pale beam of light appeared on the floor before the curtain. This timorous paleness of the distant dawn suddenly brought him peace. He felt the light gliding into the room, when it was still impossible to distinguish it from darkness. Then his fever would die down, his blood would grow calm, like a flooded river returning to its bed; an even warmth would flow through all his body, and his eyes, burning from sleeplessness, would close in spite of himself.

In the evening it was terrible to him to see the approach of the hour of sleep. He vowed that he would not give way to it, to watch the whole night through, fearing his nightmares. But in the end weariness always overcame him, and it was always when he was least on his guard that the monsters returned.

Fearful night! So sweet to most children, so terrible to some! . . . He was afraid to sleep. He was afraid of not sleeping. Waking or sleeping, he was surrounded by monstrous shapes, the phantoms of his own brain, the larvae floating in the half-day and twilight of childhood, as in the dark chiaroscuro of sickness.

But these fancied terrors were soon to be blotted out in the great Fear—that which is in the hearts of all men; that Fear which Wisdom does in vain preen itself on forgetting or denying —Death.

One day when he was rummaging in a cupboard, he came upon several things that he did not know—a child's frock and a striped bonnet. He took them in triumph to his mother, who, instead of smiling at him, looked vexed, and bade him take them back to the place where he had found them. When he hesitated to obey, and asked her why, she snatched them from him without reply, and put them on a shelf where he could not reach them. Roused to curiosity, he plied her with questions. At last she told him that there had been a little brother who had died before Jean-Christophe came into the world. He was taken aback—he had never heard tell of him. He was silent for a moment, and then tried to find out more. His mother seemed to be lost in thought; but she told him that the little brother was called Jean-Christophe like himself, but was more sensible. He put more questions to her, but she would not reply readily. She told him only that his brother was in Heaven, and was praying for them all. Jean-Christophe could get no more out of her; she bade him be quiet, and to let her get on with her work. She seemed to be absorbed in her sewing; she looked anxious, and

did not raise her eyes. But after some time she looked at him where he was in the corner, whither he had retired to sulk, began to smile, and told him to go and play outside.

These scraps of conversation profoundly agitated Jean-Christophe. There had been a child, a little boy, belonging to his mother, like himself, bearing the same name, almost exactly the same, and he was dead! Dead! He did not exactly know what that was, but it was something terrible. And they never talked of this other Jean-Christophe; he was quite forgotten. It would be the same with him if he were to die? This thought was with him still in the evening at table with his family, when he saw them all laughing and talking of trifles. So, then, it was possible that they would be gay after he was dead! Oh! he never would have believed that his mother could be selfish enough to laugh after the death of her little boy! He hated them all. He wanted to weep for himself, for his own death, in advance. At the same time he wanted to ask a whole heap of questions, but he dared not; he remembered the voice in which his mother had bid him be quiet. At last he could contain himself no longer, and one night when he had gone to bed, and Louisa came to kiss him, he asked:

'Mother, did he sleep in my bed?'

The poor woman trembled, and, trying to take on an indifferent tone of voice, she asked:

'Who?'

'The little boy who is dead,' said Jean-Christophe in a whisper.

His mother clutched him with her hands.

'Be quiet—quiet,' she said.

Her voice trembled. Jean-Christophe, whose head was leaning

against her bosom, heard her heart beating. There was a moment of silence, then she said:

'You must never talk of that, my dear . . . Go to sleep . . . No, it was not his bed.'

She kissed him. He thought he felt her cheek wet against his. He wished he could have been sure of it. He was a little comforted. There was grief in her then! Then he doubted it again the next moment, when he heard her in the next room talking in a quiet, ordinary voice. Which was true—that or what had just been? He turned about for long in his bed without finding any answer. He wanted his mother to suffer; not that he also did not suffer in the knowledge that she was sad, but it would have done him so much good, in spite of everything! He would have felt himself less alone. He slept, and next day thought no more of it.

Some weeks afterwards one of the urchins with whom he played in the street did not come at the usual time. One of them said he was ill, and they got used to not seeing him in their games. It was explained, it was quite simple. One evening Jean-Christophe had gone to bed; it was early, and from the recess in which his bed was, he saw the light in the room. There was a knock at the door. A neighbor had come to have a chat. He listened absently, telling himself stories as usual. The words of their talk did not reach him. Suddenly he heard the neighbor say: 'He is dead.' His blood stopped, for he had understood who was dead. He listened and held his breath. His parents cried out. Melchior's booming voice said:

'Jean-Christophe, do you hear? Poor Fritz is dead.'

Jean-Christophe made an effort, and replied quietly:

'Yes, papa.'

His bosom was drawn tight as in a vise.

Melchior went on:

' "Yes, papa." Is that all you say? You are not grieved by it.'

Louisa, who understood the child, said:

'Ssh! Let him sleep!'

And they talked in whispers. But Jean-Christophe, pricking his ears, gathered all the details of illness—typhoid fever, cold baths, delirium, the parents' grief. He could not breathe, a lump in his throat choked him. He shuddered. All these horrible things took shape in his mind. Above all, he gleaned that the disease was contagious—that is, that he also might die in the same way—and terror froze him, for he remembered that he had shaken hands with Fritz the last time he had seen him, and that very day had gone past the house. But he made no sound, so as to avoid having to talk, and when his father, after the neighbor had gone, asked him: 'Jean-Christophe, are you asleep?' he did not reply. He heard Melchior saying to Louisa:

'The boy has no heart.'

Louisa did not reply, but a moment later she came and gently raised the curtain and looked at the little bed. Jean-Christophe only just had time to close his eyes and imitate the regular breathing which his brothers made when they were asleep. Louisa went away on tip-toe. And yet how he wanted to keep her! How he wanted to tell her that he was afraid, and to ask her to save him, or at least to comfort him! But he was afraid of their laughing at him, and treating him as a coward; and besides, he knew only too well that nothing that they might say would be any good. And for hours he lay there in agony, thinking that he felt the disease creeping over him, and pains in his head, a stricture of the heart, and thinking in terror: 'It is the end. I am ill. I am going to die. I am going to die!' . . . Once he sat up in his bed and called to his mother in a low voice; but they were asleep, and he dared not wake them.

From that time on his childhood was poisoned by the idea of death. His nerves delivered him up to all sorts of little baseless sicknesses, to depression, to sudden transports, and fits of choking. His imagination ran riot with these troubles, and thought it saw in all of them the murderous beast which was to rob him of his life. How many times he suffered agonies, with his mother sitting only a few yards away from him, and she guessing nothing! For in his cowardice he was brave enough to conceal all his terror in a strange jumble of feeling— pride in not turning to others, shame of being afraid, and the scrupulousness of a tenderness which forbade him to trouble his mother. But he never ceased to think: 'This time I am ill. I am seriously ill. It is diphtheria . . .' He had chanced on the word 'diphtheria' . . . 'Dear God! not this time! . . .'

He had religious ideas: he loved to believe what his mother had told him, that after death the soul ascended to the Lord, and if it were pious entered into the garden of paradise. But the idea of this journey rather frightened than attracted him. He was not at all envious of the children whom God, as a recompense, according to his mother, took in their sleep and called to Him without having made them suffer. He trembled, as he went to sleep, for fear that God should indulge this whimsy at his expense. It must be terrible to be taken suddenly from the warmth of one's bed and dragged through the void into the presence of God. He imagined God as an enormous sun, with a voice of thunder. How it must hurt! It must burn the eyes, ears—all one's soul! Then, God could punish—you never know . . . And besides, that did not prevent all the other horrors which he did not know very well, though he could guess them from what he had heard—your body in a box, all alone at the bottom of a hole, lost in the crowd of those revolting cemeteries to which he was taken to pray . . . God! God! How sad! how sad! . . .

And yet it was not exactly joyous to live, and be hungry, and see your father drunk, and to be beaten, to suffer in so many ways from the wickedness of other children, from the insulting pity of grown-up persons, and to be understood by no one, not even by your mother. Everybody humiliates you, no one loves you. You are alone—alone, and matter so little! Yes; but it was just this that made him want to live. He felt in himself a surging power of wrath. A strange thing, that power! It could do nothing yet; it was as though it were afar off and gagged, swaddled, paralyzed; he had no idea what it wanted, what, later on, it would be. But it was in him; he was sure of it; he felt it stirring and crying out. To-morrow—to-morrow, what a voyage he would take! He had a savage desire to live, to punish the wicked, to do great things. 'Oh! but how I will live when I am . . .' he pondered a little—'when I am eighteen!' Sometimes he put it at twenty-one; that was the extreme limit. He thought that was enough for the domination of the world. He thought of the heroes dearest to him

—of Napoleon, and of that other more remote hero, whom he preferred, Alexander the Great. Surely he would be like them if only he lived for another twelve—ten years. He never thought of pitying those who died at thirty. They were old; they had lived their lives; it was their fault if they had failed. But to die now . . . despair! Too terrible to pass while yet a little child, and forever to be in the minds of men a little boy whom everybody thinks he has the right to scold! He wept with rage at the thought, as though he were already dead.

This agony of death tortured his childish years—corrected only by disgust with all life and the sadness of his own.

❋

NATIVE SON

RICHARD WRIGHT

[*Native Son* portrays the effects of conflicting fear and hate in the Negro youth, Bigger Thomas, whose sense of deprivation and insecurity in a world in which the white man is supreme leads him to fierce, uncontrollable resentment of those who are white and rich. While he wills to express his hate overtly, at the same time he is afraid to give it expression. Hence, to save his own face he projects his fear on to one of his fellow conspirators and indulges in violent conduct toward him. His rationalization of his action affords an interesting illustration of the way in which one may protect himself from facing an unwelcome truth. The game of 'white folks' and the illusory escape in the movie house to a world of wealth, power, and glamour suggest other compensations for the harsh realities in the life of this Negro boy. The far-reaching social consequences of the hatred and fear induced by deprivation and injustice are as clear in this experience as are the emotional effects on the individual. It is but a step from violent and irreconcilable emotional conflicts such as this to Bigger's later violently anti-social behavior. He is driven from one crime to another in his frenzied attempts to escape the bounds imposed on him and to find some expression for his tremendous vitality.]

He stood on the corner in the sunshine, watching cars and people pass. He needed more money; if he did not get more than he had now he would not know what to do with himself for the rest of the day. He wanted to see a movie; his senses hungered for it. In a movie he could dream without effort; all he had to do was lean back in a seat and keep his eyes open.

He thought of Gus and G.H. and Jack. Should he go to the poolroom and talk with them? But there was no use in his going unless they were ready to do what they had been long planning to do. If they could, it would mean some sure and quick money. From three o'clock to four o'clock in the afternoon there was no policeman on duty in the block where

From *Native Son* by Richard Wright. By permission of Harper and Brothers, 1939.

Blum's Delicatessen was and it would be safe. One of them could hold a gun on Blum and keep him from yelling; one could watch the front door; one could watch the back; and one could get the money from the box under the counter. Then all four of them could lock Blum in the store and run out through the back and duck down the alley and meet an hour later, either at the Doc's poolroom or at the South Side Boys' Club, and split the money.

Holding up Blum ought not take more than two minutes, at the most. And it would be their last job. But it would be the toughest one that they had ever pulled. All the other times they had raided newsstands, fruit stands, and apartments. And, too, they had never held up a white man before. They had always robbed Negroes. They felt that it was much easier and safer to rob their own people, for they knew that white policemen never really search diligently for Negroes who committed crimes against other Negroes. For months they had talked of robbing Blum's, but had not been able to bring themselves to do it. They had the feeling that the robbing of Blum's would be a violation of ultimate taboo; it would be a trespassing into territory where the full wrath of an alien white world would be turned loose upon them; in short, it would be a symbolic challenge of the white world's rule over them; a challenge which they yearned to make, but were afraid to. Yes; if they could rob Blum's, it would be a real hold-up, in more senses than one. In comparison, all of their other jobs had been play.

'Good-bye, Bigger.'

He looked up and saw Vera passing with a sewing kit dangling from her arm. She paused at the corner and came back to him.

'Now, what you want?'

'Bigger, please . . . You're getting a good job now. Why don't you stay away from Jack and Gus and G.H. and keep out of trouble?'

'You keep your big mouth out of my business!'

'But, Bigger!'

'Go on to school, will you!'

She turned abruptly and walked on. He knew that his mother had been talking to Vera and Buddy about him, telling them that if he got into any more trouble he would be sent to prison and not just to the reform school, where they sent him last time. He did not mind what his mother said to Buddy about him. Buddy was all right. Tough, plenty. But Vera was a sappy girl; she did not have any more sense than to believe everything she was told.

He walked toward the poolroom. When he got to the door he saw Gus half a block away, coming toward him. He stopped and waited. It was Gus who had first thought of robbing Blum's.

'Hi, Bigger!'

'What you saying, Gus?'

'Nothing. Seen G.H. or Jack yet?'

'Naw. You?'

'Naw. Say, got a cigarette?'

'Yeah.'

Bigger took out his pack and gave Gus a cigarette; he lit his and held the match for Gus. They leaned their backs against the red-brick wall of a building, smoking, their cigarettes slanting white across their black chins. To the east Bigger saw the sun burning a dazzling yellow. In the sky above him a few big white clouds drifted. He puffed silently, relaxed, his mind pleasantly vacant of purpose. Every slight movement in the street evoked a casual curiosity in him. Automatically, his eyes followed each car as it whirred over the smooth black asphalt. A woman came by and he watched the gentle sway of her body until she disappeared into a doorway. He sighed, scratched his chin and mumbled,

'Kinda warm today.'

'Yeah,' Gus said.

'You get more heat from this sun than from them old radiators at home.'

'Yeah; them old white landlords sure don't give much heat.'

'And they always knocking at your door for money.'

'I'll be glad when summer comes.'

'Me too,' Bigger said.

He stretched his arms above his head and yawned; his eyes moistened. The sharp precision of the world of steel and stone dissolved into blurred waves. He blinked and the world grew hard again, mechanical, distinct. A weaving motion in the sky made him turn his eyes upward; he saw a slender streak of billowing white blooming against the deep blue. A plane was writing high up in the air.

'Look!' Bigger said.

'What?'

'That plane writing up there,' Bigger said, pointing.

'Oh!'

They squinted at a tiny ribbon of unfolding vapor that spelled the word: Use . . . The plane was so far away that at times the strong glare of the sun blanked it from sight.

'You can hardly see it,' Gus said.

'Looks like a little bird,' Bigger breathed with childlike wonder.

'Them white boys sure can fly,' Gus said.

'Yeah,' Bigger said, wistfully. 'They get a chance to do everything.'

Noiselessly, the tiny plane looped and veered, vanishing and appearing, leaving behind it a long trail of white plumage, like coils of fluffy paste being squeezed from a tube; a plume-coil that grew and swelled and slowly began to fade into the air at the edges. The plane wrote another word: Speed . . .

'How high you reckon he is?' Bigger asked.

'I don't know. Maybe a hundred miles; maybe a thousand.'

'I could fly one of them things if I had a chance,' Bigger mumbled reflectively, as though talking to himself.

Gus pulled down the corners of his lips, stepped out from the wall, squared his shoulders, doffed his cap, bowed low and spoke with mock deference:

'Yessuh.'

'You go to hell,' Bigger said, smiling.

'Yessuh,' Gus said again.

'I could fly a plane if I had a chance,' Bigger said.

'If you wasn't black and if you had some money and if they'd let you go to that aviation school, you could fly a plane,' Gus said.

For a moment Bigger contemplated all the 'ifs' that Gus had mentioned. Then both boys broke into hard laughter, looking at each other through squinted eyes. When their laughter subsided, Bigger said in a voice that was half-question and half-statement:

'It's funny how the white folks treat us, ain't it?'

'It better be funny,' Gus said.

'Maybe they right in not wanting us to fly,' Bigger said. ' 'Cause if I took a plane up I'd take a couple of bombs along and drop 'em as sure as hell . . .'

They laughed again, still looking

upward. The plane sailed and dipped
and spread another word against the
sky: GASOLINE . . .

'Use Speed Gasoline,' Bigger mused,
rolling the words slowly from his lips.
'God, I'd like to fly up there in that
sky.'

'God'll let you fly when He gives
you your wings up in heaven,' Gus
said.

They laughed again, reclining
against the wall, smoking, the lids of
their eyes drooped softly against the
sun. Cars whizzed past on rubber
tires. Bigger's face was metallically
black in the strong sunlight. There
was in his eyes a pensive, brooding
amusement, as of a man who had
been long confronted and tantalized
by a riddle whose answer seemed always just on the verge of escaping
him, but prodding him irresistibly on
to seek its solution. The silence irked
Bigger; he was anxious to do something to evade looking so squarely at
this problem.

'Let's play "white," ' Bigger said,
referring to a game of play-acting
in which he and his friends imitated
the ways and manners of white folks.

'I don't feel like it,' Gus said.

'General!' Bigger pronounced in a
sonorous tone, looking at Gus ex-
pectantly.

'Aw, hell! I don't want to play,'
Gus whined.

'You'll be court-martialed,' Bigger
said, snapping out his words with
military precision.

'Nigger, you nuts!' Gus laughed.

'General!' Bigger tried again, determinedly.

Gus looked wearily at Bigger, then
straightened, saluted and answered:

'Yessuh.'

'Send your men over the river at
dawn and attack the enemy's left
flank,' Bigger ordered.

'Yessuh.'

'Send the Fifth, Sixth, and Sev-
enth Regiments,' Bigger said, frowning. 'And attack with tanks, gas,
planes, and infantry.'

'Yessuh!' Gus said again, saluting
and clicking his heels.

For a moment they were silent, facing each other, their shoulders thrown
back, their lips compressed to hold
down the mounting impulse to laugh.
Then they guffawed, partly at themselves and partly at the vast white
world that sprawled and towered in
the sun before them.

'Say, what's a "left flank"?' Gus
asked.

'I don't know,' Bigger said. 'I heard
it in the movies.'

They laughed again. After a bit
they relaxed and leaned against the
wall, smoking. Bigger saw Gus cup
his left hand to his ear, as though
holding a telephone receiver; and cup
his right hand to his mouth, as
though talking into a transmitter.

'Hello,' Gus said.

'Hello,' Bigger said, 'who's this?'

'This is Mr. J. P. Morgan speaking,'
Gus said.

'Yessuh, Mr. Morgan,' Bigger said;
his eyes filled with mock adulation
and respect.

'I want you to sell twenty thousand
shares of U. S. Steel in the market
this morning,' Gus said.

'At what price, suh?' Bigger asked.

'Aw, just dump 'em at any price,'
Gus said with casual irritation. 'We're
holding too much.'

'Yessuh,' Bigger said.

'And call me at my club at two
this afternoon and tell me if the
President telephoned,' Gus said.

'Yessuh, Mr. Morgan,' Bigger said.

Both of them made gestures signify-
ing that they were hanging up tele-

phone receivers; then they bent double, laughing.

'I bet that's *just* the way they talk,' Gus said.

'I wouldn't be surprised,' Bigger said.

They were silent again. Presently, Bigger cupped his hand to his mouth and spoke through an imaginary telephone transmitter.

'Hello.'

'Hello,' Gus answered. 'Who's this?'

'This is the President of the United States speaking,' Bigger said.

'Oh, yessuh, Mr. President,' Gus said.

'I'm calling a cabinet meeting this afternoon at four o'clock and you, as Secretary of State, *must* be there.'

'Well, now, Mr. President,' Gus said, 'I'm pretty busy. They raising sand over there in Germany and I got to send 'em a note . . .'

'But this is important,' Bigger said.

'What you going to take up at this cabinet meeting?' Gus asked.

'Well, you see, the niggers is raising sand all over the country,' Bigger said, struggling to keep back his laughter. 'We've got to do something with these black folks . . .'

'Oh, if it's about the niggers, I'll be right there, Mr. President,' Gus said.

They hung up imaginary receivers and leaned against the wall and laughed. A street car rattled by. Bigger sighed and swore.

'Goddammit!'

'What's the matter?'

'They don't let us do *nothing*.'

'Who?'

'The *white* folks.'

'You talk like you just now finding that out,' Gus said.

'Naw. But I just can't get used to it,' Bigger said. 'I swear to God I can't. I know I oughtn't think about it, but I can't help it. Every time I think about it I feel like somebody's poking a red-hot iron down my throat. Goddammit, look! We live here and they live there. We black and they white. They got things and we ain't. They do things and we can't. It's just like living in jail. Half the time I feel like I'm on the outside of the world peeping in through a knot-hole in the fence . . .'

'Aw, ain't no use feeling that way about it. It don't help none,' Gus said.

'You know one thing?' Bigger said.

'What?'

'Sometimes I feel like something awful's going to happen to me.' Bigger spoke with a tinge of bitter pride in his voice.

'What you mean?' Gus asked, looking at him quickly. There was fear in Gus's eyes.

'I don't know. I just feel that way. Every time I get to thinking about me being black and they being white, me being here and they being there, I feel like something awful's going to happen to me . . .'

'Aw, for Chrissakes! There ain't nothing you can do about it. How come you want to worry yourself? You black and they make the laws . . .'

'Why they make us live in one corner of the city? Why don't they let us fly planes and run ships . . .'

Gus hunched Bigger with his elbow and mumbled good-naturedly, 'Aw, nigger, quit thinking about it. You'll go nuts.'

The plane was gone from the sky and the white plumes of floating smoke were thinly spread, vanishing. Because he was restless and had time on his hands, Bigger yawned again and hoisted his arms high above his head.

'Nothing ever happens,' he complained.

'What you want to happen?'

'Anything,' Bigger said with a wide sweep of his dingy palm, a sweep that included all the possible activities of the world.

Then their eyes were riveted; a slate-colored pigeon swooped down to the middle of the steel car tracks and began strutting to and fro with ruffled feathers, its fat neck bobbing with regal pride. A street car rumbled forward and the pigeon rose swiftly through the air on wings stretched so taut and sheer that Bigger could see gold of the sun through their translucent tips. He tilted his head and watched the slate-colored bird flap and wheel out of sight over the edge of a high roof.

'Now, if I could only do that,' Bigger said.

Gus laughed.

'Nigger, you nuts.'

'I reckon we the only things in this city that can't go where we want to go and do what we want to do.'

'Don't think about it,' Gus said.

'I can't help it.'

'That's why you feeling like something awful's going to happen to you,' Gus said. 'You think too much.'

'What in hell can a man do?' Bigger asked, turning to Gus.

'Get drunk and sleep it off.'

'I can't. I'm broke.'

Bigger crushed his cigarette and took out another one and offered the package to Gus. They continued smoking. A huge truck swept past, lifting scraps of white paper into the sunshine; the bits settled down slowly.

'Gus?'

'Hunh?'

'You know where the white folks live?'

'Yeah,' Gus said, pointing eastward. 'Over across the "line"; over there on Cottage Grove Avenue.'

'Naw; they don't,' Bigger said.

'What you mean?' Gus asked, puzzled. 'Then, where do they live?'

Bigger doubled his fist and struck his solar plexus.

'Right down here in my stomach,' he said.

Gus looked at Bigger searchingly, then away, as though ashamed.

'Yeah; I know what you mean,' he whispered.

'Every time I think of 'em, I *feel* 'em,' Bigger said.

'Yeah; and in your chest and throat, too,' Gus said.

'It's like fire.'

'And sometimes you can't hardly breathe . . .'

Bigger's eyes were wide and placid, gazing into space.

'That's when I feel like something awful's going to happen to me . . .' Bigger paused, narrowed his eyes. 'Naw; it ain't like something going to happen to me. It's . . . It's like I was going to do something I can't help . . .'

'Yeah!' Gus said with uneasy eagerness. His eyes were full of a look compounded of fear and admiration for Bigger. 'Yeah; I know what you mean. It's like you going to fall and don't know where you going to land . . .'

Gus's voice trailed off. The sun slid behind a big white cloud and the street was plunged in cool shadow; quickly the sun edged forth again and it was bright and warm once more. A long sleek black car, its fenders glinting like glass in the sun, shot past them at high speed and turned a corner a few blocks away. Bigger pursed his lips and sang:

'Zoooooooooom!'

'They got everything,' Gus said.

'They own the world,' Bigger said.

'Aw, what the hell,' Gus said. 'Let's go in the poolroom.'

'O.K.'

They walked toward the door of the poolroom.

'Say, you taking that job you told us about?' Gus asked.

'I don't know.'

'You talk like you don't want it.'

'Oh, hell, yes! I want the job,' Bigger said.

They looked at each other and laughed. They went inside. The poolroom was empty, save for a fat, black man who held a half-smoked, unlit cigar in his mouth and leaned on the front counter. To the rear burned a single green-shaded bulb.

'Hi, Doc,' Bigger said.

'You boys kinda early this morning,' Doc said.

'Jack or G.H. around yet?' Bigger asked.

'Naw,' Doc said.

'Let's shoot a game,' Gus said.

'I'm broke,' Bigger said.

'I got some money.'

'Switch on the light. The balls are racked,' Doc said.

Bigger turned on the light. They lagged for first shot. Bigger won. They started playing. Bigger's shots were poor; he was thinking of Blum's, fascinated with the idea of the robbery, and a little afraid of it.

'Remember what we talked about so much?' Bigger asked in a flat, neutral tone.

'Naw.'

'Old Blum.'

'Oh,' Gus said. 'We ain't talked about that for a month. How come you think of it all of a sudden?'

'Let's clean the place out.'

'I don't know.'

'It was your plan from the start,' Bigger said.

Gus straightened and stared at Bigger, then at Doc who was looking out of the front window.

'You going to tell Doc? Can't you never learn to talk low?'

'Aw, I was just asking you, do you want to try it?'

'Naw.'

'How come? You scared 'cause he's a white man?'

'Naw. But Blum keeps a gun. Suppose he beats us to it?'

'Aw, you scared; that's all. He's a white man and you scared.'

'The hell I'm scared,' Gus, hurt and stung, defended himself.

Bigger went to Gus and placed an arm about his shoulders.

'Listen, you won't have to go in. You just stand at the door and keep watch, see? Me and Jack and G.H.'ll go in. If anybody comes along, you whistle and we'll go out the back way. That's all.'

The front door opened; they stopped talking and turned their heads.

'Here comes Jack and G.H. now,' Bigger said.

Jack and G.H. walked to the rear of the poolroom.

'What you guys doing?' Jack asked.

'Shooting a game. Wanna play?' Bigger asked.

'You asking 'em to play and I'm paying for the game,' Gus said.

They all laughed and Bigger laughed with them but stopped quickly. He felt that the joke was on him and he took a seat alongside the wall and propped his feet upon the rungs of a chair, as though he had not heard. Gus and G.H. kept on laughing.

'You niggers is crazy,' Bigger said. 'You laugh like monkeys and you ain't got nerve enough to do nothing but talk.'

'What you mean?' G.H. asked.

'I got a haul all figured out,' Bigger said.

'What haul?'

'Old Blum's.'

There was silence. Jack lit a cigarette. Gus looked away, avoiding the conversation.

'If old Blum was a black man, you-all would be itching to go. 'Cause he's white, everybody's scared.'

'I ain't scared,' Jack said. 'I'm with you.'

'You say you got it all figured out?' G.H. asked.

Bigger took a deep breath and looked from face to face. It seemed to him that he should not have to explain.

'Look, it'll be easy. There ain't nothing to be scared of. Between three and four ain't nobody in the store but the old man. The cop is way down at the other end of the block. One of us'll stay outside and watch. Three of us'll go in, see? One of us'll throw a gun on old Blum; one of us'll make for the cash box under the counter; one of us'll make for the back door and have it open so we can make a quick get-away down the back alley . . . That's all. It won't take three minutes.'

'I thought we said we wasn't never going to use a gun,' G.H. said. 'And we ain't bothered no white folks before.'

'Can't you see? This is something *big*,' Bigger said.

He waited for more objections. When none were forthcoming, he talked again.

'We can do it, if you niggers ain't scared.'

Save for the sound of Doc's whistling up front, there was silence. Bigger watched Jack closely; he knew that the situation was one in which Jack's word would be decisive. Bigger was afraid of Gus, because he knew that Gus would not hold out if Jack said yes. Gus stood at the table, toying with a cue stick, his eyes straying lazily over the billiard balls scattered about the table in the array of an unfinished game. Bigger rose and sent the balls whirling with a sweep of his hand, then looked straight at Gus as the gleaming balls kissed and rebounded from the rubber cushions, zig-zagging across the table's green cloth. Even though Bigger had asked Gus to be with him in the robbery, the fear that Gus would really go made the muscles of Bigger's stomach tighten; he was hot all over. He felt as if he wanted to sneeze and could not; only it was more nervous than wanting to sneeze. He grew hotter, tighter; his nerves were taut and his teeth were on edge. He felt that something would soon snap within him.

'Goddammit! Say something, somebody!'

'I'm in,' Jack said again.

'I'll go if the rest goes,' G.H. said.

Gus stood without speaking and Bigger felt a curious sensation—half-sensual, half-thoughtful. He was divided and pulled against himself. He had handled things just right so far; all but Gus had consented. The way things stood now there were three against Gus, and that was just as he had wanted it to be. Bigger was afraid of robbing a white man and he knew that Gus was afraid, too. Blum's store was small and Blum was alone, but Bigger could not think of robbing him without being flanked by his three pals. But even with his pals he was afraid. He had argued all of his pals but one into consenting to the robbery, and toward the lone man who held out he felt a hot hate and fear; he had transferred his fear of the whites to Gus. He hated Gus because he knew that Gus was afraid, as even he was; and he feared Gus because he felt that Gus would consent and then he would be compelled to go through with the robbery. Like a man about to shoot himself and dreading to shoot and yet knowing that he has to shoot and feeling it all at once and powerfully, he watched Gus and waited for him to say yes. But Gus did not speak. Bigger's teeth clamped so tight that his jaws ached. He edged toward Gus, not looking at Gus, but feeling the presence of Gus over all his body, through him, in and out of him, and hating himself and Gus because he felt it. Then he could not stand it any longer. The hysterical tensity of his nerves urged him to speak, to free himself. He faced Gus, his eyes red with anger and fear, his fists clenched and held stiffly to his sides.

'You black sonofabitch,' he said in a voice that did not vary in tone. 'You scared 'cause he's a white man.'

'Don't cuss me, Bigger,' Gus said quietly.

'I *am* cussing you!'

'You don't have to cuss me,' Gus said.

'Then why don't you use that black tongue of yours?' Bigger asked. 'Why don't you say what you going to do?'

'I don't have to use my tongue unless I *want* to!'

'You bastard! You scared bastard!'

'You ain't my boss,' Gus said.

'You yellow!' Bigger said. 'You scared to rob a white man.'

'Aw, Bigger. Don't say that,' G.H. said. 'Leave 'im alone.'

'He's yellow,' Bigger said. 'He won't go with us.'

'I didn't say I wouldn't go,' Gus said.

'Then, for Chrissakes, say what you going to do,' Bigger said.

Gus leaned on his cue stick and gazed at Bigger and Bigger's stomach tightened as though he were expecting a blow and were getting ready for it. His fists clenched harder. In a split second he felt how his fist and arm and body would feel if he hit Gus squarely in the mouth, drawing blood; Gus would fall and he would walk out and the whole thing would be over and the robbery would not take place. And his thinking and feeling in this way made the choking tightness rising from the pit of his stomach to his throat slacken a little.

'You see, Bigger,' began Gus in a tone that was a compromise between kindness and pride. 'You see, Bigger, you the cause of all the trouble we ever have. It's your hot temper. Now, how come you want to cuss me? Ain't I got a right to make up my mind? Naw; that ain't your way. You start cussing. You say I'm scared. It's *you* who's scared. You scared I'm going to say yes and you'll have to go through with the job . . .'

'Say that again! Say that again and I'll take one of these balls and sink it in your Goddamn mouth,' Bigger said, his pride wounded to the quick.

'Aw, for Chrissakes,' Jack said.

'You *see* how he is,' Gus said.

'Why don't you say what you going to do?' Bigger demanded.

'Aw, I'm going with you-all,' Gus said in a nervous tone that sought to hide itself; a tone that hurried on to other things. 'I'm going, but Bigger don't have to act like that. He don't have to cuss me.'

'Why didn't you say that at first?' Bigger asked; his anger amounted almost to frenzy. 'You make a man want to sock you!'

'. . . I'll help on the haul,' Gus

continued, as though Bigger had not spoken. 'I'll help just like I always help. But I'll be Goddamn if I'm taking orders from *you*, Bigger! You just a scared coward! You calling me scared so nobody'll see how scared *you* is!'

Bigger leaped at him, but Jack ran between them. G.H. caught Gus's arm and led him aside.

'Who's asking you to take orders?' Bigger said. 'I never want to give orders to a piss-sop like you!'

'You boys cut out that racket back there!' Doc called.

They stood silently about the pool table. Bigger's eyes followed Gus as Gus put his cue stick in the rack and brushed chalk dust from his trousers and walked a little distance away. Bigger's stomach burned and a hazy black cloud hovered a moment before his eyes, and left. Mixed images of violence ran like sand through his mind, dry and fast, vanishing. He could stab Gus with his knife; he could slap him; he could kick him; he could trip him up and send him sprawling on his face. He could do a lot of things to Gus for making him feel this way.

'Come on, G.H.,' Gus said.

'Where we going?'

'Let's walk.'

'O.K.'

'What we gonna do?' Jack asked. 'Meet here at three?'

'Sure,' Bigger said. 'Didn't we just decide?'

'I'll be here,' Gus said, with his back turned.

When Gus and G.H. had gone Bigger sat down and felt cold sweat on his skin. It was planned now and he would have to go through with it. His teeth gritted and the last image he had seen of Gus going through the door lingered in his mind. He could

have taken one of the cue sticks and gripped it hard and swung it at the back of Gus's head, feeling the impact of the hard wood cracking against the bottom of the skull. The tight feeling was still in him and he knew that it would remain until they were actually doing the job, until they were in the store taking the money.

'You and Gus sure don't get along none,' Jack said, shaking his head.

Bigger turned and looked at Jack; he had forgotten that Jack was still there.

'Aw, that yellow black bastard,' Bigger said.

'He's all right,' Jack said.

'He's scared,' Bigger said. 'To make him ready for a job, you have to make him scared two ways. You have to make him more scared of what'll happen to him if he don't do the job than of what'll happen to him if he pulls the job.'

'If we going to Blum's today, we oughtn't to fuss like this,' Jack said. 'We got a job on our hands, a real job.'

'Sure. Sure, I know,' Bigger said.

Bigger felt an urgent need to hide his growing and deepening feeling of hysteria; he had to get rid of it or else he would succumb to it. He longed for a stimulus powerful enough to focus his attention and drain off his energies. He wanted to run. Or listen to some swing music. Or laugh or joke. Or read a *Real Detective Story Magazine*. Or go to a movie. Or visit Bessie. All that morning he had lurked behind his curtain of indifference and looked at things, snapping and glaring at whatever had tried to make him come out into the open. But now he was out; the thought of the job at Blum's and the tilt he had had with Gus had snared him into things and his self-trust was gone. Confidence could only come again now through action so violent that it would make him forget. These were the rhythms of his life: indifference and violence; periods of abstract brooding and periods of intense desire; moments of silence and moments of anger—like water ebbing and flowing from the tug of a far-away, invisible force. Being this way was a need of his as deep as eating. He was like a strange plant blooming in the day and wilting at night; but the sun that made it bloom and the cold darkness that made it wilt were never seen. It was his own sun and darkness, a private and personal sun and darkness. He was bitterly proud of his swiftly changing moods and boasted when he had to suffer the results of them. It was the way he was, he would say; he could not help it, he would say, and his head would wag. And it was his sullen stare and the violent action that followed that made Gus and Jack and G.H. hate and fear him as much as he hated and feared himself.

'Where you want to go?' Jack asked. 'I'm tired of setting.'

'Let's walk,' Bigger said.

They went to the front door. Bigger paused and looked round the poolroom with a wild and exasperated expression, his lips tightening with resolution.

'Goin'?' Doc asked, not moving his head.

'Yeah,' Bigger said.

'See you later,' Jack said.

They walked along the street in the morning sunshine. They waited leisurely at corners for cars to pass; it was not that they feared cars, but they had plenty of time. They reached South Parkway smoking freshly lit cigarettes.

'I'd like to see a movie,' Bigger said.

'*Trader Horn's* running again at the Regal. They're bringing a lot of old pictures back.'

'How much is it?'

'Twenty cents.'

'O.K. Let's see it.'

Bigger strode silently beside Jack for six blocks. It was noon when they reached Forty-seventh Street and South Parkway. The Regal was just opening. Bigger lingered in the lobby and looked at the colored posters while Jack bought the tickets. Two features were advertised: one, *The Gay Woman,* was pictured on the posters in images of white men and white women lolling on beaches, swimming, and dancing in night clubs; the other, *Trader Horn,* was shown on the posters in terms of black men and black women dancing against a wild background of barbaric jungle. Bigger looked up and saw Jack standing at his side.

'Come on. Let's go in,' Jack said.

'O.K.'

He followed Jack into the darkened movie. The shadows were soothing to his eyes after the glare of the sun. The picture had not started and he slouched far down in a seat and listened to a pipe organ shudder in waves of nostalgic tone, like a voice humming hauntingly within him. He moved restlessly, looking round as though expecting to see someone sneaking upon him. The organ sang forth full, then dropped almost to silence.

'You reckon we'll do all right at Blum's?' he asked in a drawling voice tinged with uneasiness.

'Aw, sure,' Jack said; but his voice, too, was uneasy.

'You know, I'd just as soon go to

jail as take that damn relief job,' Bigger said.

'Don't say that. Everything'll be all right.'

'You reckon it will?'

'Sure.'

'I don't give a damn.'

'Let's think about how we'll do it, not about how we'll get caught.'

'Scared?'

'Naw. You?'

'Hell, naw!'

They were silent, listening to the organ. It sounded for a long moment on a trembling note, then died away. Then it stole forth again in whispering tones that could scarcely be heard.

'We better take our guns along this time,' Bigger said.

'O.K. But we gotta be careful. We don't wanna kill nobody.'

'Yeah. But I'll feel safer with a gun this time.'

'Gee, I wished it was three o'clock now. I wished it was over.'

'Me too.'

The organ sighed into silence and the screen flashed with the rhythm of moving shadows. There was a short newsreel which Bigger watched without much interest. Then came *The Gay Woman* in which, amid scenes of cocktail drinking, dancing, golfing, swimming, and spinning roulette wheels, a rich young white woman kept clandestine appointments with her lover while her millionaire husband was busy in the offices of a vast paper mill. Several times Bigger nudged Jack in the ribs with his elbow as the giddy young woman duped her husband and kept from him the knowledge of what she was doing.

'She sure got her old man fooled,' Bigger said.

'Looks like it. He's so busy mak-ing money he don't know what's going on,' Jack said. 'Them rich chicks'll do anything.'

'Yeah. And she's a hot looking number, all right,' Bigger said. 'Say, maybe I'll be working for folks like that if I take that relief job. Maybe I'll be driving 'em around . . .'

'Sure,' Jack said. 'Man, you ought to take that job. You don't know what you might run into. My ma used to work for rich white folks and you ought to hear the tales she used to tell . . .'

'What she say?' Bigger asked eagerly.

'Ah, man, them rich white wom-en'll go to bed with anybody, from a poodle on up. Shucks, they even have their chauffeurs. Say, if you run into anything on that new job that's too much for you to handle, let me know . . .'

They laughed. The play ran on and Bigger saw a night club floor thronged with whirling couples and heard a swing band playing music. The rich young woman was dancing and laughing with her lover.

'I'd like to be invited to a place like that just to find out what it feels like,' Bigger mused.

'Man, if them folks saw you they'd run,' Jack said. 'They'd think a gorilla broke loose from the zoo and put on a tuxedo.'

They bent over low in their seats and giggled without restraint. When Bigger sat up again he saw the picture flashing on. A tall waiter was serving two slender glasses of drinks to the rich young woman and her lover.

'I bet their mattresses is stuffed with paper dollars,' Bigger said.

'Man, them folks don't even have to turn over in their sleep,' Jack said. 'A butler stands by their beds at night, and when he hears 'em sigh, he gently rolls 'em over . . .'

They laughed again, then fell silent abruptly. The music accompanying the picture dropped to a low, rumbling note and the rich young woman turned and looked toward the front door of the night club from which a chorus of shouts and screams was heard.

'I bet it's her husband,' Jack said.

'Yeah,' Bigger said.

Bigger saw a sweating, wild-eyed young man fight his way past a group of waiters and whirling dancers.

'He looks like a crazy man,' Jack said.

'What you reckon he wants?' Bigger asked, as though he himself was outraged at the sight of the frenzied intruder.

'Damn if I know,' Jack muttered preoccupiedly.

Bigger watched the wild young man elude the waiters and run in the direction of the rich woman's table. The music of the swing band stopped and men and women scurried frantically into corners and doorways. There were shouts: *Stop 'im! Grab 'im!* The wild man halted a few feet from the rich woman and reached inside of his coat and drew forth a black object. There were more screams: *He's got a bomb! Stop 'im!* Bigger saw the woman's lover leap to the center of the floor, fling his hands high into the air and catch the bomb just as the wild man threw it. As the rich woman fainted, her lover hurled the bomb out of a window, shattering a pane. Bigger saw a white flash light up the night outside as the bomb exploded deafeningly. Then he was looking at the wild man who was now pinned to the floor by a dozen hands. He heard a woman scream: *He's a Communist!*

'Say, Jack?'

'Hunh?'

'What's a Communist?'

'A Communist is a red, ain't he?'

'Yeah; but what's a red?'

'Damn if I know. It's a race of folks who live in Russia, ain't it?'

'They must be wild.'

'Looks like it. That guy was trying to kill somebody.'

The scenes showed the wild man weeping on his knees and cursing through his tears. *I wanted to kill 'im,* he sobbed. Bigger now understood that the wild bomb-thrower was a Communist who had mistaken the rich woman's lover for her husband and had tried to kill him.

'Reds must don't like rich folks,' Jack said.

'They sure must don't,' Bigger said. 'Every time you hear about one, he's trying to kill somebody or tear things up.'

The picture continued and showed the rich young woman in a fit of remorse, telling her lover that she thanked him for saving her life, but that what had happened had taught her that her husband needed her. *Suppose it had been he?* she whimpered.

'She's going back to her old man,' Bigger said.

'Oh, yeah,' Jack said. 'They got to kiss in the end.'

Bigger saw the rich young woman rush home to her millionaire husband. There were long embraces and kisses as the rich woman and the rich man vowed never to leave each other and to forgive each other.

'You reckon folks really act like that?' Bigger asked, full of the sense of a life he had never seen.

'Sure, man. They rich,' Jack said.

'I wonder if this guy I'm going to

work for is a rich man like that?' Bigger asked.

'Maybe so,' Jack said.

'Shucks. I got a great mind to take that job,' Bigger said.

'Sure. You don't know what you might see.'

They laughed. Bigger turned his eyes to the screen, but he did not look. He was filled with a sense of excitement about his new job. Was what he had heard about rich white people really true? Was he going to work for people like you saw in the movies? If he were, then he'd see a lot of things from the inside; he'd get the dope, the low-down. He looked at *Trader Horn* unfold and saw pictures of naked black men and women whirling in wild dances and heard drums beating and then gradually the African scene changed and was replaced by images in his own mind of white men and women dressed in black and white clothes, laughing, talking, drinking and dancing. Those were smart people; they knew how to get hold of money, millions of it. Maybe if he were working for them something would happen and he would get some of it. He would see just how they did it. Sure, it was all a game and white people knew how to play it. And rich white people were not so hard on Negroes; it was the poor whites who hated Negroes. They hated Negroes because they didn't have their share of the money. His mother had always told him that rich white people liked Negroes better than they did poor whites. He felt that if he were a poor white and did not get his share of the money, then he would deserve to be kicked. Poor white people were stupid. It was the rich white people who were smart and knew how to treat people. He remembered hearing

somebody tell a story of a Negro chauffeur who had married a rich white girl and the girl's family had shipped the couple out of the country and had supplied them with money.

Yes, his going to work for the Daltons was something big. Maybe Mr. Dalton was a millionaire. Maybe he had a daughter who was a hot kind of girl; maybe she spent lots of money; maybe she'd like to come to the South Side and see the sights sometimes. Or maybe she had a secret sweetheart and only he would know about it because he would have to drive her around; maybe she would give him money not to tell.

He was a fool for wanting to rob Blum's just when he was about to get a good job. Why hadn't he thought of that before? Why take a fool's chance when other things, big things, could happen? If something slipped up this afternoon he would be out of a job and in jail, maybe. And he wasn't so hot about robbing Blum's, anyway. He frowned in the darkened movie, hearing the roll of tomtoms and the screams of black men and women dancing free and wild, men and women who were adjusted to their soil and at home in their world, secure from fear and hysteria.

'Come on, Bigger,' Jack said. 'We gotta go.'

'Hunh?'

'It's twenty to three.'

He rose and walked down the dark aisle over the soft, invisible carpet. He had seen practically nothing of the picture, but he did not care. As he walked into the lobby his insides tightened again with the thought of Gus and Blum's.

'Swell, wasn't it?'

'Yeah; it was a killer,' Bigger said.

He walked alongside Jack briskly

until they came to Thirty-ninth Street.

'We better get our guns,' Bigger said.

'Yeah.'

'We got about fifteen minutes.'

'O.K.'

'So long.'

He walked home with a mounting feeling of fear. When he reached his doorway, he hesitated about going up. He didn't want to rob Blum's; he was scared. But he had to go through with it now. Noiselessly, he went up the steps and inserted his key in the lock; the door swung in silently and he heard his mother singing behind the curtain.

Lord, I want to be a Christian,
In my heart, in my heart,
Lord, I want to be a Christian,
In my heart, in my heart . . .

He tiptoed into the room and lifted the top mattress of his bed and pulled forth the gun and slipped it inside of his shirt. Just as he was about to open the door his mother paused in her singing.

'That you, Bigger?'

He stepped quickly into the outer hallway and slammed the door and bounded headlong down the stairs. He went to the vestibule and swung through the door into the street, feeling that ball of hot tightness growing larger and heavier in his stomach and chest. He opened his mouth to breathe. He headed for Doc's and came to the door and looked inside. Jack and G.H. were shooting pool at a rear table. Gus was not there. He felt a slight lessening of nervous tension and swallowed. He looked up and down the street; very few people were out and the cop was not in sight. A clock in a window across the street told him that it was twelve

minutes to three. Well, this was it; he had to go in. He lifted his left hand and wiped sweat from his forehead in a long slow gesture. He hesitated a moment longer at the door, then went in, walking with firm steps to the rear table. He did not speak to Jack or G.H., nor they to him. He lit a cigarette with shaking fingers and watched the spinning billiard balls roll and gleam and clack over the green stretch of cloth, dropping into holes after bounding to and fro from the rubber cushions. He felt impelled to say something to ease the swelling in his chest. Hurriedly, he flicked his cigarette into a spittoon and, with twin eddies of blue smoke jutting from his black nostrils, shouted hoarsely,

'Jack, I betcha two bits you can't make it!'

Jack did not answer; the ball shot straight across the table and vanished into a side pocket.

'You would've lost,' Jack said.

'Too late now,' Bigger said. 'You wouldn't bet, so *you* lost.'

He spoke without looking. His entire body hungered for keen sensation, something exciting and violent to relieve the tautness. It was now ten minutes to three and Gus had not come. If Gus stayed away much longer, it would be too late. And Gus knew that. If they were going to do anything, it certainly ought to be done before folks started coming into the streets to buy their food for supper, and while the cop was down at the other end of the block.

'That bastard!' Bigger said. 'I knew it!'

'Oh, he'll be along,' Jack said.

'Sometimes I'd like to cut his yellow heart out,' Bigger said, fingering the knife in his pocket.

'Maybe he's hanging around some meat,' G.H. said.

'He's just scared,' Bigger said. 'Scared to rob a white man.'

The billiard balls clacked. Jack chalked his cue stick and the metallic noise made Bigger grit his teeth until they ached. He didn't like that noise; it made him feel like cutting something with his knife.

'If he makes us miss this job, I'll fix 'im, so help me,' Bigger said. 'He oughtn't be late. Every time somebody's late, things go wrong. Look at the big guys. You don't ever hear of them being late, do you? Naw! They work like clocks!'

'Ain't none of us got more guts'n Gus,' G.H. said. 'He's been with us every time.'

'Aw, shut your trap,' Bigger said.

'There you go again, Bigger,' G.H. said. 'Gus was just talking about how you act this morning. You get too nervous when something's coming off . . .'

'Don't tell me I'm nervous,' Bigger said.

'If we don't do it today, we can do it tomorrow,' Jack said.

'Tomorrow's Sunday, fool!'

'Bigger, for Chrissakes! Don't holler!' Jack said tensely.

Bigger looked at Jack hard and long, then turned away with a grimace.

'Don't tell the world what we're trying to do,' Jack whispered in a mollifying tone.

Bigger walked to the front of the store and stood looking out of the plate glass window. Then, suddenly, he felt sick. He saw Gus coming along the street. And his muscles stiffened. He was going to do something to Gus; just what, he did not know. As Gus neared he heard him whistling:

'The Merry-Go-Round Broke Down . . .' The door swung in.

'Hi, Bigger,' Gus said.

Bigger did not answer. Gus passed him and started toward the rear tables. Bigger whirled and kicked him hard. Gus flopped on his face with a single movement of his body. With a look that showed that he was looking at Gus on the floor and at Jack and G.H. at the rear table and at Doc—looking at them all at once in a kind of smiling, roving, turning-slowly glance—Bigger laughed, softly at first, then harder, louder, hysterically; feeling something like hot water bubbling inside of him and trying to come out. Gus got up and stood, quiet, his mouth open and his eyes dead-black with hate.

'Take it easy, boys,' Doc said, looking up from behind his counter, and then bending over again.

'What you kick me for?' Gus asked.

' 'Cause I wanted to,' Bigger said.

Gus looked at Bigger with lowered eyes. G.H. and Jack leaned on their cue sticks and watched silently.

'I'm going to fix you one of these days,' Gus threatened.

'Say that again,' Bigger said.

Doc laughed, straightening and looking at Bigger.

'Lay off the boy, Bigger.'

Gus turned and walked toward the rear tables. Bigger, with an amazing bound, grabbed him in the back of his collar.

'I asked you to say that again!'

'Quit, Bigger!' Gus spluttered, choking, sinking to his knees.

'Don't tell me to quit!'

The muscles of his body gave a tightening lunge and he saw his fist come down on the side of Gus's head; he had struck him really before he was conscious of doing so.

'Don't hurt 'im,' Jack said.

'I'll kill 'im,' Bigger said through shut teeth, tightening his hold on Gus's collar, choking him harder.

'T-turn m-m-m-me l-l-loose,' Gus gurgled, struggling.

'Make me!' Bigger said, drawing his fingers tighter.

Gus was very still, resting on his knees. Then, like a taut bow finding release, he sprang to his feet, shaking loose from Bigger and turning to get away. Bigger staggered back against the wall, breathless for a moment. Bigger's hand moved so swiftly that nobody saw it; a gleaming blade flashed. He made a long step, as graceful as an animal leaping, threw out his left foot and tripped Gus to the floor. Gus turned over to rise, but Bigger was on top of him, with the knife open and ready.

'Get up! Get up and I'll slice your tonsils!'

Gus lay still.

'That's all right, Bigger,' Gus said in surrender. 'Lemme up.'

'You trying to make a fool out of me, ain't you?'

'Naw,' Gus said, his lips scarcely moving.

'You Goddamn right you ain't,' Bigger said.

His face softened a bit and the hard glint in his bloodshot eyes died. But he still knelt with the open knife. Then he stood.

'Get up!' he said.

'Please, Bigger!'

'You want me to slice you?'

He stooped again and placed the knife at Gus's throat. Gus did not move and his large black eyes looked pleadingly. Bigger was not satisfied; he felt his muscles tightening again.

'Get up! I ain't going to ask you no more!'

Slowly, Gus stood. Bigger held the open blade an inch from Gus's lips.

'Lick it,' Bigger said, his body tingling with elation.

Gus's eyes filled with tears.

'Lick it, I said! You think I'm playing?'

Gus looked round the room without moving his head, just rolling his eyes in a mute appeal for help. But no one moved. Bigger's left fist was slowly lifting to strike. Gus's lips moved toward the knife; he stuck out his tongue and touched the blade. Gus's lips quivered and tears streamed down his cheeks.

'Hahahaha!' Doc laughed.

'Aw, leave 'im alone,' Jack called.

Bigger watched Gus with lips twisted in a crooked smile.

'Say, Bigger, ain't you scared 'im enough?' Doc asked.

Bigger did not answer. His eyes gleamed hard again, pregnant with another idea.

'Put your hands up, way up!' he said.

Gus swallowed and stretched his hands high along the wall.

'Leave 'im alone, Bigger,' G.H. called weakly.

'I'm doing this,' Bigger said.

He put the tip of the blade into Gus's shirt and then made an arc with his arm, as though cutting a circle.

'How would you like me to cut your belly button out?'

Gus did not answer. Sweat trickled down his temples. His lips hung wide, loose.

'Shut them liver lips of yours!'

Gus did not move a muscle. Bigger pushed the knife harder into Gus's stomach.

'Bigger!' Gus said in a tense whisper.

'Shut your mouth!'

Gus shut his mouth. Doc laughed. Jack and G.H. laughed. Then Bigger stepped back and looked at Gus with a smile.

'You clown,' he said. 'Put your hands down and set on that chair.' He watched Gus sit. 'That ought to teach you not to be late next time, see?'

'We ain't late, Bigger. We still got time . . .'

'Shut up! It *is* late!' Bigger insisted commandingly.

Bigger turned aside; then, hearing a sharp scrape on the floor, stiffened. Gus sprang from the chair and grabbed a billiard ball from the table and threw it with a half-sob and half-curse. Bigger flung his hands upward to shield his face and the impact of the ball struck his wrist. He had shut his eyes when he had glimpsed the ball sailing through the air toward him and when he opened his eyes Gus was flying through the rear door and at the same time he heard the ball hit the floor and roll away. A hard pain throbbed in his hand. He sprang forward, cursing.

'You sonofabitch!'

He slipped on a cue stick lying in the middle of the floor and tumbled forward.

'That's enough now, Bigger,' Doc said, laughing.

Jack and G.H. also laughed. Bigger rose and faced them, holding his hurt hand. His eyes were red and he stared with speechless hate.

'Just keep laughing,' he said.

'Behave yourself, boy,' Doc said.

'Just keep laughing,' Bigger said again, taking out his knife.

'Watch what you're doing now,' Doc cautioned.

'Aw, Bigger,' Jack said, backing away toward the rear door.

'You done spoiled things now,' G.H. said. 'I reckon that was what you wanted . . .'

'You go to hell!' Bigger shouted, drowning out G.H.'s voice.

Doc bent down behind the counter and when he stood up he had something in his hand which did not show. He stood there laughing. White spittle showed at the corners of Bigger's lips. He walked to the billiard table, his eyes on Doc. Then he began to cut the green cloth on the table with long sweeping strokes of his arm. He never took his eyes from Doc's face.

'Why, you sonofabitch!' Doc said. 'I ought to shoot you, so help me God! Get out, before I call a cop!'

Bigger walked slowly past Doc, looking at him, not hurrying, and holding the open knife in his hand. He paused in the doorway and looked back. Jack and G.H. were gone.

'Get out of here!' Doc said, showing a gun.

'Don't you like it?' Bigger asked.

'Get out before I shoot you!' Doc said. 'And don't you ever set your black feet inside here again!'

Doc was angry and Bigger was afraid. He shut the knife and slipped it in his pocket and swung through the door to the street. He blinked his eyes from the bright sunshine; his nerves were so taut that he had difficulty in breathing. Halfway down the block he passed Blum's store; he looked out of the corners of his eyes through the plate glass window and saw that Blum was alone and the store was empty of customers. Yes; they would have had time to rob the store; in fact, they still had time. He had lied to Gus and G.H. and Jack. He walked on; there was not a policeman in sight. Yes; they could have robbed the store and could have gotten away. He hoped the fight he had had with Gus covered up what he was trying to hide. At least the fight made him feel the equal of them. And he felt the equal of Doc, too; had he not slashed his table and dared him to use his gun?

He had an overwhelming desire to be alone; he walked to the middle of the next block and turned into an alley. He began to laugh, softly, tensely; he stopped still in his tracks and felt something warm roll down his cheek and he brushed it away. 'Jesus,' he breathed. 'I laughed so hard I cried.' Carefully, he dried his face on his coat sleeve, then stood for two whole minutes staring at the shadow of a telephone pole on the alley pavement. Suddenly he straightened and walked on with a single expulsion of breath. 'What the hell!' He stumbled violently over a tiny crack in the pavement. 'Goddamn!' he said. When he reached the end of the alley, he turned into a street, walking slowly in the sunshine, his hands jammed deep into his pockets, his head down, depressed.

He went home and sat in a chair by the window, looking out dreamily.

'That you, Bigger?' his mother called from behind the curtain.

'Yeah,' he said.

'What you run in here and run out out for, a little while ago?'

'Nothing.'

'Don't you go and get into no trouble, now, boy.'

'Aw, Ma! Leave me alone.'

He listened awhile to her rubbing clothes on the metal washboard, then he gazed abstractedly into the street, thinking of how he had felt when he fought Gus in Doc's poolroom. He was relieved and glad that in an hour he was going to see about that job at the Dalton place. He was disgusted with the gang; he knew that what had happened today put an end to his being with them in any more jobs. Like a man staring regretfully but hopelessly at the stump of a cut-off arm or leg, he knew that the fear of robbing a white man had had hold of him when he started that fight with Gus; but he knew it in a way that kept it from coming to his mind in the form of a hard and sharp idea. His confused emotions had made him feel instinctively that it would be better to fight Gus and spoil the plan of the robbery than to confront a white man with a gun. But he kept this knowledge of his fear thrust firmly down in him; his courage to live depended upon how successfully his fear was hidden from his consciousness. He had fought Gus because Gus was late; that was the reason his emotions accepted and he did not try to justify himself as being responsible to them for what he did, even though they had been involved as deeply as he in the planned robbery. He felt that same way toward everyone. As long as he could remember, he had never been responsible to anyone. The moment a situation became so that it exacted something of him, he rebelled. That was the way he lived; he passed his days trying to defeat or gratify powerful impulses in a world he feared.

THE RED BADGE OF COURAGE

STEPHEN CRANE

[In *The Red Badge of Courage* we see the vacillation of the soldier who alternately faces the problem of combat and retreats from it, acknowledges his fear and at once suppresses it. However, as he becomes increasingly aware of his comrades, he loses his sense of personal identity, acts blindly and automatically, and experiences sensations varying from 'blistering sweetness' to the 'rage of a driven beast.' His anger at the enemy is transferred to an anger at the 'swirling battle phantoms choking him.'

After his flight he conjures up dreams of the conquering hero who strikes forward in the face of death, he romanticizes over the magnificent pathos of his dead body, he rationalizes his inaction, he magnifies his self-hate, he tortures himself with imaginings of the derision and contempt of his comrades. But in the end it is the thought of them that frees him. The validity of this experience has been recently corroborated by psychiatrists who have studied the psychoneuroses of soldiers and civilians during war crises and have found that the desire for social approval is a compelling drive in steeling the individual to the ordeals of invasion or combat.]

The youth was in a little trance of astonishment. So they were at last going to fight. On the morrow, perhaps, there would be a battle, and he would be in it. For a time he was obliged to labor to make himself believe. He could not accept with assurance an omen that he was about to mingle in one of those great affairs of the earth.

He had, of course, dreamed of battles all his life—of vague and bloody conflicts that had thrilled him with their sweep and fire. In visions he had seen himself in many struggles. He had imagined peoples secure in the shadow of his eagle-eyed prowess. But awake he had regarded battles as crimson blotches on the pages of the past. He had put them as things of the bygone with his thought-images of heavy crowns and high castles. There was a portion of the world's history which he had regarded as the time of wars, but it, he thought, had been long gone over the horizon and had disappeared forever.

From his home his youthful eyes had looked upon the war in his own country with distrust. It must be some sort of a play affair. He had long despaired of witnessing a Greeklike struggle. Such would be no more, he had said. Men were better, or more timid. Secular and religious education had effaced the throat-grappling instinct, or else firm finance held in check the passions.

He had burned several times to enlist. Tales of great movements shook the land. They might not be distinctly Homeric, but there seemed to be much glory in them. He had read of marches, sieges, conflicts, and he had longed to see it all. His busy mind had drawn for him large pic-

From *The Red Badge of Courage* by Stephen Crane. By permission of D. Appleton-Century Co., Inc.

tures extravagant in color, lurid with breathless deeds.

But his mother had discouraged him. She had affected to look with some contempt upon the quality of his war ardor and patriotism. She could calmly seat herself and with no apparent difficulty give him many hundreds of reasons why he was of vastly more importance on the farm than on the field of battle. She had had certain ways of expression that told him that her statements on the subject came from a deep conviction. Moreover, on her side, was his belief that her ethical motive in the argument was impregnable.

At last, however, he had made firm rebellion against this yellow light thrown upon the color of his ambitions. The newspapers, the gossip of the village, his own picturings, had aroused him to an uncheckable degree. They were in truth fighting finely down there. Almost every day the newspapers printed accounts of a decisive victory.

One night, as he lay in bed, the winds had carried to him the clangoring of the church bell as some enthusiast jerked the rope frantically to tell the twisted news of a great battle. This voice of the people rejoicing in the night had made him shiver in a prolonged ecstasy of excitement. Later, he had gone down to his mother's room and had spoken thus: 'Ma, I'm going to enlist.'

'Henry, don't you be a fool,' his mother had replied. She had then covered her face with the quilt. There was an end to the matter for that night.

Nevertheless, the next morning he had gone to a town that was near his mother's farm and had enlisted in a company that was forming there. When he had returned home his mother was milking the brindle cow. Four others stood waiting. 'Ma, I've enlisted,' he had said to her diffidently. There was a short silence. 'The Lord's will be done, Henry,' she had finally replied, and had then continued to milk the brindle cow.

When he had stood in the doorway with his soldier's clothes on his back, and with the light of excitement and expectancy in his eyes almost defeating the glow of regret for the home bonds, he had seen two tears leaving their trails on his mother's scarred cheeks.

Still, she had disappointed him by saying nothing whatever about returning with his shield or on it. He had privately primed himself for a beautiful scene. He had prepared certain sentences which he thought could be used with touching effect. But her words destroyed his plans. She had doggedly peeled potatoes and addressed him as follows: 'You watch out, Henry, an' take good care of yerself in this here fighting business —you watch out, an' take good care of yerself. Don't go a-thinkin' you can lick the hull rebel army at the start, because yeh can't. Yer jest one little feller amongst a hull lot of others, and yeh've got to keep quiet an' do what they tell yeh. I know how you are, Henry.'

*   *   *

From his home he had gone to the seminary to bid adieu to many schoolmates. They had thronged about him with wonder and admiration. He had felt the gulf now between them and he swelled with pride. He and some of his fellows who had donned blue were quite overwhelmed with privileges for all of one afternoon, and it had been a very delicious thing. They had strutted.

A certain light-haired girl had made vivacious fun at his martial spirit, but there was another and darker girl whom he had gazed at steadfastly, and he thought she grew demure and sad at sight of his blue and brass. As he had walked down the path between the rows of oaks, he had turned his head and detected her at a window watching his departure. As he perceived her, she had immediately begun to stare up through the high tree branches at the sky. He had seen a good deal of flurry and haste in her movement as she changed her attitude. He often thought of it.

On the way to Washington his spirit had soared. The regiment was fed and caressed at station after station until the youth had believed that he must be a hero. There was a lavish expenditure of bread and cold meats, coffee, and pickles and cheese. As he basked in the smiles of the girls and was patted and complimented by the old men, he had felt growing within him the strength to do mighty deeds of arms.

After complicated journeyings with many pauses, there had come months of monotonous life in a camp. He had had the belief that real war was a series of death struggles with small time in between for sleep and meals; but since his regiment had come to the field the army had done little but sit still and try to keep warm.

He was brought then gradually back to his old ideas. Greeklike struggles would be no more. Men were better, or more timid. Secular and religious education had effaced the throat-grappling instinct, or else firm finance held in check the passions.

He had grown to regard himself merely as a part of a vast blue demonstration. His province was to look out, as far as he could, for his personal comfort. For recreation he could twiddle his thumbs and speculate on the thoughts which must agitate the minds of the generals. Also, he was drilled and drilled and reviewed.

The only foes he had seen were some pickets along the river bank. They were a sun-tanned, philosophical lot, who sometimes shot reflectively at the blue pickets. When reproached for this afterward, they usually expressed sorrow, and swore by their gods that the guns had exploded without their permission. The youth, on guard duty one night, conversed across the stream with one of them. He was a slightly ragged man, who spat skillfully between his shoes and possessed a great fund of bland and infantile assurance. The youth liked him personally.

'Yank,' the other had informed him, 'yer a right dum good feller.' This sentiment, floating to him upon the still air, had made him temporarily regret war.

Various veterans had told him tales. Some talked of gray, bewhiskered hordes who were advancing with relentless curses and chewing tobacco with unspeakable valor; tremendous bodies of fierce soldiery who were sweeping along like the Huns. Others spoke of tattered and eternally hungry men who fired despondent powders. 'They'll charge through hell's fire an' brimstone t' git a holt on a haversack, an' sech stomachs ain't a-lastin' long,' he was told. From the stories, the youth imagined the red, live bones sticking out through slits in the faded uniforms.

Still, he could not put a whole faith in veterans' tales, for recruits were their prey. They talked much of smoke, fire, and blood, but he could not tell how much might be lies.

They persistently yelled 'Fresh fish!' at him, and were in no wise to be trusted.

However, he perceived now that it did not greatly matter what kind of soldiers he was going to fight, so long as they fought, which fact no one disputed. There was a more serious problem. He lay in his bunk pondering upon it. He tried to mathematically prove to himself that he would not run from a battle.

Previously he had never felt obliged to wrestle too seriously with this question. In his life he had taken certain things for granted, never challenging his belief in ultimate success, and bothering little about means and roads. But here he was confronted with a thing of moment. It had suddenly appeared to him that perhaps in a battle he might run. He was forced to admit that as far as war was concerned he knew nothing of himself.

A sufficient time before he would have allowed the problem to kick its heels at the outer portals of his mind, but now he felt compelled to give serious attention to it.

A little panic-fear grew in his mind. As his imagination went forward to a fight, he saw hideous possibilities. He contemplated the lurking menaces of the future, and failed in an effort to see himself standing stoutly in the midst of them. He recalled his visions of broken-bladed glory, but in the shadow of the impending tumult he suspected them to be impossible pictures.

He sprang from the bunk and began to pace nervously to and fro. 'Good Lord, what's th' matter with me?' he said aloud.

He felt that in this crisis his laws of life were useless. Whatever he had learned of himself was here of no avail. He was an unknown quantity. He saw that he would again be obliged to experiment as he had in early youth. He must accumulate information of himself, and meanwhile he resolved to remain close upon his guard lest those qualities of which he knew nothing should everlastingly disgrace him. 'Good Lord!' he repeated in dismay.

*　　*　　*

He became aware that the furnace roar of the battle was growing louder. Great brown clouds had floated to the still heights of air before him. The noise, too, was approaching. The woods filtered men and the fields became dotted.

As he rounded a hillock, he perceived that the roadway was now a crying mass of wagons, teams, and men. From the heaving tangle issued exhortations, commands, imprecations. Fear was sweeping it all along. The cracking whips bit and horses plunged and tugged. The white-topped wagons strained and stumbled in their exertions like fat sheep.

The youth felt comforted in a measure by this sight. They were all retreating. Perhaps, then, he was not so bad after all. He seated himself and watched the terror-stricken wagons. They fled like soft, ungainly animals. All the roarers and lashers served to help him to magnify the dangers and horrors of the engagement that he might try to prove to himself that the thing with which men could charge him was in truth a symmetrical act. There was an amount of pleasure to him in watching the wild march of this vindication.

Presently the calm head of a forward-going column of infantry appeared in the road. It came swiftly on. Avoiding the obstructions gave it the sinuous movement of a serpent. The men at the head butted mules with their musket stocks. They prodded teamsters indifferent to all howls. The men forced their way through parts of the dense mass by strength. The blunt head of the column pushed. The raving teamsters swore many strange oaths.

The commands to make way had the ring of a great importance in them. The men were going forward to the heart of the din. They were to confront the eager rush of the enemy. They felt the pride of their onward movement when the remainder of the army seemed trying to dribble down this road. They tumbled teams about with a fine feeling that it was no matter so long as their column got to the front in time. This importance made their faces grave and stern. And the backs of the officers were very rigid.

As the youth looked at them the black weight of his woe returned to him. He felt that he was regarding a procession of chosen beings. The separation was as great to him as if they had marched with weapons of flame and banners of sunlight. He could never be like them. He could have wept in his longings.

He searched about in his mind for an adequate malediction for the indefinite cause, the thing upon which men turn the words of final blame. It —whatever it was—was responsible for him, he said. There lay the fault.

The haste of the column to reach the battle seemed to the forlorn young man to be something much finer than stout fighting. Heroes, he thought, could find excuses in that long seething lane. They could retire with perfect self-respect and make excuses to the stars.

He wondered what those men had eaten that they could be in such haste to force their way to grim chances of death. As he watched his envy grew until he thought that he wished to change lives with one of them. He would have liked to have used a tremendous force, he said, throw off himself and become a better. Swift pictures of himself, apart, yet in himself, came to him—a blue desperate figure leading lurid charges with one knee forward and a broken blade high—a blue, determined figure standing before a crimson and steel assault, getting calmly killed on a high place before the eyes of all. He thought of the magnificent pathos of his dead body.

These thoughts uplifted him. He felt the quiver of war desire. In his ears, he heard the ring of victory. He knew the frenzy of a rapid successful charge. The music of the trampling feet, the sharp voices, clanking arms of the column near him made him soar on the red wings of war. For a few moments he was sublime.

He thought that he was about to start for the front. Indeed, he saw a picture of himself, dust-stained, haggard, panting, flying to the front at the proper moment to seize and throttle the dark, leering witch of calamity.

Then the difficulties of the thing began to drag at him. He hesitated, balancing awkwardly on one foot.

He had no rifle; he could not fight with his hands, said he resentfully to his plan. Well, rifles could be had for the picking. They were extraordinarily profuse.

Also, he continued, it would be a miracle if he found his regiment. Well, he could fight with any regiment.

He started forward slowly. He stepped as if he expected to tread upon some explosive thing. Doubts and he were struggling.

He would truly be a worm if any of his comrades should see him returning thus, the marks of his flight upon him. There was a reply that the intent fighters did not care for what happened rearward saving that no hostile bayonets appeared there. In the battle-blur his face would, in a way, be hidden, like the face of a cowled man.

But then he said that his tireless fate would bring forth, when the strife lulled for a moment, a man to ask of him an explanation. In imagination he felt the scrutiny of his companions as he painfully labored through some lies.

Eventually, his courage expended itself upon these objections. The debates drained him of his fire.

He was not cast down by this defeat of his plan, for, upon studying the affair carefully, he could not but admit that the objections were very formidable.

Furthermore, various ailments had begun to cry out. In their presence he could not persist in flying high with the wings of war; they rendered it almost impossible for him to see himself in a heroic light. He tumbled headlong.

He discovered that he had a scorching thirst. His face was so dry and grimy that he thought he could feel his skin crackle. Each bone of his body had an ache in it, and seemingly threatened to break with each movement. His feet were like two sores. Also, his body was calling for food. It was more powerful than a direct hunger. There was a dull, weight-like feeling in his stomach, and, when he tried to walk, his head swayed and he tottered. He could not see with

distinctness. Small patches of green mist floated before his vision.

While he had been tossed by many emotions, he had not been aware of ailments. Now they beset him and made clamor. As he was at last compelled to pay attention to them, his capacity for self-hate was multiplied. In despair, he declared that he was not like those others. He now conceded it to be impossible that he should ever become a hero. He was a craven loon. Those pictures of glory were piteous things. He groaned from his heart and went staggering off.

A certain mothlike quality within him kept him in the vicinity of the battle. He had a great desire to see, and to get news. He wished to know who was winning.

He told himself that, despite his unprecedented suffering, he had never lost his greed for a victory, yet, he said, in a half-apologetic manner to his conscience, he could not but know that a defeat for the army this time might mean many favorable things for him. The blows of the enemy would splinter regiments into fragments. Thus, many men of courage, he considered, would be obliged to desert the colors and scurry like chickens. He would appear as one of them. They would be sullen brothers in distress, and he could then easily believe he had not run any farther or faster than they. And if he himself could believe in his virtuous perfection, he conceived that there would be small trouble in convincing all others.

He said, as if in excuse for this hope, that previously the army had encountered great defeats and in a few months had shaken off all blood and tradition of them, emerging as bright and valiant as a new one; thrusting out of sight the memory of disaster, and appearing with the valor and confidence of unconquered legions. The shrilling voices of the people at home would pipe dismally for a time, but various generals were usually compelled to listen to these ditties. He of course felt no compunctions for proposing a general as a sacrifice. He could not tell who the chosen for the barbs might be, so he could center no direct sympathy upon him. The people were afar and he did not conceive public opinion to be accurate at long range. It was quite probable they would hit the wrong man who, after he had recovered from his amazement, would perhaps spend the rest of his days in writing replies to the songs of his alleged failure. It would be very unfortunate, no doubt, but in this case a general was of no consequence to the youth.

In a defeat there would be a roundabout vindication of himself. He thought it would prove, in a manner, that he had fled early because of his superior powers of perception. A serious prophet upon predicting a flood should be the first man to climb a tree. This would demonstrate that he was indeed a seer.

A moral vindication was regarded by the youth as a very important thing. Without salve, he could not, he thought, wear the sore badge of his dishonor through life. With his heart continually assuring him that he was despicable, he could not exist without making it, through his actions, apparent to all men.

If the army had gone gloriously on he would be lost. If the din meant that now his army's flags were tilted forward he was a condemned wretch. He would be compelled to doom himself to isolation. If the men were advancing, their indifferent feet were trampling upon his chances for a successful life.

As these thoughts went rapidly through his mind, he turned upon them and tried to thrust them away. He denounced himself as a villain. He said that he was the most unutterably selfish man in existence. His mind pictured the soldiers who would place their defiant bodies before the spear of the yelling battle fiend, and as he saw their dripping corpses on an imagined field, he said that he was their murderer.

Again he thought that he wished he was dead. He believed that he envied a corpse. Thinking of the slain, he achieved a great contempt for some of them, as if they were guilty for thus becoming lifeless. They might have been killed by lucky chances, he said, before they had had opportunities to flee or before they had been really tested. Yet they would receive laurels from tradition. He cried out bitterly that their crowns were stolen and their robes of glorious memories were shams. However, he still said that it was a great pity he was not as they.

A defeat of the army had suggested itself to him as a means of escape from the consequences of his fall. He considered now, however, that it was useless to think of such a possibility. His education had been that success for that mighty blue machine was certain; that it would make victories as a contrivance turns out buttons. He presently discarded all his speculations in the other direction. He returned to the creed of soldiers.

When he perceived again that it was not possible for the army to be defeated, he tried to bethink him of a fine tale which he could take back to his regiment, and with it turn the expected shafts of derision.

But, as he mortally feared these shafts, it became impossible for him to invent a tale he felt he could trust. He experimented with many schemes, but threw them aside one by one as flimsy. He was quick to see vulnerable places in them all.

Furthermore, he was much afraid that some arrow of scorn might lay him mentally low before he could raise his protecting tale.

He imagined the whole regiment saying: 'Where's Henry Fleming? He run, didn't 'e? Oh, my!' He recalled various persons who would be quite sure to leave him no peace about it. They would doubtless question him with sneers, and laugh at his stammering hesitation. In the next engagement they would try to keep watch of him to discover when he would run.

Wherever he went in camp, he would encounter insolent and lingeringly cruel stares. As he imagined himself passing near a crowd of comrades, he could hear some one say, 'There he goes!'

Then, as if the heads were moved by one muscle, all the faces were turned toward him with wide, derisive grins. He seemed to hear some one make a humorous remark in a low tone. At it the others all crowed and cackled. It was a slang phrase.

*   *   *

The colonel came running along back of the line. There were other officers following him. 'We must charge 'm!' they shouted. 'We must charge 'm!' they cried with resentful voices, as if anticipating a rebellion against this plan by the men.

The youth, upon hearing the shouts, began to study the distance between him and the enemy. He made vague calculations. He saw that to be firm soldiers they must go forward. It would be death to stay in the present place, and with all the circumstances to go backward would exalt too many others. Their hope was to push the galling foes away from the fence.

He expected that his companions, weary and stiffened, would have to be driven to this assault, but as he turned toward them he perceived with a certain surprise that they were giving quick and unqualified expressions of assent. There was an ominous, clanging overture to the charge when the shafts of the bayonets rattled upon the rifle barrels. At the yelled words of command the soldiers sprang forward in eager leaps. There was new and unexpected force in the movement of the regiment. A knowledge of its faded and jaded condition made the charge appear like a paroxysm, a display of the strength that comes before a final feebleness. The men scampered in insane fever of haste, racing as if to achieve a sudden success before an exhilarating fluid should leave them. It was a blind and despairing rush by the collection of men in dusty and tattered blue, over a green sward and under a sapphire sky, toward a fence, dimly outlined in smoke, from behind which spluttered the fierce rifles of enemies.

The youth kept the bright colors to the front. He was waving his free arm in furious circles, the while shrieking mad calls and appeals, urging on those that did not need to be urged, for it seemed that the mob of blue men hurling themselves on the dangerous group of rifles were again grown suddenly wild with an enthusiasm of unselfishness. From the many firings starting toward them, it looked as if they would merely succeed in making a great sprinkling of corpses on the grass between their former position and the fence. But they were in a state of frenzy, perhaps because of forgotten vanities, and it made an exhibition of sublime recklessness. There was no obvious questioning, nor figurings, nor diagrams. There were, apparently, no considered loopholes. It appeared that the swift wings of their desires would have shattered against the iron gates of the impossible.

He himself felt the daring spirit of a savage religion-mad. He was capable of profound sacrifices, a tremendous death. He had no time for dissections, but he knew that he thought of the bullets only as things that could prevent him from reaching the place of his endeavor. There were subtle flashings of joy within him that thus should be his mind.

He strained all his strength. His eyesight was shaken and dazzled by the tension of thought and muscle. He did not see anything excepting the mist of smoke gashed by the little knives of fire, but he knew that in it lay the aged fence of a vanished farmer protecting the snuggled bodies of the gray men.

As he ran a thought of the shock of contact gleamed in his mind. He expected a great concussion when the two bodies of troops crashed together. This became a part of his wild battle madness. He could feel the onward swing of the regiment about him and he conceived of a thunderous, crushing blow that would prostrate the resistance and spread consternation and amazement for miles. The flying regiment was going to have a catapultian effect. This dream made him run faster among his comrades, who were giving vent to hoarse and frantic cheers.

But presently he could see that many of the men in gray did not intend to abide the blow. The smoke, rolling, disclosed men who ran, their faces still turned. These grew to a crowd, who retired stubbornly. Individuals wheeled frequently to send a bullet at the blue wave.

But at one part of the line there was a grim and obdurate group that made no movement. They were settled firmly down behind posts and rails. A flag, ruffled and fierce, waved over them and their rifles dinned fiercely.

The blue whirl of men got very near, until it seemed that in truth there would be a close and frightful scuffle. There was an expressed disdain in the opposition of the little group, that changed the meaning of the cheers of the men in blue. They became yells of wrath, directed, personal. The cries of the two parties were now in sound an interchange of scathing insults.

They in blue showed their teeth; their eyes shone all white. They launched themselves as at the throats of those who stood resisting. The space between dwindled to an insignificant distance.

The youth had centered the gaze of his soul upon that other flag. Its possession would be high pride. It would express bloody minglings, near blows. He had a gigantic hatred for those who made great difficulties and complications. They caused it to be as a craved treasure of mythology, hung amid tasks and contrivances of danger.

He plunged like a mad horse at it. He was resolved it should not escape if wild blows and darings of blows could seize it. His own emblem, quivering and aflare, was winging toward the other. It seemed there would shortly be an encounter of strange beaks and claws, as of eagles.

The swirling body of blue men came to a sudden halt at close and disastrous range and roared a swift volley. The group in gray was split and broken by this fire, but its riddled body still fought. The men in blue yelled again and rushed in upon it.

The youth, in his leapings, saw, as through a mist, a picture of four or five men stretched upon the ground or writhing upon their knees with bowed heads as if they had been stricken by bolts from the sky. Tottering among them was the rival color bearer, whom the youth saw had been bitten vitally by the bullets of the last formidable volley. He perceived this man fighting a last struggle, the struggle of one whose legs are grasped by demons. It was a ghastly battle. Over his face was the bleach of death, but set upon it were the dark and hard lines of desperate purpose. With this terrible grin of resolution he hugged his precious flag to him and was stumbling and staggering in his design to go the way that led to safety for it.

But his wounds always made it seem that his feet were retarded, held, and he fought a grim fight, as with invisible ghouls fastened greedily upon his limbs. Those in advance of the scampering blue men, howling cheers, leaped at the fence. The despair of the lost was in his eyes as he glanced back at them.

*   *   *

At this point of its march the division curved away from the field and went winding off in the direction of the river. When the significance of this movement had impressed itself upon the youth he turned his head and looked over his shoulder toward the trampled and *débris*-strewed ground. He breathed a breath of new satisfaction. He finally nudged his friend. 'Well, it's all over,' he said to him.

His friend gazed backward. 'B' Gawd, it is,' he assented. They mused.

For a long time the youth was obliged to reflect in a puzzled and uncertain way. His mind was undergoing a subtle change. It took moments for it to cast off its battleful ways and resume its accustomed course of thought. Gradually his brain emerged from the clogged clouds, and at last he was enabled to more closely comprehend himself and circumstance.

He understood then that the existence of shot and countershot was in the past. He had dwelt in a land of strange, squalling upheavals and had come forth. He had been where there was red of blood and black of passion, and he was escaped. His first thoughts were given to rejoicings at this fact.

Later he began to study his deeds, his failures, and his achievements. Thus, fresh from scenes where many of his usual machines of reflection had been idle, from where he had proceeded sheeplike, he struggled to marshal all his acts.

At last they marched before him clearly. From this present view point he was enabled to look upon them in spectator fashion and to criticise them with some correctness, for his new condition had already defeated certain sympathies.

Regarding his procession of memory he felt gleeful and unregretting, for in it his public deeds were paraded in great and shining prominence. Those performances which had been witnessed by his fellows marched now in wide purple and gold, having various deflections. They went gayly with music. It was pleasure to watch these things. He spent delightful minutes viewing the gilded images of memory.

He saw that he was good. He recalled with a thrill of joy the respectful comments of his fellows upon his conduct.

Nevertheless, the ghost of his flight from the first engagement appeared to him and danced. There were small shoutings in his brain about these matters. For a moment he blushed, and the light of his soul flickered with shame.

A specter of reproach came to him. There loomed the dogging memory of the tattered soldier—he who, gored by bullets and faint for blood, had fretted concerning an imagined wound in another; he who had loaned his last of strength and intellect for the tall soldier; he who, blind with weariness and pain, had been deserted in the field.

For an instant a wretched chill of sweat was upon him at the thought that he might be detected in the thing. As he stood persistently before his vision, he gave vent to a cry of sharp irritation and agony.

His friend turned. 'What's the matter, Henry?' he demanded. The youth's reply was an outburst of crimson oaths.

As he marched along the little branch-hung roadway among his prattling companions this vision of cruelty brooded over him. It clung near him always and darkened his view of these deeds in purple and gold. Whichever way his thoughts turned they were followed by the somber phantom of the desertion in the fields. He looked stealthily at his companions, feeling sure that they must discern in his face evidences of this pursuit. But they were plodding in ragged array, discussing with quick tongues the accomplishments of the late battle.

'Oh, if a man should come up an' ask me, I'd say we got a dum good lickin'.'

'Lickin'—in yer eye! We ain't licked, sonny. We're goin' down here aways, swing aroun', an' come in behint 'em.'

'Oh, hush, with your comin' in behint 'em. I've seen all 'a that I wanta. Don't tell me about comin' in behint—'

'Bill Smithers, he ses he'd rather been in ten hundred battles than been in that heluva hospital. He ses they got shootin' in th' night-time, an' shells dropped plum among 'em in th' hospital. He ses sech hollerin' he never see.'

'Hasbrouck? He's th' best off'cer in this here reg'ment. He's a whale.'

'Didn't I tell yeh we'd come aroun' in behint 'em? Didn't I tell yeh so? We—'

'Oh, shet yeh mouth!'

For a time this pursuing recollection of the tattered man took all elation from the youth's veins. He saw his vivid error, and he was afraid that it would stand before him all his life. He took no share in the chatter of his comrades, nor did he look at them or know them, save when he felt sudden suspicion that they were seeing his thoughts and scrutinizing each detail of the scene with the tattered soldier.

Yet gradually he mustered force to put the sin at a distance. And at last his eyes seemed to open to some new ways. He found that he could look back upon the brass and bombast of his earlier gospels and see them truly. He was gleeful when he discovered that he now despised them.

With this conviction came a store of assurance. He felt a quiet manhood, nonassertive but of sturdy and strong blood. He knew that he would no more quail before his guides wherever they should point. He had been to touch the great death, and found that, after all, it was but the great death. He was a man.

So it came to pass that as he trudged from the place of blood and wrath his soul changed. He came from hot plowshares to prospects of clover tranquilly, and it was as if hot plowshares were not. Scars faded as flowers.

It rained. The procession of weary soldiers became a bedraggled train, despondent and muttering, marching with churning effort in a trough of liquid brown mud under a low, wretched sky. Yet the youth smiled, for he saw that the world was a world for him, though many discovered it to be made of oaths and walking sticks. He had rid himself of the red sickness of battle. The sultry nightmare was in the past. He had been an animal blistered and sweating in the heat and pain of war. He turned now with a lover's thirst to images of tranquil skies, fresh meadows, cool brooks—an existence of soft and eternal peace.

Over the river a golden ray of sun came through the hosts of leaden rain clouds.

❋

WAR AND PEACE
LEO TOLSTOY

[In Tolstoy's panoramic novel, *War and Peace,* we find unequalled insight into the inner conflicts of varying types of individuals in time of war. We come to understand the process by which the emotions of idealistic youth may be caught up in identification with a cause symbolized by the person of a leader, whether he be Alexander I of Russia, Napoleon, or Hitler. The sensitive Rostov, wandering among the campfires and dreaming of the happiness of dying before his Emperor's eyes, is taunted by his more extroverted friend Denisov: 'To be sure he'd no one to fall in love with in the field, so he's fallen in love with the Tsar.' Rostov resents Denisov's flippancy—'It's such a lofty, such a sublime feeling.' The author comments, 'He really was in love with the Tsar and the glory of the Russian arms and the hope of coming victory.'

But if, to many, war means the loss of personal identity in devotion to something greater than themselves, to others it may offer limitless possibilities for the power their proud natures crave. Although Prince Andrew later renounces war and personal glory, at this moment his attitude strikingly supports Adler's analysis of the drive for power as dominant in human life.]

From *War and Peace* by Leo Tolstoy. Reprinted by permission of the Oxford University Press, London.

The day after the meeting of Boris and Rostov the review of the Austrian and Russian troops was held, both of those freshly arrived and those who had been campaigning under Kutuzov. The two emperors, the Russian and his heir the Tsarevich, and the Austrian with the archduke, inspected the Allied army of eighty thousand men.

From early morning the smart, clean, and trim troops were on the move, forming up on the field before the fortress. Now thousands of feet and bayonets moved and, with banners flying, stopped at their officers' command, turned, and took position at intervals, wheeling round other similar masses of infantry in different uniforms; now were heard the rhythmic beat of hoofs and the jungle of showy cavalry in blue, red, and green braided uniforms, with the smartly dressed bandsmen in front mounted on black, roan, or grey horses; then again, spreading out with the brazen clatter of the polished shining cannon that jolted on their gun-carriages, and with the smell of linstocks, came the artillery, creeping between the infantry and cavalry and taking up their appointed positions. Not only the generals in full parade uniforms, with their thin or thick waists drawn in to the narrowest limits, and their red necks squeezed into their collars, wearing sashes and all their decorations; not only the elegant officers with pomaded hair, but every soldier with his freshly washed and shaved face and his weapons as clean and shining as it was possible to make them, and every horse groomed until its coat shone like satin and every hair of its wetted mane lay smooth —all felt that something was happening which was no trifle, but an important and solemn affair. Every general

and every soldier was conscious of his own insignificance, aware of being but a drop in that ocean of men, and was yet at the same time conscious of his power as part of that enormous whole.

From early morning there had been strenuous activities and exertions, and by ten o'clock all had been brought to its appointed order. The ranks stood on the vast field. The whole army was extended in three lines. In front was the cavalry, behind it the artillery, and behind that again the infantry.

A space like a road was left between each line of troops. Three different parts of that army were sharply distinguishable from one another: Kutuzov's fighting army (with the Pavlograds on the right flank of the front line), those that had recently arrived from Russia (both Guards and regiments of the line), and the Austrian troops. But they all stood in the same lines, in the same order, and under one commander.

Like wind through the leaves ran the excited whisper, 'They're coming! They're coming!' Alarmed voices were heard, and a wave of bustle of final preparation passed through the whole army.

In front, from the direction of Olmütz, appeared an approaching group. At that moment, though the day was calm, a light gust of wind blew over the army slightly agitating the streamers on the lances, and the unfolded standards which fluttered against their staves. It was as if by that slight motion the army itself expressed its joy at the approach of the emperors. One voice was heard shouting, 'Attention!' Then, like the crowing of cocks before dawn, this was repeated by other voices from various sides. All became silent.

In the death-like stillness only the tramp of horses was heard. They were the horses of the emperors' suites. The emperors rode up to the flank, and the trumpets of the first cavalry regiment began to play a general march. It seemed that not only the trumpeters were playing, but that the entire army itself, rejoicing at the emperors' approach, naturally burst into music. Among these sounds one young kindly voice, that of the Emperor Alexander, was clearly heard. He gave the greeting, and the first regiment roared 'Hurrah' so deafeningly, continuously, and joyfully that the men were themselves awed by their multitude and the immensity of the power they constituted.

Rostov, standing in the front lines of Kutuzov's army, which the emperor approached first, experienced the same feeling as every other man in that army: a feeling of self-forgetfulness, a proud consciousness of the might of him who was the cause of this triumph, and a passionate attraction towards him.

He felt that at a single word from that man all this immense mass (and he himself, an insignificant atom attached to it) would go through fire and water, commit crime, die, perform deeds of highest heroism, and therefore he could not but tremble and his heart stand still at the imminence of that word.

'Hurrah! Hurrah! Hurrah!' thundered voices from all sides, one regiment after another receiving the Tsar with the strains of the march, and then 'Hurrah!' . . . Then the General March and again 'Hurrah!' 'Hurrah!' growing ever stronger, and increasing and merging into a deafening roar.

Before the emperor reached it each regiment seemed by its silence and immobility to be a lifeless body; but as soon as he came up the regiment became animated, their thunder joining in the roar of the whole line he had already passed. Through the terrible and deafening sound of those voices, among the masses of troops standing motionless as if turned to stone in their squares, moved carelessly but symmetrically and above all freely the hundreds of riders composing the suites, and in front of them two men—the emperors. It was upon them that the undivided, tensely passionate attention of that whole mass of men was concentrated.

The handsome young Emperor Alexander, in the uniform of the Horse Guards and wearing a three-cornered hat base forward, with his pleasant face and resonant though not loud voice, attracted every one's attention.

Rostov was not far from the trumpeters, and with his keen sight had recognized the emperor and watched his approach. When he was within twenty steps and Nicholas could clearly distinguish every detail of his handsome, happy, young face, he experienced a feeling of tenderness and ecstasy such as he had never known before. Everything—every trait and every movement—seemed to him enchanting.

Having halted in front of the Pavlograds, the Tsar said something in French to the Austrian emperor and smiled.

Seeing that smile Rostov himself involuntarily smiled and felt a yet stronger flow of love for his sovereign. He wanted to show that love somehow, and, knowing that this was impossible, was ready to cry. The Tsar called the commander of the regiment and said a few words to him.

'Oh God, what would happen to me if the emperor spoke to me?' thought Rostov. 'I should die of joy!'

The emperor·addressed the officers also: 'I thank you all, gentlemen, I thank you with all my heart'; to Rostov every word sounded like a voice from heaven.

How happily would he have died at once for his Tsar!

'You have deserved the St. George's standards and you will be worthy of them.'

'Oh, to die, to die for him!' thought Rostov.

The Tsar said something else which Rostov could not hear, and the soldiers, straining their lungs, shouted 'Hurrah!'

Rostov, leaning over his saddle, shouted 'Hurrah!' too with all his might, wishing to injure himself by that shout, only to express his rapture more fully.

The emperor stayed a few minutes in front of the Hussars, as if undecided.

'How can the emperor be undecided?' thought Rostov, but then even this indecision appeared to him majestic and enchanting like everything else that the emperor did.

That hesitation lasted only a moment. The emperor's foot, in the narrow-pointed boot fashionable at that period, touched the flank of the thoroughbred bay mare he rode; his hand in a white glove gathered up the reins, and he started again, accompanied by the irregularly swaying sea of aides-de-camp. Farther and farther away he rode, stopping in front of other regiments, till at last only his white plumes were visible to Rostov from amid the suites that surrounded the emperors.

Among the gentlemen of the suites Rostov noticed Bolkonski sitting his horse indolently and carelessly. He recalled their quarrel of yesterday, and was again confronted by the question whether he ought or ought not to challenge Bolkonski. 'Of course not!' he now thought. 'Is it worth thinking or speaking about it at such a moment? At a time of such love, such rapture, and such self-renunciation, what do all our quarrels and offences matter? I love and forgive everybody now.'

When the emperor had passed nearly all the regiments, the troops began a ceremonial march past him, and Rostov on Bedouin, recently purchased from Denisov, rode past too at the rear of his squadron—that is, alone and in full view of the emperor.

Before he reached him, Rostov, who was a splendid rider, spurred Bedouin twice, and successfully got him into the showy trot natural to the high-spirited animal. Bending his foaming muzzle to his chest, his tail extended, Bedouin, also conscious of the emperor's eye upon him, passed splendidly, as if flying through the air without touching the ground at all, and lifting his feet with a high and graceful action.

Rostov himself, his legs well back and his stomach drawn in, and feeling himself one with his steed, with a frowning but blissful face rode past the emperor 'like a vewy devil,' as Denisov expressed it.

'Fine fellows, the Pavlograds!' remarked the emperor.

'Oh God, how happy I should be if he ordered me to leap into the fire this instant!' thought Rostov.

When the review was over both the newly arrived men and Kutuzov's alike came together in groups and began to speak about awards, about the Austrians and their uniforms, about the front, about Bonaparte, and how badly the latter would now fare, especially when another army corps arrived from Essen and Prussia took our side.

But most of all, in each group, the talk was of the Emperor Alexander. Every word of his was repeated and every gesture, and they went into ecstasies about him.

All had but one wish: to advance under the emperor's command as soon as possible against the enemy. Commanded by the emperor himself it would be impossible not to vanquish any one, whoever he might be; that, after the review, was the thought of Rostov and the majority of the officers.

After the review all were surer of victory than the winning of two battles could have made them.

*   *   *

The council of war, at which Prince Andrew had not succeeded in expressing his opinion as he had hoped to do, created in him a vague and uneasy impression. Who was right—Dolgorukov and Weyrother, or Kutuzov, Langeron, and the others who did not approve of the plan of attack—he did not know. 'But was it really not possible for Kutuzov to lay his views plainly before the emperor? Was it possible,' thought he, 'that on account of court and personal considerations tens of thousands of lives, and my life, *my* life,' he thought, 'had to be risked?'

'Yes, it is quite possible that I shall be killed to-morrow,' he thought. And suddenly, at this thought of death, a whole chain of most distant and most intimate memories rose up in his imagination; he remembered his last departing from his father and his wife; he remembered the days when he first loved her! He thought of her pregnancy, and felt sorry for her and for himself. In a nervously emotional and softened mood he went out of the hut in which Nesvitzki and he were billeted, and began pacing up and down before it.

The night was foggy, and through the fog the moonlight gleamed mysteriously. 'Yes, to-morrow, to-morrow!' he thought. 'To-morrow everything may be at an end for me.' All these memories may be no more, none of them will any more have a meaning for me. To-morrow perhaps—even certainly . . . I have a presentiment that I shall for the first time have to show all I can do.' And his fancy pictured the battle, its loss, the concentration of the fighting at one point, and the perplexity of all the commanders. And now that happy moment, that Toulon for which he has waited so long, at last confronts him. Firmly and clearly he expresses his opinion to Kutuzov and Weyrother and the emperors. Everybody is struck by the justice of his views, but no one undertakes to carry them out, so he takes a regiment, a division—stipulates that no one is to interfere with his arrangements—leads his division to the critical point, and gains the victory alone. 'But death and suffering?' suggests another voice. Prince Andrew, however, gave that voice no answer, but went on dreaming of his triumphs. The dispositions for the next battle are made by him alone. He only has the title of an officer on duty in Kutuzov's army, but he alone does everything. The next battle is gained by him alone. Kutuzov is removed, and he is appointed . . . 'Well, and then?' asked the other voice. 'And then if, before that, you are not ten times wounded, killed or betrayed, well, . . . what then? . . .

'Well then,' Prince Andrew answered himself, 'I don't know what will happen, and don't wish to know, and can't, but if I want this: want glory, want to be known to men, want to be loved by them, it is not my fault that I want it, and want nothing but that, and live only for that. Yes, for that alone! I shall never tell any one, but, oh God! what am I to do if I love nothing but fame and men's love? Death, wounds, the loss of family—I fear nothing. And precious and dear as many persons are to me—father, sister, wife—those dearest to me, yet, dreadful and unnatural as it seems, I would give them all for a moment of glory, of triumph over men, of love from men I don't know and never shall know, for the love of these men here,' he thought, as he listened to the voices in Kutuzov's courtyard. The voices were those of the orderlies who were packing up; one voice, probably the coachman's, was teasing Kutuzov's old cook, whom Prince Andrew knew, and who was called Pete. He was saying 'Pete! I say, Pete.'

'Well?' returned the old man.

'Pete! Go thrash the wheat!' said the wag.

'Oh, go to the devil!' called out a voice drowned by the laughter of the orderlies and servants.

'All the same, I love and value nothing but triumph over them all, I value this mystic power and glory that is floating here above me in this mist!'

THE LEARNING PROCESS

. . . Who shall parcel out
His intellect by geometric rules,
Split like a province into round and square?
Who knows the individual hour in which
His habits were first sown, even as a seed?

—WORDSWORTH

IN the individual's physical make-up, his family relationships, his environment, economic and social, we have found factors determining the growth of his personality. The processes by which it is shaped, the way the various inner and outer forces condition one emotionally and intellectually, afford endless ground for study and interpretation by psychologists and educators. They tell us that the infant responds to a stimulus with a simple, automatic response of pleasure or pain. Pavlov's experiment in which the dog reacts to the secondary stimulus without the presence of the initial stimulus is the basis not only of the biologist's explanation of human behavior but also the foundation of the psychiatrist's interpretation of man's actions. Just as the dog or the chimpanzee reacts automatically to the stimulus, so the human being, whose faculties for reasoning and analysis will not mature until he is about eighteen years old. The pleasure-pain response of the child becomes modified, however, by his experience in life. The imposition of punishment or expression of approval by his parents plays a large part in determining his later responses to stimuli; so too the strictures of society govern his behavior. But always the response even of the adult is grounded on the initial sensation of pleasure or pain deriving from the thalamus or old brain. As the child matures these affective responses become more and more fixed through repetition, just as tires retracing the same road leave deeper and deeper imprints. This pathway magnetically attracts subsequent stimuli although as the child matures the stimulus may traverse the longer pathway beyond the magnetic course and enter into the region of the new brain or cortex. Here the response may be modified by the exercise of intelligence, reason, and foresight, a calling up of the experience of the individual and the race. Only by the exercise of the evaluational faculties of the brain can the personality achieve integration and keep its orientation to reality.

The creative artist, concerned with the inevitability of a character's

229

acts and decisions in the light of what has happened before, may implicitly suggest this intricate and subtle process at work.

*

SWANN'S WAY
MARCEL PROUST

[Proust suggests how the sense impressions of early childhood, the associations that have grown up, often unconsciously, about simple, vivid moments of sight, sound, smell, touch, and taste are the stimulus to many of our later emotional attitudes. He portrays vividly the way in which a single moment of sense experience long forgotten, recalled by an accidental association, may afford the clue to understanding of a personality and its intricate world of emotional and intellectual relationships. The taste of the madeleine dipped in tea becomes the key to a half-buried past which the writer can now re-create and explore.]

Many years had elapsed during which nothing of Combray, save what was comprised in the theatre and the drama of my going to bed there, had any existence for me, when one day in winter, as I came home, my mother, seeing that I was cold, offered me some tea, a thing I did not ordinarily take. I declined at first, and then, for no particular reason, changed my mind. She sent out for one of those short, plump little cakes called 'petites madeleines,' which look as though they had been moulded in the fluted scallop of a pilgrim's shell. And soon, mechanically, weary after a dull day with the prospect of a depressing morrow, I raised to my lips a spoonful of the tea in which I had soaked a morsel of the cake. No sooner had the warm liquid, and the crumbs with it, touched my palate than a shudder ran through my whole body, and I stopped, intent upon the extraordinary changes that were taking place. An exquisite pleasure had invaded my senses, but individual, detached, with no suggestion of its origin. And at once the vicissitudes of life had become indifferent to me, its disasters innocuous, its brevity illusory—this new sensation having had on me the effect which love has of filling me with a precious essence; or rather this essence was not in me, it was myself. I had ceased now to feel mediocre, accidental, mortal. Whence could it have come to me, this all-powerful joy? I was conscious that it was connected with the taste of tea and cake, but that it infinitely transcended those savours, could not, indeed, be of the same nature as theirs. Whence did it come? What did it signify? How could I seize upon and define it?

I drink a second mouthful, in which I find nothing more than in

From *Swann's Way* by Marcel Proust. Reprinted by permission of Random House, Inc.

the first, a third, which gives me rather less than the second. It is time to stop; the potion is losing its magic. It is plain that the object of my quest, the truth, lies not in the cup but in myself. The tea has called up in me, but does not itself understand, and can only repeat indefinitely, with a gradual loss of strength, the same testimony; which I, too, cannot interpret, though I hope at least to be able to call upon the tea for it again and to find it there presently, intact and at my disposal, for my final enlightenment. I put down my cup and examine my own mind. It is for it to discover the truth. But how? What an abyss of uncertainty whenever the mind feels that some part of it has strayed beyond its own borders; when it, the seeker, is at once the dark region through which it must go seeking, where all its equipment will avail it nothing. Seek? More than that: create. It is face to face with something which does not so far exist, to which it alone can give reality and substance, which it alone can bring into the light of day.

And I begin again to ask myself what it could have been, this unremembered state which brought with it no logical proof of its existence, but only the sense that it was a happy, that it was a real state in whose presence other states of consciousness melted and vanished. I decide to attempt to make it reappear. I retrace my thoughts to the moment at which I drank the first spoonful of tea. I find again the same state, illumined by no fresh light. I compel my mind to make one further effort, to follow and recapture once again the fleeting sensation. And that nothing may interrupt it in its course I shut out every obstacle, every extraneous idea,

I stop my ears and inhibit all attention to the sounds which come from the next room. And then, feeling that my mind is growing fatigued without having any success to report, I compel it for a change to enjoy that distraction which I have just denied it, to think of other things, to rest and refresh itself before the supreme attempt. And then for the second time I clear an empty space in front of it. I place in position before my mind's eye the still recent taste of that first mouthful, and I feel something start within me, something that leaves its resting-place and attempts to rise, something that has been embedded like an anchor at a great depth; I do not know yet what it is, but I can feel it mounting slowly; I can measure the resistance, I can hear the echo of great spaces traversed.

Undoubtedly what is thus palpitating in the depths of my being must be the image, the visual memory which, being linked to that taste, has tried to follow it into my conscious mind. But its struggles are too far off, too much confused; scarcely can I perceive the colourless reflection in which are blended the uncapturable whirling medley of radiant hues, and I cannot distinguish its form, cannot invite it, as the one possible interpreter, to translate to me the evidence of its contemporary, its inseparable paramour, the taste of cake soaked in tea; cannot ask it to inform me what special circumstance is in question, of what period in my past life.

Will it ultimately reach the clear surface of my consciousness, this memory, this old, dead moment which the magnetism of an identical moment has travelled so far to importune, to disturb, to raise up out of the very depths of my being? I cannot tell. Now that I feel nothing, it has stopped, has perhaps gone down again into its darkness, from which who can say whether it will ever rise? Ten times over I must essay the task, must lean down over the abyss. And each time the natural laziness which deters us from every difficult enterprise, every work of importance, has urged me to leave the thing alone, to drink my tea and to think merely of the worries of to-day and of my hopes for to-morrow, which let themselves be pondered over without effort or distress of mind.

And suddenly the memory returns. The taste was that of the little crumb of madeleine which on Sunday mornings at Combray (because on those mornings I did not go out before church-time), when I went to say good day to her in her bedroom, my aunt Leonie used to give me, dipping it first in her own cup of real or of lime-flower tea. The sight of the little madeleine had recalled nothing to my mind before I tasted it; perhaps because I had so often seen such things in the interval, without tasting them, on the trays in pastry-cooks' windows, that their image had dissociated itself from those Combray days to take its place among others more recent; perhaps because of those memories, so long abandoned and put out of mind, nothing now survived, everything was scattered; the forms of things, including that of the little scallop-shell of pastry, so richly sensual under its severe, religious folds, were either obliterated or had been so long dormant as to have lost the power of expansion which would have allowed them to resume their place in my consciousness. But when from a long-distant past nothing sub-

sists, after the people are dead, after the things are broken and scattered, still, alone, more fragile, but with more vitality, more unsubstantial, more persistent, more faithful, the smell and taste of things remain poised a long time, like souls, ready to remind us, waiting and hoping for their moment, amid the ruins of all the rest; and bear unfaltering, in the tiny and almost impalpable drop of their essence, the vast structure of recollection.

And once I had recognised the taste of the crumb of madeleine soaked in her decoction of lime-flowers which my aunt used to give me (although I did not yet know and must long postpone the discovery of why this memory made me so happy) immediately the old grey house upon the street, where her room was, rose up like the scenery of a theatre to attach itself to the little pavilion, opening on to the garden, which had been built out behind it for my parents (the isolated panel which until that moment had been all that I could see); and with the house the town, from morning to night and in all weathers, the Square where I was sent before luncheon, the streets along which I used to run errands, the country roads we took when it was fine. And just as the Japanese amuse themselves by filling a porcelain bowl with water and steeping in it little crumbs of paper which until then are without character or form, but, the moment they become wet, stretch themselves and bend, take on colour and distinctive shape, become flowers or houses or people, permanent and recognisable, so in that moment all the flowers in our garden and in M. Swann's park, and the water-lilies on the Vivonne and the good folk of the village and their little dwellings and the parish church and the whole of Combray and of its surroundings, taking their proper shapes and growing solid, sprang into being, town and gardens alike, from my cup of tea.

❊

DEATH OF A HERO

RICHARD ALDINGTON

[The mental and emotional confusions of a boy in the process of learning what the world of adults expects of him are well portrayed by Richard Aldington. He recognizes sense impressions as the first teachers and knows that they are often in conflict with the codes and mores of a child's elders. The stupidities of much of the sex education given to children and the feelings of guilt and fear it may induce are suggested in this passage.]

George, the younger, liked Hamborough best perhaps, Martin's Point next, Pamber hardly at all, and he detested Dullborough, the town which contained his father's offices and the minor public school which he attended.

The mind of a very young child is not very interesting. It has imagination and wonder, but too unregulated, too bizarre, too 'quaint', too credulous. Does it matter very much that George babbled o' white lobsters, stirred up frogs in a bucket, thought that the word 'mist' meant sunset, and was easily persuaded that a sort of milk pudding he detested had been made from an ostrich's egg? Of course a good deal of adult imagination consists in people's persuading themselves that they can see white lobsters, just as their poetry consists in persuading themselves that the milk pudding *did* come out of the ostrich's egg. The child at least is honest, which is something. But on the whole the young child-mind is boring.

The intellect wakes earlier than the feelings, curiosity before the passions. The child asks the scientist's Why? before he asks the poet's How? George read little primers on Botany and Geology and the Story of the Stars, and collected butterflies, and wanted to do chemistry, and hated Greek. And then one evening the world changed. It was at Martin's Point. All one night the South-West wind had streamed over the empty downs, sweeping up in a crescendo of sound to a shrill ecstasy of speed, sinking into abrupt sobs of dying vigour, while underneath steadily, unyieldingly, streamed and roared the major volume of the storm. The windows rattled. Rain pelted on the panes, oozed and bubbled through the joints of the woodwork. The sea, dimly visible at dusk, rolled furiously—tossing

From *Death of a Hero* by Richard Aldington. By permission of Covici-Friede, Inc., New York, 1929.

long breakers on the rocks, and made a tumult of white horses in the Channel. Even the largest ships took shelter. In the irregular harmony of that storm George went to sleep in his narrow lonely child's bed, and who knows what Genius, what Puck, what elfin spirit of Beauty came riding on the storm from the South, and shed the juice of what magic herb on his closed eyes? All next day the gale blew with ever diminishing violence. It was a half holiday, and no games on account of the wet. After lunch, George went to his room, and sank absorbed in his books, his butterflies, his moths, his fossils. He was aroused by a sudden glare of yellow sunlight. The storm had blown itself out. The last clouds, broken in lurid ragged-edged fragments, were sailing gently over a soft blue sky. Soon even they were gone. George opened the window, and leaned out. The heavy dank smell of wet earth-mould came up to him with its stifling hyacinth-like quality; the rain-drenched privet was almost over-sweet; the young poplar leaves twinkled and trembled in the last gusts, shaking down rapid chains of diamonds. But it was all fresh, fresh with the clarity of air which follows a great gale, with the scentless purity of young leaves, the drenched grasses of the empty downs. The sun moved majestically and imperceptibly downwards in a widening pool of gold, which faded, as the great ball vanished, into pure clear hard green and blue. One, two, a dozen blackbirds and linnets and thrushes were singing; and as the light faded they dwindled to one blackbird tune of exquisite melancholy and purity.

Beauty is in us, not outside us. We recognize our own beauty in the patterns of the infinite flux. Light, form, movement, glitter, scent, sound, suddenly apprehended as givers of delight, as interpreters of the inner vitality, not as the customary aspect of things. A boy, caught for the first time in a kind of ecstasy, brooding on the mystery of beauty.

A penetrating voice came up the stairs:

'Georgie! Georgie! Come out of that stuffy room at once! I want you to get me something from Gilpin's.'

What perverse instinct tells them when to strike? How do they learn to break the crystal mood so unerringly? Why do they hate the mystery so much?

Long before he was fifteen George was living a double life—one life for school and home, another for himself. Consummate dissimulation of youth, fighting for the inner vitality and the mystery. How amusingly, but rather tragically he fooled them. How innocent-seemingly he played the fine healthy barbarian schoolboy, even to the slang and the hateful games. Be ye soft as doves and cunning as serpents. He's such a *real* boy, you know —viz., not an idea in his head, no suspicion of the mystery. 'Rippin' game of rugger to-day, Mother. I scored two tries.' Upstairs was that volume of Keats, artfully abstracted from the shelves.

A double row of huge old poplars beside the narrow brook swayed and danced in the gales, rustled in the late spring breeze, stood spirelike heavy in July sunlight—a stock-in-trade of spires without churches left mysteriously behind by some mediaeval architect. Chestnut trees hung over the walks built on the old town walls. In late May after rain the sweet musty scent filled the lungs and nostrils, and sheets of white and pink petals hid the asphalt. In summer the tiled roofs of the old town were soft deep orange and red, speckled with lemon-coloured lichens. In winter the snow drifted down the streets and formed a tessellated pattern of white and black in the cobbled market-place. The sound of footsteps echoed in the deserted streets. The clock bells from the Norman tower, with its curious bulbous Dutch cupola, rang so leisurely, marking a fabulous Time.

Said the gardener:

'It's a rum thing, Master George, them rabbits don't drink, and they makes water; and the chickens don't make water, but they drinks it.'

Insoluble problem, capricious de-crees of Providence.

Confirmation classes.

'You'll have to go and see old Squish.'

'What's he say to you?'

'Oh, he gives you a lot of jaw, and asks you if you know any smut.'

In the School Chapel. Full-dress Preparation Class for Confirmation. The Head in academic hood and sur-plice entered the pulpit. Whispers sank to intimidated silence, dramati-cally prolonged by the hawk-faced man silently bullying the rows of im-mature eyes. Then in slow, deliberate, impressive tones:

'Within ten years one half of you boys will be DEAD!'

Moral: prepare to meet Thy God, and avoid smut.

But did he know, that blind prophet?

Was he inspired, that stately hypo-crite?

Like a moral vulture he leaned over and tortured his palpitating prey.

Motionless in body, they writhed within, as he painted dramatically the penalties of Vice and Sin, drew pictures of Hell. But did he know? Did he know the hell they were going to within ten years, did he know *how* soon most of their names would be on the Chapel wall? How he must have enjoyed composing that inscrip-tion to those 'who went forth un-falteringly, and proudly laid down their lives for King and Country'!

One part of the mystery was called SMUT. If you were smutty you went mad and had to go into a lunatic asy-lum. Or you 'contracted a loathsome disease' and your nose fell off.

The pomps and vanities of this wicked world, and all the sinful lusts of the flesh. So it was wicked, like be-ing smutty, to feel happy when you looked at things and read Keats? Per-haps you went mad that way too and your eyes fell out?

'That's what makes them lay eggs,' said the little girl, swinging her long golden hair and laughing, as the cock leaped on a hen.

O dreadful, O wicked little girl, you're talking smut to me. You'll go mad, I shall go mad, our noses will drop off. O please don't talk like that, please, please.

From fornication and all other deadly sins . . . What is fornication? Have I committed fornication? Is that the holy word for smut? Why don't they tell me what it means, why is it 'the foulest thing a decent man can commit'? When that thing hap-pened in the night it must have been fornication; I shall go mad and my nose will drop off.

Hymn Number . . . A few more years shall roll.

How wicked I must be.

Are there two religions? A few

more years shall roll, in ten years half of you boys will be dead. Smut, nose dropping off, fornication and all other deadly sins. Oh, wash me in Thy Precious Blood, and take my sins away. Blood, Smut. And then the other—a draught of vintage that has been cooled a long age in the deep-delved earth, tasting of Flora and the country green, dance and Provençal song, and sun-burned mirth? Listening to the sound of the wind as you fell asleep; watching the blue butterflies and the Small Coppers hovering and settling on the great scented lavender bush; taking off your clothes and letting your body slide into a cool deep clear rock-pool, while the grey kittiwakes clamoured round the sun-white cliffs and the scent of seaweeds and salt water filled you; watching the sun go down and trying to write something of what it made you feel, like Keats; getting up very early in the morning and riding out along the white empty lanes on your bicycle; wanting to be alone and think about things and feeling strange and happy and ecstatic—was that another religion? Or was that all Smut and Sin? Best not speak of it, best keep it all hidden. I can't help it, if it is Smut and Sin. Is 'Romeo and Juliet' smut? It's in the same book where you do parsing and analysis out of 'King John.' Seize on the white wonder of dear Juliet's hand and steal immortal blessing from her lips . . .

But more than words about things were things themselves. You looked and looked at them, and then you wanted to put down what they looked like, re-arrange them in patterns. In the drawing class they made you look at a dirty whitish cube, cylinder and cone, and you drew and re-drew hard outlines which weren't there. But for yourself you wanted to get the colours of things and how they faded into each other and how they formed themselves—or did you form them?—into exciting patterns. It was so much more fun to paint things than even to read what Keats and Shakespeare thought about them. George spent all his pocket-money on paints and water-colour blocks. For a long time he hadn't much to look at, even in reproductions. He had Cruikshank and Quiz illustrations, which he didn't much care for; and a reproduction of a Bougereau which he hated, and two Rossetti pictures which he rather liked, and a catalogue of the Tate Collection which gave him photographs of a great many horrible Watts and Frank Dicksees. Best of all, he liked an album of coloured reproductions of Turner's water-colours. Then, one spring, George Augustus took him to Paris for a few days. They did an 'educative' visit to the Louvre, and George simply leaped at the Italians and became very pre-Raphaelite and adored the Primitives. He was quite feverish for weeks after he got back, unable to talk of anything else. Isabel was worried about him—it was so *unboyish*, so, well, really, quite *unhealthy*, all this silly craze for pictures, and spending hours and hours crouching over paint-blocks, instead of being in the fresh air. So much nicer for the boy to be manly. Wasn't he old enough to have a gun license and learn to kill things?

So George had a gun license, and went out every morning in the autumn shooting. He killed several plovers and a wood pigeon. Then one frosty November morning he fired into a flock of plovers, killed one, and wounded another, which fell down on the crisp grass with such a wail of despair. 'If you wing a bird, pick it up and wring its neck,' he had been told. He picked up the struggling, heaving little mass of feathers, and with infinite repugnance and shut eyes, tried to wring its neck. The bird struggled and squawked. George wrung harder and convulsively—and the whole head came off in his hand. The shock was unspeakable. He left the wretched body, and hurried home shuddering. Never again, never, never again would he kill things. He oiled his gun dutifully, as he had been told to do, put it away, and never touched it again. At nights he was haunted by the plover's wail and by the ghastly sight of the headless bleeding bird's body. In the daytime he thought of them. He could forget them when he went out and sketched the calm trees and fields, or tried to design in his tranquil room. He plunged more deeply into painting than ever, and thus ended one of the many attempts to 'make a man' of George Winterbourne.

The business of 'making a man' of him was pursued at School, but with little more success, even with the aid of compulsion.

'The type of boy we aim at turning out,' the Head used to say to impressed parents, 'is a thoroughly manly fellow. We prepare for the Universities, of course, but our pride is in our excellent Sports Record. There is an O.T.C., organized by Sergeant-Major Brown (who served throughout the South African War), and officered by the masters who have been trained in the Militia. Every boy must undergo six months' training, and is then competent to take up arms for his Country in an emergency.'

The parents murmured polite approval, though rather tender mothers hoped the discipline was not too strict and 'the guns not too heavy for young arms.' The Head was contemptuously and urbanely reassuring. On such occasions he invariably quoted those stirring and indeed immortal lines of Rudyard Kipling, which end up 'you'll be a man, my son.' It is *so* important to know how to kill. Indeed, unless you know how to kill you cannot possibly be a Man, still less a Gentleman.

❀

CONFESSIONS

JEAN-JACQUES ROUSSEAU

[That permanent injury may be done to a child by unjust punishment is suggested by Rousseau. We see in this account from his *Confessions* how his childhood world was changed when those on whose justice and kindness he had relied failed to recognize the rights of his personality. To this harsh experience, Rousseau believed, might be traced much of the intensely emotional hatred of authority and tyranny that characterized him in later life. This insight of Rousseau's into the springs of his own actions is supported by modern psychologists. They see in the child's resentment of an authority he

Reprinted from *Confessions* by Jean-Jacques Rousseau, by permission of and special arrangement with Alfred A. Knopf, Inc., authorized publishers.

believes unjust the origins of his later attitudes toward society. He may, like Rousseau, in his intense individualism, initiate movements of social reform, or he may turn so violently against all authority that he becomes a criminal.]

One day I was learning my lesson by myself in the room next to the kitchen. The servant had put Mademoiselle Lambercier's combs in front of the fire-place to dry. When she came back to fetch them, she found one with a whole row of teeth broken. Who was to blame for the damage? No one except myself had entered the room. On being questioned, I denied that I had touched the comb. M. and Mademoiselle Lambercier both began to admonish, to press, and to threaten me; I obstinately persisted in my denial; but the evidence was too strong, and outweighed all my protestations, although it was the first time that I had been found to lie so boldly. The matter was regarded as serious, as in fact it deserved to be. The mischievousness, the falsehood, the obstinacy appeared equally deserving of punishment; but this time it was not by Mademoiselle Lambercier that chastisement was inflicted. My uncle Bernard was written to, and he came. My poor cousin was accused of another equally grave offense; we were involved in the same punishment. It was terrible. Had they wished to look for the remedy in the evil itself and to deaden for ever my depraved senses, they could not have set to work better, and for a long time my senses left me undisturbed.

They could not draw from me the desired confession. Although I was several times brought up before them and reduced to a pitiable condition, I remained unshaken. I would have endured death, and made up my mind to do so. Force was obliged to yield to the diabolical obstinacy of a child—as they called my firmness. At last I emerged from this cruel trial, utterly broken, but triumphant.

It is now nearly fifty years since this incident took place, and I have no fear of being punished again for the same thing. Well, then, I declare in the sight of heaven that I was innocent of the offense, that I neither broke nor touched the comb, that I never went near the fire-place, and had never even thought of doing so. It would be useless to ask me how the damage was done: I do not know, and I cannot understand; all that I know for certain is, that I had nothing to do with it.

Imagine a child, shy and obedient in ordinary life, but fiery, proud, and unruly in his passions: a child who had always been led by the voice of reason and always treated with gentleness, justice, and consideration, who had not even a notion of injustice, and who for the first time becomes acquainted with so terrible an example of it on the part of the very people whom he most loves and respects! What an upset of ideas! what a disturbance of feelings! what revolution in his heart, in his brain, in the whole of his little intellectual and moral being! Imagine all this, I say, if possible. As for myself, I feel incapable of disentangling and following up the least trace of what then took place within me.

I had not yet sense enough to feel how much appearances were against me, and to put myself in the place of the others. I kept to my own place, and all that I felt was the harshness of a frightful punishment for an offense which I had not committed. The bodily pain, although severe, I felt but little: all I felt was indignation, rage, despair. My cousin, whose case was almost the same, and who had been punished for an involuntary mistake as if it had been a premeditated act, following my example, flew into a rage, and worked himself up to the same pitch of excitement as myself. Both in the same bed, we embraced each other with convulsive transports: we felt suffocated; and when at length our young hearts, somewhat relieved, were able to vent their wrath, we sat upright in bed and began to shout, times without number, with all our might: *Carnifex! carnifex! carnifex!*

While I write these words, I feel that my pulse beats faster; those moments will always be present to me though I should live a hundred thousand years. That first feeling of violence and injustice has remained so deeply graven on my soul, that all the ideas connected with it bring back to me my first emotion; and this feeling, which, in its origin, had reference only to myself, has become so strong in itself and so completely detached from all personal interest, that, when I see or hear of any act of injustice—whoever is the victim of it, and wherever it is committed—my heart kindles with rage, as if the effect of it recoiled upon myself. When I read of the cruelties of a ferocious tyrant, the crafty atrocities of a rascally priest, I would gladly set out to plunge a dagger into the heart of such wretches, although I had to die for it a hundred times. I have often put myself in a perspiration, pursuing or stoning a cock, a cow, a dog, or any animal which I saw tormenting another merely because it felt itself the stronger. This impulse may be natural to me, and I believe that it is; but the profound impression left upon me by the first injustice I suffered was too long and too strongly connected with it, not to have greatly strengthened it.

With the above incident the tranquillity of my childish life was over. From that moment I ceased to enjoy a pure happiness, and even at the present day I feel that the recollection of the charms of my childhood ceases there.

❀

BRAVE NEW WORLD

Aldous Huxley

[An amusing satire on systems of conditioning children, grounded upon Pavlov's theory, is Aldous Huxley's *Brave New World*. Exaggerated though it is, his account has validity as an illustration of the way in which conditioned responses begin to be formed soon after birth and, whether deliberately or accidentally determined, explain our likes and dislikes, our idiosyncrasies, our emotional attitudes, our mature interests and beliefs. Such a picture may be especially alarming when one considers the way in which children in totali-

From *Brave New World*, by Aldous Huxley. By permission of Harper and Brothers.

tarian countries today are being taught to accept the ideas which best serve the state.]

Mr. Foster was left in the Decanting Room. The D.H.C. and his students stepped into the nearest lift and were carried up to the fifth floor.

INFANT NURSERIES. NEO-PAVLOVIAN CONDITIONING ROOMS, announced the notice board.

The Director opened a door. They were in a large bare room, very bright and sunny; for the whole of the southern wall was a single window. Half a dozen nurses, trousered and packeted in the regulation white viscose-linen uniform, their hair aseptically hidden under white caps, were engaged in setting out bowls of roses in a long row across the floor. Big bowls, packed tight with blossom. Thousands of petals, ripe-blown and silkily smooth, like the cheeks of innumerable little cherubs, but of cherubs, in that bright light, not exclusively pink and Aryan, but also luminously Chinese, also Mexican, also apoplectic with too much blowing of celestial trumpets, also pale as death, pale with the posthumous whiteness of marble.

The nurses stiffened to attention as the D.H.C. came in.

'Set out the books,' he said curtly.

In silence the nurses obeyed his command. Between the rose bowls the books were duly set out—a row of nursery quartos opened invitingly each at some gaily coloured image of beast or fish or bird.

'Now bring in the children.'

They hurried out of the room and returned in a minute or two, each pushing a kind of tall dumb-waiter laden, on all its four wire-netted shelves, with eight-month-old babies, all exactly alike (a Bokanovsky Group, it was evident) and all (since their caste was Delta) dressed in khaki.

'Put them down on the floor.'

The infants were unloaded.

'Now turn them so that they can see the flowers and books.'

Turned, the babies at once fell silent, then began to crawl towards those clusters of sleek colours, those shapes so gay and brilliant on the white pages. As they approached, the sun came out of a momentary eclipse behind a cloud. The roses flamed up as though with a sudden passion from within; a new and profound significance seemed to suffuse the shining pages of the books. From the ranks of the crawling babies came little squeals of excitement, gurgles and twitterings of pleasure.

The Director rubbed his hands. 'Excellent!' he said. 'It might almost have been done on purpose.'

The swiftest crawlers were already at their goal. Small hands reached out uncertainly, touched, grasped, unpetaling the transfigured roses, crumpling the illuminated pages of the books. The Director waited until all were happily busy. Then, 'Watch carefully,' he said. And, lifting his hand, he gave the signal.

The Head Nurse, who was standing by a switchboard at the other end of the room, pressed down a little lever.

There was a violent explosion. Shriller and ever shriller, a siren shrieked. Alarm bells maddeningly sounded.

The children started, screamed; their faces were distorted with terror.

'And now,' the Director shouted (for the noise was deafening), 'now we proceed to rub in the lesson with a mild electric shock.'

He waved his hand again, and the Head Nurse pressed a second lever. The screaming of the babies suddenly changed its tone. There was something desperate, almost insane, about the sharp spasmodic yelps to which they now gave utterance. Their little bodies twitched and stiffened; their limbs moved jerkily as if to the tug of unseen wires.

'We can electrify that whole strip of floor,' bawled the Director in explanation. 'But that's enough,' he signalled to the nurse.

The explosions ceased, the bells stopped ringing, the shriek of the siren died down from tone to tone into silence. The stiffly twitching bodies relaxed, and what had become the sob and yelp of infant maniacs broadened out once more into the normal howl of ordinary terror.

'Offer them the flowers and the books again.'

The nurses obeyed, but at the approach of the roses, at the mere sight of those gaily-coloured images of pussy and cock-a-doodle-doo and baa-baa black sheep, the infants shrank away in horror; the volume of their howling suddenly increased.

'Observe,' said the Director triumphantly, 'observe.'

Books and loud noises, flowers and electric shocks—already in the infant mind these couples were compromisingly linked; and after two hundred repetitions of the same or a similar lesson would be wedded indissolubly. What man has joined, nature is powerless to put asunder.

'They'll grow up with what the psychologists used to call an "instinctive" hatred of books and flowers. Reflexes unalterably conditioned. They'll be safe from books and botany all their lives.' The Director turned to his nurses. 'Take them away again.'

Still yelling, the khaki babies were loaded on to their dumbwaiters and wheeled out, leaving behind them the smell of sour milk and a most welcome silence.

One of the students held up his hand; and though he could see quite well why you couldn't have lower-caste people wasting the Community's time over books, and that there was always the risk of their reading something which might undesirably de-condition one of their reflexes, yet . . . well, he couldn't understand about the flowers. Why go to the trouble of making it psychologically impossible for Deltas to like flowers?

Patiently the D.H.C. explained. If the children were made to scream at the sight of a rose, that was on grounds of high economic policy. Not so very long ago (a century or thereabouts), Gammas, Deltas, even Epsilons, had been conditioned to like flowers—flowers in particular and wild nature in general. The idea was to make them want to be going out into the country at every available opportunity, and so compel them to consume transport.

'And didn't they consume transport?' asked the student.

'Quite a lot,' the D.H.C. replied. 'But nothing else.'

Primroses and landscapes, he pointed out, have one grave defect; they are gratuitous. A love of nature keeps no factories busy. It was decided to abolish the love of nature, at any rate among the lower classes; to abolish the love of nature, but *not* the tendency to consume transport. For of course it was essential that they should keep on going to the country, even though they hated it. The problem was to find an economically sounder reason for consuming transport than a mere affection for primroses and landscapes. It was duly found.

'We condition the masses to hate the country,' concluded the Director. 'But simultaneously we condition them to love all country sports. At the same time, we see to it that all country sports shall entail the use of elaborate apparatus. So that they consume manufactured articles as well as transport. Hence those electric shocks.'

'I see,' said the student, and was silent, lost in admiration.

There was a silence; then, clearing his throat, 'Once upon a time,' the Director began, 'while our Ford was still on earth, there was a little boy called Reuben Rabinovitch. Reuben was the child of Polish-speaking parents.' The Director interrupted himself. 'You know what Polish is, I suppose?'

'A dead language.'

'Like French and German,' added another student, officiously showing off his learning.

'And "parent"?' questioned the D.H.C.

There was an uneasy silence. Several of the boys blushed. They had not yet learned to draw the significant but often very fine distinction between smut and pure science. One, at last, had the courage to raise a hand.

'Human beings used to be . . .' he hesitated; the blood rushed to his cheeks. 'Well, they used to be viviparous.'

'Quite right.' The Director nodded approvingly.

'And when the babies were decanted . . .'

' "Born," ' came the correction.

'Well, then they were parents—I mean, not the babies, of course; the other ones.' The poor boy was overwhelmed with confusion.

'In brief,' the Director summed up, 'the parents were the father and the mother.' The smut that was really science fell with a crash into the boys' eye-avoiding silence. 'Mother,' he repeated loudly, rubbing in the science; and, leaning back in his chair, 'These,' he said gravely, 'are unpleasant facts; I know it. But then most historical facts *are* unpleasant.'

He returned to Little Reuben—to Little Reuben, in whose room, one evening, by an oversight, his father and mother (crash, crash!) happened to leave the radio turned on.

('For you must remember that in those days of gross viviparous reproduction, children were always brought up by their parents and not in State Conditioning Centres.')

While the child was asleep, a broadcast programme from London suddenly started to come through; and the next morning, to the astonishment of his crash and crash (the more daring of the boys ventured to grin at one another), Little Reuben woke up repeating word for word a long lecture by that curious old writer ('one of the very few whose works have been permitted to come down to us'), George Bernard Shaw, who was speaking, according to a well-authenticated tradition, about his own genius. To Little Reuben's wink and snigger, this lecture was, of course, perfectly incomprehensible and, imagining that their child had suddenly gone mad, they sent for a doctor. He, fortunately, understood English, recognized the discourse as that which Shaw had broadcasted the previous evening, realized the significance of what had happened, and sent a letter to the medical press about it.

'The principle of sleep-teaching, or

hypnopaedia, had been discovered.' The D.H.C. made an impressive pause.

The principle had been discovered, but many, many years were to elapse before that principle was usefully applied.

'The case of Little Reuben occurred only twenty-three years after Our Ford's first T-Model was put on the market.' (Here the Director made a sign of the T on his stomach and all the students reverently followed suit.) 'And yet . . .'

Furiously the students scribbled. *Hypnopaedia, first used officially in A.F. 214. Why not before? Two reasons. (a) . . .'*

'These early experimenters,' the D.H.C. was saying, 'were on the wrong track. They thought that hypnopaedia could be made an instrument of intellectual education . . .'

(A small boy asleep on his right side, the right arm stuck out, the right hand hanging limp over the edge of the bed. Through a round grating in the side of a box a voice speaks softly.)

'The Nile is the longest river in Africa and the second in length of all the rivers of the globe. Although falling short of the length of the Mississippi-Missouri, the Nile is at the head of all the rivers as regards the length of its basin, which extends through 35 degrees of latitude . . .'

At breakfast the next morning, 'Tommy,' some one says, 'do you know which is the longest river in Africa?' A shaking of the head. 'But don't you remember something that begins: The Nile is the . . .'

'The — Nile — is — the — longest — river — in — Africa — and — the — second — in — length — of — all — the — rivers — of — the — globe . . .' The words come rushing out. 'Although — falling — short — of . . .'

'Well now, which is the longest river in Africa?'

The eyes are blank. 'I don't know.'

'But the Nile, Tommy.'

'The — Nile — is — the — longest — river — in — Africa — and — the — second . . .'

'Then which river is the longest, Tommy?'

Tommy bursts into tears. 'I don't know,' he howls.

That howl, the Director made it plain, discouraged the earliest investigators. The experiments were abandoned. No further attempt was made to teach children the length of the Nile in their sleep. Quite rightly. You can't learn a science unless you know what it's all about.

'Whereas, if they'd only started on *moral* education,' said the Director, leading the way towards the door. The students followed him, desperately scribbling as they walked and all the way up in the lift. 'Moral education, which ought never, in any circumstances, to be rational.'

'Silence, silence,' whispered a loud speaker as they stepped out at the fourteenth floor, and 'Silence, silence,' the trumpet mouths indefatigably repeated at intervals down every corridor. The students and even the Director himself rose automatically to the tips of their toes. They were Alphas, of course; but even Alphas have been well conditioned. 'Silence, silence.' All the air of the fourteenth floor was sibilant with the categorical imperative.

Fifty yards of tiptoeing brought them to a door which the Director cautiously opened. They stepped over the threshold into the twilight of a shuttered dormitory. Eighty cots stood in a row against the wall. There was a sound of light regular breathing and a continuous murmur, as of very faint voices remotely whispering.

A nurse rose as they entered and came to attention before the Director.

'What's the lesson this afternoon?' he asked.

'We had Elementary Sex for the first forty minutes,' she answered. 'But now it's switched over to Elementary Class Consciousness.'

The Director walked slowly down the long line of cots. Rosy and relaxed with sleep, eighty little boys and girls lay softly breathing. There was a whisper under every pillow. The D.H.C. halted and, bending over one of the little beds, listened attentively.

'Elementary Class Consciousness, did you say? Let's have it repeated a little louder by the trumpet.'

At the end of the room a loud speaker projected from the wall. The Director walked up to it and pressed a switch.

'... all wear green,' said a soft but very distinct voice, beginning in the middle of a sentence, 'and Delta Children wear khaki. Oh no, I don't want to play with Delta children. And Epsilons are still worse. They're too stupid to be able to read or write. Besides they wear black, which is such a beastly colour. I'm so glad I'm a Beta.'

There was a pause; then the voice began again.

'Alpha children wear grey. They work much harder than we do, because they're so frightfully clever. I'm really awfully glad I'm a Beta, because I don't work so hard. And then we are much better than the Gammas and Deltas. Gammas are stupid. They all wear green, and Delta children wear khaki. Oh no, I *don't* want to play with Delta children.

And Epsilons are still worse. They're too stupid to be able . . .'

The Director pushed back the switch. The voice was silent. Only its thin ghost continued to mutter from beneath the eighty pillows.

'They'll have that repeated forty or fifty times more before they wake; then again on Thursday, and again on Saturday. A hundred and twenty times three times a week for thirty months. After which they go on to a more advanced lesson.'

Roses and electric shocks, the khakis of Deltas and a whiff of asafoetida—wedded indissolubly before the child can speak. But wordless conditioning is crude and wholesale; cannot bring home the finer distinctions, cannot inculcate the more complex courses of behaviour. For that there must be words, but words without reason. In brief, hypnopaedia.

'The greatest moralizing and socializing force of all time.'

The students took it down in their little books. Straight from the horse's mouth.

Once more the Director touched the switch.

'. . . so frightfully clever,' the soft, insinuating, indefatigable voice was saying. 'I'm really awfully glad I'm a Beta, because . . .'

Not so much like drops of water, though water, it is true, can wear holes in the hardest granite; rather, drops of liquid sealing-wax, drops that adhere, incrust, incorporate themselves with what they fall on, till finally the rock is all one scarlet blob.

'Till at last the child's mind *is* these suggestions, and the sum of the suggestions *is* the child's mind. And not the child's mind only. The adult's mind too—all his life long. The mind that judges and desires and decides—made up of these suggestions. But all these suggestions are *our* suggestions!' The Director almost shouted in his triumph. 'Suggestions from the State.'

He banged the nearest table. 'It therefore follows . . .'

A noise made him turn around.

'Oh, Ford!' he said in another tone, 'I've gone and woken the children.'

Part Two

ADJUSTMENT AND MALADJUSTMENT OF THE PERSONALITY

✻   ✻   ✻   ✻   ✻   ✻   ✻

DREAMS AND THE UNCONSCIOUS

Cease, dreams, the images of day desires,
To model forth the passions of the morrow.

—SAMUEL DANIEL

ALTHOUGH dreams in ancient times were often regarded with superstitious awe, the dreams of ordinary human beings were not considered worthy of the psychologist's attention until about sixty years ago,
when Sigmund Freud ventured upon a serious consideration of dreams
as part of his study and treatment of mental patients. The furor he
aroused is well known, but the chief ideas developed by Freud have colored all subsequent study of the problem, and his underlying theses are
now rather generally accepted, although some psychologists still hold
that dreams represent a more or less random play of associations. For
understanding of his theories one must refer to his own compendious
volumes of studies painstakingly compiled and revised through the years
up to his death in 1939, but we may note here a few salient points. Basic
to his entire theory is his concept of sexual drives as the primary motivating principle of behavior. As the child develops in his social environment, he learns that he must repress these impulses. The repressive
agency Freud often referred to as the censor. All wishes and impulses
incompatible with this moral self are forced down into the unconscious.
But every tendency or instinct, even when it is not on the level of the conscious, seeks active expression. In sleep the repressive agency is more or
less off guard, and the repressed sexual wishes can partially express themselves as dreams. And yet even in sleep, according to Freud, the moral
nature is not in complete abeyance, and for this reason the repressed
wishes may still not find direct expression. By means of such mechanisms
as symbolism and distortion of the true dream content, the individual is
kept from any shock which would disturb his moral nature. The problem
of the analyst, then, becomes that of finding the true meaning of the
dream symbols, for it seems more than probable that dreams are in some
way aspects of the sentiments, moods, wishes, fears of the personality,
and that the visions of the sleeping state may throw light on the forces
that make us what we are.

THE OUTWARD ROOM

Millen Brand

[The method employed by Freud was that of free-association of the elements of the dream or the day-dream, for he insisted that the latter is also significant. This free-association technique of the psychoanalyst is well illustrated by the passage from *The Outward Room*. The patient, who has been mentally ill since the death of a loved brother, flees from reality and rejects life. She is eventually freed by acknowledging her real emotions, apparent in her dreams, and by allowing herself to love again.]

'Hello,' Dr. Revlin said as she entered his office, getting up and taking her hand. 'It's a nice day, isn't it? Have you been out?'

'No—'

He noticed. 'Something is troubling you,' he said.

'Yes.'

'What?'

She was suddenly afraid to speak.

'Yes, tell me. We've been through much together, haven't we? And I'm your friend, no?'

She said, 'You are.'

'You'll tell me then?'

'May I tell you afterward?'

He hesitated. 'All right,' he said.

She lay down on a couch, according to their routine, and he drew a shade, darkening the room. He sat down to one side, out of range of her sight. All she knew of him now was his voice.

'As you've something important to tell me later, we'll get right to business. Let's hope this won't interfere; for the time being put it out of your mind.'

He waited.

'What did you dream last night,' he said.

'Nothing.'

'Resistance today. Or is it—? No, try to remember.'

'I'm sure I didn't dream—'

'You've remembered before when you thought you hadn't dreamed. Try to think.'

'I can't.' Yet she was yielding, her mood changing. She said, 'When I woke up, there was nothing on my mind. I even forgot I was in the hospital.'

'That's interesting. Tell me a little more about it.'

'That's all, I had just forgotten.'

'No, how was it—did you feel you were home, before you came to the hospital?'

'I don't know, I didn't think of anything. But I was happy.'

'Good! You were happy and didn't realize you were in the hospital. When you wake up and find you are in the hospital, you're unhappy, is that right?'

'In a way.'

'Why "in a way"?'

'I—all right, I'm unhappy.'

'I wish you could tell me what you meant by "in a way." I want to know.'

'I can't, I don't know.'

'Let's try again. If you had woken up at home before you came to the

From *The Outward Room* by Millen Brand. By permission of Simon and Schuster, Inc.

hospital, would you have been happy?'

'Yes, you know that!'

He paused. 'Then you would like to be the way you were then.'

'I know what you want to make me say. Can you bring back my brother?' she said.

He sighed.

'Let's start again differently. Suppose now, right now, you woke up somewhere and were not at the hospital—would you be happy then?'

'Yes, in a way—but not as happy as the other way.'

'Why would it make you happier now, to be out of the hospital? Do you mean you want to be well?'

She said nothing.

'Would it be just that it meant you were well that would make you happy?'

'Stop!'

'You would be happier if you were outside, whether you were well or not?'

'Yes.'

'But why?'

'Isn't there reason enough? Here everybody knows, they see my brother's death, my own death.'

'You're not dead.'

She said nothing.

'If you were not well, you would have to come back.'

She still said nothing.

'Outside then you would forget your brother's death?'

'No, I'd—have it alone, for a while.'

He waited a minute and said, 'Is there any other reason why you would be happier outside?'

'No.'

'You're sure? Be honest.'

She hesitated. 'Yes,' she said.

'To have escaped me, could that be it?'

She felt her face flushing. 'Yes.'

'Tell me, had you thought of trying to escape?'

'Please, Doctor—'

'Tell me.'

'I've always thought of it—not seriously, perhaps.'

'All thought is serious. And what you think about this is very serious.' He paused. 'Let me tell you something, there have been people who were about to undergo an operation, one that would mean life or death to them. At the last moment, with all arrangements made, they take a train, go away somewhere—in order not to go through with the operation. Possibly that's what you want to do?'

'I see what you mean.'

'I think you know we're reaching a kind of—that we're coming towards something. Perhaps what you are going to tell me is the same as what I am going to tell you. But first I'm interested in your dream.'

'How can I think?'

'You can. Don't think of when you woke up. Think back into the night.'

She lay quietly, her thoughts out of control. But she was experienced and kept pressing back, backward to the night. All thought would stop, meeting darkness—then begin again.

'Yes. I did dream. I was acting in a play, in costume, and I was taking two parts, at the same time.' The dream formed before her eyes, sudden, spreading out. She could feel as much as see, it was hard to put into words. What she said would not be the dream, and it would be the dream. 'Go on,' he said. 'As one person I was very tall, a giant—as the other I was very small. No, that isn't it,' she said. 'Yes it is! Go on.' 'I felt really that I was the tall person and somebody else was the small person, but it was myself too. Is that possible?'

'Yes. It's all just as you remember. Go on.'

'The small person was my servant and I felt very scornful towards her. No—' 'Yes, you were scornful. But tell me, was there anything—why, in what way did you feel scornful?'

'I don't know.'

'This is important. Did you express it in any way?'

Farther in. 'Yes.' How did he know? 'I took my servant's mail and opened it. I think I even read it to her and she couldn't do anything about it.'

'That's very interesting. Was there anything else? Think of the dream carefully.'

'We, that is both of us, were wearing a strange kind of clothing.'

'What kind?'

'It was like a costume, like historical plays.'

'Good. Can you remember anything else?'

'No.'

'All right, let's see what we can do with it—does it mean anything to you?'

'No.'

'Let's go over it. You're a giant and the servant is very small, what can that mean?'

'I can't think—no, I can't think of anything.'

'How about the dress?'

'I don't think of anything.'

'Try.'

'Yes.' It came to her suddenly. '*Gulliver's Travels.*'

'That's very interesting.' He paused. 'Yes, that must be it.'

'But I didn't think of *Gulliver's Travels* in the dream.'

'No. You just thought of it now. But there is some connection.'

'Why? Anybody might have thought of it.' She felt angry.

'Perhaps. But why Gulliver? Why not David and Goliath, or Jack and the Giant Killer—you see it isn't so simple. No, you thought of it because it really is connected with your dream. That's how it works, the laws are rather strong.'

She said nothing.

'Now let's see if perhaps there isn't some connection. A giant—' He paused. 'Is the giant Gulliver in Lilliput, or is it a Brobdignagian?'

'I don't know.'

'I'd say a Brobdignagian, do you know why?'

'No.'

'Perhaps you do. Think.'

'The Brobdignagians made Gulliver a kind of servant, a slave. They kept him in a cage.'

'Yes, that's what I was thinking of. By the way, you know your Gulliver very well. Did you read it as a child?'

'Yes.'

'When?'

'When I was five or six, I guess.'

'Did your father or mother ever read it to you?'

'My father.'

'Were there pictures in the book?'

'Yes—oh, I remember. There was one picture, the hat, yes I can see it—it's the same as in the dream.'

'What?'

'The servant looked like Gulliver in this picture.'

'Well, now we're getting somewhere.' He stopped. 'Then let's go back. Why did you think you were the same person?'

'I don't know.'

'This may be rather important. Try association.'

After a long wait, she said, 'One flesh.'

'Why "one flesh"?'

'We were the same person.'

'Any more associations?'

'My father used to say to my mother, "You're my better half." '

Immediately, as if excited, he asked, 'How young were you when you first heard your father make that remark, about the "better half"?'

'I don't know, I can't remember that.'

'Tell me this. You've mentioned before that your father was weaker than your mother. Could you have felt it when you were five, six?'

'Maybe.'

'How did he seem weaker, at that time?'

'My mother always ordered him around. I can remember her doing that. Oh, I remember—the mail. She used to open his letters and read them—'

'So that's the letters.'

'It made him angry.'

'Is there anything more about the dream?'

'Yes, there's something. But I don't know whether it's worth mentioning.'

He said irritably, 'You know everything is worth mentioning.'

'I remember how as the giant I wasn't entirely sure I was superior to the servant.'

'Yes, that's good. It all fits together. Gulliver in the story had a good mind, he knew more than the giant. And haven't you sometimes admitted to me your father was a remarkable man, that he had a quality of mind, not practical, but still superior somehow to your mother's?'

'Yes—'

'You realize it now better than you did as a child.'

'Yes, I do.'

'Well, you've explained the dream to me. And I haven't forced you to, have I, except to make you tell me?'

'No, I agree that that's the meaning of the dream.'

He paused. 'And it's close, like most of your dreams, to the whole problem of your illness. I said before that to-day we were going to talk things over as we never had before. You want to do this, don't you? We're going to, as they say, put the cards on the table.'

'Yes.'

'I want you to let me do most of the talking for a while now, and just answer what I ask you. Is this arrangement all right?'

'Yes.'

'You know for a long time certain things have kept coming up, recurring. I had hoped they would give you an understanding of yourself, without my help—without my telling you too much. And I think you've come near it, some of it you know and much more of it you must guess. But it isn't enough, you don't really know it. And so I think the time has come to go farther—to sum the whole thing up quite fully and plainly. I believe it's the best. You may not see it now, but some time you will. And I have in mind too something else, to help you. Now, have you enough courage, will you go through with it?'

'Yes, I will,' she said.

'All right. Then I'll tell you. It won't be easy for you. I don't know how it may affect you; maybe you'll be angry and won't believe me at all. But I think you ought to have it stated, put before you. Try not to argue, just listen to what I say.'

She remained silent, looking upward, waiting.

'Here it is, then. At the center of your dream, clearly, you became your mother, you were putting yourself in her place in relation to your father. The letters, the "better half," everything shows it. It's just another proof of something I've told you, that almost all children go through a period when they fall in love with the parent, the one of the opposite sex. It's an old story now, well-known. And being in love with one parent, children are jealous of the other parent —you were jealous of your mother. During the period of your childhood represented by this dream, you were in love with your father, but not as much as at first. Already your father seemed inferior to you. Later you substituted your brother for him, who was stronger and took after your mother—'

'No!'

'Remember, it isn't a matter of belief now, just listen.' He went steadily on, 'At a certain age, towards the end of childhood, the child, daughter in your case, becomes reconciled with the mother in order to be freed from the father. Then she can find her love outside of the family—she is identified with her mother; she can reach full adult love.' He paused. 'As I told you, your brother was substituted for your father, but it would have made no difference. Unfortunately your brother's death occurred just when you were beginning to free yourself from him and because of it, you have never been able to go on, past his death.'

'No, I can't believe it. It's just words, it's just the way you want it. It isn't like that in me.'

'You know, I'm not basing what I say on this one dream. All the material, all I've uncovered, hundreds, thousands of details support what I've told you. You say it's the way I want it—that isn't fair, I don't care about theories—I'm not trying to prove a case, I'm trying to help you.'

She said nothing.

'At least you've kept your promise, you've listened to me. You don't have to believe me now; just remember what I've said. Remember it carefully.' She heard him move in his chair. 'And now we come to what I mentioned before—something else I've thought of, to help you.'

'Yes—'

'In a month or so, I want you to have your parents come to see you.'

'No!'

'I know how you feel towards your parents—you think they killed your brother, but I hope by the time they come, I can make you overcome this feeling. At least enough so that you can see them—'

'No, please!'

'You say your father was tired the day of your brother's death and asked your brother to drive the car. And so, remotely speaking, he killed him. However, no reasonable person—'

'He did!'

'Remember—'

'He had no right to have a car. We were always poor, never had money, and yet he kept the car. An old one, a death trap. And my mother let him. It was my mother's fault as well as his—'

'You can make it look the way you want, but it isn't that really. That's what you'll have to see. By the time your parents come—I'll tell you— This is the final thing I've wanted to tell you. In the situation in which you were placed, something you could not know happened. It's a very delicate thing to explain to you, and you must forgive me if I'm too blunt. You know that unconsciously you must have felt some guilt about your love for your brother—'

'No!'

'It must have been a very strong love, it must have been that to do what it did to you.'

She was silent.

'So it was a help to you, when you

had to make a new adjustment to life, to blame your parents. Unconsciously, you said, "If I'm guilty, they're guilty too. They killed him." ' He paused. 'I've been as honest as I can. It's been hard to tell you all this. I haven't wanted to hurt you. I hope when you see your parents, things will suddenly become clear to you. In the meantime, with what you know, your mind can be more at rest. You know there is nothing else now, nothing unknown. And I count on you to be brave, to go on working with me, not to try to escape. Tomorrow, much of the pain of this talk will be gone. You'll find that your father's intelligence, which you have, will begin to help you. And this is very important —remember, even if this experiment I'm counting on fails, even then you can still have hope.'

✳

A CHAPTER ON DREAMS

ROBERT LOUIS STEVENSON

[Recognition of the absence of the moral element in the dream life is found in Stevenson's *A Chapter on Dreams*. The writer makes significant observations on the relation between his dreams and his processes of creation. He indicates that the moral was often later imposed by his waking conscience on the stories that came to him in sleep. The completely amoral character of his dreams is revealed in the account of his dream of a man who killed his father and loved his stepmother. The Freudian pattern here needs no comment. An analyst would perhaps have told Stevenson that the woman became stepmother rather than mother only out of deference to the censor.]

The past is all of one texture— whether feigned or suffered—whether acted out in three dimensions, or only witnessed in that small theatre of the brain which we keep brightly lighted all night long, after the jets are down, and darkness and sleep reign undisturbed in the remainder of the body. There is no distinction on the face of our experiences; one is vivid indeed, and one dull, and one pleasant, and another agonising to remember; but which of them is what we call true, and which a dream, there is not one hair to prove. The past stands on a precarious footing; another straw split in the field of metaphysic, and behold us robbed of it. There is scarce a family that can count four generations but lays a claim to some dormant title or some castle and estate: a claim not prosecutable in any court of law, but flattering to the fancy and a great alleviation of idle hours. A man's claim to his own past is yet less valid. A paper might turn up (in proper story-book fashion) in the secret drawer of an old ebony secretary, and restore your family to its ancient honours, and reinstate mine in a certain West Indian islet (not far from St. Kitt's, as beloved tradition hummed in my young ears) which was once ours, and is now unjustly some one else's, and for that matter (in the state of the sugar trade) is not worth anything to anybody. I do not say that these revolutions are likely; only no man can deny that they are possible; and the past, on the other hand, is lost for ever: our old days and deeds, our old selves, too, and the very world in which these scenes were acted, all brought down to the same faint residuum as a last night's dream, to some incontinuous images, and an echo in the chambers of the brain. Not an hour, not a mood, not a glance of the eye, can we revoke; it is all gone, past conjuring. And yet conceive us robbed of it, conceive that little thread of memory that we trail behind us broken at the pocket's edge; and in what naked nullity should we be left! for we only guide ourselves, and only know ourselves, by these air-painted pictures of the past.

Upon these grounds, there are some among us who claim to have lived longer and more richly than their neighbours; when they lay asleep they claim they were still active; and among the treasures of memory that all men review for their amusement, these count in no second place the harvests of their dreams. There is one of this kind whom I have in my eye, and whose case is perhaps unusual enough to be described. He was from a child an ardent and uncomfortable dreamer. When he had a touch of fever at night, and the room swelled and shrank, and his clothes, hanging on a nail, now loomed up instant to the bigness of a church, and now drew away into a horror of infinite distance and infinite littleness, the poor soul was very well aware of what must follow, and struggled hard against the approaches of that slumber which was the beginning of sorrows. But his struggles were in vain; sooner or later the night-hag would have him by the throat, and pluck him, strangling and screaming, from his sleep. His dreams were at times commonplace enough, at times very strange: at times they were almost formless, he would be haunted, for instance, by nothing more definite than a certain hue of brown, which he did not mind in the least while he was awake, but feared and loathed while he was dreaming; at times, again, they took on every detail of circumstance, as when once he supposed he must swallow the populous world, and awoke screaming with the horror of the thought. The two chief troubles of his very narrow existence —the practical and everyday trouble of school tasks and the ultimate and airy one of hell and judgment—were often confounded together into one appalling nightmare. He seemed to himself to stand before the Great White Throne; he was called on, poor little devil, to recite some form of words, on which his destiny depended; his tongue stuck, his memory was blank, hell gaped for him; and he would awake, clinging to the curtain-rod with his knees to his chin.

These were extremely poor experiences, on the whole; and at that time of life my dreamer would have very willingly parted with his power of dreams. But presently, in the course of his growth, the cries and physical contortions passed away, seemingly for ever; his visions were still for the most part miserable, but they were more constantly supported; and he would awake with no more extreme symptom than a flying heart, a freezing scalp, cold sweats, and the speechless midnight fear. His dreams, too, as befitted a mind better stocked with particulars, became more circumstantial, and had more the air and continuity of life. The look of the world beginning to take hold on his attention, scenery came to play a part in his sleeping as well as in his waking thoughts, so that he would take long, uneventful journeys and see strange towns and beautiful places as he lay in bed. And, what is more significant, an odd taste that he had for the Georgian costume and for stories laid in that period of English history, began to rule the features of his dreams; so that he masqueraded there in a three-cornered hat, and was much engaged with Jacobite conspiracy between the hour for bed and that for breakfast. About the same time, he began to read in his dreams—tales, for the most part, and for the most part after the manner of G. P. R. James, but so incredibly more vivid and moving than any printed book, that he has ever since been malcontent with literature.

And then, while he was yet a student, there came to him a dream-adventure which he has no anxiety to repeat; he began, that is to say, to dream in sequence and thus to lead a double life—one of the day, one of the night—one that he had every reason to believe was the true one, another that he had no means of proving to be false. I should have said he studied, or was by way of studying, at Edinburgh College, which (it may be supposed) was how I came to know him. Well, in his dream-life, he passed a long day in the surgical theatre, his heart in his mouth, his teeth on edge, seeing monstrous malformations and the abhorred dexterity of surgeons. In a heavy, rainy, foggy evening he came forth into the South Bridge, turned up the High Street, and entered the door of a tall *land*, at the top of which he supposed himself to lodge. All night long, in his wet clothes, he climbed the stairs, stair

after stair in endless series, and at every second flight a flaring lamp with a reflector. All night long, he brushed by single persons passing downward— beggarly women of the street, great, weary, muddy labourers, poor scarecrows of men, pale parodies of women —but all drowsy and weary like himself, and all single, and all brushing against him as they passed. In the end, out of a northern window, he would see day beginning to whiten over the Firth, give up the ascent, turn to descend, and in a breath be back again upon the streets, in his wet clothes, in the wet, haggard dawn, trudging to another day of monstrosities and operations. Time went quicker in the life of dreams, some seven hours (as near as he can guess) to one; and it went, besides, more intensely, so that the gloom of these fancied experiences clouded the day, and he had not shaken off their shadow ere it was time to lie down and to renew them. I cannot tell how long it was that he endured this discipline; but it was long enough to leave a great black blot upon his memory, long enough to send him, trembling for his reason, to the doors of a certain doctor; whereupon with a simple draught he was restored to the common lot of man.

The poor gentleman has since been troubled by nothing of the sort; indeed, his nights were for some while like other men's, now blank, now chequered with dreams, and these sometimes charming, sometimes appalling, but except for an occasional vividness, of no extraordinary kind. I will just note one of these occasions, ere I pass on to what makes my dreamer truly interesting. It seemed to him that he was in the first floor of a rough hill-farm. The room showed some poor efforts at gentility, a carpet on the floor, a piano, I think, against the wall; but, for all these refinements, there was no mistaking he was in a moorland place, among hillside people, and set in miles of heather. He looked down from the window upon a bare farmyard, that seemed to have been long disused. A great, uneasy stillness lay upon the world. There was no sign of the farmfolk or of any live stock, save for an old, brown, curly dog of the retriever breed, who sat close in against the wall of the house and seemed to be dozing. Something about the dog disquieted the dreamer; it was quite a nameless feeling, for the beast looked right enough—indeed, he was so old and dull and dusty and broken-down, that he should rather have awakened pity; and yet the conviction came and grew upon the dreamer that this was no proper dog at all, but something hellish. A great many dozing summer flies hummed about the yard; and presently the dog thrust forth his paw, caught a fly in his open palm, carried it to his mouth like an ape, and looking suddenly up at the dreamer in the window, winked to him with one eye. The dream went on, it matters not how it went; it was a good dream as dreams go; but there was nothing in the sequel worthy of that devilish brown dog. And the point of interest for me lies partly in that very fact: that having found so singular an incident, my imperfect dreamer should prove unable to carry the tale to a fit end and fall back on indescribable noises and indiscriminate horrors. It would be different now; he knows his business better!

For, to approach at last the point: This honest fellow had long been in the custom of setting himself to sleep with tales, and so had his father before him; but these were irresponsible inventions, told for the teller's pleasure, with no eye to the crass public or the thwart reviewer: tales where a thread might be dropped, or one adventure quitted for another, on fancy's least suggestion. So that the little people who manage man's internal theatre had not as yet received a very rigorous training; and played upon their stage like children who should have slipped into the house and found it empty, rather than like drilled actors performing a set piece to a huge hall of faces. But presently my dreamer began to turn his former amusement of story-telling to (what is called) account; by which I mean that he began to write and sell his tales. Here was he, and here were the little people who did that part of his business, in quite new conditions. The stories must now be trimmed and pared and set on all fours, they must run from a beginning to an end and fit (after a manner) with the laws of life; the pleasure, in one word, had become a business; and that not only for the dreamer, but for the little people of his theatre. These understood the change as well as he. When he lay down to prepare himself for sleep, he no longer sought amusement, but printable and profitable tales; and after he had dozed off in his box-seat, his little people continued their evolutions with the same mercantile designs. All other forms of dream deserted him but two; he still occasionally reads the most delightful books, he still visits at times the most delightful places; and it is perhaps worthy of note that to these same places, and to one in particular, he returns at intervals of months and years, finding new field-paths, visiting new neighbours, beholding that happy valley under new effects of noon and dawn and sunset. But all the rest of the family of visions is quite lost to him: the common, mangled version of yesterday's affairs, the raw-head-and-bloody-bones nightmare, rumoured to be the child of toasted cheese—these and their like are gone; and, for the most part, whether awake or asleep, he is simply occupied—he or his little people—in consciously making stories for the market. This dreamer (like many other persons) has encountered some trifling vicissitudes of fortune. When the bank begins to send letters and the butcher to linger at the back gate, he sets to belabouring his brains after a story, for that is his readiest money-winner; and behold! at once the little people begin to bestir themselves in the same quest, and labour all night long, and all night long set before him truncheons of tales upon their lighted theatre. No fear of his being frightened now; the flying heart and the frozen scalp are things bygone; applause, growing applause, growing interest, growing exultation in his own cleverness (for he takes all the credit), and at last a jubilant leap to wakefulness, with the cry, 'I have it, that'll do!' upon his lips: with such and similar emotions he sits at these nocturnal dramas, with such outbreaks, like Claudius in the play, he scatters the performance in the midst. Often enough the waking is a disappointment: he has been too deep asleep, as I explain the thing; drowsiness has gained his little people, they have gone stumbling and maundering through their parts; and the play, to the awakened mind, is seen to be a tissue of absurdities. And yet how often have these sleepless Brownies done him honest service, and given him, as he sat idly taking his pleasure in the boxes, better tales than he could fashion for himself.

Here is one, exactly as it came to him. It seemed he was the son of a very rich and wicked man, the owner of broad acres and a most damnable temper. The dreamer (and that was the son) had lived much abroad, on purpose to avoid his parent; and when at length he returned to England, it was to find him married again to a young wife, who was supposed to suffer cruelly and to loathe her yoke. Because of this marriage (as the dreamer indistinctly understood) it was desirable for father and son to have a meeting; and yet both being proud and both angry, neither would condescend upon a visit. Meet they did accordingly, in a desolate, sandy country by the sea; and there they quarrelled, and the son, stung by some intolerable insult, struck down the father dead. No suspicion was aroused; the dead man was found and buried, and the dreamer succeeded to the broad estates, and found himself installed under the same roof with his father's widow, for whom no provision had been made. These two lived very much alone, as people may after a bereavement, sat down to table together, shared the long evenings, and grew daily better friends; until it seemed to him of a sudden that she was prying about dangerous matters, that she had conceived a notion of his guilt, that she watched him and tried him with questions. He drew back from her company as men draw back from a precipice suddenly discovered; and yet so strong was the attraction that he would drift again and again into the old intimacy, and again and again be startled back by some suggestive question or some inexplicable meaning in her eye. So they lived at cross purposes, a life full of broken dialogue, challenging glances, and suppressed passion; until, one day, he saw the woman slipping from the house in a veil, followed her to the station, followed her in the train to the seaside country, and out over the sandhills to the very place where the murder was done. There she began to grope among the bents, he watching her, flat upon his face; and presently she had something in her hand—I cannot remember what it was, but it was deadly evidence against the dreamer—and as she held it up to look at it, perhaps from the shock of the discovery, her foot slipped, and she hung at some peril on the brink of the tall sand-wreaths. He had no thought but to spring up and rescue her; and there they stood face to face, she with that deadly matter openly in her hand—his very presence on the spot another link of proof. It was plain she was about to speak, but this was more than he could bear—he could bear to be lost, but not to talk of it with his destroyer; and he cut her short with trivial conversation. Arm in arm, they returned together to the train, talking he knew not what, made the journey back in the same carriage, sat down to dinner, and passed the evening in the drawing-room as in the past. But suspense and fear drummed in the dreamer's bosom. 'She has not denounced me yet'—so his thoughts ran—'when will she denounce me? Will it be tomorrow?' And it was not tomorrow, nor the next day, nor the next; and their life settled back on the old terms, only that she seemed kinder than before, and that as for him, the burthen of his suspense and wonder grew daily more unbearable, so that he wasted away like a man with a disease. Once, indeed, he broke all bounds of decency, seized an occasion when she was abroad, ransacked her room, and at last, hidden away among her jewels, found the damning evidence. There he stood, holding this thing, which was his life, in the hollow of his hand, and marvelling at her inconsequent behaviour, that she should seek, and keep, and yet not use it; and then the door opened, and behold herself. So, once more, they stood, eye to eye, with the evidence between them; and once more she raised to him a face brimming with some communication; and once more he shied away from speech and cut her off. But before he left the room, which he had turned upside down, he laid back his death-warrant where he had found it; and at that, her face lighted up. The next thing he heard, she was explaining to her maid, with some ingenious falsehood, the disorder of her things. Flesh and blood could bear the strain no longer; and I think it was the next morning (though chronology is always hazy in the theatre of the mind) that he burst from his reserve. They had been breakfasting together in one corner of a great, parqueted, sparely-furnished room of many windows; all the time of the meal she had tortured him with sly allusions; and no sooner were the servants gone, and these two protagonists alone together, than he leaped to his feet. She too sprang up, with a pale face; with a pale face, she heard him as he raved out his complaint: Why did she torture him so? she knew all, she knew he was no enemy to her; why did she not denounce him at once? what signified her whole behaviour? why did she torture him? and yet again, why did she torture him? And when he had done, she fell upon her knees, and with out-stretched hands: 'Do you not understand?' she cried. 'I love you!'

Hereupon, with a pang of wonder and mercantile delight, the dreamer awoke. His mercantile delight was not of long endurance; for it soon became plain that in this spirited tale there were unmarketable elements; which is just the reason why you have it here so briefly told. But his wonder has still kept growing; and I think the reader's will also, if he consider it ripely. For now he sees why I speak of the little people as of substantive inventors and performers. To the end they had kept their secret. I will go bail for the dreamer (having excellent grounds for valuing his candour) that he had no guess whatever at the motive of the woman—the hinge of the whole well-invented plot—until the instant of that highly dramatic declaration. It was not his tale; it was the little people's! And, observe: not only was the secret kept, the story was told with really guileful craftsmanship. The conduct of both actors is (in the cant phrase) psychologically correct, and the emotion aptly graduated up to the surprising climax. I am awake now, and I know this trade; and yet I cannot better it. I am awake, and I live by this business; and yet I could not outdo—could not perhaps equal—that crafty artifice (as of some old, experienced carpenter of plays, some Dennery or Sardou) by which the same situation is twice presented and the two actors twice brought face to face over the evidence, only once it is in her hand, once in his—and these in their due order, the least dramatic first. The more I think of it, the more I am moved to press upon the world my question: Who are the Little People? They are near connections of the dreamer's, beyond doubt; they share in his financial worries and have an eye to the bank-book; they share

plainly in his training; they have plainly learned like him to build the scheme of a considerate story and to arrange emotion in progressive order; only I think they have more talent; and one thing is beyond doubt, they can tell him a story piece by piece, like a serial, and keep him all the while in ignorance of where they aim. Who are they, then? and who is the dreamer?

Well, as regards the dreamer, I can answer that, for he is no less a person than myself;—as I might have told you from the beginning, only that the critics murmur over my consistent egotism;—and as I am positively forced to tell you now, or I could advance but little farther with my story. And for the Little People what shall I say they are but just my Brownies, God bless them! who do one-half my work for me while I am fast asleep, and in all human likelihood, do the rest for me as well, when I am wide awake and fondly suppose I do it for myself. That part which is done while I am sleeping is the Brownies' part beyond contention; but that which is done when I am up and about is by no means necessarily mine, since all goes to show the Brownies have a hand in it even then. Here is a doubt that much concerns my conscience. For myself—what I call I, my conscious ego, the denizen of the pineal gland unless he has changed his residence since Descartes, the man with the conscience and the variable bank-account, the man with the hat and the boots, and the privilege of voting and not carrying his candidate at the general elections—I am sometimes tempted to suppose he is no storyteller at all, but a creature as matter of fact as any cheesemonger or any cheese, and a realist bemired up to the ears in actuality; so that, by that account, the whole of my published fiction should be the single-handed product of some Brownie, some Familiar, some unseen collaborator, whom I keep locked in a back garret, while I get all the praise and he but a share (which I cannot prevent him getting) of the pudding. I am an excellent adviser, something like Molière's servant; I pull back and I cut down; and I dress the whole in the best words and sentences that I can find and make; I hold the pen, too; and I do the sitting at the table, which is about the worst of it; and when all is done, I make up the manuscript and pay for the registration; so that, on the whole, I have some claim to share, though not so largely as I do, in the profits of our common enterprise.

I can but give an instance or so of what part is done sleeping and what part awake, and leave the reader to share what laurels there are, at his own nod, between myself and my collaborators; and to do this I will first take a book that a number of persons have been polite enough to read, the *Strange Case of Dr. Jekyll and Mr. Hyde.* I had long been trying to write a story on this subject, to find a body, a vehicle, for that strong sense of man's double being which must at times come in upon and overwhelm the mind of every thinking creature. I had even written one, *The Travelling Companion,* which was returned by an editor on the plea that it was a work of genius and indecent, and which I burned the other day on the ground that it was not a work of genius, and that *Jekyll* had supplanted it. Then came one of those financial fluctuations to which (with an elegant modesty) I have hitherto referred in the third person. For two days I went about racking my brains

for a plot of any sort; and on the second night I dreamed the scene at the window, and a scene afterward split in two, in which Hyde, pursued for some crime, took the powder and underwent the change in the presence of his pursuers. All the rest was made awake, and consciously, although I think I can trace in much of it the manner of my Brownies. The meaning of the tale is therefore mine, and had long pre-existed in my garden of Adonis, and tried one body after another in vain; indeed, I do most of the morality, worse luck! and my Brownies have not a rudiment of what we call a conscience. Mine, too, is the setting, mine the characters. All that was given me was the matter of three scenes, and the central idea of a voluntary change becoming involuntary. Will it be thought ungenerous, after I have been so liberally ladling out praise to my unseen collaborators, if I here toss them over, bound hand and foot, into the arena of the critics? For the business of the powders, which so many have censured, is, I am relieved to say, not mine at all but the Brownies'. Of another tale, in case the reader should have glanced at it, I may say a word: the not very defensible story of *Olalla.* Here the court, the mother, the mother's niche, Olalla, Olalla's chamber, the meetings on the stair, the broken window, the ugly scene of the bite, were all given me in bulk and detail as I have tried to write them; to this I added only the external scenery (for in my dream I never was beyond the court), the portrait, the characters of Felipe and the priest, the moral, such as it is, and the last pages, such as, alas! they are. And I may even say that in this case the moral itself was given me; for it arose immediately on a comparison of the mother and the daughter, and from the hideous trick of atavism in the first. Sometimes a parabolic sense is still more undeniably present in a dream; sometimes I cannot but. suppose my Brownies have been aping Bunyan, and yet in no case with what would possibly be called a moral in a tract; never with the ethical narrowness; conveying hints instead of life's larger limitations and that sort of sense which we seem to perceive in the arabesque of time and space.

For the most part, it will be seen, my Brownies are somewhat fantastic, like their stories hot and hot, full of passion and the picturesque, alive with animating incident; and they have no prejudice against the supernatural. But the other day they gave me a surprise, entertaining me with a love-story, a little April comedy, which I ought certainly to hand over to the author of *A Chance Acquaintance,* for he could write it as it should be written, and I am sure (although I mean to try) that I cannot.— But who would have supposed that a Brownie of mine should invent a tale for Mr. Howells?

❇

BLUE VOYAGE

CONRAD AIKEN

[In *Blue Voyage* Conrad Aiken takes us into the intensely sensitive mind of a writer, Demarest, by means of a stream-of-consciousness technique, in which there is often no border line between dream, daydream, and objective happening. In this passage Demarest interprets his own dream, revealing insight into the social and family conditioning that has heightened his introversion and his feeling of inferiority.]

It was manifest to Demarest that he had got into the wrong place. It was totally unfamiliar. He walked quietly along the side of the grape-arbour and then, cautiously, passed under a fragrant trellis overgrown with roses. He emerged upon a wide lawn enclosed with trees and flowers, where a garden party was in progress. A score of glitteringly-dressed men and women stood talking, sauntered here and there, or set cups down on flower-decked tables. How horrible! He felt out of place, furtive and shabby, an intruder. But how was he to escape? He couldn't recall where he had got in. Was it over a wall? . . . He turned back through the trellis, hearing behind him a mild laughter. He looked down, and saw that his shoes were covered with mud and that his trousers were torn. Passing this time to the left of the grape-arbour, he hurried along the narrow path of deep soft turf, and was horrified to encounter a group of ladies coming in. They looked at him with hard eyes. Perhaps they thought he was some kind of a gardener? . . . This, then, might be the way out? . . .

From *Blue Voyage* by Conrad Aiken. By permission of Charles Scribner's Sons.

A flunkey in knee breeches eyed him suspiciously. Then he saw a green wooden gate; but just as he was about to open it, there came a loud knock at the other side, which was at once terrifyingly repeated, repeated—

'Bath's ready, sir.'

He groaned with relief, waking . . . The ship, of course! he was on a ship. He relaxed, becoming conscious of the regular remote throbbing of the engines. His coat, hanging on the stateroom door, sidled a little . . . That curious dream! It was just a new version, nevertheless, of the familiar theme—his absurd 'inferiority complex.' Good God! Was he destined never to escape it? Why was it that he never could be at his ease with those who were socially his equals— only at ease with his 'inferiors'? It was very strange. Formal occasions, polite people, froze him to the marrow: he couldn't remain himself . . . It was not that he hadn't had every opportunity to become accustomed to them,—for all the rest of the family were happily and intensely social . . . Mary and Tom adored parties, and so had his mother . . . But he had always been instinctively hostile to such things; and while he recognized in himself a passionate attachment for the fine and rich—by way of environment—he wanted the fine and rich freed from the 'social'; and moreover, every so often he wanted a good deep foaming bath in the merely vulgar. An occasional debauch was imperative,—whether it was only a visit to a cheap vaudeville, with its jazz, its spangles, its coarse jokes, its 'Chase me, boys—I issue trading stamps,'—or a shabby little clandestine adventure of his own, in which his motive was largely, if not entirely, curiosity . . . It was precisely this damned inferiority complex that had put him at such an initial disadvantage with Cynthia. By the time he had succeeded in adjusting himself, psychologically, to her exquisite old-worldliness, the dim, deep constellations of refinements and manners amid which she so statelily moved, and by the time he had put out of his mind the feeling that he was a mere ugly duckling, and had scraped from his shoes (metaphorically speaking) the mud of the brief, violent, disgusting Helen Shafter affair: by this time Cynthia had left London and gone to the continent. Gone! and that was the end . . . He shut his eyes in a spasm of pain.

✳

ULYSSES

JAMES JOYCE

[The following passage is a selection from the forty pages of Molly Bloom's unpunctuated stream-of-consciousness monologue which concludes James Joyce's *Ulysses*. It affords a fine illustration of the fabric of the unconscious, in which are linked in random association, memories of the past, sense impressions of the moment, and anticipations of the future. Mrs. Bloom, lying

From *Ulysses* by James Joyce. By special permission of Random House, Inc.

in bed beside her sleeping husband, whom she scorns, recalls her first conquest over him and plans the ruses by which she expects to capture her latest lover, 'Blazes' Boylan.]

. . . let me see if I can doze off 1 2 3 4 5 what kind of flowers are those they invented like the stars the wallpaper in Lombard street was much nicer the apron he gave me was like that something only I only wore it twice better lower this lamp and try again so as I can get up early Ill go to Lambes there beside Findlaters and get them to send us some flowers to put about the place in case he brings him home tomorrow today I mean no no Fridays an unlucky day first I want to do the place up someway the dust grows in it I think while Im asleep then we can have music and cigarettes I can accompany him first I must clean the keys of the piano with milk whatll I wear shall I wear a white rose or those fairy cakes in Liptons I love the smell of a rich big shop at 7½d. a lb or the other ones with the cherries in them and the pinky sugar 11d a couple of lbs of course a nice plant for the middle of the table Id get that cheaper in wait wheres this I saw them not long ago I love flowers Id love to have the whole place swimming in roses God of heaven theres nothing like nature the wild mountains then the sea and the waves rushing then the beautiful country with fields of oats and wheat and all kind of things and all the fine cattle going about that would do your heart good to see rivers and lakes and flowers all sorts of shapes and smells and colours springing up even out of the ditches primroses and violets nature it is as for them saying theres no God I wouldnt give a snap of my two fingers for all their learning why dont they go and create something I often asked him atheists or whatever they call themselves go and wash the cobbles off themselves first then they go howling for the priest and they dying and why why because theyre afraid of hell on account of their bad conscience ah yes I know them well who was the first person in the universe before there was anybody that made it all who ah that they dont know neither do I so there you are they might as well try to stop the sun from rising tomorrow the sun shines for you he said the day we were lying among the rhododendrons on Howth head in the grey tweed suit and his straw hat the day I got him to propose to me yes first I gave him the bit of seedcake out of my mouth and it was leapyear like now yes 16 years ago my God after that long kiss I near lost my breath yes he said I was a flower of the mountain yes so we are flowers all a womans body yes that was one true thing he said in his life and the sun shines for you today yes that was why I liked him because I saw he understood or felt what a woman is and I knew I could always get round him and I gave him all the pleasure I could leading him on till he asked me to say yes and I wouldnt answer first only looked out over the sea and the sky I was thinking of so many things he didnt know of Mulvey and Mr. Stanhope and Hester and father and old captain Groves and the sailors playing all birds fly and I say stoop and washing up dishes they called it on the pier and the sentry in front of the governors house with the thing round his white helmet poor devil half roasted and the Spanish girls laughing in their shawls and their tall combs and the auctions in the morning the Greeks and the jews and the Arabs and the devil knows who else from all the ends of Europe and Duke street and the fowl market all clucking outside Larby Sharons and the poor donkeys slipping half asleep and the vague fellows in the cloaks asleep in the shade on the steps and the big wheels of the carts of the bulls and the old castle thousands of years old yes and those handsome Moors all in white and turbans like kings asking you to sit down in their little bit of a shop and Ronda with the old windows of the posadas glancing eyes a lattice hid for her lover to kiss the iron and the wineshops half open at night and the castanets and the night we missed the boat at Algeciras the watchman going about serene with his lamp and O that awful deepdown torrent O and the sea the sea crimson sometimes like fire and the glorious sunsets and the figtrees in the Alameda gardens yes and all the queer little streets and pink and blue and yellow houses and the rosegardens and the jessamine and geraniums and cactuses and Gibraltar as a girl where I was a Flower of the mountain yes when I put the rose in my hair like the Andalusian girls used or shall I wear a red yes and how he kissed me under the Moorish wall and I thought as well him as another and then I asked him with my eyes to ask again yes and then he asked me would I yes to say yes my mountain flower and first I put my arms around him yes and drew him down to me so he could feel my breasts all perfume yes and his heart was going like mad and yes I said yes I will Yes.

✳

CONFESSIONS OF AN ENGLISH OPIUM-EATER
THOMAS DE QUINCEY

[The process of association is analyzed by De Quincey, who was aware of the way in which daydreams merge into the dreams of sleep in vivid sense perceptions. The picture-making faculties of the mind in sleep were of especial interest to De Quincey, who made significant observations on the recall in dreams of forgotten childhood memories. The drug to which De Quincey was addicted served temporarily to heighten his normal powers of perception and feeling. Childhood fears, feelings of guilt, amorous desires, fantasies of persecution and suffering hero motifs are all apparent in his *Confessions*.]

The Pains of Opium

*   *   *

I now pass to what is the main subject of these latter confessions, to the history and journal of what took place in my dreams; for these were the immediate and proximate cause of my acutest suffering.

The first notice I had of any important change going on in this part of my physical economy was from the reawakening of a state of eye generally incident to childhood, or exalted states of irritability. I know not whether my reader is aware that many children, perhaps most, have a power of painting, as it were, upon the darkness, all sorts of phantoms: in some that power is simply a mechanic affection of the eye; others have a voluntary or a semi-voluntary power to dismiss or to summon them; or, as a child once said to me when I questioned him on this matter, 'I can tell them to go, and they go; but sometimes they come when I don't tell them to come.' Whereupon I told him that he had almost as unlimited a command over apparitions as a Roman centurion over his soldiers.—In the middle of 1817, I think it was, that this faculty became positively distressing to me: at night, when I lay awake in bed, vast processions passed along in mournful pomp; friezes of never-ending stories, that to my feelings were as sad and solemn as if they were stories drawn from times before Oedipus or Priam, before Tyre, before Memphis. And, at the same time, a corresponding change took place in my dreams; a theatre seemed suddenly opened and lighted up within my brain, which presented, nightly, spectacles of more than earthly splendour. And the four following facts may be mentioned, as noticeable at this time:

1. That, as the creative state of the eye increased, a sympathy seemed to arise between the waking and the dreaming states of the brain in one point—that whatsoever I happened to call up and to trace by a voluntary act upon the darkness was very apt to transfer itself to my dreams; so that I feared to exercise this faculty; for, as Midas turned all things to gold, that yet baffled his hopes and defrauded his human desires, so whatsoever things capable of being visually represented I did but think of in the darkness, immediately shaped themselves into phantoms of the eye; and, by a process apparently no less inevitable, when thus once traced in faint and visionary colours, like writings in sympathetic ink, they were drawn out, by the fierce chemistry of my dreams, into insufferable splendour that fretted my heart.

2. For this and all other changes in my dreams were accompanied by deep-seated anxiety and gloomy melancholy, such as are wholly incommunicable by words. I seemed every night to descend—not metaphorically, but literally to descend—into chasms and sunless abysses, depths below depths, from which it seemed hopeless that I could ever reascend. Nor did I, by waking, feel that I *had* reascended. This I do not dwell upon; because the state of gloom which attended these gorgeous spectacles, amounting at least to utter darkness, as of some suicidal despondency, cannot be approached by words.

3. The sense of space and in the end the sense of time were both powerfully affected. Buildings, landscapes, etc., were exhibited in proportions so vast as the bodily eye is not fitted to receive. Space swelled, and was amplified to an extent of unutterable infinity. This, however, did not disturb me so much as the vast expansion of time. I sometimes seemed to have lived for seventy or one hundred years in one night; nay, sometimes had feelings representative of a millennium, passed in that time, or, however, of a duration far beyond the limits of any human experience.

4. The minutest incidents of childhood, or forgotten scenes of later

years, were often revived. I could not be said to recollect them; for if I had been told of them when waking, I should not have been able to acknowledge them as parts of my past experience. But placed as they were before me, in dreams like intuitions, and clothed in all their evanescent circumstances and accompanying feelings, I *recognized* them instantaneously. I was once told by a near relative of mine that having in her childhood fallen into a river, and being on the very verge of death but for the critical assistance which reached her, she saw in a moment her whole life, in its minutest incidents, arrayed before her simultaneously as in a mirror; and she had a faculty developed as suddenly for comprehending the whole and every part. This, from some opium experiences of mine, I can believe; I have, indeed, seen the same thing asserted twice in modern books, and accompanied by a remark which I am convinced is true, namely, that the dread book of account which the Scriptures speak of is, in fact, the mind itself of each individual. Of this, at least, I feel assured, that there is no such thing as *forgetting* possible to the mind; a thousand accidents may and will interpose a veil between our present consciousness and the secret inscriptions on the mind; accidents of the same sort will also rend away this veil; but alike, whether veiled or unveiled, the inscription remains forever; just as the stars seem to withdraw before the common light of day, whereas, in fact, we all know that it is the light which is drawn over them as a veil, and that they are waiting to be revealed, when the obscuring daylight shall have withdrawn.

Having noticed these four facts as memorably distinguishing my dreams from those of health, I shall now cite a case illustrative of the first fact; and shall then cite any others that I remember, either in their chronological order, or any other that may give them more effect as pictures to the reader.

I had been in youth, and ever since for occasional amusement, a great reader of Livy, whom I confess that I prefer, both for style and matter, to any other of the Roman historians; and I had often felt as most solemn and appalling sounds, and most emphatically representative of the majesty of the Roman people, the two words so often occurring in Livy—*Consul Romanus;* especially when the consul is introduced in his military character. I mean to say, that the words *king, sultan, regent,* etc., or any other titles of those who embody in their own persons the collective majesty of a great people, had less power over my reverential feelings. I had also, though no great reader of history, made myself minutely and critically familiar with one period of English history, namely, the period of the Parliamentary War, having been attracted by the moral grandeur of some who figured in that day, and by the many interesting memoirs which survive those unquiet times. Both these parts of my lighter reading, having furnished me often with matter of reflection, now furnished me with matter for my dreams. Often I used to see, after painting upon the blank darkness a sort of rehearsal whilst waking, a crowd of ladies, and perhaps a festival, and dances. And I heard it said, or I said to myself, 'These are English ladies from the unhappy times of Charles I. These are the wives and daughters of those who met in peace, and sat at the same tables, and were allied by marriage or by blood; and yet, after a certain day in August, 1642, never smiled upon each other again, nor met but in the field of battle; and at Marston Moor, at Newbury, or at Naseby, cut asunder all ties of love by the cruel sabre, and washed away in blood the memory of ancient friendship.' The ladies danced, and looked as lovely as at the court of George IV. Yet I knew, even in my dream, that they had been in the grave for nearly two centuries. This pageant would suddenly dissolve; and, at a clapping of hands, would be heard the heart-quaking sound of *Consul Romanus;* and immediately came 'sweeping by,' in gorgeous paludaments, Paulus, or Marius girt round by a company of centurions, with the crimson tunic hoisted on a spear, and followed by the *alalagmos* of the Roman legions.

Many years ago, when I was looking over Piranesi's *Antiquities of Rome,* Mr. Coleridge, who was standing by, described to me a set of plates by that artist, called his *Dreams,* and which record the scenery of his own visions during the delirium of a fever: some of them (I describe only from memory of Mr. Coleridge's account) representing vast Gothic halls; on the floor of which stood all sorts of engines and machinery, wheels, cables, pulleys, levers, catapults, etc., etc., expressive of enormous power put forth, and resistance overcome. Creeping along the sides of the walls, you perceived a staircase; and upon it, groping his way upwards, was Piranesi himself. Follow the stairs a little further, and you perceive it to come to a sudden, abrupt termination, without any balustrade, and allowing no step onwards to him who had reached the extremity, except into the depths below. Whatever is to become of poor Piranesi, you suppose, at least,

that his labours must in some way terminate here. But raise your eyes, and behold a second flight of stairs still higher; on which again Piranesi is perceived, by this time standing on the very brink of the abyss. Again elevate your eye, and a still more aërial flight of stairs is beheld; and again is poor Piranesi busy on his aspiring labours; and so on, until the unfinished stairs and Piranesi both are lost in the upper gloom of the hall. With the same power of endless growth and self-reproduction did my architecture proceed in dreams. In the early stage of my malady, the splendours of my dreams were indeed chiefly architectural; and I beheld such pomp of cities and palaces as was never yet beheld in the clouds, what in many the clouds. From a great modern poet I cite the part of a passage which describes, as an appearance actually beheld by the waking eye, unless in of its circumstances I saw frequently in sleep:

The appearance, instantaneously disclosed,
Was of a mighty city—boldly say
A wilderness of building, sinking far
And self-withdrawn into a wondrous depth,
Far sinking into splendour—without end!
Fabric it seemed of diamond, and of gold,
With alabaster domes and silver spires,
And blazing terrace upon terrace, high
Uplifted; here, serene pavilions bright,
In avenues disposed; there towers begirt
With battlements that on their restless fronts
Bore stars—illumination of all gems!
By earthly nature had the effect been wrought
Upon the dark materials of the storm
Now pacified; on them, and on the coves,
And mountain-steeps and summits, whereunto
The vapours had receded—taking there
Their station under a cerulean sky, etc.

The sublime circumstance—'battlements that on their *restless* fronts bore stars'—might have been copied from my architectural dreams, for it often occurred. We hear it reported of Dryden, and of Fuseli in modern times, that they thought proper to eat raw meat for the sake of obtaining splendid dreams: how much better, for such a purpose, to have eaten opium, which yet I do not remember that any poet is recorded to have done, except the dramatist Shadwell; and in ancient days, Homer is, I think, rightly reputed to have known the virtues of opium.

To my architecture succeeded dreams of lakes and silvery expanses of water: these haunted me so much, that I feared (though possibly it will appear ludicrous to a medical man) that some dropsical state or tendency of the brain might thus be making itself (to use a metaphysical word) *objective* and the sentient organ *project* itself as its own object. For two months I suffered greatly in my head —a part of my bodily structure which had hitherto been so clear from all touch or taint of weakness (physically, I mean) that I used to say of it, as the last Lord Orford said of his stomach, that it seemed likely to survive the rest of my person. Till now I had never felt a headache even, or any the slightest pain, except rheumatic pains caused by my own folly. However, I got over this attack, though it must have been verging on something very dangerous.

The waters now changed their character—from translucent lakes, shining like mirrors, they now became seas and oceans. And now came a tremendous change, which, unfolding itself slowly like a scroll, through many months, promised an abiding torment; and, in fact, it never left me until the winding up of my case. Hitherto the human face had mixed often in my dreams, but not despotically, nor with any special power of tormenting. But now that which I have called the tyranny of the human face began to unfold itself. Perhaps some part of my London life might be answerable for this. Be that as it may, now it was that upon the rocking waters of the ocean the human face began to appear; the sea appeared paved with innumerable faces, upturned to the heavens; faces imploring, wrathful, despairing, surged upwards by thousands, by myriads, by generations, by centuries: my agitation was infinite, my mind tossed, and surged with the ocean.

May, 1818.—The Malay has been a fearful enemy for months. I have been every night, through his means, transported into Asiatic scenes. I know not whether others share in my feelings on this point; but I have often thought that if I were compelled to forego England, and to live in China, and among Chinese manners and modes of life and scenery, I should go mad. The causes of my horror lie deep, and some of them must be common to others. Southern Asia, in general, is the seat of awful images and associations. As the cradle of the human race, it would alone have a dim and reverential feeling connected with it. But there are other reasons. No man can pretend that the wild, barbarous, and capricious superstitions of Africa, or of savage tribes elsewhere, affect him in the way that he is affected by the ancient, monumental, cruel, and elaborate religions of Indostan, etc. The mere antiquity of Asiatic things, of their institutions, histories, modes of faith, etc., is so impressive, that to me the vast age of the race and name overpowers the sense of youth in the individual. A young Chinese seems to me an antediluvian man renewed. Even Englishmen, though not bred in any knowledge of such institutions, cannot but shudder at the mystic sublimity of *castes* that have flowed apart, and refused to mix, through such immemorial tracts of time; nor can any man fail to be awed by the names of the Ganges, or the Euphrates. It contributes much to these feelings, that Southern Asia is, and has been for thousands of years, the part of the earth most swarming with human life, the great *officina gentium*. Man is a weed in those regions. The vast empires, also, into which the enormous population of Asia has always been cast, give a further sublimity to the feelings associated with all oriental names or images. In China, over and above what it has in common with the rest of Southern Asia, I am terrified by the modes of life, by the manners, and the barrier of utter abhorrence, and want of sympathy, placed between us by feelings deeper than I can analyze. I could sooner live with lunatics, or brute animals. All this, and much more than I can say, or have time to say, the reader must enter into, before he can comprehend the unimaginable horror which these dreams of oriental imagery, and mythological tortures, impressed upon me. Under the connecting feeling of tropical heat and vertical sunlights, I brought together all creatures, birds, beasts, reptiles, all trees and plants, usages and appearances, that are found in all tropical regions, and assembled them together in China or Indostan. From kindred feelings, I soon brought Egypt and all her gods under the same law. I was stared at, hooted at, grinned at, chattered at, by monkeys, by paro-quets, by cockatoos. I ran into pagodas, and was fixed, for centuries, at the summit, or in secret rooms: I was the idol; I was the priest; I was worshiped; I was sacrificed. I fled from the wrath of Brama through all the forests of Asia: Vishnu hated me; Seeva laid wait for me. I came suddenly upon Isis and Osiris; I had done a deed, they said, which the ibis and the crocodile trembled at. I was buried for a thousand years in stone coffins, with mummies and sphinxes, in narrow chambers at the heart of eternal pyramids. I was kissed, with cancerous kisses, by crocodiles; and laid, confounded with all unutterable slimy things, amongst reeds and Nilotic mud.

I thus give the reader some slight abstraction of my oriental dreams, which always filled me with such amazement at the monstrous scenery that horror seemed absorbed, for a while, in sheer astonishment. Sooner or later came a reflux of feeling that swallowed up the astonishment, and left me, not so much in terror, as in hatred and abomination of what I saw. Over every form, and threat, and punishment, and dim sightless incarceration, brooded a sense of eternity and infinity that drove me into an oppression as of madness. Into these dreams only, it was, with one or two slight exceptions, that any circumstances of physical horror entered. All before had been moral and spiritual terrors. But here the main agents were ugly birds, or snakes, or crocodiles, especially the last. The cursed crocodile became to me the object of more horror than almost all the rest. I was compelled to live with him; and (as was always the case, almost, in my dreams) for centuries. I escaped sometimes, and found myself in Chinese houses with cane tables, etc. All the feet of the tables, sofas, etc., soon became instinct with life: the abominable head of the crocodile, and his leering eyes, looked out at me, multiplied into a thousand repetitions; and I stood loathing and fascinated. And so often did this hideous reptile haunt my dreams that many times the very same dream was broken up in the very same way: I heard gentle voices speaking to me (I hear everything when I am sleeping), and instantly I awoke: it was broad noon, and my children were standing, hand in hand, at my bedside; come to show me their coloured shoes, or new frocks, or to let me see them dressed for going out. I protest that so awful was the transition from the damned crocodile, and the other unutterable monsters and abortions of my dreams, to the sight of innocent *human* natures and of infancy, that, in the mighty and sudden revulsion of mind, I wept, and could not forbear it, as I kissed their faces.

June, 1819.—I have had occasions to remark, at various periods of my life, that the deaths of those whom we love, and, indeed, the contemplation of death generally, is (*caeteris paribus*) more affecting in summer than in any other season of the year. And the reasons are these three, I think: first, that the visible heavens in summer appear far higher, more distant, and (if such a solecism may be excused) more infinite; the clouds by which chiefly the eye expounds the distance of the blue pavilion stretched over our heads are in summer more voluminous, massed, and accumulated in far grander and more towering piles; secondly, the light and the appearances of the declining and the setting sun are much more fitted to be types and characters of the infinite; and, thirdly (which is the main rea-

son), the exuberant and riotous prodigality of life naturally forces the mind more powerfully upon the antagonist thought of death, and the wintry sterility of the grave. For it may be observed generally that, wherever two thoughts stand related to each other by a law of antagonism, and exist, as it were, by mutual repulsion, they are apt to suggest each other. On these accounts it is that I find it impossible to banish the thought of death when I am walking alone in the endless days of summer; and any particular death, if not more affecting, at least haunts my mind more obstinately and besiegingly in that season. Perhaps this cause, and a slight incident which I omit, might have been the immediate occasions of the following dream, to which, however, a predisposition must always have existed in my mind; but, having been once roused, it never left me, and split into a thousand fantastic varieties, which often suddenly reunited, and composed again the original dream.

I thought that it was a Sunday morning in May; that it was Easter Sunday, and as yet very early in the morning. I was standing, as it seemed to me, at the door of my own cottage. Right before me lay the very scene which could really be commanded from that situation, but exalted, as was usual, and solemnized by the power of dreams. There were the same mountains, and the same lovely valley at their feet; but the mountains were raised to more than Alpine height, and there was interspace far larger between them of meadows and forest lawns; the hedges were rich with white roses; and no living creature was to be seen, excepting that in the green churchyard there were cattle tranquilly reposing upon the verdant graves, and particularly round about the grave of a child whom I had tenderly loved, just as I had really beheld them, a little before sunrise in the same summer, when that child died. I gazed upon the well-known scene, and I said aloud (as I thought) to myself, 'It yet wants much of sunrise; and it is Easter Sunday; and that is the day on which they celebrate the first-fruits of resurrection. I will walk abroad; old griefs shall be forgotten today; for the air is cool and still, and the hills are high, and stretch away to heaven; and the forest-glades are as quiet as the churchyard; and with the dew I can wash the fever from my forehead, and then I shall be unhappy no longer.' And I turned, as if to open my garden gate; and immediately I saw upon the left a scene far different; but which yet the power of dreams had reconciled into harmony with the other. The scene was an Oriental one; and there also it was Easter Sunday, and very early in the morning. And at a vast distance were visible, as a stain upon the horizon, the domes and cupolas of a great city—an image or faint abstraction, caught perhaps in childhood from some picture of Jerusalem. And not a bow-shot from me, upon a stone, and shaded by Judean palms, there sat a woman; and I looked; and it was—Ann! She fixed her eyes upon me earnestly; and I said to her at length: 'So then I have found you at last.' I waited: but she answered me not a word. Her face was the same as when I saw it last, and yet again how different! Seventeen years ago, when the lamplight fell upon her face, as for the last time I kissed her lips (lips, Ann, that to me were not polluted), her eyes were streaming with tears: the tears were now wiped away; she seemed more beautiful than she was at that time, but in all other points

the same, and not older. Her looks were tranquil, but with unusual solemnity of expression; and I now gazed upon her with some awe, but suddenly her countenance grew dim, and, turning to the mountains, I perceived vapors rolling between us; in a moment, all had vanished; thick darkness came on; and, in the twinkling of an eye, I was far away from mountains, and by lamplight in Oxford Street, walking again with Ann —just as we walked seventeen years before, when we were both children.

As a final specimen, I cite one of a different character, from 1820.

The dream commenced with a music which now I often heard in dreams—a music of preparation and of awakening suspense; a music like the opening of the Coronation Anthem, and which, like *that,* gave the feeling of a vast march—of infinite cavalcades filing off—and the tread of innumerable armies. The morning was come of a mighty day—a day of crisis and of final hope for human nature, then suffering some mysterious eclipse, and laboring in some dread extremity. Somewhere, I knew not where—somehow, I knew not how —by some beings, I knew not whom —a battle, a strife, an agony, was conducting—was evolving like a great drama, or piece of music; with which my sympathy was the more insupportable from my confusion as to its place, its cause, its nature, and its possible issue. I, as is usual in dreams (where, of necessity, we make ourselves central to every movement), had the power, and yet had not the power, to decide it. I had the power, if I could raise myself, to will it, and yet again had not the power, for the weight of twenty Atlantics was upon me, or the oppression of inexpiable guilt. 'Deeper than ever plummet sounded,'

I lay inactive. Then, like a chorus, the passion deepened. Some greater interest was at stake; some mightier cause than ever yet the sword had pleaded, or trumpet had proclaimed. Then came sudden alarms: hurryings to and fro: trepidations of innumerable fugitives, I knew not whether from the good cause or the bad: darkness and lights: tempest and human faces: and at last, with the sense that all was lost, female forms, and the features that were worth all the world to me, and but a moment allowed—and clasped hands, and heart-breaking partings, and then—everlasting farewells! and with a sigh, such as the caves of hell sighed when the incestuous mother uttered the abhorrent name of death, the sound was reverberated—everlasting farewells! and again and yet again reverberated—everlasting farewells!

And I awoke in struggles, and cried aloud—'I will sleep no more!'

※

THE GUERMANTES WAY

Marcel Proust

[The relation between the sleeping and waking associative processes was a problem of great interest to Proust. The passage to follow reveals his keen understanding of the workings of the mind and the role played by sensation, association, and memory in shaping our lives.]

. . . Before going to bed I decided to leave the room in order to explore the whole of my fairy kingdom. I walked down a long gallery which did me homage successively with all that it had to offer me if I could not sleep, an armchair placed waiting in a corner, a spinet, on a table against the wall, a bowl of blue crockery filled with cinerarias, and, in an old frame, the phantom of a lady of long ago whose powdered hair was starred with blue flowers, holding in her hand a bunch of carnations. When I came to the end, the bare wall in which no door opened said to me simply: 'Now you must turn and go back, but, you see, you are at home, the house is yours,' while the soft carpet, not to be left out, added that if I did not sleep that night I could easily come in barefoot, and the unshuttered windows, looking out over the open country, assured me that they would hold a sleepless vigil and that, at whatever hour I chose to come in, I need not be afraid of disturbing anyone. And behind a hanging curtain I surprised only a little closet which, stopped by the wall and unable to escape any farther, had hidden itself there with a guilty conscience and gave me a frightened stare from its little round window, glowing blue in the moonlight. I went to bed, but the presence of the eiderdown quilt, of the pillars, of the neat fireplace, by straining my attention to a pitch beyond that of Paris, prevented me from letting myself go upon my habitual train of

From *The Guermantes Way* by Marcel Proust. Reprinted by permission of Random House, Inc.

fancies. And as it is this particular state of strained attention that enfolds our slumbers, acts upon them, modifies them, brings them into line with this or that series of past impressions, the images that filled my dreams that first night were borrowed from a memory entirely distinct from that on which I was in the habit of drawing. If I had been tempted while asleep to let myself be swept back upon my ordinary current of remembrance, the bed to which I was not accustomed, the comfortable attention which I was obliged to pay to the position of my various limbs when I turned over were sufficient to correct my error, to disentangle and to keep running the new thread of my dreams. It is the same with sleep as with our perception of the external world. It needs only a modification in our habits to make it poetic, it is enough that while undressing we should have dozed off unconsciously upon the bed, for the dimensions of our dreamworld to be altered and its beauty felt. We awake, look at our watch, see 'four o'clock'; it is only four o'clock in the morning, but we imagine that the whole day has gone by, so vividly does this nap of a few minutes unsought by us, appear to have come down to us from the skies, by virtue of some divine right, fullbodied, vast, like an Emperor's orb of gold. In the morning, while worrying over the thought that my grandfather was ready, and was waiting for me to start on our walk along the Méséglise way, I was awakened by the blare of a regimental band which passed every day beneath my windows. But on several occasions—and I mention these because one cannot properly describe human life unless one shews it soaked in the sleep in which it plunges, which, night after night, sweeps round it as a promontory is encircled by the sea—the intervening layer of sleep was strong enough to bear the shock of the music and I heard nothing. On the other mornings it gave way for a moment; but, still velvety with the refreshment of having slept, my consciousness (like those organs by which, after a local anaesthetic, a cauterisation, not perceived at first, is felt only at the very end and then as a faint burning smart) was touched only gently by the shrill points of the fifes which caressed it with a vague, cool, matutinal warbling; and after this brief interruption in which the silence had turned to music it relapsed into my slumber before even the dragoons had finished passing, depriving me of the latest opening buds of the sparkling clangorous nosegay. And the zone of my consciousness which its springing stems had brushed was so narrow, so circumscribed with sleep that later on, when Saint-Loup asked me whether I had heard the band, I was no longer certain that the sound of its brasses had not been as imaginary as that which I heard during the day echo, after the slightest noise, from the paved streets of the town. Perhaps I had heard it only in a dream, prompted by my fear of being awakened, or else of not being awakened and so not seeing the regiment march past. For often, when I was still asleep at the moment when, on the contrary, I had supposed that the noise would awaken me, for the next hour I imagined that I was awake, while still drowsing, and I enacted to myself with tenuous shadow-shapes on the screen of my slumber the various scenes of which it deprived me but at which I had the illusion of looking on.

What one had meant to do during

the day, as it turns out, sleep intervening, one accomplished only in one's dreams, that is to say after it has been distorted by sleep into following another line than one would have chosen when awake. The same story branches off and has a different ending. When all is said, the world in which we live when we are asleep is so different that people who have difficulty in going to sleep seek first of all to escape from the waking world. After having desperately, for hours on end, with shut eyes, revolved in their minds thoughts similar to those which they would have had with their eyes open, they take heart again on noticing that the last minute has been crawling under the weight of an argument in formal contradiction of the laws of thought, and their realization of this, and the brief 'absence' to which it points, indicate that the door is now open through which they will perhaps be able, presently, to escape from the perception of the real, to advance to a resting-place more or less remote on the other side, which will mean their having a more or less 'good' night. But already a great stride has been made when we turn our back on the real, when we reach the cave in which 'auto-suggestions' prepare—like witches—the hell-broth of imaginary maladies or of the recurrence of nervous disorders, and watch for the hour at which the storm that has been gathering during our unconscious sleep will break with sufficient force to make sleep cease.

Not far thence is the secret garden in which grow like strange flowers the kinds of sleep, so different one from another, the sleep induced by datura, by the multiple extracts of ether, the sleep of belladonna, of opium, of valerian, flowers whose petals remain shut until the day when the predestined visitor shall come and, touching them, bid them open, and for long hours inhale the aroma of their peculiar dreams into a marvelling and bewildered being. At the end of the garden stands the convent with open windows through which we hear voices repeating the lessons learned before we went to sleep, which we shall know only at the moment of awakening; while, a presage of that moment, sounds the resonant tick of that inward alarum which our preoccupation has so effectively regulated that when our housekeeper comes in with the warning: 'It is seven o'clock,' she will find us awake and ready. On the dim walls of that chamber which opens upon our dreams, within which toils without ceasing that oblivion of the sorrows of love whose task, interrupted and brought to nought at times by a nightmare big with reminiscence, is ever speedily resumed, hang, even after we are awake, the memories of our dreams, but so overshadowed that often we catch sight of them for the first time only in the broad light of the afternoon when the ray of a similar idea happens by chance to strike them; some of them brilliant and harmonious while we slept, but already so distorted that, having failed to recognise them, we can but hasten to lay them in the earth like dead bodies too quickly decomposed or relics so seriously damaged, so nearly crumbling into dust that the most skilful restorer could not bring them back to their true form or make anything of them. Near the gate is the quarry to which our heavier slumbers repair in search of substances which coat the brain with so unbreakable a glaze that, to awaken the sleeper, his own will is obliged, even on a golden morning, to smite him with mighty blows, like a young Siegfried. Beyond this, again, are the nightmares of which the doctors foolishly assert that they tire us more than does insomnia, whereas on the contrary they enable the thinker to escape from the strain of thought; those nightmares with their fantastic picture-books in which our relatives who are dead are shewn meeting with a serious accident which at the same time does not preclude their speedy recovery. Until then we keep them in a little rat-cage, in which they are smaller than white mice and, covered with big red spots, out of each of which a feather sprouts, engage us in Ciceronian dialogues. Next to this picture-book is the revolving disc of awakening, by virtue of which we submit for a moment to the tedium of having to return at once to a house which was pulled down fifty years ago, the memory of which is gradually effaced as sleep grows more distant by a number of others, until we arrive at that memory which the disc presents only when it has ceased to revolve and which coincides with what we shall see with opened eyes.

Sometimes I had heard nothing, being in one of those slumbers into which we fall as into a pit from which we are heartily glad to be drawn up a little later, heavy, overfed, digesting all that has been brought to us (as by the nymphs who fed the infant Hercules) by those agile, vegetative powers whose activity is doubled while we sleep.

That kind of sleep is called 'sleeping like lead,' and it seems as though one has become, oneself, and remains for a few moments after such a sleep is ended, simply a leaden image. One is no longer a person. How then, seeking for one's mind, one's personality, as one seeks for a thing that is lost, does one recover one's own self rather than any other? Why, when one begins again to think, is it not another personality than yesterday's that is incarnate in one? One fails to see what can dictate the choice, or why, among the millions of human beings any one of whom one might be, it is on him who one was overnight that unerringly one lays one's hand? What is it that guides us, when there has been an actual interruption—whether it be that our unconsciousness has been complete or our dreams entirely different from ourself? There has indeed been death, as when the heart has ceased to beat and a rhythmical friction of the tongue revives us. No doubt the room, even if we have seen it only once before, awakens memories to which other, older memories cling. Or were some memories also asleep in us of which we now become conscious? The resurrection at our awakening—after that healing attack of mental alienation which is sleep—must after all be similar to what occurs when we recapture a name, a line, a refrain that we had forgotten. And perhaps the resurrection of the soul after death is to be conceived as a phenomenon of memory.

I KNOCK AT THE DOOR

SEAN O'CASEY

[Sean O'Casey presents a story of a small boy who finds escape from physical suffering, social inferiority, and deprivation in daydreams and fantasies. His mother has required him to go to Sunday School because of the insistence of the curate—a 'black-whiskered, snug-souled gollywog gospel-cook who brightened up the will of God with his own.' Johnny has been seriously ill with an eye affliction which still troubles him, although one suspects that his mother is partially right in believing that the prospect of Sunday School tends to revive his pain. The situation is presented largely through the thoughts that pass through Johnny's mind as, soaked by the rain, and tormented by a bully on his way to church, he now sits unhappy and shivering in the hard pew.]

Give your feet a good wipe on the mat, warned Miss Valentine, so that you won't soil the carpet in the aisle, as she went off to her place in the choir, to help in singing loud praises to God.

Johnny rubbed and rubbed his feet in the sodden mat, trying to get some of the water from his boots that were more sodden than the mat under them; and taking off his saturated cap, with drops of rain from his hair trickling down his cheeks, he went into the church and crept quietly into a pew on the north aisle, sitting down on the edge of the seat so that his rain-soaked trousers would press the less on his legs.

Then the bell gave a last little tinkle, and late-comers hurried in, and, after bending their heads down for a second or two in silent prayer to show everybody they had made no mistake and were in the right place, settled themselves in their seats and waited for the service to begin. Massey, passing by, caught sight of Johnny, and at once turned aside, sidled into the pew, and perched himself on the seat beside him.

Oul' Hunter, and his curate, a tall thin man, came out of the vestry and moved slowly over to their places in the chancel, one to the right, the other to the left, to the piping of a tune on the organ. Both knelt in silent prayer a little longer than any member of the congregation, because, of course, they were parsons. Then the tall thin curate began murmuring in a thin tired voice, while all the congregation stood up on their hind legs, O Lord correct me, but with judgment, not in Thine anger, lest Thou bring me to nothing. Dearly beloved brethren, the scriptures moveth us in sundry places to acknowledge and confess our manifold sins and wickedness.

—How would you like to have a swing outa Hunter's whiskers? asked Massey.

Johnny said hush, and giggled, screwed up his face seriously, for he

From *I Knock at the Door*, by Sean O'Casey. By permission of the Macmillan Company.

was afraid that he would laugh out loud at the picture rushing into his mind of Hunter yellin' 'n yellin' while he was swingin' outa his whiskers, swing-swong swing-swong, now we're off to London Town, safe 'n sound in Hunter's whiskers, take your seats, take your seats, please, for I wish Massey hadn' come into my pew, 'cause he'll do somethin' to make me laugh, 'n Hunter'll tell me ma about it 'n turn her against me for days, 'n I hate the hard 'n cold look comin' into her eyes when Hunter howls a complaint against me; for even when I try to make up to her she'll shake her head 'n say No, Johnny, I'm black out with you for what you done in church; now we're kneelin' down to say the general confession, all together boys, one, two, three, 'n away, I beseech you, as many as are here present, to accompany me with a pure heart 'n humble voice to the throne of His heavenly grace, saying after me, that if it hadn' been rainin' we'd ha' gone to the zoo today, but, next Sunday, me 'n da 'n ma are goin' first thing while you are streelin' off to Sunday school to cod with the monkeys that the rest of our life hereafter may be pure and holy so that at the last you have to be snappy on accounta if you weren't quick the buggers 'ud snap a bit outa your fingers 'n you have to be careful for the keeper's always knockin' about pryin' to see what you're up to, for me da says he knew a fella was pulled for squirtin' a chew of tobacco into a monkey's eye so that he squealed out, let us worship 'n fall down 'n kneel before the Lord our maker, an' the elephant's dangerous to thrick with, always eatin' spuds 'n carrots 'n cakes just like us to sit down while oul' Hunter's readin' the lessons in his white surplice an' the tall thin curate listenin' in his white surplice with a solemn pus on him waitin' his turn to read the second lesson, for the day I grow up to be a man I'll go to sea as a skipper of a three-masted schooner with mainsail 'n foresail 'n jibsail 'n topgallants 'n I'll run up 'n down the ratlines same as you'd run up an' down stairs standin' steady in the crow's nest when she pitches fore 'n when she pitches aft, an' I believe in the holy catholic church, the communion of saints, the forgiveness of sins and the life ever sailin' an' sailin' thousands 'n thousands of miles over blue seas 'n green seas and black seas 'n red seas, an' I'll live on islands where honey's flowin' down the trees with none to eat it 'n none to share it but meself an' there'll be birds like thrushes only red 'n bigger, 'n birds like gulls only blue 'n bigger, 'n there'll be no goin' to Sunday school or church in the mornin' or in the evenin' 'cause everyone'll be happy, for there's Hunter goin' to preach, settlin' his glasses on his nose 'n coughin' a little before startin' on his sermon, sayin' somethin' about becoming followers of the Lord having heard the word in much affliction he rambled on an' rumbled on an' gambled on an' ambled on an' scrambled on an' mummy-mummy-mumbled on an' yambled on an' yumbled on an' scambled on an' scumbled on an' humbled on an' grumbled on an' stummy-stummy-stumbled on an' tumbled on an' fumbled on an' jumbled on an' drumbled on an' numbled on an' bummy-bummy-bumbled on, while here 'm I sittin' in the pew shiverin' cold as cold can be with me wet clothes clingin' to me back 'n stickin' to me legs.

At last the sermon ends, an' up we

get on our pins to sing a hymn, fortified forth in Thy name, oh Lord, I
go, my daily labour to pursue; Thee,
only Thee, resolved to know, in all
I think, or speak, or do, well, so I
will, so help me God, to stand in me
trousers without lettin' me legs touch
them. Kneelin' down we get the
blessin' an' then stream out down the
aisles towards the door into the porch
to see the rain pouring outa the
heavens and peltin' off the pavement.

THE NEUROSES

All our lives long, every day and every hour, we are engaged in
the process of accommodating our changed and unchanged selves
to changed and unchanged surroundings; living, in fact, is nothing else than this process of accommodation; when we fail in it
a little we are stupid, when we fail flagrantly we are mad, when
we suspend it temporarily we sleep, when we give up the attempt
altogether we die.

—SAMUEL BUTLER

WE have seen in the preceding pages that there is not always an
harmonious functioning of the total personality, that the individual is often in conflict with himself, with other individuals, or with society
in general. The degree to which the various elements of one's personality are in harmony determines the extent of his mental health. Carlyle's
exclamation on being told that Margaret Fuller had decided to accept
the universe—'Gad, she had better!'—is remarkably like the point of view
of modern psychiatrists that one must either accept the world as it is,
with all of its imperfections, and adjust one's desires to the realm of the
attainable, or he must cease to be a social being and retreat into a private
world dominated by his impulses and desires. But there is much variety
in the manner in which one may accept the universe. In these selections
we shall find that the individuals portrayed indulge in behavior usually
regarded as neurotic; that is to say, they have made certain adaptations
to their environment which may not have brought them happiness or
even contentment; indeed these responses—or dynamisms—may not have
met with social approbation, but they have none the less served to keep
the personality to some degree in touch with reality.

There are infinite shadings of neurotic expression, from the minor
emotional and physical idiosyncrasies that make us individuals to the
more strongly fixed manifestations that warp the personality and endanger
its stability. Any influence which diverts the development of one's emotional life from its normal cycle, or arrests it at a certain point, may induce neurotic behavior. In general, psychiatrists recognize certain phases
of normal development from infancy to adulthood. The infant's earliest
pleasurable sensations have their origin in his own body—the narcissistic
stage. Shortly thereafter his pleasure in self is transferred to a love object
outside of himself, normally the mother or a mother substitute. But occasionally the emotional life of the child is arrested at the period of self-
absorption. Like so many of the ancient myths, the story of Narcissus,

the youth who fell in love with his own image, embodies a profound psychological truth. A striking modern expression of this narcissistic phase, arrested and developed into neurotic manifestations, is Benét's picture of Lucy, the Southern belle, in *John Brown's Body*. Her self love makes her regard with horror the thought of anyone else's possessing the body of whose beauty she is so enamoured. Standing before the mirror she kisses her little white shoulders and murmurs to her image:

> 'Honey, I love you,' she whispered, 'I love you, honey.
> Nobody loves you like I do, do they, sugar?
> Nobody knows but Lucy how sweet you are.
> You mustn't get married, honey. You mustn't leave me.
> We'll always be pretty and sweet to all of them, won't we, honey?
> We'll always have beaus to dance with and tunes to dance to,
> But you mustn't leave me, honey. I couldn't bear it.
> You mustn't leave me for any man.' [1]

Normally the child progresses from engrossment in himself to love of another object, usually the mother who protects him and serves his needs. The usual course of development of the male child is from love of his mother, through interest in companions of his own age and sex, to interest in one of the opposite sex, or adult heterosexuality. If the child is female, a more complex emotional cycle must be traversed. From the child's initial interest in her self, her love interest is centered first upon her mother, then upon her father, and thence to a father substitute and adult heterosexuality. But life cannot be reduced to such a simple formula. Innumerable factors may divert and obstruct this development. Denied acceptance by her mother, the child may continue to look for affection from a mother substitute. In *The Well of Loneliness* the father's fervent wish for a son shut out all thought that the child his wife was bearing might conceivably be a daughter.[2] When his wishes were thwarted by the birth of a baby girl, the father continued to regard his daughter as a son, whom he christened Stephen. The mother, repelled by Stephen's likeness to her father, was filled with an inexplicable antagonism for her daughter. Inevitably the girl sensed her mother's aversion and unconsciously identified herself with her father in her hope of winning her mother's affection. While her turning to the maid, Collins, as a mother substitute represents a normal stage of the child's emotional development, her later emotional dependence on individuals of her own sex illustrates the arresting of the normal cycle and the inability to advance to adult heterosexuality.

1 Stephen Vincent Benét, *John Brown's Body*, Farrar & Rinehart Inc., N. Y., 1928, p. 275.
2 Radclyffe Hall, *The Well of Loneliness*, N. Y., Covici-Friede, Inc.

MADAME BOVARY

Gustave Flaubert

[A narcissistic woman who has matured physically but is emotionally infantile is Madame Bovary. Life is interesting to her only in terms of audience approval. Hence she lapses into a state of slovenliness and apathy when there is no one but her dull husband to see her; she longs for violent pleasures (a regression to the pleasure-pain response of the infant), and when there is no satisfaction of her longings, she reacts physically. Her conversion—a disguised expression of repressed emotional energy—takes the form of heart palpitations. Her original romantic illusions regarding marriage having failed to coincide with the facts, she can no longer accept reality. One is reminded of Carlyle, whose definition of happiness points to the necessity of decreasing one's demands from life, or of Count Korzybski who suggests the need of looking upon life with minimal rather than maximal expectations, so that the discrepancy between the expectation and the fact will not lead to a disintegration of the personality. Before Madame Bovary escapes from the boredom of marriage to an extra-marital relationship, she alternates between reveling in her virtue and rationalizing her desires. She projects her guilt upon her husband, Charles, and when her conscience remains unrelieved, she wishes that he would beat her. Her flight from reality continues as she seeks to identify herself first with a mystical Creator and later with the heroine of the opera; finally she deludes herself into imagining that the male actor is singling her out for his amorous attention.]

. . . Why, at least, was not her husband one of those men of taciturn passions who work at their books all night, and at last, when about sixty, the age of rheumatism sets in, wear a string of orders on their ill-fitting black coat? She could have wished this name of Bovary, which was hers, had been illustrious, to see it displayed at the booksellers', repeated in the newspapers, known to all France. But Charles had no ambition. An Yvetot doctor whom he had lately met in consultation had somewhat humiliated him at the very bedside of the patient, before the assembled relatives. When, in the evening, Charles told her this anecdote, Emma inveighed loudly against his colleague. Charles was much touched. He kissed her forehead with a tear in his eyes. But she was angered with shame; she felt a wild desire to strike him; she went to open the window in the passage and breathed in the fresh air to calm herself.

'What a man! what a man!' she said in a low voice, biting her lips.

Besides, she was becoming more irritated with him. As he grew older his manner grew heavier; at dessert he cut the corks of the empty bottles, after eating he cleaned his teeth with his tongue; in taking soup he made

From *Madame Bovary* by Gustave Flaubert. Reprinted by permission of Random House, Inc.

a gurgling noise with every spoonful; and, as he was getting fatter, the puffed-out cheeks seemed to push the eyes, always small, up to the temples.

Sometimes Emma tucked the red borders of his undervest into his waistcoat, rearranged his cravat, and threw away the dirty gloves he was going to put on: and this was not, as he fancied, for himself; it was for herself, by a diffusion of egotism, of nervous irritation. Sometimes, too, she told him of what she had read, such as a passage in a novel, of a new play, or an anecdote of the 'upper ten' that she had seen in a feuilleton; for, after all, Charles was something, an ever-open ear, an ever-ready approbation. She confided many a thing to her greyhound. She would have done so to the logs in the fireplace or to the pendulum of the clock.

At bottom of her heart, however, she was waiting for something to happen. Like shipwrecked sailors, she turned despairing eyes upon the solitude of her life, seeking afar off some white sail in the mists of the horizon. She did not know what this chance would be, what wind would bring it her, towards what shore it would drive her, if it would be a shallop or a three-decker, laden with anguish or full of bliss to the portholes. But each morning, as she awoke, she hoped it would come that day; she listened to every sound, sprang up with a start, wondered that it did not come; then at sunset, always more saddened, she longed for the morrow.

Spring came round. With the first warm weather, when the pear-trees began to blossom, she suffered from dyspnœa.

From the beginning of July she counted how many weeks there were to October, thinking that perhaps the Marquis d'Andervilliers would give another ball at Vaubyessard. But all September passed without letters or visits.

After the ennui of this disappointment her heart once more remained empty, and then the same series of days recommenced. So now they would thus follow one another, always the same, immovable, and bringing nothing. Other lives, however flat, had at least the chance of some event. One adventure sometimes brought with it infinite consequences and the scene changed. But nothing happened to her; God had willed it so! The future was a dark corridor, with its door at the end shut fast.

She gave up music. What was the good of playing? Who would hear her? Since she could never, in a velvet gown with short sleeves, striking with her light fingers the ivory keys of an Erard at a concert, feel the murmur of ecstasy envelop her like a breeze, it was not worth while boring herself with practising. Her drawing cardboard and her embroidery she left in the cupboard. What was the good? What was the good? Sewing irritated her. 'I have read everything,' she said to herself. And she sat there making the tongs red-hot, or looked at the rain falling.

How sad she was on Sundays when vespers sounded! She listened with dull attention to each stroke of the cracked bell. A cat slowly walking over some roof put up his back in the pale rays of the sun. The wind on the highroad blew up clouds of dust. Afar off a dog sometimes howled; and the bell, keeping time, continued its monotonous ringing that died away over the fields.

But the people came out from church. The women in waxed clogs, the peasants in new blouses, the little bareheaded children skipping along in front of them, all were going home. And till nightfall, five or six men, always the same, stayed playing at corks in front of the large door of the inn.

The winter was severe. The windows every morning were covered with rime, and the light shining through them, dim as through ground-glass, sometimes did not change the whole day long. At four o'clock the lamp had to be lighted.

On fine days she went down into the garden. The dew had left on the cabbages a silver lace with long transparent threads spreading from one to the other. No birds were to be heard; everything seemed asleep, the espalier covered with straw, and the vine, like a great sick serpent under the coping of the wall, along which, on drawing near, one saw the many-footed woodlice crawling. Under the spruce by the hedgerow, the curé in the three-cornered hat reading his breviary had lost his right foot, and the very plaster, scaling off with the frost, had left white scabs on his face.

Then she went up again, shut her door, put on coals, and fainting with the heat of the hearth, felt her boredom weigh more heavily than ever. She would have liked to go down and talk to the servant, but a sense of shame restrained her.

Every day at the same time the schoolmaster in a black skull-cap opened the shutters of his house, and the rural policeman, wearing his sabre over his blouse, passed by. Night and morning the post-horses, three by three, crossed the street to water at the pond. From time to time the bell of a public-house door rang, and when it was windy one could hear the little brass basins that served as signs for the hairdresser's shop creaking on their two rods. This shop had as decoration an old engraving of a fashion-plate stuck against a window-pane and the wax bust of a woman with yellow hair. He, too, the hairdresser, lamented his wasted calling, his hopeless future, and dreaming of some shop in a big town—at Rouen, for example, overlooking the harbour, near the theatre—he walked up and down all day from the mairie to the church, sombre and waiting for customers. When Madame Bovary looked up, she always saw him there, like a sentinel on duty, with his skull-cap over his ears and his vest of lasting.

Sometimes in the afternoon outside the window of her room, the head of a man appeared, a swarthy head with black whiskers, smiling slowly, with a broad, gentle smile that showed his white teeth. A waltz immediately began, and on the organ, in a little drawing-room, dancers the size of a finger, women in pink turbans, Tyroleans in jackets, monkeys in frock-coats, gentlemen in knee-breeches, turned and turned between the sofas, the consoles, multiplied in the bits of looking-glass held together at their corners by a piece of gold paper. The man turned his handle, looking to the right and left, and up at the windows. Now and again, while he shot out a long squirt of brown saliva against the milestone, with his knee he raised his instrument, whose hard straps tired his shoulder; and now, doleful and drawling, or gay and hurried, the music escaped from the box, droning through a curtain of pink taffeta under a brass claw in arabesque. They were airs played in other places at the theatres, sung in drawing-rooms, danced to at night under lighted lustres, echoes of the world that reached even to Emma. Endless sarabands ran through her head, and, like an Indian dancing-girl on the flowers of a carpet, her thoughts leapt with the notes, swung from dream to dream, from sadness to sadness. When the man had caught some coppers in his cap, he drew down an old cover of blue cloth, hitched his organ on to his back, and went off with a heavy tread. She watched him going.

But it was above all the meal-times that were unbearable to her, in this small room on the ground-floor, with its smoking stove, its creaking door, the walls that sweated, the damp flags; all the bitterness in life seemed served up on her plate, and with the smoke of the boiled beef there rose from her secret soul whiffs of sickliness. Charles was a slow eater; she played with a few nuts, or, leaning on her elbow, amused herself with drawing lines along the oilcloth tablecover with the point of her knife.

She now let everything in her household take care of itself, and Madame Bovary senior, when she came to spend part of Lent at Tostes, was much surprised at the change. She who was formerly so careful, so dainty, now passed whole days without dressing, wore grey cotton stockings, and burnt tallow candles. She kept saying they must be economical since they were not rich, adding that she was very contented, very happy, that Tostes pleased her very much, with other speeches that closed the mouth of her mother-in-law. Besides, Emma no longer seemed inclined to follow her advice; once even, Madame Bovary having thought fit to maintain that mistresses ought to keep an eye on the religion of their servants, she had answered with so angry a look and so cold a smile that the good woman did not try it again.

Emma was growing difficile, capricious. She ordered dishes for herself,

then she did not touch them; one day drank only pure milk, and the next cups of tea by the dozen. Often she persisted in not going out, then, stifling, threw open the windows and put on light dresses. After she had well scolded her servant she gave her presents or sent her out to see neighbours, just as she sometimes threw beggars all the silver in her purse, although she was by no means tender-hearted or easily accessible to the feelings of others, like most country-bred people, who always retain in their souls something of the horny hardness of the paternal hands.

Towards the end of February old Rouault, in memory of his cure, himself brought his son-in-law a superb turkey, and stayed three days at Tostes. Charles being with his patients, Emma kept him company. He smoked in the room, spat on the firedogs, talked farming, calves, cows, poultry, and municipal council, so that when he left she closed the door on him with a feeling of satisfaction that surprised even herself. Moreover she no longer concealed her contempt for anything or anybody, and at times she set herself to express singular opinions, finding fault with that which others approved, and approving things perverse and immoral, all of which made her husband open his eyes widely.

Would this misery last for ever? Would she never issue from it? Yet she was as good as all the women who were living happily. She had seen duchesses at Vaubyessard with clumsier waists and commoner ways, and she execrated the injustice of God. She leant her head against the walls to weep; she envied lives of stir; longed for masked balls, for violent pleasures, with all the wildness, that she did not know, but that these must surely yield.

She grew pale and suffered from palpitations of the heart. Charles prescribed valerian and camphor baths. Everything that was tried only seemed to irritate her the more.

On certain days she chattered with feverish rapidity, and this over-excitement was suddenly followed by a state of torpor, in which she remained without speaking, without moving. What then revived her was pouring a bottle of eau-de-cologne over her arms.

As she was constantly complaining about Tostes, Charles fancied that her illness was no doubt due to some local cause, and fixing on this idea, began to think seriously of setting up elsewhere.

From that moment she drank vinegar, contracted a sharp little cough, and completely lost her appetite.

It cost Charles much to give up Tostes after living there four years and 'when he was beginning to get on there.' Yet if it must be! He took her to Rouen to see his old master. It was a nervous complaint; change of air was needed.

After looking about him on this side and on that, Charles learnt that in the Neufchâtel arrondissement there was a considerable market-town called Yonville-l'Abbaye, whose doctor, a Polish refugee, had decamped a week before. Then he wrote to the chemist of the place to ask the number of the population, the distance from the nearest doctor, what his predecessor had made a year, and so forth; and the answer being satisfactory, he made up his mind to move towards the spring, if Emma's health did not improve.

One day when, in view of her departure, she was tidying a drawer, something pricked her finger. It was a wire of her wedding-bouquet. The orange blossoms were yellow with dust and the silver-bordered satin ribbons frayed at the edges. She threw it into the fire. It flared up more quickly than dry straw. Then it was like a red bush in the cinders, slowly devoured. She watched it burn. The little pasteboard berries burst, the wire twisted, the gold lace melted; and the shrivelled paper corollas, fluttering like black butterflies at the back of the stove, at last flew up the chimney.

When they left Tostes in the month of March, Madame Bovary was pregnant.

* * *

Emma grew thinner, her cheeks paler, her face longer. With her black hair, her large eyes, her aquiline nose, her birdlike walk, and always silent now, did she not seem to be passing through life scarcely touching it, and to bear on her brow the vague impress of some divine destiny? She was so sad and so calm, at once so gentle and so reserved, that near her one felt oneself seized by an icy charm, as we shudder in churches at the perfume of the flowers mingling with the cold of the marble. The others even did not escape from this seduction. The chemist said—

'She is a woman of great parts, who wouldn't be misplaced in a sub-prefecture.'

The housewives admired her economy, the patients her politeness, the poor her charity.

But she was eaten up with desires, with rage, with hate. That dress with the narrow folds hid a distracted heart, of whose torment those chaste lips said nothing. She was in love with Léon, and sought solitude that she might with the more ease delight in his image. The sight of his form troubled the voluptuousness of this meditation. Emma thrilled at the sound of his step; then in his presence the emotion subsided, and afterwards there remained to her only an immense astonishment that ended in sorrow.

Léon did not know that when he left her in despair she rose after he had gone to see him in the street. She concerned herself about his comings and goings; she watched his face; she invented quite a history to find an excuse for going to his room. The chemist's wife seemed happy to her to sleep under the same roof, and her thoughts constantly centered upon this house, like the 'Lion d'Or' pigeons, who came there to dip their red feet and white wings in its gutters. But the more Emma recognized her love, the more she crushed it down, that it might not be evident, that she might make it less. She would have liked Léon to guess it, and she imagined chances, catastrophes that should facilitate this. What restrained her was, no doubt, idleness and fear, and a sense of shame also. She thought she had repulsed him too much, that the time was past, that all was lost. Then, pride, the joy of being able to say to herself, 'I am virtuous,' and to look at herself in the glass taking resigned poses, consoled her a little for the sacrifice she believed she was making.

Then the lusts of the flesh, the longing for money, and the melancholy of passion all blended themselves into one suffering, and instead of turning her thoughts from it, she clave to it the more, urging herself to pain, and seeking everywhere occasion for it. She was irritated by an ill-served dish or by a half-open door; bewailed the velvets she had not, the happiness she had missed, her too exalted dreams, her narrow home.

What exasperated her was that Charles did not seem to notice her anguish. His conviction that he was making her happy seemed to her an imbecile insult, and his sureness on this point ingratitude. For whose sake, then, was she virtuous? Was it not for him, the obstacle to all felicity, the cause of all misery, and, as it were, the sharp clasp of that complex strap that buckled her in on all sides?

On him alone, then, she concentrated all the various hatreds that resulted from her boredom, and every effort to diminish only augmented it; for this useless trouble was added to the other reasons for despair, and contributed still more to the separation between them. Her own gentleness to herself made her rebel against him. Domestic mediocrity drove her to lewd fancies, marriage tenderness to adulterous desires. She would have liked Charles to beat her, that she might have a better right to hate him, to revenge herself upon him. She was surprised sometimes at the atrocious conjectures that came into her thoughts, and she had to go on smiling, to hear repeated to her at all hours that she was happy, to pretend to be happy, to let it be believed.

Yet she had loathing of this hypocrisy. She was seized with the temptation to flee somewhere with Léon to try a new life; but at once a vague chasm full of darkness opened within her soul.

'Besides, he no longer loves me,' she thought. 'What is to become of me? What help is to be hoped for, what consolation, what solace?'

She was left broken, breathless, inert, sobbing in a low voice, with flowing tears.

'Why don't you tell master?' the servant asked her when she came in during these crises.

'It is the nerves,' said Emma. 'Do not speak to him of it; it would worry him.'

'Ah! yes,' Félicité went on, 'you are just like La Guérine, Père Guérin's daughter, the fisherman at Pollet, that I used to know at Dieppe before I came to you. She was so sad, so sad, to see her standing upright on the threshold of her house, she seemed to you like a winding-sheet spread out before the door. Her illness, it appears, was a kind of fog that she had in her head, and the doctors could not do anything, nor the priest either. When she was taken too bad she went off quite alone to the seashore, so that the customs officer, going his rounds, often found her lying flat on her face, crying on the shingle. Then, after her marriage, it went off, they say.'

'But with me,' replied Emma, 'it was after marriage that it began.'

*　　*　　*

The winter was severe, Madame Bovary's convalescence slow. When it was fine they wheeled her armchair to the window that overlooked the square, for she now had an antipathy to the garden, and the blinds on that side were always down. She wished the horse to be sold; what she formerly liked now displeased her. All her ideas seemed to be limited to the care of herself. She stayed in bed taking little meals, rang for the servant to inquire about her gruel or to chat with her. The snow on the market-roof threw a white, still light into the room; then the rain began to fall; and Emma waited daily with a mind full of eagerness for the inevitable return of some trifling events which

nevertheless had no relation to her. The most important was the arrival of the 'Hirondelle' in the evening. Then the landlady shouted out, and other voices answered, while Hippolyte's lantern, as he fetched the boxes from the boot, was like a star in the darkness. At midday Charles came in; then he went out again; next she took some beef-tea, and towards five o'clock, as the day drew in, the children coming back from school, dragging their wooden shoes along the pavement, knocked the clapper of the shutters with their rulers one after the other.

It was at this hour that Monsieur Bournisien came to see her. He inquired after her health, gave her news, exhorted her to religion in a coaxing little gossip that was not without its charm. The mere thought of his cassock comforted her.

One day, when at the height of her illness, she had thought herself dying, and had asked for the communion; and, while they were making the preparations in her room for the sacrament, while they were turning the night-table covered with syrups into an altar, and while Félicité was strewing dahlia flowers on the floor, Emma felt some power passing over her that freed her from her pains, from all perception, from all feeling. Her body, relieved, no longer thought; another life was beginning; it seemed to her that her being, mounting toward God, would be annihilated in that love like a burning incense that melts into vapour. The bed-clothes were sprinkled with holy water, the priest drew from the holy pyx the white wafer; and it was fainting with a celestial joy that she put out her lips to accept the body of the Saviour presented to her. The curtains of the alcove floated gently round her like clouds, and the rays of the two tapers burning on the night-table seemed to shine like dazzling halos. Then she let her head fall back, fancying she heard in space the music of seraphic harps, and perceived in an azure sky, on a golden throne in the midst of saints holding green palms, God the Father, resplendent with majesty, who with a sign sent to earth angels with wings of fire to carry her away in their arms.

This splendid vision dwelt in her memory as the most beautiful thing that it was possible to dream, so that now she strove to recall her sensation, that still lasted, however, but in a less exclusive fashion and with a deeper sweetness. Her soul, tortured by pride, at length found rest in Christian humility, and, tasting the joy of weakness, she saw within herself the destruction of her will, that must have left a wide entrance for the inroads of heavenly grace. There existed, then, in the place of happiness, still greater joys,—another love beyond all loves, without pause and without end, one that would grow eternally! She saw amid the illusions of her hope a state of purity floating above the earth mingling with heaven, to which she aspired. She wanted to become a saint. She bought chaplets and wore amulets; she wished to have in her room, by the side of her bed, a reliquary set in emeralds that she might kiss it every evening.

The curé marvelled at this humour, although Emma's religion, he thought, might, from its fervour, end by touching on heresy, extravagance. But not being much versed in these matters, as soon as they went beyond a certain limit he wrote to Monsieur Boulard, bookseller to Monsignor, to send him 'something good for a lady who was very clever.' The bookseller, with as much indifference as if he had been sending off hardware to niggers, packed up, pell-mell, everything that was then the fashion in the pious book trade. There were little manuals in questions and answers, pamphlets of aggressive tone after the manner of Monsieur de Maistre, and certain novels in rose-coloured bindings and with a honied style, manufactured by troubadour seminarists or penitent blue-stockings. There were the 'Think of it; the Man of the World at Mary's Feet, by Monsieur de ! ! !, décoré with many Orders'; 'The Errors of Voltaire, for the Use of the Young,' &c.

Madame Bovary's mind was not yet sufficiently clear to apply herself seriously to anything; moreover, she began this reading in too much hurry. She grew provoked at the doctrines of religion; the arrogance of the polemic writings displeased her by their inveteracy in attacking people she did not know; and the secular stories, relieved with religion, seemed to her written in such ignorance of the world, that they insensibly estranged her from the truths for whose proof she was looking. Nevertheless, she persevered; and when the volume slipped from her hands, she fancied herself seized with the finest Catholic melancholy that an ethereal soul could conceive.

As for the memory of Rodolphe, she had thrust it back to the bottom of her heart, and it remained there more solemn and more motionless than a king's mummy in a catacomb. An exhalation escaped from this embalmed love, that, penetrating through everything, perfumed with tenderness the immaculate atmosphere in which she longed to live. When she knelt on her Gothic prie-Dieu, she addressed to the Lord the same suave words that she had murmured formerly to her lover in the outpourings of adultery. It was to make faith come; but no delights descended from the heavens, and she arose with tired limbs and with a vague feeling of a gigantic dupery.

This searching after faith, she thought, was only one merit the more, and in the pride of her devoutness Emma compared herself to those grand ladies of long ago whose glory she had dreamed of over a portrait of La Vallière, and who, trailing with so much majesty the lace-trimmed trains of their long gowns, retired into solitudes to shed at the feet of Christ all the tears of hearts that life had wounded.

Then she gave herself up to excessive charity. She sewed clothes for the poor, she sent wood to women in childbed; and Charles one day, on coming home, found three good-for-nothings in the kitchen seated at the table eating soup. She had her little girl, whom during her illness her husband had sent back to the nurse, brought home. She wanted to teach her to read; even when Berthe cried, she was not vexed. She had made up her mind to resignation, to universal indulgence. Her language about everything was full of ideal expressions. She said to her child, 'Is your stomach-ache better, my angel?'

*   *   *

Her heart began to beat as soon as she reached the vestibule. She involuntarily smiled with vanity on seeing the crowd rushing to the right by the other corridor while she went up the staircase to the reserved seats. She was as pleased as a child to push with her finger the large tapestried door. She breathed in with all her might the dusty smell of the lobbies, and when she was seated in her box she bent forward with the air of a duchess.

The theatre was beginning to fill; opera-glasses were taken from their cases, and the subscribers, catching sight of one another, were bowing. They came to seek relaxation in the fine arts after the anxieties of business; but 'business' was not forgotten; they still talked cottons, spirits of wine, or indigo. The heads of old men were to be seen, inexpressive and peaceful, with their hair and complexions looking like silver medals tarnished by steam of lead. The young beaux were strutting about in the pit, showing in the opening of their waistcoats their pink or apple-green cravats, and Madame Bovary from above admired them leaning on their canes with golden knobs in the open palm of their yellow gloves.

Now the lights of the orchestra were lit, the lustre, let down from the ceiling, throwing by the glimmering of its facets a sudden gaiety over the theatre; then the musicians came in one after the other; and first there was the protracted hubbub of the brasses grumbling, violins squeaking, cornets trumpeting, flutes and flageolets fifing. But three knocks were heard on the stage, a rolling of drums began, the brass instruments played some chords, and the curtain rising, discovered a country-scene.

It was the cross-roads of a wood, with a fountain shaded by an oak to the left. Peasants and lords with plaids on their shoulders were singing a hunting-song together; then a captain suddenly came on, who evoked the spirit of evil by lifting both his arms to heaven. Another appeared; they went away, and the hunters started afresh.

She felt herself transported to the reading of her youth, into the midst of Walter Scott. She seemed to hear through the mist the sound of the Scotch bagpipes re-echoing over the heather. Then her remembrance of the novel helping her to understand the libretto, she followed the story phrase by phrase, while vague thoughts that came back to her dispersed at once again with the bursts of music. She gave herself up to the lullaby of the melodies, and felt all her being vibrate as if the violin bows were drawn over her nerves. She had not eyes enough to look at the costumes, the scenery, the actors, the painted trees that shook when any one walked, and the velvet caps, cloaks, swords—all those imaginary things that floated amid the harmony as in the atmosphere of another world. But a young woman stepped forward, throwing a purse to a squire in green. She was left alone, and the flute was heard like the murmur of a fountain or the warbling of birds. Lucie attacked her cavatina in G major bravely. She plained of love; she longed for wings. Emma, too, fleeing from life, would have liked to fly away in an embrace. Suddenly, Edgar-Lagardy appeared.

He had that splendid pallor that gives something of the majesty of marble to the ardent races of the South. His vigorous form was tightly clad in a brown-coloured doublet; a small chiselled poniard hung against his left thigh, and he cast round laughing looks showing his white teeth. They said that a Polish princess having heard him sing one night on the beach at Biarritz, where he mended boats, had fallen in love with him. She had ruined herself for him. He had deserted her for other women, and this sentimental celebrity did not fail to enhance his artistic reputation. The diplomatic mummer took care always to slip into his advertisements some poetic phrase on the fascination of his person and the susceptibility of his soul. A fine organ, imperturbable coolness, more temperament than intelligence, more power of emphasis than real singing, made up the charm of this admirable charlatan nature, in which there was something of the hairdresser and the toreador.

From the first scene he evoked enthusiasm. He pressed Lucie in his arms, he left her, he came back, he seemed desperate; he had outbursts of rage, then elegiac gurglings of infinite sweetness, and the notes escaped from his bare neck full of sobs and kisses. Emma leant forward to see him, clutching the velvet of the box with her nails. She was filling her heart with these melodious lamentations that were drawn out to the accompaniment of the double-basses, like the cries of the drowning in the tumult of a tempest. She recognized all the intoxication and the anguish that had almost killed her. The voice of the prima donna seemed to her to be but echoes of her conscience, and this illusion that charmed her as some very thing of her own life. But no one on earth had loved her with such love. He had not wept like Edgar that last moonlit night when they said, 'To-morrow! to-morrow!' The theatre rang with cheers; they recommenced the entire movement; the lovers spoke of the flowers on their tomb, of vows, exile, fate, hopes; and when they uttered the final adieu, Emma gave a sharp cry that mingled with the vibrations of the last chords.

'But why,' asked Bovary, 'does that gentleman persecute her?'

'No, no!' she answered; 'he is her lover!'

'Yet he vows vengeance on her family, while the other one who came on before said, "I love Lucie and she loves me!" Besides, he went off with her father arm in arm. For he certainly is her father, isn't he—the ugly little man with a cock's feather in his hat?'

Despite Emma's explanations, as soon as the recitative duet began in which Gilbert lays bare his abominable machinations to his master Ashton, Charles, seeing the false troth-ring that is to deceive Lucie, thought it was a love-gift sent by Edgar. He confessed, moreover, that he did not understand the story because of the music, which interfered very much with the words.

'What does it matter?' said Emma. 'Do be quiet!'

'Yes, but you know,' he went on, leaning against her shoulder, 'I like to understand things.'

'Be quiet! be quiet!' she cried impatiently.

Lucie advanced, half supported by her women, a wreath of orange blossoms in her hair, and paler than the white satin of her gown. Emma dreamed of her marriage day; she saw herself at home again amid the corn in the little path as they walked to the church. Oh, why had not she, like this woman, resisted, implored? She, on the contrary, had been joyous, without seeing the abyss into which she was throwing herself. Ah! if in the freshness of her beauty, before the soiling of marriage and the disillusions of adultery, she could have anchored her life upon some great, strong heart, then virtue, tenderness, voluptuousness, and duty blending, she would never have fallen from so high a happiness. But that happiness, no doubt, was a lie invented for the despair of all desire. She now knew the smallness of the passions that art exaggerated. So, striving to divert her thoughts, Emma determined now to see in this reproduction of her sorrows only a plastic fantasy, well enough to please the eye, and she even smiled internally with disdainful pity when at the back of the stage under the velvet hangings a man appeared in a black coat.

His large Spanish hat fell at a gesture he made, and immediately the instruments and the singers began the sextet. Edgar, flashing with fury, dominated all the others with his clearer voice; Ashton hurled homicidal provocation at him in deep notes; Lucie uttered her shrill plaint, Arthur at one side, his modulated tones in the middle register, and the bass of the minister pealed forth like an organ, while the voices of the women repeating his words took them up in chorus delightfully. They were all in a row gesticulating, and anger, vengeance, jealousy, terror, and stupefaction breathed forth at once from their half-opened mouths. The outraged lover brandished his naked sword; his guipure ruffle rose with jerks to the movements of his chest, and he walked from right to left with long strides, clanking against the boards the silver-gilt spurs of his soft boots, widening out at the ankles. He, she thought, must have an inexhaustible love to lavish it upon the crowd with such effusion. All her small fault-findings faded before the poetry of the part that absorbed her; and, drawn towards this man by the illusion of the character, she tried to imagine to herself his life—that life resonant, extraordinary, splendid, and that might have been hers if fate had willed it. They would have known one another, loved one another. With him, through all the kingdoms of Europe she would have travelled from capital to capital, sharing his fatigues and his pride, picking up the flowers thrown to him, herself embroidering his costumes. Then each evening, at the back of a box, behind the golden trellis-work, she would have drunk in eagerly the expansions of this soul that would have sung for her alone; from the stage, even as he acted, he would have looked at her. But the mad idea seized her that he was looking at her; it was certain. She longed to run to his arms, to take refuge in his strength, as in the incarnation of love itself, and to say to him, to cry out, 'Take me away! carry me with you! let us go! Thine, thine! all my ardour and all my dreams!'

The curtain fell.

The smell of gas mingled with that of the breaths, the waving of the fans, made the air more suffocating. Emma wanted to go out; the crowd filled the corridors, and she fell back in her armchair with palpitations that choked her. Charles, fearing that she would faint, ran to the refreshment-room to get a glass of barley-water.

※

SONS AND LOVERS

D. H. LAWRENCE

[It may be that the love interest fails to extend beyond the immediate family, and the father, mother, brother, or sister constitutes the sole object of emotional interest. Such a relationship may be overtly expressed, or it may operate unconsciously and militate against progression to heterosexual love. No one has more powerfully presented the experience of the Oedipus complex, the fixation of emotional interest upon the mother, than D. H. Lawrence, whose own emotional conflicts are obviously the basis of *Sons and Lovers*. For Paul, as for Lawrence himself, a satisfactory adult relationship with a woman was forever impossible because of his emotional bondage to his mother. His relation to Miriam became one of torment as his ambivalent feelings toward her found expression at one moment in tender words and actions and at another in sadistic mental probings and denials of his love.]

At this time he was beginning to question the orthodox creed. He was twenty-one and she was twenty. She was beginning to dread the spring: he became so wild, and hurt her so much. All the way he went cruelly smashing her beliefs. Edgar enjoyed it. He was by nature critical and rather dispassionate. But Miriam suffered exquisite pain, as, with an intellect like a knife, the man she loved examined her religion in which she lived and moved and had her being. But he did not spare her. He was cruel. And when they went alone he was even more fierce, as if he would kill her soul. He bled her beliefs till she almost lost consciousness.

'She exults—she exults as she carries him off from me,' Mrs. Morel cried in her heart when Paul had gone. 'She's not like an ordinary woman, who can leave me my share in him. She wants to absorb him. She wants to draw him out and absorb him till there is nothing left of him, even for himself. He will never be a man on his own feet—she will suck him up.' So the mother sat, and battled and brooded bitterly.

And he, coming home from his walks with Miriam, was wild with torture. He walked biting his lips and with clenched fists, going at a great rate. Then, brought up against a stile, he stood for some minutes, and did not move. There was a great hollow of darkness fronting him, and on the black upslopes patches of tiny lights, and in the lowest trough of the night, a flare of the pit. It was all weird and dreadful. Why was he torn so, almost bewildered, and unable to move? Why did his mother sit at home and suffer? And why did he hate Miriam, and feel so cruel towards her, at the thought of his mother? If Miriam caused his mother suffering, then he hated her—and he easily hated her. Why did she make him feel as if he were uncertain of himself, insecure, an indefinite thing, as if he had not sufficient sheathing to prevent the night and the space breaking into him? How he hated her! And then, what a rush of tenderness and humility!

Suddenly he plunged on again, running home. His mother saw on him the marks of some agony, and she said nothing. But he had to make her talk to him. Then she was angry with him for going so far with Miriam.

'Why don't you like her, mother?' he cried in despair.

'I don't know, my boy,' she replied piteously. 'I'm sure I've tried to like her. I've tried and tried, but I can't— I can't.'

And he felt dreary and hopeless between the two.

Spring was the worst time. He was changeable, and intense and cruel. So he decided to stay away from her. Then came the hours when he knew Miriam was expecting him. His mother watched him growing restless. He could not go on with his work. He could do nothing. It was as if something were drawing his soul out toward Willey Farm. Then he put on his hat and went, saying nothing. And his mother knew he was gone. And as soon as he was on the way he sighed with relief. And when he was with her he was cruel again.

One day in March he lay on the bank of Nethermere, with Miriam sitting beside him. It was a glistening, white-and-blue day. Big clouds, so brilliant, went by overhead, while shadows stole along on the water. The clear spaces in the sky were of clean, cold blue. Paul lay on his back in the old grass, looking up. He could not bear to look at Miriam. She seemed to want him, and he resisted. He resisted all the time. He wanted now to give her passion and tenderness, and he could not. He felt that she wanted the soul out of his body, and not him. All his strength and energy she drew into herself through some channel which united them. She did not want to meet him, so that there were two of them, man and woman together. She wanted to draw all of him into her. It urged him to an intensity like madness, which fascinated him, as drug-taking might.

He was discussing Michael Angelo. It felt to her as if she were fingering the very quivering tissue, the very protoplasm of life, as she heard him. It gave her her deepest satisfaction.

And in the end it frightened her. There he lay in the white intensity of his search, and his voice gradually filled her with fear, so level it was, almost inhuman, as if in a trance.

'Don't talk any more,' she pleaded softly, laying her hand on his forehead.

He lay quite still, almost unable to move. His body was somewhere discarded.

'Why not? Are you tired?'

'Yes, and it wears you out.'

He laughed shortly, realizing.

'Yet you always make me like it,' he said.

'I don't wish to,' she said, very low.

'Not when you've gone too far, and you feel you can't bear it. But your unconscious self always asks it of me. And I suppose I want it.'

He went on, in his dead fashion:

'If only you could want *me*, and not want what I can reel off for you!'

'I!' she cried bitterly—'I! Why, when would you let me take you?'

'Then it's my fault,' he said, and, gathering himself together, he got up and began to talk trivialities. He felt insubstantial. In a vague way he hated her for it. And he knew he was as much to blame himself. This, however, did not prevent his hating her.

One evening about this time he had walked along the home road with her. They stood by the pasture leading down to the wood, unable to part. As the stars came out the clouds closed. They had glimpses of their own constellation, Orion, towards the west. His jewels glimmered for a moment, his dog ran low, struggling with difficulty through the spume of cloud.

Orion was for them chief in significance among the constellations. They had gazed at him in their strange, surcharged hours of feeling, until they seemed themselves to live in every one of his stars. This evening Paul had been moody and perverse. Orion had seemed just an ordinary constellation to him. He had fought against his glamour and fascination. Miriam was watching her lover's mood carefully. But he said nothing that gave him away, till the moment came to part, when he stood frowning gloomily at the gathered clouds, behind which the great constellation must be striding still.

There was to be a little party at his house the next day, at which she was to attend.

'I shan't come and meet you,' he said.

'Oh, very well; it's not very nice out,' she replied slowly.

'It's not that—only they don't like me to. They say I care more for you than for them. And you understand, don't you? You know it's only friendship.'

Miriam was astonished and hurt for him. It had cost him an effort. She left him, wanting to spare him any further humiliation. A fine rain blew in her face as she walked along the road. She was hurt deep down; and she despised him for being blown about by any wind of authority. And in her heart of hearts, unconsciously, she felt that he was trying to get away from her. This she would never have acknowledged. She pitied him.

*   *   *

'If *I* wanted you to go to Selby on Friday night, I can imagine the scene,' said Mrs. Morel. 'But you're never too tired to go if *she* will come for you. Nay, you neither want to eat nor drink then.'

'I can't let her go alone.'

'Can't you? And why does she come?'

'Not because I ask her.'

'She doesn't come without you want her—'

'Well, what if I *do* want her—' he replied.

'Why, nothing, if it was sensible or reasonable. But to go trapseing up there miles and miles in the mud, coming home at midnight, and got to go to Nottingham in the morning—'

'If I hadn't, you'd be just the same.'

'Yes, I should, because there's no sense in it. Is she *so* fascinating that you must follow her all that way?' Mrs. Morel was bitterly sarcastic. She sat still, with averted face, stroking with a rhythmic, jerked movement, the black sateen of her apron. It was a movement that hurt Paul to see.

'I do like her,' he said, 'but—'

'*Like* her!' said Mrs. Morel, in the same biting tones. 'It seems to me you like nothing and nobody else. There's neither Annie, nor me, nor anyone now for you.'

'What nonsense, mother—you know I don't love her—I—I tell you I *don't* love her—she doesn't even walk with my arm, because I don't want her to.'

'Then why do you fly to her so often!'

'I *do* like to talk to her—I never said I didn't. But I *don't* love her.'

'Is there nobody else to talk to?'

'Not about the things we talk of . . . There's lots of things that you're not interested in, that—'

'What things?'

Mrs. Morel was so intense that Paul began to pant.

'Why—painting—and books. *You* don't care about Herbert Spencer.'

'No,' was the sad reply. 'And *you* won't at my age.'

'Well, but I do now—and Miriam does—'

'And how do you know,' Mrs.

Morel flashed defiantly, 'that *I* shouldn't. Do you ever try me!'

'But you don't, mother, you know you don't care whether a picture's decorative or not; you don't care what *manner* it is in.'

'How do you know I don't care? Do you ever try me? Do you ever talk to me about these things, to try?'

'But it's not that that matters to you, mother, you know it's not.'

'What is it, then—what is it, then, that matters to me?' she flashed. He knitted his brows with pain.

'You're old, mother, and we're young.'

He only meant that the interests of *her* age were not the interests of his. But he realized the moment he had spoken that he had said the wrong thing.

'Yes, I know it well—I am old. And therefore I may stand aside; I have nothing more to do with you. You only want me to wait on you—the rest is for Miriam.'

He could not bear it. Instinctively he realized that he was life to her. And, after all, she was the chief thing to him, the only supreme being.

'You know it isn't, mother, you know it isn't!'

She was moved to pity by his cry.

'It looks a great deal like it,' she said, half putting aside her despair.

'No, mother—I really don't love her. I talk to her, but I want to come home to you.'

He had taken off his collar and tie, and rose, bare-throated, to go to bed. As he stooped to kiss his mother, she threw her arms round his neck, hid her face on his shoulder, and cried, in a whimpering voice, so unlike her own that he writhed in agony:

'I can't bear it. I could let another woman—but not her. She'd leave me no room, not a bit of room—'

And immediately he hated Miriam bitterly.

'And I've never—you know, Paul —I've never had a husband—not really—'

He stroked his mother's hair, and his mouth was on her throat.

'And she exults so in taking you from me—she's not like ordinary girls.'

'Well, I don't love her, mother,' he murmured, bowing his head and hiding his eyes on her shoulder in misery. His mother kissed him a long, fervent kiss.

'My boy!' she said, in a voice trembling with passionate love.

Without knowing, he gently stroked her face.

'There,' said his mother, 'now go to bed. You'll be *so* tired in the morning.' As she was speaking she heard her husband coming. 'There's your father—now go.' Suddenly she looked at him almost as if in fear. 'Perhaps I'm selfish. If you want her, take her, my boy.'

His mother looked so strange, Paul kissed her, trembling.

'Ha—mother!' he said softly.

Morel came in, walking unevenly. His hat was over one corner of his eye. He balanced in the doorway.

'At your mischief again?' he said venomously.

Mrs. Morel's emotion turned into sudden hate of the drunkard who had come in thus upon her.

'At any rate, it is sober,' she said.

'H'm—h'm—h'm!' he sneered. He went into the passage, hung up his hat and coat. Then they heard him go down three steps to the pantry. He returned with a piece of pork-pie in his fist. It was what Mrs. Morel had bought for her son.

'Nor was that bought for you. If you can give me no more than twenty-five shillings, I'm sure I'm not going to buy you pork-pie to stuff, after you've swilled a bellyful of beer.'

'Wha-at—wha-at!' snarled Morel, toppling in his balance. 'Wha-at—not for me?' He looked at the piece of meat and crust, and suddenly, in a vicious spurt of temper, flung it into the fire.

Paul started to his feet.

'Waste your own stuff!' he cried.

'What—what!' suddenly shouted Morel, jumping up and clenching his fist. 'I'll show yer, yer young jockey!'

'All right!' said Paul viciously, putting his head on one side. 'Show me!'

He would at that moment dearly have loved to have a smack at something. Morel was half crouching, fists up, ready to spring. The young man stood, smiling with his lips.

'Ussha!' hissed the father, swiping round with a great stroke just past his son's face. He dared not, even though so close, really touch the young man, but swerved an inch away.

'Right!' said Paul, his eyes upon the side of his father's mouth, where in another instant his fist would have hit. He ached for that stroke. But he heard a faint moan from behind. His mother was deadly pale, and dark at the mouth. Morel was dancing up to deliver another blow.

'Father!' said Paul, so that the word rang.

Morel started, and stood at attention.

'Mother!' moaned the boy. 'Mother!'

She began to struggle with herself. Her open eyes watched him, although she could not move. Gradually she was coming to herself. He laid her down on the sofa, and ran upstairs for a little whisky, which at least she could sip. The tears were hopping down his face. As he kneeled in front of her he did not cry, but the tears ran down his face quickly. Morel, on the opposite side of the room, sat with his elbows on his knees glaring across.

'What's-a-matter with 'er?' he asked.

'Faint!' replied Paul.

'H'm!'

The elderly man began to unlace his boots. He stumbled off to bed. His last fight was fought in that home.

Paul kneeled there, stroking his mother's hand.

'Don't be poorly, mother—don't be poorly!' he said time after time.

'It's nothing, my boy,' she murmured.

At last he rose, fetched in a large piece of coal, and raked the fire. Then he cleared the room, put everything straight, laid the things for breakfast, and brought his mother's candle.

'Can you go to bed, mother?'

'Yes, I'll come.'

'Sleep with Annie, mother, not with him.'

'No. I'll sleep in my own bed.'

'Don't sleep with him, mother.'

'I'll sleep in my own bed.'

She rose, and he turned out the gas, then followed her closely upstairs, carrying her candle. On the landing he kissed her close.

'Good-night, mother.'

'Good-night,' she said.

He pressed his face upon the pillow in a fury of misery. And yet, somewhere in his soul, he was at peace because he still loved his mother best. It was the bitter peace of resignation.

The efforts of his father to con-ciliate him next day were a great humiliation to him.

Everybody tried to forget the scene.

* * *

'At any rate, mother, I s'll never marry,' he said.

'Ay, they all say that, my lad. You've not met the one yet. Only wait a year or two.'

'But I shan't marry, mother. I shall live with you, and we'll have a servant.'

'Ay, my lad, it's easy to talk. We'll see when the time comes.'

'What time? I'm nearly twenty-three.'

'Yes, you're not one that would marry young. But in three years' time—'

'I shall be with you just the same.'

'We'll see, my boy, we'll see.'

'But you don't want me to marry?'

'I shouldn't like to think of you going through your life without anybody to care for you and do—no.'

'And you think I ought to marry?'

'Sooner or later every man ought.'

'But you'd rather it were later.'

'It would be hard—and very hard. It's as they say:

' "A son's my son till he takes him a wife,
But my daughter's my daughter the whole of her life." '

'And you think I'd let a wife take me from you?'

'Well, you wouldn't ask her to marry your mother as well as you,' Mrs. Morel smiled.

'She could do what she liked; she wouldn't have to interfere.'

'She wouldn't—till she'd got you—and then you'd see.'

'I never will see. I'll never marry while I've got you—I won't.'

'But I shouldn't like to leave you with nobody, my boy,' she cried.

'You're not going to leave me. What are you? Fifty-three! I'll give you till seventy-five. There you are, I'm fat and forty-four. Then I'll marry a staid body. See!'

His mother sat and laughed.

'Go to bed,' she said—'go to bed.'

'And we'll have a pretty house, you and me, and a servant, and it'll be just all right. I s'll perhaps be rich with my painting.'

'Will you go to bed!'

'And then you s'll have a pony-carriage. See yourself—a little Queen Victoria trotting round.'

'I tell you go to bed,' she laughed.

He kissed her and went. His plans for the future were always the same.

❊

PIERRE AND JEAN

Guy de Maupassant

[While the mechanism of repression enables one to obliterate from consciousness feelings irreconcilable with the demands of the ego or the pressure of one's conscience, the buried feelings may arise to the surface in strange and often disguised forms. Sadism is a perverted form of pleasure attained through inflicting pain on another. Its corollary, masochism, is a means of sexual gratification through having pain inflicted upon oneself. Their origin can best be explained through the child's association of punishment with sexual pleasure. In Maupassant's *Pierre and Jean* Pierre's love for his mother, his jealousy of his younger brother who is his mother's favorite, and his sense of horror in the realization that his mother has committed adultery, are given sadistic expression in his uncontrollable impulses to torture her.]

For a week or two nothing occurred at the Rolands'. The father went fishing; Jean, with his mother's help, was furnishing and settling himself; Pierre, very gloomy, never was seen excepting at meal-times.

His father having asked him, one evening: 'Why the deuce do you always come in with a face as cheerful as a funeral? This is not the first time I have remarked it,' the doctor replied: 'The fact is, I am terribly conscious of the burden of life.'

The old man had not a notion what he meant, and with an aggrieved look he went on: 'It really is too bad. Ever since we had the good luck to come into this legacy, everyone seems unhappy. It is as though some accident had befallen us, as if we were in mourning for someone.'

'I *am* in mourning for someone,' said Pierre.

'You are? For whom?'

'For someone you never knew, and of whom I was too fond.'

Roland imagined that his son alluded to some girl with whom he had had some love-passages, and he said: 'A woman, I suppose.'

From *Pierre and Jean* by Guy de Maupassant, translated by Ernest Boyd. By permission of Alfred A. Knopf, Inc.

'Yes, a woman.'

'Dead?'

'No. Worse. Ruined!'

'Ah!'

Though he was startled by this unexpected confidence, in his wife's presence too, and by his son's strange tone about it, the old man made no further inquiries, for in his opinion such affairs did not concern a third person.

Madame Roland affected not to hear; she seemed ill and was very pale. Several times already her husband, surprised to see her sit down as if she were dropping into her chair, and to hear her gasp as if she could not draw her breath, had said:

'Really, Louise, you look very ill; you tire yourself too much with helping Jean. Give yourself a little rest. *Sacristi!* The rascal is in no hurry, as he is a rich man.'

She shook her head without a word.

But to-day her pallor was so great that Roland remarked on it again.

'Come, come,' said he, 'this will not do at all, my dear old woman. You must take care of yourself.' Then, addressing his son, 'You surely must see that your mother is ill. Have you questioned her, at any rate?'

Pierre replied: 'No; I had not noticed that there was anything the matter with her.'

At this Roland was angry.

'But it stares you in the face, confound you! What on earth is the good of your being a doctor if you cannot even see that your mother is out of sorts? Why, look at her, just look at her! Really, a man might die under his very eyes and this doctor would never think there was anything the matter!'

Madame Roland was panting for breath, and so white that her husband exclaimed:

'She is going to faint!'

'No, no, it is nothing—I shall get better directly—it is nothing.'

Pierre had gone up to her and was looking at her steadily.

'What ails you?' he said. And she repeated, in an undertone:

'Nothing, nothing—I assure you, nothing.'

Roland had gone to fetch some vinegar; he now returned, and, handing the bottle to his son, he said:

'Here—do something to ease her. Have you felt her heart?'

As Pierre bent over her to feel her pulse, she pulled away her hand so vehemently that she struck it against a chair which was standing by.

'Come,' said he, in icy tones, 'let me see what I can do for you, as you are ill.'

Then she raised her arm and held it out to him. Her skin was burning, the blood throbbing in short irregular leaps.

'You are certainly ill,' he murmured. 'You must take something to quiet you. I will write you a prescription.' And as he wrote, stooping over the paper, a low sound of choked sighs, smothered, quick breathing, and suppressed sobs made him suddenly look round at her. She was weeping, her hands covering her face.

Roland, quite distracted, asked her:

'Louise, Louise, what is the matter with you? What on earth ails you?'

She did not answer, but seemed racked by some deep and dreadful grief. Her husband tried to take her hands from her face, but she resisted him, repeating:

'No, no, no.'

He appealed to his son.

'But what is the matter with her? I never saw her like this.'

'It is nothing,' said Pierre. 'She is a little hysterical.'

And he felt as if it were a comfort to him to see her suffering thus, as if this anguish mitigated his resentment and diminished his mother's load of opprobrium. He looked at her as a judge satisfied with his day's work.

Suddenly she rose, rushed to the door with such a swift impulse that it was impossible to forestall or to stop her, and ran off to lock herself into her room.

Roland and the doctor were left face to face.

'Can you make head or tail of it?' said the father.

'Oh, yes,' said the other. 'It is a little nervous disturbance, not alarming or surprising; such attacks may very likely recur from time to time.'

They did in fact recur, almost every day; and Pierre seemed to bring them on with a word, as if he had the clue to her strange and new disorder. He would discern in her face a lucid interval of peace and, with the willingness of a torturer, would, with a word, revive the anguish that had been lulled for a moment.

But he, too, was suffering as cruelly as she. It was dreadful pain to him that he could no longer love her or respect her, that he must put her on the rack. When he had laid bare the bleeding wound which he had opened in her woman's, her mother's heart, when he felt how wretched and desperate she was, he would go out alone, wander about the town, so torn by remorse, so broken by pity, so grieved to have thus hammered her with his scorn as her son, that he longed to fling himself into the sea and put an end to it all by drowning himself.

Ah, how gladly now would he have forgiven her! But he could not, for he was incapable of forgetting. If only he could have desisted from making her suffer! But this again he could not, suffering as he did himself. He went home to his meals, full of relenting resolutions; then, as soon as he saw her, as soon as he met her eye—formerly so clear and frank, now so evasive, frightened, and bewildered—he struck at her in spite of himself, unable to suppress the treacherous words which would rise to his lips.

The disgraceful secret, known to them alone, goaded him up against her. It was a poison flowing in his veins and giving him an impulse to bite like a mad dog.

❈

DIARY

Cotton Mather

[One may rationalize in such a way as to make the gratification of one's desires acceptable to one's conscience. Cotton Mather's *Diary* illustrates the dilemma of a religious fanatic whose sublimated emotions have a strong sexual basis which his moral nature compels him to deny. He rationalizes his conduct by regarding the woman he favors as a 'gift of God,' thereby rendering her acceptable to his conscience as well as to his desire.]

From *Collections* of the Massachusetts Historical Society, 7th series. By permission of the Massachusetts Historical Society.

Feb. 1702-03.

'February begins with a very astonishing Trial.

'There is a young Gentlewoman of incomparable Accomplishments. No Gentlewoman in the English *America* has a more polite Education. She is one of rare Witt and Sense; and of a comely Aspect; and extremely winning in her Conversation, and she has a Mother of an extraordinary Character for her Piety.

'This young Gentlewoman first Addresses me with diverse Letters, and then makes me a Visit at my House; wherein she gives me to understand that she has long had a more than ordinary Value for my Ministry; and that since my present Condition has given her more of Liberty to think of me, she must confess herself charmed with my Person, to such a Degree, that she could not but break in upon me, with her most importunate Requests, that I would make her mine; and that the highest Consideration she had in it, was her eternal Salvation, for if she were mine, she could not but hope the Effect of it would be, that she should also be Christ's.

*   *   *

'I was in a great Strait, how to treat so polite a Gentlewoman, thus applying herself unto me . . . I desired, that there might be Time taken, to see what would be the wisest and fittest Resolution.

'In the mean time, if I could not make her my own, I should be glad of being any way instrumental, to make her the Lord's.

*   *   *

'She is not much more than twenty years old. [Mather at the time was 39.] I Know she has been a very aiery Person. Her Reputation has been under some Disadvantage.

'What Snares may be laying for me, I know not. Much Prayer with Fasting and Patience, must be my way to encounter them.

'I think, how would my Lord Jesus Christ Himself treat a returning Sinner.'

Feb. 12 The XLI st Year.

'As for my special soul-harassing Point; I did some Dayes ago . . . vehemently beg . . . that it might be desisted from, and that I might not be kill'd by hearing any more of it. Yett such was my flexible tenderness as to be conquered by the importunities of several, to allow further Interviews. But I resolved, that I would make them turn chiefly upon the most glorious Design in the World. I did accordingly . . . with all the Charms I could imagine, draw that witty Gentlewoman unto tearful Expressions of her Consent, unto all the Articles of her Marriage and Union with the Great L[ord] Redeemer . . .

[Feb.]

'*20 d. 12 m. Satureday*. My grevious Distresses, (occasion'd especially by the late Addresses made unto me . . .) cause me to fall down before the Lord, with Prayers and with Tears continually . . .

'And that I may be left utterly destitute of all humane Support, my Relatives, thro' their extreme Distaste at the Talk of my Respects for the Person, above mentioned; and lest I should over-value her; do treat me with unsupportable Strangeness and Harshness.

'*Lord, I am oppressed; undertake for me!*

*   *   *

'As for the ingenious Child, that sollicits my Respects unto her, I cry to the Lord, with Fervency and Agony and Floods of Tears, that she may be the Lord's; and that her Union and Marriage to the Lord Jesus Christ, may be the Effect of the Discourses I have had with her. But I also resign her, and offer her unto the Lord; and earnestly profess unto Him, that tho' I sett a great Value upon her, yett I can deny myself everything in the World, that the Glory of His Name, and my Service to His Name, shall oblige me to part withal.

* * *

[March]
'I am now under incredible Disadvantages. The Design of Satan, to entangle me in a Match that might have proved ruinous to my Family, or my Ministry, is defeated, by my Resolution totally to reject the Addresses of the young Gentlewoman to me; which I do, for the sake of the Lord Jesus Christ, whose Name, I see will suffer, if I accept her . . .

'But then, Satan has raised up an horrid Storm of Reproach upon me, both for my Earliness in courting a Gentlewoman, and especially for my courting of a Person whom they generally apprehend as disagreeable to my Character. And here is hazard, lest my Usefulness be horribly Ruined, by the Clamour of the rash People on this Occasion, before there can be due Measures taken to quiet them; and my Civility to the Person who has address'd me, will not lett me utter what would most effectually quiet them.

'I am a man greatly assaulted by Satan . . .

'My Spirit is excessively broken. There is Danger of my dying suddenly, with smothered Griefs and Fears . . .

* * *

[April]
'27 d. 1 m. Satureday. Was ever man more tempted, than the miserable Mather!

'Sometimes, Temptations to Impurities; and sometimes to Blasphemy, and Atheism, and the Abandonment of all Religion, as a meer Delusion; and sometimes, to Self-Destruction itself. These, even these, O miserable Mather, do follow thee, with an astonishing Fury. But I fall down into the Dust, on my Study-floor, with Tears before the Lord; and then they quickly vanish; tis fair weather again. Lord! what wilt thou do with me!

'I am under singular Distress. What I would on many Accounts prefer, as the most eligible and honourable Condition; would be to continue all the rest of my little Time, in an unspotted widowhood.

'But my Family suffers by it, in several instances.

'My Father presses me frequently and fervently, that I would by no means take up Resolutions to continue in my widowhood . . .

'But I foresee, and already suffer, a worse Encumbrance. The Applications, which the Gentlewoman . . . has made unto me, have occasioned very many misrepresentations of me, among a foolish People. The coarse, tho' just, Usage that she has had from me, will also put her upon a thousand Inventions. I shall be continually every week, persecuted with some Noise and Nonsense carried about the Town concerning me. The Persecution of the Lyes daily invented about me, will be, I see insupportable. All the Friends I have in the World, perswade me, that I shall have no way to gett from under these Confusions, but by proceeding unto another marriage.

'Lord, help me, what shall I do? I am a miserable man.

* * *

[July]
'*10 d. 5 m. Satureday*
'. . . God is going to build up my Family, in a far more important and illustrious Instance.

'He showes me a Gentlewoman within two Houses of my own; a Gentlewoman of Piety and Probity, and a most unspotted Reputation; a Gentlewoman of good Witt and Sense, and Discretion at ordering an Household; a Gentlewoman of incomparable Sweetness in her Temper, and Humour, a Gentlewoman honourably descended and related; and a very comely person . . . She was married, and quickly left a Widow about four years ago, and is now near thirty years of Age.

* * *

[August]
'*18 d. 6 m. Wednesday.* THIS is the Day, the joyful Day, wherein my glorious Lord JESUS CHRIST brings me, to the rich Harvest of my Prayers, my Tears, my Resignations. I am in the Evening of this Day, to receive a most lovely Creature, and such a Gift of Heaven unto me, and mine, that the Sense thereof almost as often as I ponder thereon, dissolves me into Tears of Joy.'

❋

MACBETH

WILLIAM SHAKESPEARE

[When one's pattern of behavior arouses feelings of guilt, one's defense may take the form of a reaction-formation, a protective device whereby one unconsciously covers up the disorder, crime, or sexual aberration in one's life by an exaggerated expression of orderliness, honesty, or protestation of purity. In Maugham's play, *The Circle,* Arnold's obsession for orderliness, and in his story, *Miss Thompson,* the missionary's zeal are graphic illustrations of this mechanism at work. Similar in motivation to the reaction-formation is the compulsion neurosis whereby one unconsciously disguises his guilt through seemingly irrational but persistently repeated acts. Lady Macbeth, who dares not face her guilt in her waking state, gives expression to it in her sleep in a compulsive cleansing of her hands.]

DOCTOR. I have two nights watched with you, but can perceive no truth in your report. When was it she last walked?

GENTLEWOMAN. Since his majesty went into the field, I have seen her rise from her bed, throw her nightgown upon her, unlock her closet, take forth paper, fold it, write upon 't, read it, afterwards seal it, and again return to bed; yet all this while in a most fast sleep.

DOCTOR. A great perturbation in nature, to receive at once the benefit of sleep and do the effects of watching! In this slumbery agitation, besides her walking and other actual performances, what, at any time, have you heard her say?

GENTLEWOMAN. That, sir, which I will not report after her.

DOCTOR. You may to me, and 'tis most meet you should.

GENTLEWOMAN. Neither to you nor any one, having no witness to confirm my speech.

Enter LADY MACBETH, *with a taper.*

Lo you! here she comes. This is her very guise; and, upon my life, fast asleep. Observe her; stand close.

DOCTOR. How came she by that light?

GENTLEWOMAN. Why, it stood by her: she has light by her continually; 'tis her command.

DOCTOR. You see, her eyes are open.

GENTLEWOMAN. Ay, but their sense is shut.

DOCTOR. What is it she does now? Look, how she rubs her hands.

GENTLEWOMAN. It is an accustomed action with her, to seem thus washing her hands. I have known her to continue in this a quarter of an hour.

LADY MACBETH. Yet here's a spot.

DOCTOR. Hark! she speaks. I will set down what comes from her, to satisfy my remembrance the more strongly.

LADY MACBETH. Out, damned spot! out, I say! One; two: why, then, 'tis time to do't. Hell is murky! Fie, my lord, fie! a soldier, and afeard? What need we fear who knows it, when none can call our power to account? Yet who would have thought the old man to have had so much blood in him?

DOCTOR. Do you mark that?

LADY MACBETH. The Thane of Fife had a wife: where is she now? What! will these hands ne'er be clean? No more o' that, my lord, no more o' that: you mar all with this starting.

DOCTOR. Go to, go to; you have known what you should not.

GENTLEWOMAN. She has spoke what she should not, I am sure of that: Heaven knows what she has known.

LADY MACBETH. Here's the smell of the blood still: all the perfumes of Arabia will not sweeten this little hand. Oh! oh! oh!

DOCTOR. What a sigh is there! The heart is sorely charged.

GENTLEWOMAN. I would not have such a heart in my bosom for the dignity of the whole body.

DOCTOR. Well, well, well.

GENTLEWOMAN. Pray God it be, sir.

DOCTOR. This disease is beyond my practice: yet I have known those which have walked in their sleep who have died holily in their beds.

LADY MACBETH. Wash your hands, put on your nightgown; look not so pale. I tell you yet again, Banquo's buried; he cannot come out on's grave.

DOCTOR. Even so?

LADY MACBETH. To bed, to bed; there's knocking at the gate. Come, come come, come, give me your hand. What's done cannot be undone. To bed, to bed, to bed. *(Exit.*

DOCTOR. Will she go now to bed?

GENTLEWOMAN. Directly.

DOCTOR. Foul whisperings are abroad. Unnatural deeds

Do breed unnatural troubles; infected minds

To their deaf pillows will discharge their secrets;

More needs she the divine than the physician.

God, God forgive us all! Look after her;

Remove from her the means of all annoyance,

And still keep eyes upon her. So, good-night:

My mind she has mated, and amaz'd my sight.

I think, but dare not speak.

GENTLEWOMAN. Good-night, good doctor. *(Exeunt.*

RICHARD THE SECOND

WILLIAM SHAKESPEARE

[Frustration of all kinds is frequently met by recourse to the mechanism of exhibitionism, which varies widely in expression. We are familiar with the adolescent in every classroom who must throw spit balls or say startling and unconventional things in order to gain attention; we are also aware of erotic display of the body, sometimes called to the attention of the police but more often authorized by producers of burlesque shows. While we do not become unduly worried by the temper tantrums of the eight-year-old, we regard such lapses on the part of the chronologically adult as regressive, a reverting to an inferior stage of emotional development. In *Richard II* the wounded egotism and sense of guilt of the deposed young king find expression in exhibitionistic behavior when, in a hysterical frenzy of self-pity, he calls for a mirror in which to examine himself, then dashes it to the floor.]

BOLINGBROKE. Are you contented to resign the crown?

KING RICHARD. Ay, no; no, ay; for I must nothing be;
Therefore no no, for I resign to thee.
Now mark me how I will undo myself:
I give this heavy weight from off my head,
And this unwieldy sceptre from my hand,
The pride of kingly sway from out my heart;
With mine own tears I wash away my balm,
With mine own hands I give away my crown,
With mine own tongue deny my sacred state,
With mine own breath release all duteous rites:
All pomp and majesty I do forswear;
My manors, rents, revenues, I forego;
My acts, decrees, and statutes I deny:
God pardon all oaths that are broke to me!
God keep all vows unbroke are made to thee!
Make me, that nothing have, with nothing griev'd,
And thou with all pleas'd, that hast all achiev'd!
Long mayst thou live in Richard's seat to sit,
And soon lie Richard in an earthy pit!
God save King Henry, unking'd Richard says,
And send him many years of sunshine days!
What more remains?

NORTHUMBERLAND. (*Offering a paper.*)
No more, but that you read
These accusations and these grievous crimes
Committed by your person and your followers
Against the state and profit of this land;
That, by confessing them, the souls of men
May deem that you are worthily depos'd.

KING RICHARD. Must I do so? and must I ravel out
My weav'd-up follies? Gentle Northumberland,
If thy offences were upon record,
Would it not shame thee in so fair a troop
To read a lecture of them? If thou wouldst,
There shouldst thou find one heinous article,
Containing the deposing of a king,
And cracking the strong warrant of an oath,

Mark'd with a blot, damn'd in the book
of heaven.
Nay, all of you that stand and look upon
me,
Whilst that my wretchedness doth bait
myself,
Though some of you with Pilate wash
your hands,
Showing an outward pity; yet you Pilates
Have here deliver'd me to my sour cross,
And water cannot wash away your sin.

NORTHUMBERLAND. My lord, dispatch;
read o'er these articles.

KING RICHARD. Mine eyes are full of
tears, I cannot see:
And yet salt water blinds them not so
much
But they can see a sort of traitors here.
Nay, if I turn mine eyes upon myself,
I find myself a traitor with the rest;
For I have given here my soul's consent
To undeck the pompous body of a king;
Made glory base and sovereignty a slave,
Proud majesty a subject, state a peasant.

NORTHUMBERLAND. My lord,—

KING RICHARD. No lord of thine, thou
haught insulting man,
Nor no man's lord; I have no name, no
title,
No, not that name was given me at the
font,
But 'tis usurp'd: alack the heavy day!
That I have worn so many winters out,
And know not now what name to call
myself.
O! that I were a mockery king of snow,
Standing before the sun of Bolingbroke,
To melt myself away in water-drops.
Good king, great king,—and yet not
greatly good,
An if my word be sterling yet in Eng-
land,
Let it command a mirror hither straight,
That it may show me what a face I have,
Since it is bankrupt of his majesty.

BOLINGBROKE. Go some of you and fetch
a looking-glass. (Exit an Attendant.

NORTHUMBERLAND. Read o'er this paper
while the glass doth come.

KING RICHARD. Fiend! thou torment'st
me ere I come to hell.

BOLINGBROKE. Urge it no more, my Lord
Northumberland.

NORTHUMBERLAND. The commons will
not then be satisfied.

KING RICHARD. They shall be satisfied:
I'll read enough
When I do see the very book indeed
Where all my sins are writ, and that's
myself.

(Re-enter Attendant, with a glass.

Give me the glass, and therein will I read.
No deeper wrinkles yet? Hath sorrow
struck
So many blows upon this face of mine
And made no deeper wounds? O, flat-
tering glass!
Like to my followers in prosperity,
Thou dost beguile me. Was this face the
face
That every day under his household roof
Did keep ten thousand men? Was this
the face
That like the sun did make beholders
wink?
Was this the face that fac'd so many
follies,
And was at last out-fac'd by Bolingbroke?
A brittle glory shineth in this face:
As brittle as the glory is the face;

(Dashes the glass against the ground.

For there it is, crack'd in a hundred
shivers
Mark, silent king, the moral of this sport,
How soon my sorrow hath destroy'd my
face.

BOLINGBROKE. The shadow of your sorrow hath destroy'd
The shadow of your face.

KING RICHARD.   Say that again.
The shadow of my sorrow! Ha! let's see:
'Tis very true, my grief lies all within;
And these external manners of laments
Are merely shadows to the unseen grief
That swells with silence in the tortur'd
soul;
There lies the substance: and I thank
thee, king,
For thy great bounty, that not only givest
Me cause to wail, but teachest me the
way
How to lament the cause. I'll beg one
boon,

And then be gone and trouble you no
more.
Shall I obtain it?

BOLINGBROKE. Name it, fair cousin.

KING RICHARD. 'Fair cousin'! I am
greater than a king;
For when I was a king, my flatterers
Were then but subjects; being now a subject,
I have a king here to my flatterer.
Being so great, I have no need to beg.

BOLINGBROKE. Yet ask.

KING RICHARD. And shall I have?

BOLINGBROKE. You shall.

KING RICHARD. Then give me leave to
go.

BOLINGBROKE. Whither?

KING RICHARD. Whither you will, so I
were from your sights.

BOLINGBROKE. Go, some of you convey
him to the Tower.

KING RICHARD. O, good! convey? conveyers are you all,
That rise thus nimbly by a true king's
fall.

(*Exeunt* KING RICHARD *and Guard.*

※

JEAN-CHRISTOPHE

ROMAIN ROLLAND

[Jean-Christophe, the sensitive, talented boy-musician, was always an introvert, but his tendencies to introversion became exaggerated to the point of neurotic manifestations by the ridicule and scorn of his family and associates. At fourteen he was forced to assume the financial burden of his family by giving music lessons to stupid little girls who taunted him with his physical awkwardness. At night, miserable in evening dress-suit, he was on exhibition at the palace, where the Princess made him play music he loathed and improvise sentimental themes for her. The physical ailments to which he was subject during this period illustrate the conversion mechanisms by which a person may unconsciously seek escape from intolerable realities. This device failing in its end, Jean-Christophe found escape from his burdens in compensatory dreams of himself as the great artist of the future, admired by those who once scorned him.]

He would go up to his room, which he shared with his brothers, and never was he so overwhelmed by disgust and despair with his life as at the moment when in his attic, with its stifling smell, he was at last permitted to take off the halter of his misery. He had hardly the heart to undress himself. Happily, no sooner did his head touch the pillow than he would sink into a heavy sleep which deprived him of all consciousness of his troubles.

But he had to get up by dawn in summer, and before dawn in winter. He wished to do his own work. It was all the free time that he had between five o'clock and eight. Even then he had to waste some of it by work to command, for his title of *Hof Musi-*

From *Jean-Christophe* by Romain Rolland. By permission of Henry Holt and Co., Inc.

cus and his favor with the Grand Duke exacted from him official compositions for the Court festivals.

So the very source of his life was poisoned. Even his dreams were not free, but, as usual, this restraint made them only the stronger. When nothing hampers action, the soul has fewer reasons for action, and the closer the walls of Jean-Christophe's prison of care and banal tasks were drawn about him, the more his heart in its revolt felt its independence. In a life without obstacles he would doubtless have abandoned himself to chance and to the voluptuous sauntering of adolescence. As he could be free only for an hour or two a day, his strength flowed into that space of time like a river between walls of rock. It is a good discipline for art for a man to confine his efforts between unshakable bounds. In that sense it may be said that misery is a master, not only of thought, but of style; it teaches sobriety to the mind as to the body. When time is doled out and thoughts measured, a man says no word too much, and grows accustomed to thinking only what is essential; so he lives at double pressure, having less time for living.

This had happened in Jean-Christophe's case. Under his yoke he took full stock of the value of liberty and he never frittered away the precious minutes with useless words or actions. His natural tendency to write diffusely, given up to all the caprice of a mind sincere but indiscriminating, found correction in being forced to think and do as much as possible in the least possible time. Nothing had so much influence on his artistic and moral development—not the lessons of his masters, nor the example of the masterpieces. During the years when the character is formed he came to consider music as an exact language, in which every sound has a meaning, and at the same time he came to loathe those musicians who talk without saying anything.

And yet the compositions which he wrote at this time were still far from expressing himself completely, because he was still very far from having completely discovered himself. He was seeking himself through the mass of acquired feelings which education imposes on a child as second nature. He had only intuitions of his true being, until he should feel the passions of adolescence, which strip the personality of its borrowed garments as a thunder-clap purges the sky of the mists that hang over it. Vague and great forebodings were mingled in him with strange memories, of which he could not rid himself. He raged against these lies; he was wretched to see how inferior what he wrote was to what he thought; he had bitter doubts of himself. But he could not resign himself to such a stupid defeat. He longed passionately to do better, to write great things, and always he missed fire. After a moment of illusion as he wrote, he saw that what he had done was worthless. He tore it up; he burned everything that he did; and, to crown his humiliation, he had to see his official works, the most mediocre of all, preserved, and he could not destroy them—the concerto, *The Royal Eagle*, for the Prince's birthday and the cantata, *The Marriage of Pallas*, written on the occasion of the marriage of Princess Adelaide—published at great expense in *éditions de luxe*, which perpetuated his imbecilities for posterity; for he believed in posterity. He wept in his humiliation.

Fevered years! No respite, no release—nothing to create a diversion from such maddening toil; no games, no friends. How should he have them? In the afternoon, when other children played, young Jean-Christophe, with his brows knit in attention, was at his place in the orchestra in the dusty and ill-lighted theatre; and in the evening, when other children were abed, he was still there, sitting in his chair, bowed with weariness.

No intimacy with his brothers. The younger, Ernest, was twelve. He was a little ragamuffin, vicious and impudent, who spent his days with other rapscallions like himself, and from their company had caught not only deplorable manners, but shameful habits which good Jean-Christophe, who had never so much as suspected their existence, was horrified to see one day. The other, Rodolphe, the favorite of Uncle Theodore, was to go into business. He was steady, quiet, but sly. He thought himself much superior to Jean-Christophe, and did not admit his authority in the house, although it seemed natural to him to eat the food that he provided. He had espoused the cause of Theodore and Melchior's ill-feeling against Jean-Christophe and used to repeat their absurd gossip. Neither of the brothers cared for music, and Rodolphe, in imitation of his uncle, affected to despise it. Chafing against Jean-Christophe's authority and lectures—for he took himself very seriously as the head of the family—the two boys had tried to rebel; but Jean-Christophe, who had lusty fists and the consciousness of right, sent them packing. Still they did not for that cease to do with him as they liked. They abused his credulity, and laid traps for him, into which he invariably fell. They used to extort money from him with barefaced lies, and

laughed at him behind his back. Jean-Christophe was always taken in. He had so much need of being loved that an affectionate word was enough to disarm his rancor. He would have forgiven them everything for a little love. But his confidence was cruelly shaken when he heard them laughing at his stupidity after a scene of hypocritical embracing which had moved him to tears, and they had taken advantage of it to rob him of a gold watch, a present from the Prince, which they coveted. He despised them, and yet went on letting himself be taken in from his unconquerable tendency to trust and to love. He knew it. He raged against himself, and he used to thrash his brothers soundly when he discovered once more that they had tricked him. That did not keep him from swallowing almost immediately the fresh hook which it pleased them to bait for him.

A more bitter cause of suffering was in store for him. He learned from officious neighbors that his father was speaking ill of him. After having been proud of his son's successes, and having boasted of them everywhere, Melchior was weak and shameful enough to be jealous of them. He tried to decry them. It was stupid to weep; Jean-Christophe could only shrug his shoulders in contempt. It was no use being angry about it, for his father did not know what he was doing, and was embittered by his own downfall. The boy said nothing. He was afraid, if he said anything, of being too hard; but he was cut to the heart.

They were melancholy gatherings at the family evening meal round the lamp, with a spotted cloth, with all the stupid chatter and the sound of the jaws of these people whom he despised and pitied, and yet loved in spite of everything. Only between himself and his brave mother did Jean-Christophe feel a bond of affection. But Louisa, like himself, exhausted herself during the day, and in the evening she was worn out and hardly spoke, and after dinner used to sleep in her chair over her darning. And she was so good that she seemed to make no difference in her love between her husband and her three sons. She loved them all equally. Jean-Christophe did not find in her the trusted friend that he so much needed.

So he was driven in upon himself. For days together he would not speak, fulfilling his tiresome and wearing task with a sort of silent rage. Such a mode of living was dangerous, especially for a child at a critical age, when he is most sensitive, and is exposed to every agent of destruction and the risk of being deformed for the rest of his life. Jean-Christophe's health suffered seriously. He had been endowed by his parents with a healthy constitution and a sound and healthy body; but his very healthiness only served to feed his suffering when the weight of weariness and too early cares had opened up a gap by which it might enter. Quite early in life there were signs of grave nervous disorders. When he was a small boy he was subject to fainting-fits and convulsions and vomiting whenever he encountered opposition. When he was seven or eight, about the time of the concert, his sleep had been troubled. He used to talk, cry, laugh and weep in his sleep, and this habit returned to him whenever he had too much to think of. Then he had cruel headaches, sometimes shooting pains at the base of his skull or the top of his head, sometimes a leaden heaviness. His eyes troubled him. Sometimes it was as though red-hot needles were piercing his eyeballs. He was subject to fits of dizziness, when he could not see to read, and had to stop for a minute or two. Insufficient and unsound food and irregular meals ruined the health of his stomach. He was racked by internal pains or exhausted by diarrhea. But nothing brought him more suffering than his heart. It beat with a crazy irregularity. Sometimes it would leap in his bosom, and seem like to break; sometimes it would hardly beat at all, and seem like to stop. At night his temperature would vary alarmingly; it would change suddenly from fever-point to next to nothing. He would burn, then shiver with cold, pass through agony. His throat would go dry; a lump in it would prevent his breathing. Naturally his imagination took fire. He dared not say anything to his family of what he was going through, but he was continually dissecting it with a minuteness which either enlarged his sufferings or created new ones. He decided that he had every known illness one after the other. He believed that he was going blind, and as he sometimes used to turn giddy as he walked, he thought that he was going to fall down dead. Always that dreadful fear of being stopped on his road, of dying before his time, obsessed him, overwhelmed him, and pursued him. Ah, if he had to die, at least let it not be now, not before he had tasted victory! . . .

Victory . . . the fixed idea which never ceases to burn within him without his being fully aware of it—the idea which bears him up through all his disgust and fatigues and the stagnant morass of such a life! A dim and great foreknowledge of what he will be some day, of what he is already! . . . What is he? A sick, nervous child, who plays the violin in the orchestra and writes mediocre concertos? No; far more than such a child. That is no more than the wrapping, the seeming of a day; that is not his Being. There is no connection between his Being and the existing shape of his face and thought. He knows that well. When he looks at himself in the mirror he does not know himself. That broad red face, those prominent eyebrows, those little sunken eyes, that short thick nose, that sullen mouth—the whole mask, ugly and vulgar, is foreign to himself. Neither does he know himself in his writings. He judges, he knows that what he does and what he is are nothing; and yet he is sure of what he will be and do. Sometimes he falls foul of such certainty as a vain lie. He takes pleasure in humiliating himself and bitterly mortifying himself by way of punishment. But his certainty endures; nothing can alter it. Whatever he does, whatever he thinks, none of his thoughts, actions, or writings contain him or express him. He knows, he has this strange presentiment, that the more that he is, is not contained in the present but is what he *will be,* what he *will be to-morrow. He will be!* . . . He is fired by that faith, he is intoxicated by that light! Ah, if only *To-day* does not block the way! If only he does not fall into one of the cunning traps which *To-day* is forever laying for him!

So he steers his bark across the sea of days, turning his eyes neither to right nor left, motionless at the helm, with his gaze fixed on the bourne, the refuge, the end that he has in sight. In the orchestra, among the talkative musicians, at table with his own family, at the Palace, while he is playing without a thought of what he is playing, for the entertainment of Royal folk—it is in that future, that future which a speck may bring toppling to earth—no matter, it is in that that he lives.

He is at his old piano, in his garret, alone. Night falls. The dying light of day is cast upon his music. He strains his eyes to read the notes until the last ray of light is dead. The tenderness of hearts that are dead breathed forth from the dumb page fills him with love. His eyes are filled with tears. It seems to him that a beloved creature is standing behind him, that soft breathing caresses his cheek, that two arms are about his neck. He turns, trembling. He feels, he knows, that he is not alone. A soul that loves and is loved is there, near him. He groans aloud because he cannot perceive it, and yet that shadow of bitterness falling upon his ecstasy has sweetness, too. Even sadness has its light. He thinks of his beloved masters, of the genius that is gone, though its soul lives on in the music which it had lived in its life. His heart is overflowing with love; he dreams of the superhuman happiness which must have been the lot of these glorious men, since the reflection only of their happiness is still so much aflame. He dreams of being like them, of giving out such love as this, with lost rays to lighten his misery with a godlike smile. In his turn to be a god, to give out the warmth of joy, to be a sun of life! . . .

Alas! if one day he does become the equal of those whom he loves, if he does achieve that brilliant happiness for which he longs, he will see the illusion that was upon him . . .

PICTOR IGNOTUS

FLORENCE, 15—

ROBERT BROWNING

[Another form of flight from reality is to be found in Browning's portrait of *Pictor Ignotus,* the neurotic painter whose egotism is wounded by criticism. He withdraws into himself and refuses to paint anything but conventional figures on cloister walls.]

I could have painted pictures like that
    youth's
  Ye praise so. How my soul springs up!
    No bar
Stayed me—ah, thought which saddens
    while it soothes!
  —Never did fate forbid me, star by
    star,
To outburst on your night with all my
    gift
  Of fires from God; nor would my flesh
    have shrunk
From seconding my soul, with eyes up-
    lift
  And wide to heaven, or, straight like
    thunder, sunk
To the center, of an instant; or around
  Turned calmly and inquisitive, to scan
The license and the limit, space and
    bound,
  Allowed to truth made visible in man.
And, like that youth ye praise so, all I
    saw,
  Over the canvas could my hand have
    flung,
Each face obedient to its passion's law,
  Each passion clear proclaimed without
    a tongue;
Whether Hope rose at once in all the
    blood,
  A-tiptoe for the blessing of embrace,
Or Rapture drooped the eyes, as when
    her brood
  Pull down the nesting dove's heart to
    its place;
Or Confidence lit swift the forehead up,
  And locked the mouth fast, like a
    castle braved—

O human faces, hath it spilt, my cup?
  What did ye give me that I have not
    saved?
Nor will I say I have not dreamed (how
    well!)
  Of going—I, in each new picture—
    forth,
As, making new hearts beat and bosoms
    swell,
  To Pope or Kaiser, East, West, South,
    or North,
Bound for the calmly satisfied great State,
  Or glad aspiring little burgh, it went,
Flowers cast upon the car which bore
    the freight,
  Through old streets named afresh from
    the event,
Till it reached home, where learned age
    should greet
  My face, and youth, the star not yet
    distinct
Above his hair, lie learning at my feet!—
  Oh, thus to live, I and my picture,
    linked
With love about, and praise, till life
    should end,
  And then not go to heaven, but linger
    here,
Here on my earth, earth's every man my
    friend—
  The thought grew frightful, 'twas so
    wildly dear!
But a voice changed it. Glimpses of such
    sights
  Have scared me, like the revels through
    a door
Of some strange house of idols at its rites!

This world seemed not the world it was
before;
Mixed with my loving trusting ones, there
trooped
. . . Who summoned those cold faces
that begun
To press on me and judge me? Though I
stooped
Shrinking, as from the soldiery a nun,
They drew me forth, and spite of me . . .
enough!
These buy and sell our pictures, take
and give,
Count them for garniture and household-
stuff,
And where they live needs must our
pictures live
And see their faces, listen to their prate,
Partakers of their daily pettiness,
Discussed of—'This I love, or this I hate,
This likes me more, and this affects me
less!'
Wherefore I chose my portion. If at
whiles
My heart sinks, as monotonous I paint

These endless cloisters and eternal aisles
With the same series, Virgin, Babe, and
Saint,
With the same cold calm beautiful re-
gard—
At least no merchant traffics in my
heart;
The sanctuary's gloom at least shall ward
Vain tongues from where my pictures
stand apart;
Only prayer breaks the silence of the
shrine
While, blackening in the daily candle-
smoke,
They molder on the damp wall's traver-
tine,
'Mid echoes the light footstep never
woke.
So, die my pictures! surely, gently die!
O youth, men praise so—holds their
praise its worth?
Blown harshly, keeps the trump its golden
cry?
Tastes sweet the water with such specks
of earth?

❋

THE MOON AND SIXPENCE

Somerset Maugham

[The interaction between what Freud calls the Id, the Ego, and the Super-ego is dramatically reflected in *The Moon and Sixpence,* a fictional biography of the painter, Gauguin. It is interesting to observe the ambivalence in Blanche's attitude toward Strickland: before his arrival, her protestation of hate, her trembling, tears, and convulsive shaking, her premonition of harm; after his arrival, her yielding to him in spite of his obvious indifference to her as a person. Insight into her compulsion is to be found in the active function-ing of her Super-ego, a carry-over from her earlier experience of seduction and desertion and the attendant sense of shame and guilt. Her suicide repre-sents the ultimate retreat from social responsibility for which her previous reactions have prepared us.

In Strickland we find a man whose Id impulses are given unlimited re-lease; he makes no attempt to orient to reality in terms of the bourgeois mores to which he had responded, at least passively, for the greater part of his life.

He passionately decries woman's desire for power, thus projecting (i.e. transference of one's own sense of guilt or inadequacy to another) his own drive for domination upon the defenseless woman whom he has made to suffer. He turns to art as an escape from his uncontrollable desires, and the author suggests at the end of the novel that his lurid but striking use of color and form represents the sublimation of the perverse and tyrannical demands of his nature.]

Dirk was going home to dinner, and I proposed to find a doctor and bring him to see Strickland; but when we got down into the street, fresh after the stuffy attic, the Dutchman begged me to go immediately to his studio. He had something in mind which he would not tell me, but he insisted that it was very necessary for me to accompany him. Since I did not think a doctor could at the moment do any more than we had done, I consented. We found Blanche Stroeve laying the table for dinner. Dirk went up to her, and took both her hands.

'Dear one, I want you to do something for me,' he said.

She looked at him with the grave cheerfulness which was one of her charms. His red face was shining with sweat, and he had a look of comic agitation, but there was in his round, surprised eyes an eager light.

'Strickland is very ill. He may be dying. He is alone in a filthy attic, and there is not a soul to look after him. I want you to let me bring him here.'

She withdrew her hands quickly, I had never seen her make so rapid a movement, and her cheeks flushed.

'Oh, no.'

'Oh, my dear one, don't refuse. I couldn't bear to leave him where he is. I shouldn't sleep a wink for thinking of him.'

'I have no objection to your nursing him.'

Her voice was cold and distant.

'But he'll die.'

'Let him.'

Stroeve gave a little gasp. He wiped his face. He turned to me for support, but I did not know what to say.

'He's a great artist.'

'What do I care? I hate him.'

'Oh, my love, my precious, you don't mean that. I beseech you to let me bring him here. We can make him comfortable. Perhaps we can save him. He shall be no trouble to you. I will do everything. We'll make him up a bed in the studio. We can't let him die like a dog. It would be inhuman.'

'Why can't he go to a hospital?'

'A hospital! He needs the care of loving hands. He must be treated with infinite tact.'

I was surprised to see how moved she was. She went on laying the table, but her hands trembled.

'I have no patience with you. Do you think if you were ill he would stir a finger to help you?'

'But what does that matter? I should have you to nurse me. It wouldn't be necessary. And besides, I'm different; I'm not of any importance.'

'You have no more spirit than a mongrel cur. You lie down on the ground and ask people to trample on you.'

Stroeve gave a little laugh. He thought he understood the reason of his wife's attitude.

'Oh, my poor dear, you're thinking of that day he came here to look at my pictures. What does it matter if he didn't think them any good? It was stupid of me to show them to him. I dare say they're not very good.'

He looked round the studio ruefully. On the easel was a half-finished picture of a smiling Italian peasant, holding a bunch of grapes over the head of a dark-eyed girl.

'Even if he didn't like them he should have been civil. He needn't have insulted you. He showed that he despised you, and you lick his hand. Oh, I hate him.'

'Dear child, he has genius. You don't think I believe that I have it. I wish I had; but I know it when I see it, and I honour it with all my heart. It's the most wonderful thing in the world. It's a great burden to its possessors. We should be very tolerant with them, and very patient.'

I stood apart, somewhat embarrassed by the domestic scene, and wondered why Stroeve had insisted on my coming with him. I saw that his wife was on the verge of tears.

'But it's not only because he's a genius that I ask you to let me bring him here; it's because he's a human being, and he is ill and poor.'

'I will never have him in my house —never.'

Stroeve turned to me.

'Tell her that it's a matter of life and death. It's impossible to leave him in that wretched hole.'

'It's quite obvious that it would be much easier to nurse him here,' I said, 'but of course it would be very inconvenient. I have an idea that someone will have to be with him day and night.'

'My love, it's not you who would shirk a little trouble.'

'If he comes here, I shall go,' said Mrs. Stroeve violently.

'I don't recognize you. You're so good and kind.'

'Oh, for goodness sake, let me be. You drive me to distraction.'

Then at last the tears came. She sank into a chair, and buried her face in her hands. Her shoulders shook convulsively. In a moment Dirk was on his knees beside her, with his arms round her, kissing her, calling her all sorts of pet names, and the facile tears ran down his own cheeks. Presently she released herself and dried her eyes.

'Leave me alone,' she said, not unkindly; and then to me, trying to smile: 'What must you think of me?'

Stroeve, looking at her with perplexity, hesitated. His forehead was all puckered, and his red mouth set in a pout. He reminded me oddly of an agitated guinea-pig.

'Then it's No, darling?' he said at last.

She gave a gesture of lassitude. She was exhausted.

'The studio is yours. Everything belongs to you. If you want to bring him here, how can I prevent you?'

A sudden smile flashed across his round face.

'Then you consent? I knew you would. Oh, my precious.'

Suddenly she pulled herself together. She looked at him with haggard eyes. She clasped her hands over her heart as though its beating were intolerable.

'Oh, Dirk, I've never since we met asked you to do anything for me.'

'You know there's nothing in the world that I wouldn't do for you.'

'I beg you not to let Strickland come here. Anyone else you like. Bring a thief, a drunkard, any outcast off the streets, and I promise you

I'll do anything I can for them gladly. But I beseech you not to bring Strickland here.'

'But why?'

'I'm frightened of him. I don't know why, but there's something in him that terrifies me. He'll do us some great harm. I know it. I feel it. If you bring him here it can only end badly.'

'But how unreasonable!'

'No, no, I know I'm right. Something terrible will happen to us.'

'Because we do a good action?'

She was panting now, and in her face was a terror which was inexplicable. I do not know what she thought. I felt that she was possessed by some shapeless dread which robbed her of all self-control. As a rule she was so calm; her agitation now was amazing. Stroeve looked at her for a while with puzzled consternation.

'You are my wife; you are dearer to me than anyone in the world. No one shall come here without your entire consent.'

She closed her eyes for a moment, and I thought she was going to faint. I was a little impatient with her; I had not suspected that she was so neurotic a woman. Then I heard Stroeve's voice again. It seemed to break oddly on the silence.

'Haven't you been in bitter distress once when a helping hand was held out to you? You know how much it means. Wouldn't you like to do someone a good turn when you have the chance?'

The words were ordinary enough, and to my mind there was in them something so hortatory that I almost smiled. I was astonished at the effect they had on Blanche Stroeve. She started a little, and gave her husband a long look. His eyes were fixed on the ground. I did not know why he seemed embarrassed. A faint colour came into her cheeks, and then her face became white—more than white, ghastly; you felt that the blood had shrunk away from the whole surface of her body; and even her hands were pale. A shiver passed through her. The silence of the studio seemed to gather body, so that it became an almost palpable presence. I was bewildered.

'Bring Strickland here, Dirk. I'll do my best for him.'

'My precious,' he smiled.

He wanted to take her in his arms, but she avoided him.

'Don't be affectionate before strangers, Dirk,' she said. 'It makes me feel such a fool.'

Her manner was quite normal again, and no one could have told that so shortly before she had been shaken by such a great emotion.

*　　*　　*

We arrived at the house in which I lived. I would not ask him to come in with me, but walked up the stairs without a word. He followed me, and entered the apartment on my heels. He had not been in it before, but he never gave a glance at the room I had been at pains to make pleasing to the eye. There was a tin of tobacco on the table, and, taking out his pipe, he filled it. He sat down on the only chair that had no arms and tilted himself on the back legs.

'If you're going to make yourself at home, why don't you sit in an arm-chair?' I asked irritably.

'Why are you concerned about my comfort?'

'I'm not,' I retorted, 'but only about my own. It makes me uncomfortable to see someone sit on an uncomfortable chair.'

He chuckled, but did not move. He smoked on in silence, taking no further notice of me, and apparently was absorbed in thought. I wondered why he had come.

Until long habit has blunted the sensibility, there is something disconcerting to the writer in the instinct which causes him to take an interest in the singularities of human nature so absorbing that his moral sense is powerless against it. He recognises in himself an artistic satisfaction in the contemplation of evil which a little startles him; but sincerity forces him to confess that the disapproval he feels for certain actions is not nearly so strong as his curiosity in their reasons. The character of a scoundrel, logical and complete, has a fascination for his creator which is an outrage to law and order. I expect that Shakespeare devised Iago with a gusto which he never knew when, weaving moonbeams with his fancy, he imagined Desdemona. It may be that in his rogues the writer gratifies instincts deep-rooted in him, which the manners and customs of a civilised world have forced back to the mysterious recesses of the subconscious. In giving to the character of his invention flesh and bones he is giving life to that part of himself which finds no other means of expression. His satisfaction is a sense of liberation.

The writer is more concerned to know than to judge.

There was in my soul a perfectly genuine horror of Strickland, and side by side with it a cold curiosity to discover his motives. I was puzzled by him, and I was eager to see how he regarded the tragedy he had caused in the lives of people who had used him with so much kindness. I applied the scalpel boldly.

'Stroeve told me that picture you painted of his wife was the best thing you've ever done.'

Strickland took his pipe out of his mouth, and a smile lit up his eyes.

'It was great fun to do.'

'Why did you give it to him?'

'I'd finished it. It wasn't any good to me.'

'Do you know that Stroeve nearly destroyed it?'

'It wasn't altogether satisfactory.'

He was quiet for a moment or two, then he took his pipe out of his mouth again, and chuckled.

'Do you know that the little man came to see me?'

'Weren't you rather touched by what he had to say?'

'No; I thought it damned silly and sentimental.'

'I suppose it escaped your memory that you'd ruined his life?' I remarked.

He rubbed his bearded chin reflectively.

'He's a very bad painter.'

'But a very good man.'

'And an excellent cook,' Strickland added derisively.

His callousness was inhuman, and in my indignation I was not inclined to mince my words.

'As a mere matter of curiosity I wish you'd tell me, have you felt the smallest twinge of remorse for Blanche Stroeve's death?'

I watched his face for some change of expression, but it remained impassive.

'Why should I?' he asked.

'Let me put the facts before you. You were dying, and Dirk Stroeve took you into his own house. He nursed you like a mother. He sacrificed his time and his comfort and his money for you. He snatched you from the jaws of death.'

Strickland shrugged his shoulders.

'The absurd little man enjoys doing things for other people. That's his life.'

'Granting that you owed him no gratitude, were you obliged to go out of your way to take his wife from him? Until you came on the scene they were happy. Why couldn't you leave them alone?'

'What makes you think they were happy?'

'It was evident.'

'You are a discerning fellow. Do you think she could ever have forgiven him for what he did for her?'

'What do you mean by that?'

'Don't you know why he married her?'

I shook my head.

'She was a governess in the family of some Roman prince, and the son of the house seduced her. She thought he was going to marry her. They turned her out into the street neck and crop. She was going to have a baby, and she tried to commit suicide. Stroeve found her and married her.'

'It was just like him. I never knew anyone with so compassionate a heart.'

I had often wondered why that ill-assorted pair had married, but just that explanation had never occurred to me. That was perhaps the cause of the peculiar quality of Dirk's love for his wife. I had noticed in it something more than passion. I remembered also how I had always fancied that her reserve concealed I know not what; but now I saw in it more than the desire to hide a shameful secret. Her tranquillity was like the sullen calm that broods over an island which has been swept by a hurricane. Her cheerfulness was the cheerfulness of despair. Strickland interrupted my reflections with an observation the profound cynicism of which startled me.

'A woman can forgive a man for the harm he does her,' he said, 'but she can never forgive him for the sacrifices he makes on her account.'

'It must be reassuring to you to know that you certainly run no risk of incurring the resentment of the women you come in contact with,' I retorted.

A slight smile broke on his lips.

'You are always prepared to sacrifice your principles for a repartee,' he answered.

'What happened to the child?'

'Oh, it was still-born, three or four months after they were married.'

Then I came to the question which had seemed to me most puzzling.

'Will you tell me why you bothered about Blanche Stroeve at all?'

He did not answer for so long that I nearly repeated it.

'How do I know?' he said at last. 'She couldn't bear the sight of me. It amused me.'

'I see.'

He gave a sudden flash of anger.

'Damn it all, I wanted her.'

But he recovered his temper immediately, and looked at me with a smile.

'At first she was horrified.'

'Did you tell her?'

'There wasn't any need. She knew. I never said a word. She was frightened. At last I took her.'

I do not know what there was in the way he told me this that extraordinarily suggested the violence of his desire. It was disconcerting and rather horrible. His life was strangely divorced from material things, and it was as though his body at times wreaked a fearful revenge on his spirit. The satyr in him suddenly took possession, and he was powerless in the grip of an instinct which had all the strength of the primitive forces of nature. It was an obsession so complete that there was no room in his soul for prudence or gratitude.

'But why did you want to take her away with you?' I asked.

'I didn't,' he answered, frowning. 'When she said she was coming I was nearly as surprised as Stroeve. I told her that when I'd had enough of her she'd have to go, and she said she'd risk that.' He paused a little. 'She had a wonderful body, and I wanted to paint a nude. When I'd finished my picture I took no more interest in her.'

'And she loved you with all her heart.'

He sprang to his feet and walked up and down the small room.

'I don't want love. I haven't time for it. It's weakness. I am a man, and sometimes I want a woman. When I've satisfied my passion I'm ready for other things. I can't overcome my desire, but I hate it; it imprisons my spirit; I look forward to the time when I shall be free from all desire and can give myself without hindrance to my work. Because women can do nothing except love, they've given it a ridiculous importance. They want to persuade us that it's the whole of life. It's an insignificant part. I know lust. That's normal and healthy. Love is a disease. Women are the instruments of my pleasure; I have no patience with their claim to be helpmates, partners, companions.'

I had never heard Strickland speak so much at one time. He spoke with a passion of indignation. But neither here nor elsewhere do I pretend to give his exact words; his vocabulary was small, and he had no gift for framing sentences, so that one had to piece his meaning together out of interjections, the expression of his face, gestures and hackneyed phrases.

'You should have lived at a time when women were chattels and men the masters of slaves,' I said.

'It just happens that I am a completely normal man.'

I could not help laughing at this remark, made in all seriousness; but he went on, walking up and down the room like a caged beast, intent on expressing what he felt, but found such difficulty in putting coherently.

'When a woman loves you she's not satisfied until she possesses your soul. Because she's weak, she has a rage for domination, and nothing less will satisfy her. She has a small mind, and she resents the abstract which she is unable to grasp. She is occupied with material things, and she is jealous of the ideal. The soul of man wanders through the uttermost regions of the universe, and she seeks to imprison it in the circle of her account-book. Do you remember my wife? I saw Blanche little by little trying all her tricks. With infinite patience she prepared to snare me and bind me. She wanted to bring me down to her level; she cared nothing for me, she only wanted me to be hers. She was willing to do everything in the world for me except the one thing I wanted; to leave me alone.'

I was silent for a while.

'What did you expect her to do when you left her?'

'She could have gone back to Stroeve,' he said irritably. 'He was ready to take her.'

'You're inhuman,' I answered. 'It's as useless to talk to you about these things as to describe colours to a man who was born blind.'

He stopped in front of my chair, and stood looking down at me with an expression in which I read a contemptuous amazement.

'Do you really care a twopenny

damn if Blanche Stroeve is alive or dead?'

I thought over his question, for I wanted to answer it truthfully, at all events, to my soul.

'It may be a lack of sympathy in myself if it does not make any great difference to me that she is dead. Life had a great deal to offer her. I think it's terrible that she should have been deprived of it in that cruel way, and I am ashamed because I do not really care.'

'You have not the courage of your convictions. Life has no value. Blanche Stroeve didn't commit suicide because I left her, but because she was a foolish and unbalanced woman. But we've talked about her quite enough; she was an entirely unimportant person. Come, and I'll show you my pictures.'

He spoke as though I were a child that needed to be distracted. I was sore, but not with him so much as with myself. I thought of the happy life that pair had led in the cosy studio in Montmartre, Stroeve and his wife, their simplicity, kindness, and hospitality; it seemed to me cruel that it should have been broken to pieces by a ruthless chance; but the cruellest thing of all was that in fact it made no great difference. The world went on, and no one was a penny the worse for all that wretchedness. I had an idea that Dirk, a man of greater emotional reactions than depth of feeling, would soon forget; and Blanche's life, begun with who knows what bright hopes and what dreams, might just as well have never been lived. It all seemed useless and inane.

Strickland had found his hat, and stood looking at me.

'Are you coming?'

'Why do you seek my acquaintance?' I asked him. 'You know that I hate and despise you.'

He chuckled good-humouredly.

'Your only quarrel with me really is that I don't care a twopenny damn what you think about me.'

I felt my cheeks grow red with sudden anger. It was impossible to make him understand that one might be outraged by his callous selfishness. I longed to pierce his armour of complete indifference. I knew also that in the end there was truth in what he said. Unconsciously, perhaps, we treasure the power we have over people by their regard for our opinion of them, and we hate those upon whom we have no such influence. I suppose it is the bitterest wound to human pride. But I would not let him see that I was put out.

'Is it possible for any man to disregard others entirely?' I said, though more to myself than to him. 'You're dependent on others for everything in existence. It's a preposterous attempt to try to live only for yourself and by yourself. Sooner or later you'll be ill and tired and old, and then you'll crawl back into the herd. Won't you be ashamed when you feel in your heart the desire for comfort and sympathy? You're trying an impossible thing. Sooner or later the human being in you will yearn for the common bonds of humanity.'

'Come and look at my pictures.'

'Have you ever thought of death?'

'Why should I? It doesn't matter.'

I stared at him. He stood before me, motionless, with a mocking smile in his eyes; but for all that, for a moment I had an inkling of a fiery, tortured spirit, aiming at something greater than could be conceived by anything that was bound up with the flesh. I had a fleeting glimpse of a pursuit of the ineffable. I looked at the man before me in his shabby clothes, with his great nose and shining eyes, his red beard and untidy hair; and I had a strange sensation that it was only an envelope, and I was in the presence of a disembodied spirit.

'Let us go and look at your pictures,' I said.

※　　　※　　　※　　　※　　　※　　　※　　　※

THE PSYCHOSES

Cans't thou not minister to a mind diseas'd
Pluck from the memory a rooted sorrow,
Raze out the written troubles of the brain,
And with some sweet oblivious antidote
Cleanse the stuff'd bosom of that perilous stuff
Which weighs upon the heart?

—SHAKESPEARE

IN the preceding section we have noted how relative a concept is normality. Most of the behavior patterns represented are responses which, although common to all, have been carried to excess. The most normal individual will rationalize at one time or another in order that his self-regard may not be diminished, but only the neurotic will permit his life to be built upon rationalization. So too, the normal person will engage now and then in idle daydreaming, but while his daydreams will be only a momentary transgression from reality, those of the neurotic individual will occupy a larger portion of his waking hours. So long as the latter knows that he is daydreaming, however, and can at will be roused to action, he has not lost complete touch with reality. When he ceases to exercise control over his fantasy life, when he can no longer distinguish between the dream and the reality, then his sanity may be questioned. For in psychotic behavior the manifestations we have called neurotic are carried to excess. No longer is there an interplay between one's primitive impulses and the repressing forces of the personality; one is no longer governed either by his own moral scruples or by his desire for social approval. The conflicting elements of one's personality have ceased to strive for ascendancy, as in the neurotic, and one's behavior is no longer modified or controlled by logic or reason. Although the psychotic manifestations illustrated in the pages to follow differ in kind and degree, they all reflect a lack of orientation to the world of reality and indicate the complete dissociation of the personality. In short, the psychosis demonstrates one's inability to accept life on its own terms.

PAUL'S CASE

Willa Cather

[The interaction of many forces shaping the human personality is responsible for Paul's tragedy. His physical frailty, the fact that his mother died when he was a small child, his father's petty tyrannies, the stupidity of his teachers, the mores of Cordelia Street all contributed to making Paul a neurotic personality, a problem child at home and at school. But he was not defenseless. In the various realms of art he found escape: he identified himself with the successful opera singer who lived luxuriously and received the adulation of the crowd; he experienced sweet oblivion in his contemplation of the masters at the art gallery; when he listened to the symphony he found liberation from the yellow wallpaper which symbolized his home on drab Cordelia Street. The punitive efforts of his teachers did not affect him, for he had recourse to various kinds of exhibitionism; and he could protect his ego further in his fantasy lying at the expense of his schoolmates. But when these escapes were cut off, Paul was no longer able to reconcile the demands of his own nature with those of society. The inhibitions which his training had imposed upon him were thrust off. In complete defiance of the laws of society he must retreat from the real world, since it was no longer bearable. This total splitting of the personality, or schizophrenia, was inevitable after Paul was denied the neurotic substitutions which had previously served to keep him partially oriented to reality. The time bombs set in early years had exploded.]

It was Paul's afternoon to appear before the faculty of the Pittsburgh High School to account for his various misdemeanours. He had been suspended a week ago, and his father had called at the Principal's office and confessed his perplexity about his son. Paul entered the faculty room suave and smiling. His clothes were a trifle outgrown, and the tan velvet on the collar of his open overcoat was frayed and worn; but for all that there was something of the dandy about him, and he wore an opal pin in his neatly knotted black four-in-hand, and a red carnation in his buttonhole. This latter adornment the faculty somehow felt was not properly significant of the contrite spirit befitting a boy under the ban of suspension.

Paul was tall for his age and very thin, with high, cramped shoulders and a narrow chest. His eyes were remarkable for a certain hysterical brilliancy, and he continually used them in a conscious, theatrical sort of way, peculiarly offensive in a boy. The pupils were abnormally large, as though he were addicted to belladonna, but there was a glassy glitter about them which that drug does not produce.

When questioned by the Principal as to why he was there, Paul stated, politely enough, that he wanted to

From *Youth and the Bright Medusa* by Willa Cather. By permission of Alfred A. Knopf, Publishers.

come back to school. This was a lie, but Paul was quite accustomed to lying; found it, indeed, indispensable for overcoming friction. His teachers were asked to state their respective charges against him, which they did with such a rancour and aggrievedness as evinced that this was not a usual case. Disorder and impertinence were among the offenses named, yet each of his instructors felt that it was scarcely possible to put into words the real cause of the trouble, which lay in a sort of hysterically defiant manner of the boy's; in the contempt which they all knew he felt for them, and which he seemingly made not the least effort to conceal. Once, when he had been making a synopsis of a paragraph at the blackboard, his English teacher had stepped to his side and attempted to guide his hand. Paul had started back with a shudder and thrust his hands violently behind him. The astonished woman could scarcely have been more hurt and embarrassed had he struck at her. The insult was so involuntary and definitely personal as to be unforgettable. In one way and another, he had made all his teachers, men and women alike, conscious of the same feeling of physical aversion. In one class he habitually sat with his hand shading his eyes; in another he always looked out of the window during the recitation; in another he made a running commentary on the lecture, with humorous intent.

His teachers felt this afternoon that his whole attitude was symbolized by his shrug and his flippantly red carnation flower, and they fell upon him without mercy, his English teacher leading the pack. He stood through it smiling, his pale lips parted over his white teeth. (His lips were continually twitching, and he had a habit of raising his eyebrows that was contemptu-ous and irritating to the last degree.) Older boys than Paul had broken down and shed tears under that ordeal, but his set smile did not once desert him, and his only sign of discomfort was the nervous trembling of the fingers that toyed with the buttons of his overcoat, and an occasional jerking of the other hand which held his hat. Paul was always smiling, always glancing about him, seeming to feel that people might be watching him and trying to detect something. This conscious expression, since it was as far as possible from boyish mirthfulness, was usually attributed to insolence or 'smartness.'

As the inquisition proceeded, one of his instructors repeated an impertinent remark of the boy's, and the Principal asked him whether he thought that a courteous speech to make to a woman. Paul shrugged his shoulders slightly and his eyebrows twitched.

'I don't know,' he replied. 'I didn't mean to be polite or impolite, either. I guess it's a sort of way I have of saying things regardless.'

The Principal asked him whether he didn't think that a way it would be well to get rid of. Paul grinned and said he guessed so. When he was told that he could go, he bowed gracefully and went out. His bow was like a repetition of the scandalous red carnation.

His teachers were in despair, and his drawing master voiced the feeling of them all when he declared there was something about the boy which none of them understood. He added: 'I don't believe that smile of his comes altogether from insolence; there's something sort of haunted about it. The boy is not strong, for one thing. There is something wrong about the fellow.'

The drawing master had come to realize that, in looking at Paul, one saw only his white teeth and the forced animation of his eyes. One warm afternoon the boy had gone to sleep at his drawing-board, and his master had noted with amazement what a white, blue-veined face it was; drawn and wrinkled like an old man's about the eyes, the lips twitching even in his sleep.

His teachers left the building dissatisfied and unhappy; humiliated to have felt so vindictive toward a mere boy, to have uttered this feeling in cutting terms, and to have set each other on, as it were, in the gruesome game of intemperate reproach. One of them remembered having seen a miserable street cat set at bay by a ring of tormentors.

As for Paul, he ran down the hill whistling the Soldiers' Chorus from *Faust*, looking wildly behind him now and then to see whether some of his teachers were not there to witness his light-heartedness. As it was now late in the afternoon and Paul was on duty that evening as usher at Carnegie Hall, he decided that he would not go home to supper.

When he reached the concert hall the doors were not yet open. It was chilly outside, and he decided to go up into the picture gallery—always deserted at this hour—where there were some of Raffelli's gay studies of Paris streets and an airy blue Venetian scene or two that always exhilarated him. He was delighted to find no one in the gallery but the old guard, who sat in the corner, a newspaper on his knee, a black patch over one eye and the other closed. Paul possessed himself of the place and walked confidently up and down, whistling under his breath. After a while he sat down before a blue Rico

and lost himself. When he bethought him to look at his watch, it was after seven o'clock and he rose with a start and ran downstairs, making a face at Augustus Caesar, peering out from the cast-room, and an evil gesture at the Venus of Milo as he passed her on the stairway.

When Paul reached the ushers' dressing-room half-a-dozen boys were there already, and he began excitedly to tumble into his uniform. It was one of the few that at all approached fitting, and Paul thought it very becoming—though he knew the tight, straight coat accentuated his narrow chest, about which he was exceedingly sensitive. He was always excited while he dressed, twanging all over to the tuning of the strings and the preliminary flourishes of the horns in the music-room; but tonight he seemed quite beside himself, and he teased and plagued the boys until, telling him that he was crazy, they put him down on the floor and sat on him.

Somewhat calmed by his suppression, Paul dashed out to the front of the house to seat the early comers. He was a model usher. Gracious and smiling he ran up and down the aisles. Nothing was too much trouble for him; he carried messages and brought programs as though it were his greatest pleasure in life, and all the people in his section thought him a charming boy, feeling that he remembered and admired them. As the house filled, he grew more and more vivacious and animated, and the colour came to his cheeks and lips. It was very much as though this were a great reception and Paul were the host. Just as the musicians came out to take their places, his English teacher arrived with checks for the seats which a prominent manufacturer had taken for the season. She betrayed some embarrassment when she handed Paul the tickets, and a *hauteur* which subsequently made her feel very foolish. Paul was startled for a moment, and had the feeling of wanting to put her out; what business had she here among all these fine people and gay colours? He looked her over and decided that she was not appropriately dressed and must be a fool to sit downstairs in such togs. The tickets had probably been sent her out of kindness, he reflected, as he put down a seat for her, and she had about as much right to sit there as he had.

When the symphony began Paul sank into one of the rear seats with a long sigh of relief, and lost himself as he had done before the Rico. It was not that symphonies, as such, meant anything in particular to Paul, but the first sigh of the instruments seemed to free some hilarious spirit within him; something that struggled there like the Genius in the bottle found by the Arab fisherman. He felt a sudden zest of life; the lights danced before his eyes and the concert hall blazed into unimaginable splendour. When the soprano soloist came on, Paul forgot even the nastiness of his teacher's being there, and gave himself up to the peculiar intoxication such personages always had for him. The soloist chanced to be a German woman, by no means in her first youth, and the mother of many children; but she wore a satin gown and a tiara, and she had that indefinable air of achievement, that world-shine upon her, which always blinded Paul to any possible defects.

After a concert was over, Paul was often irritable and wretched until he got to sleep,—and tonight he was even more than usually restless. He had the feeling of not being able to let down; of its being impossible to give up this delicious excitement which was the only thing that could be called living at all. During the last number he withdrew and, after hastily changing his clothes in the dressing-room, slipped out to the side door where the singer's carriage stood. Here he began pacing rapidly up and down the walk, waiting to see her come out.

Over yonder the Schenley, in its vacant stretch, loomed big and square through the fine rain, the windows of its twelve stories glowing like those of a lighted cardboard house under a Christmas tree. All the actors and singers of any importance stayed there when they were in the city, and a number of the big manufacturers of the place lived there in the winter. Paul had often hung about the hotel, watching the people go in and out, longing to enter and leave schoolmasters and dull care behind him forever.

At last the singer came out, accompanied by the conductor, who helped her into her carriage and closed the door with a cordial '*Auf Wiedersehen*'—which set Paul to wondering whether she were not an old sweetheart of his. Paul followed the carriage over to the hotel, walking so rapidly as not to be far from the entrance when the singer alighted and disappeared behind the swinging glass doors which were opened by a negro in a tall hat and a long coat. In the moment that the door was ajar, it seemed to Paul that he, too, entered. He seemed to feel himself go after her up the steps, into the warm, lighted building, into an exotic, a tropical world of shiny, glistening surfaces and basking ease. He reflected upon the mysterious dishes that were brought into the dining-room, the green bottles in buckets of ice, as he had seen them in the supper party pictures of the Sunday supplement. A quick gust of wind brought the rain down with sudden vehemence, and Paul was startled to find that he was still outside in the slush of the gravel driveway; that his boots were letting in the water and his scanty overcoat was clinging wet about him; that the lights in front of the concert hall were out, and that the rain was driving in sheets between him and the orange glow of the windows above him. There it was, what he wanted—tangibly before him like the fairy world of a Christmas pantomime; as the rain beat in his face, Paul wondered whether he were destined always to shiver in the black night outside, looking up at it.

He turned and walked reluctantly toward the car tracks. The end had to come some time; his father in his night-clothes at the top of the stairs, explanations that did not explain, hastily improvised fictions that were forever tripping him up, his upstairs room and its horrible yellow wallpaper, the creaking bureau with the greasy plush collar-box, and over his painted wooden bed the pictures of George Washington and John Calvin, and the framed motto, 'Feed my Lambs,' which had been worked in red worsted by his mother, whom Paul could not remember.

Half an hour later Paul alighted from the Negley Avenue car and went slowly down one of the side streets off the main thoroughfare. It was a highly respectable street, where all the houses were exactly alike, and where business men of moderate means begot and reared large families of children, all of whom went to Sabbath-school and learned the shorter catechism, and were interested in arithmetic; all of whom were as exactly alike as their homes, and of a

piece with the monotony in which they lived. Paul never went up Cordelia Street without a shudder of loathing. His home was next the house of the Cumberland minister. He approached it tonight with the nerveless sense of defeat, the hopeless feeling of sinking back forever into ugliness and commonness that he had always had when he came home. The moment he turned into Cordelia Street he felt the waters close above his head. After each of these orgies of living, he experienced all the physical depression which follows a debauch; the loathing of respectable beds, of common food, of a house permeated by kitchen odours; a shuddering repulsion for the flavourless, colourless mass of everyday existence; a morbid desire for cool things and soft lights and fresh flowers.

The nearer he approached the house, the more absolutely unequal Paul felt to the sight of it all; his ugly sleeping chamber; the cold bathroom with the grimy zinc tub, the cracked mirror, the dripping spigots; his father, at the top of the stairs, his hairy legs sticking out from his nightshirt, his feet thrust into carpet slippers. He was so much later than usual that there would certainly be inquiries and reproaches. Paul stopped short before the door. He felt that he could not be accosted by his father tonight; that he could not toss again on that miserable bed. He would not go in. He would tell his father that he had no car-fare, and it was raining so hard he had gone home with one of the boys and stayed all night.

Meanwhile, he was wet and cold. He went around to the back of the house and tried one of the basement windows, found it open, raised it cautiously, and scrambled down the cellar wall to the floor. There he stood, holding his breath, terrified by the noise he had made; but the floor above him was silent, and there was no creak on the stairs. He found a soap-box, and carried it over to the soft ring of light that streamed from the furnace door, and sat down. He was horribly afraid of rats, so he did not try to sleep, but sat looking distrustfully at the dark, still terrified lest he might have awakened his father. In such reactions, after one of the experiences which made days and nights out of the dreary blanks of the calendar, when his senses were deadened, Paul's head was always singularly clear. Suppose his father had heard him getting in at the window and had come down and shot him for a burglar? Then, again, suppose his father had come down, pistol in hand, and he had cried out in time to save himself, and his father had been horrified to think how nearly he had killed him? Then, again, suppose a day should come when his father would remember that night, and wish there had been no warning cry to stay his hand? With this last supposition Paul entertained himself until daybreak.

The following Sunday was fine; the sodden November chill was broken by the last flash of autumnal summer. In the morning Paul had to go to church and Sabbath-school, as always. On seasonable Sunday afternoons the burghers of Cordelia Street usually sat out on their front 'stoops,' and talked to their neighbours on the next stoop, or called to those across the street in neighborly fashion. The men sat placidly on gay cushions placed upon the steps that led down to the sidewalk, while the women, in their Sunday 'waists,' sat in rockers on the cramped porches, pretending to be greatly at their ease. The children played in the streets; there were so many of them that the place resembled the recreation grounds of a kindergarten. The men on the steps —all in their shirt sleeves, their vests unbuttoned—sat with their legs well apart, their stomachs comfortably protruding, and talked of the prices of things, or told anecdotes of the sagacity of their various chiefs and overlords. They occasionally looked over the multitude of squabbling children, listened affectionately to their high-pitched, nasal voices, smiling to see their own proclivities reproduced in their offspring, and interspersed their legends of the iron kings with remarks about their sons' progress at school, their grades in arithmetic, and the amounts they had saved in their toy banks.

On this last Sunday of November, Paul sat all the afternoon on the lowest step of his 'stoop,' staring into the street, while his sisters, in their rockers, were talking to the minister's daughters next door about how many shirt-waists they had made in the last week, and how many waffles some one had eaten at the last church supper. When the weather was warm, and his father was in a particularly jovial frame of mind, the girls made lemonade, which was always brought out in a red-glass pitcher, ornamented with forget-me-nots in blue enamel. This the girls thought very fine, and the neighbours joked about the suspicious colour of the pitcher.

Today Paul's father, on the top step, was talking to a young man who shifted a restless baby from knee to knee. He happened to be the young man who was daily held up to Paul as a model, and after whom it was his father's dearest hope that he would pattern. This young man was of a ruddy complexion, with a compressed, red mouth, and faded, near-sighted eyes, over which he wore thick spectacles, with gold bows that curved about his ears. He was clerk to one of the magnates of a great steel corporation, and was looked upon in Cordelia Street as a young man with a future. There was a story that, some five years ago—he was now barely twenty-six—he had been a trifle 'dissipated,' but in order to curb his appetites and save the loss of time and strength that a sowing of wild oats might have entailed, he had taken his chief's advice, oft reiterated to his employés, and at twenty-one had married the first woman whom he could persuade to share his fortunes. She happened to be an angular schoolmistress, much older than he, who also wore thick glasses, and who had now borne him four children, all near-sighted, like herself.

The young man was relating how his chief, now cruising in the Mediterranean, kept in touch with all the details of the business, arranging his office hours on his yacht just as though he were at home, and 'knocking off work enough to keep two stenographers busy.' His father told, in turn, the plan his corporation was considering, of putting in an electric railway plant at Cairo. Paul snapped his teeth; he had an awful apprehension that they might spoil it all before he got there. Yet he rather liked to hear these legends of the iron kings, that were told and retold on Sundays and holidays; these stories of palaces in Venice, yachts on the Mediterranean, and high play at Monte Carlo appealed to his fancy, and he was interested in the triumphs of cash boys who had become famous, though he had no mind for the cash boy stage.

After supper was over, and he had helped to dry the dishes, Paul nervously asked his father whether he could go to George's to get some help in his geometry, and still more nervously asked for car-fare. This latter request he had to repeat, as his father, on principle, did not like to hear requests for money, whether much or little. He asked Paul whether he could not go to some boy who lived nearer, and told him that he ought not to leave his school work until Sunday; but he gave him the dime. He was not a poor man, but he had a worthy ambition to come up in the world. His only reason for allowing Paul to usher was that he thought a boy ought to be earning a little.

Paul bounded upstairs, scrubbed the greasy odour of dish-water from his hands with the ill-smelling soap he hated, and then shook over his fingers a few drops of violet water from the bottle he kept hidden in his drawer. He left the house with his geometry conspicuously under his arm, and the moment he got out of Cordelia Street and boarded a downtown car, he shook off the lethargy of two deadening days, and began to live again.

The leading juvenile of the permanent stock company which played at one of the downtown theatres was an acquaintance of Paul's, and the boy had been invited to drop in at the Sunday-night rehearsals whenever he could. For more than a year Paul had spent every available moment loitering about Charley Edwards' dressing-room. He had won a place among Edwards' following not only because the young actor, who could not afford to employ a dresser, often found him useful, but because he recognized in Paul something akin to what churchmen term 'vocation.'

It was at the theatre and at Carnegie Hall that Paul really lived; the rest was but a sleep and a forgetting. This was Paul's fairy tale, and it had for him all the allurement of a secret love. The moment he inhaled the gassy, painty, dusty odour behind the scenes, he breathed like a prisoner set free, and felt within him the possibility of doing or saying splendid, brilliant things. The moment the cracked orchestra beat out the overture from *Martha,* or jerked at the serenade from *Rigoletto,* all stupid and ugly things slid from him, and his senses were deliciously, yet delicately fired.

Perhaps it was because, in Paul's world, the natural nearly always wore the guise of ugliness, that a certain element of artificiality seemed to him necessary in beauty. Perhaps it was because his experience of life elsewhere was so full of Sabbath-school picnics, petty economies, wholesome advice as to how to succeed in life, and the unescapable odours of cooking, that he found this existence so alluring, these smartly clad men and women so attractive, that he was so moved by these starry apple orchards that bloomed perennially under the lime-light.

It would be difficult to put it strongly enough how convincingly the stage entrance of that theatre was for Paul the actual portal of Romance. Certainly none of the company ever suspected it, least of all Charley Edwards. It was very like the old stories that used to float about London of fabulously rich Jews, who had subterranean halls, with palms, and fountains, and soft lamps and richly apparelled women who never saw the disenchanting light of London day. So, in the midst of that smoke-palled city, enamoured of figures and grimy toil, Paul had his secret temple, his wishing-carpet, his

bit of blue-and-white Mediterranean shore bathed in perpetual sunshine.

Several of Paul's teachers had a theory that his imagination had been perverted by garish fiction; but the truth was, he scarcely ever read at all. The books at home were not such as would either tempt or corrupt a youthful mind, and as for reading the novels that some of his friends urged upon him—well, he got what he wanted much more quickly from music; any sort of music, from an orchestra to a barrel organ. He needed only the spark, the indescribable thrill that made his imagination master of his senses, and he could make plots and pictures enough of his own. It was equally true that he was not stage-struck—not, at any rate, in the usual acceptation of that expression. He had no desire to become an actor, any more than he had to become a musician. He felt no necessity to do any of these things; what he wanted was to see, to be in the atmosphere, float on the wave of it, to be carried out, blue league after blue league, away from everything.

After a night behind the scenes, Paul found his school-room more than ever repulsive; the hard floors and naked walls; the prosy men who never wore frock coats, or violets in their button-holes; the women with their dull gowns, shrill voices, and pitiful seriousness about prepositions that govern the dative. He could not bear to have the other pupils think, for a moment, that he took these people seriously; he must convey to them that he considered it all trivial, and was there only by way of a joke, anyway. He had autograph pictures of all the members of the stock company which he showed his classmates, telling them the most incredible stories of his familiarity with these people, of his acquaintance with the soloists who came to Carnegie Hall, his suppers with them and the flowers he sent them. When these stories lost their effect, and his audience grew listless, he would bid all the boys good-bye, announcing that he was going to travel for a while; going to Naples, to California, to Egypt. Then, next Monday, he would slip back, conscious and nervously smiling; his sister was ill, and he would have to defer his voyage until spring.

Matters went steadily worse with Paul at school. In the itch to let his instructors know how heartily he despised them, and how thoroughly he was appreciated elsewhere, he mentioned once or twice that he had no time to fool with theorems; adding— with a twitch of the eyebrows and a touch of that nervous bravado which so perplexed them—that he was helping the people down at the stock company; they were old friends of his.

The upshot of the matter was, that the Principal went to Paul's father, and Paul was taken out of school and put to work. The manager at Carnegie Hall was told to get another usher in his stead; the doorkeeper at the theatre was warned not to admit him to the house; and Charley Edwards remorsefully promised the boy's father not to see him again.

The members of the stock company were vastly amused when some of Paul's stories reached them—especially the women. They were hard-working women, most of them supporting indolent husbands or brothers, and they laughed rather bitterly at having stirred the boy to such fervid and florid inventions. They agreed with the faculty and with his father, that Paul's was a bad case.

The east-bound train was plowing through a January snow-storm; the dull dawn was beginning to show gray when the engine whistled a mile out of Newark. Paul started up from the seat where he had lain curled in uneasy slumber, rubbed the breath-misted window glass with his hand, and peered out. The snow was whirling in curling eddies above the white bottom lands, and the drifts lay already deep in the fields and along the fences, while here and there the long dead grass and dried weed stalks protruded black above it. Lights shone from the scattered houses, and a gang of labourers who stood beside the track waved their lanterns.

Paul had slept very little, and he felt grimy and uncomfortable. He had made the all-night journey in a day coach because he was afraid if he took a Pullman he might be seen by some Pittsburgh business man who had noticed him in Denny & Carson's office. When the whistle woke him, he clutched quickly at his breast pocket, glancing about him with an uncertain smile. But the little, clay-bespattered Italians were still sleeping, the slatternly women across the aisle were in open-mouthed oblivion, and even the crumby, crying babies were for the nonce stilled. Paul settled back to struggle with his impatience as best he could.

When he arrived at the Jersey City Station, he hurried through his breakfast, manifestly ill at ease and keeping a sharp eye about him. After he reached the Twenty-third Street Station, he consulted a cabman, and had himself driven to a men's furnishing establishment which was just opening for the day. He spent upward of two hours there, buying with endless reconsidering and great care. His new street suit he put on in the fitting-room; the frock coat and dress clothes he had bundled into the cab with his new shirts. Then he drove to a hatter's and a shoe house. His next errand was at Tiffany's, where he selected silver-mounted brushes and a scarf-pin. He would not wait to have his silver marked, he said. Lastly, he stopped at a trunk shop on Broadway, and had his purchases packed into various traveling bags.

It was a little after one o'clock when he drove up to the Waldorf, and, after settling with the cabman, went into the office. He registered from Washington; said his mother and father had been abroad, and that he had come down to await the arrival of their steamer. He told his story plausibly and had no trouble, since he offered to pay for them in advance, in engaging his rooms; a sleeping-room, sitting-room and bath.

Not once, but a hundred times Paul had planned this entry into New York. He had gone over every detail of it with Charley Edwards, and in his scrapbook at home there were pages of description about New York hotels, cut from the Sunday papers.

When he was shown to his sitting-room on the eighth floor, he saw at a glance that everything was as it should be; there was but one detail in his mental picture that the place did not realize, so he rang for the bell boy and sent him down for flowers. He moved about nervously until the boy returned, putting away his new linen and fingering it delightedly as he did so. When the flowers came, he put them hastily into water, and then tumbled into a hot bath. Presently he came out of his white bath-room, resplendent in his new silk underwear, and playing with the tassels of his red robe. The snow was whirling so fiercely outside his windows that he could scarcely see across the street; but within, the air was deliciously soft and fragrant. He put the violets and jonquils on the tabouret beside the couch, and threw himself down with a long sigh, covering himself with a Roman blanket. He was thoroughly tired; he had been in such haste, he had stood up to such a strain, covered so much ground in the last twenty-four hours, that he wanted to think how it had all come about. Lulled by the sound of the wind, the warm air, and the cool fragrance of the flowers, he sank into deep, drowsy retrospection.

It had been wonderfully simple; when they had shut him out of the theatre and concert hall, when they had taken away his bone, the whole thing was virtually determined. The rest was a mere matter of opportunity. The only thing that at all surprised him was his own courage—for he realized well enough that he had always been tormented by fear, a sort of apprehensive dread that, of late years, as the meshes of the lies he had told closed about him, had been pulling the muscles of his body tighter and tighter. Until now, he could not remember a time when he had not been dreading something. Even when he was a little boy, it was always there—behind him, or before, or on either side. There had always been the shadowed corner, the dark place into which he dared not look, but from which something seemed always to be watching him—and Paul had done things that were not pretty to watch, he knew.

But now he had a curious sense of relief, as though he had at last thrown the gauntlet to the thing in the corner.

Yet it was but a day since he had been sulking in the traces; but yesterday afternoon that he had been sent to the bank with Denny & Carson's deposit as usual—but this time he was instructed to leave the book to be balanced. There was above two thousand dollars in checks, and nearly a thousand in the bank notes which he had taken from the book and quietly transferred to his pocket. At the bank he had made out a new deposit slip. His nerves had been steady enough to permit of his returning to the office, where he had finished his work and asked for a full day's holiday tomorrow, Saturday, giving a perfectly reasonable pretext. The bank book, he knew, would not be returned before Monday or Tuesday, and his father would be out of town for the next week. From the time he slipped the bank notes into his pocket until he boarded the night train for New York, he had not known a moment's hesitation.

How astonishingly easy it had all been; here he was, the thing done; and this time there would be no awakening, no figure at the top of the stairs. He watched the snowflakes whirling by his window until he fell asleep.

When he awoke, it was four o'clock in the afternoon. He bounded up with a start; one of his precious days gone already! He spent nearly an hour in dressing, watching every stage of his toilet carefully in the mirror. Everything was quite perfect; he was exactly the kind of boy he had always wanted to be.

When he went downstairs, Paul took a carriage and drove up Fifth Avenue toward the Park. The snow had somewhat abated; carriages and tradesmen's wagons were hurrying soundlessly to and fro in the winter twilight; boys in woolen mufflers were shoveling off the doorsteps; the avenue stages made fine spots of colour against the white street. Here and there on the corners were stands, with whole flower gardens blooming behind glass windows, against which the snowflakes stuck and melted; violets, roses, carnations, lilies of the valley—somehow vastly more lovely and alluring that they blossomed thus unnaturally in the snow. The Park itself was a wonderful stage winter piece.

When he returned, the pause of the twilight had ceased, and the tune of the streets had changed. The snow was falling faster, lights streamed from the hotels that reared their many stories fearlessly up into the storm, defying the raging Atlantic winds. A long, black stream of carriages poured down the avenue, intersected here and there by other streams, tending horizontally. There were a score of cabs about the entrance of his hotel, and his driver had to wait. Boys in livery were running up and down the red velvet carpet laid from the door to the street. Above, about, within it all, was the rumble and roar, the hurry and toss of thousands of human beings as hot for pleasure as himself, and on every side of him towered the glaring affirmation of the omnipotence of wealth.

The boy set his teeth and drew his shoulders together in a spasm of realization; the plot of all dramas, the text of all romances, the nerve-stuff of all sensations was whirling about him like the snowflakes. He burnt like a faggot in a tempest.

When Paul came down to dinner, the music of the orchestra floated up the elevator shaft to greet him. As he stepped into the thronged corridor, he sank back into one of the chairs against the wall to get his breath. The lights, the chatter, the perfumes, the bewildering medley of colour—he had, for a moment, the feeling of not being able to stand it. But only for a moment; these were his own people, he told himself. He went slowly about the corridors, through the writing-rooms, smoking-rooms, reception-rooms, as though he were exploring the chambers of an enchanted palace, built and peopled for him alone.

When he reached the dining-room he sat down at a table near a window. The flowers, the white linen, the many-coloured wine glasses, the gay toilettes of the women, the low popping of corks, the undulating repetitions of the *Blue Danube* from the orchestra, all flooded Paul's dream with bewildering radiance. When the roseate tinge of his champagne was added—that cold, precious bubbling stuff that creamed and foamed in his glass—Paul wondered that there were honest men in the world at all. This was what all the world was fighting for, he reflected; this was what all the struggle was about. He doubted the reality of his past. Had he ever known a place called Cordelia Street, a place where fagged-looking business men boarded the early car? Mere rivets in a machine they seemed to Paul,—sickening men, with combings of children's hair always hanging to their coats, and the smell of cooking in their clothes. Cordelia Street—ah, that belonged to another time and country! Had he not always been thus, had he not sat here night after night, from as far back as he could remember, looking pensively over just such shimmering textures, and slowly twirling the stem of a glass like this one between his thumb and middle finger? He rather thought he had.

He was not in the least abashed or lonely. He had no especial desire to meet or to know any of these people; all he demanded was the right to look on and conjecture, to watch the pageant. The mere stage properties were all he contended for. Nor was he lonely later in the evening, in his loge at the Opera. He was entirely rid of his nervous misgivings, of his forced aggressiveness, of the imperative desire to show himself different from his surroundings. He felt now that his surroundings explained him. Nobody questioned his purple; he had only to wear it passively. He had only to glance down at his dress coat to reassure himself that here it would be impossible for any one to humiliate him.

He found it hard to leave his beautiful sitting-room to go to bed that night, and sat long watching the raging storm from his turret window. When he went to sleep, it was with the lights turned on in his bedroom; partly because of his old timidity, and partly so that, if he should wake in the night, there would be no wretched moment of doubt, no horrible suspicion of yellow wall-paper, or of Washington and Calvin above his bed.

On Sunday morning the city was practically snowbound. Paul breakfasted late, and in the afternoon he fell in with a wild San Francisco boy, a freshman at Yale, who said he had run down for a 'little flyer' over Sunday. The young man offered to show Paul the night side of the town, and the two boys went off together after dinner, not returning to the hotel until seven o'clock the next morning. They had started out in the confiding warmth of a champagne friendship, but their parting in the elevator was singularly cool. The freshman pulled himself together to make his train, and Paul went to bed. He awoke at two o'clock in the afternoon, very thirsty and dizzy, and rang for ice-water, coffee, and the Pittsburgh paper.

On the part of the hotel management, Paul excited no suspicion. There was this to be said for him, that he wore his spoils with dignity and in no way made himself conspicuous. His chief greediness lay in his ears and eyes, and his excesses were not offensive ones. His dearest pleasures were the gray winter twilights in his sitting-room; his quiet enjoyment of his flowers, his clothes, his wide divan, his cigarette and his sense of power. He could not remember a time when he had felt so at peace with himself. The mere release from the necessity of petty lying, lying every day and every day, restored his self-respect. He had never lied for pleasure, even at school; but to make himself noticed and admired, to assert his difference from other Cordelia Street boys; and he felt a good deal more manly, more honest, even, now that he had no need for boastful pretensions, now that he could, as his actor friends used to say, 'dress the part.' It was characteristic that remorse did not occur to him. His golden days went by without a shadow, and he made each as perfect as he could.

On the eighth day after his arrival in New York, he found the whole affair exploited in the Pittsburgh papers, exploited with a wealth of detail which indicated that local news of a sensational nature was at a low ebb. The firm of Denny & Carson announced that the boy's father had refunded the full amount of his theft, and that they had no intention of prosecuting. The Cumberland minister had been interviewed, and expressed his hope of yet reclaiming the motherless lad, and Paul's Sabbath-school teacher declared that she would spare no effort to that end. The rumour had reached Pittsburgh that the boy had been seen in a New York hotel, and his father had gone East to find him and bring him home.

Paul had just come in to dress for dinner; he sank into a chair, weak in the knees, and clasped his head in his hands. It was to be worse than jail, even; the tepid waters of Cordelia Street were to close over him finally and forever. The gray monotony stretched before him in hopeless, unrelieved years; Sabbath-school, Young People's Meeting, the yellow-papered room, the damp dish-towels; it all rushed back upon him with sickening vividness. He had the old feeling that the orchestra had suddenly stopped, the sinking sensation that the play was over. The sweat broke out on his face, and he sprang to his feet, looked about him with his white, conscious smile, and winked at himself in the mirror. With something of the childish belief in miracles with which he had so often gone to class, all his lessons unlearned, Paul dressed and dashed whistling down the corridor to the elevator.

He had no sooner entered the dining-room and caught the measure of the music, than his remembrance was lightened by his old elastic power of claiming the moment, mounting with it, and finding it all-sufficient. The glare and glitter about him, the mere scenic accessories had again, and for the last time, their old potency. He would show himself that he was game, he would finish the thing splendidly. He doubted, more than ever, the existence of Cordelia Street, and for the first time he drank his wine recklessly. Was he not, after all, one of these fortunate beings? Was he not still himself, and in his own place? He drummed a nervous accompaniment to the music and looked about him, telling himself over and over that it had paid.

He reflected drowsily, to the swell of the violin and the chill sweetness of his wine, that he might have done it more wisely. He might have caught an outbound steamer and been well out of their clutches before now. But the other side of the world had seemed too far away and too uncertain then; he could not have waited for it; his need had been too sharp. If he had to choose over again, he would do the same thing tomorrow. He looked affectionately about the dining-room, now gilded with a soft mist. Ah, it had paid indeed!

Paul was awakened next morning by a painful throbbing in his head and feet. He had thrown himself across the bed without undressing, and had slept with his shoes on. His limbs and hands were lead-heavy, and his tongue and throat were parched. There came upon him one of those fateful attacks of clearheadedness that never occurred except when he was physically exhausted and his nerves hung loose. He lay still and closed his eyes and let the tide of his realities wash over him.

His father was in New York; 'stopping at some joint or other,' he told himself. The memory of successive summers on the front stoop fell upon him like a weight of black water. He had not a hundred dollars left; and he knew now, more than ever, that money was everything, the wall that stood between all he loathed and all he wanted. The thing was winding itself up; he had thought of that on his first glorious day in New York, and had even provided a way to snap

the thread. It lay on his dressing-table now; he had got it out last night when he came blindly up from dinner,—but the shiny metal hurt his eyes, and he disliked the look of it, anyway.

He rose and moved about with a painful effort, succumbing now and again to attacks of nausea. It was the old depression exaggerated; all the world had become Cordelia Street. Yet somehow he was not afraid of anything, was absolutely calm; perhaps because he had looked into the dark corner at last, and knew. It was bad enough, what he saw there; but somehow not so bad as his long fear of it had been. He saw everything clearly now. He had a feeling that he had made the best of it, that he had lived the sort of life he was meant to live, and for half an hour he sat staring at the revolver. But he told himself that was not the way, so he went downstairs and took a cab to the ferry.

When Paul arrived at Newark, he got off the train and took another cab, directing the driver to follow the Pennsylvania tracks out of the town. The snow lay heavy on the roadways and had drifted deep in the open fields. Only here and there the dead grass or dried weed stalks projected, singularly black, above it. Once well into the country, Paul dismissed the carriage and walked, floundering along the tracks, his mind a medley of irrelevant things. He seemed to hold in his brain an actual picture of everything he had seen that morning. He remembered every feature of both his drivers, the toothless old woman from whom he had bought the red flowers in his coat, the agent from whom he had got his ticket, and all of his fellow-passengers on the ferry. His mind, unable to cope with vital matters near at hand, worked feverishly and deftly at sorting and grouping these images. They made for him a part of the ugliness of the world, of the ache in his head, and the bitter burning on his tongue. He stooped and put a handful of snow into his mouth as he walked, but that, too, seemed hot. When he reached a little hillside, where the tracks ran through a cut some twenty feet below him, he stopped and sat down.

The carnations in his coat were drooping with the cold, he noticed; all their red glory over. It occurred to him that all the flowers he had seen in the show windows that first night must have gone the same way, long before this. It was only one splendid breath they had, in spite of their brave mockery at the winter outside the glass. It was a losing game in the end, it seemed, this revolt against the homilies by which the world is run. Paul took one of the blossoms carefully from his coat and scooped a little hole in the snow, where he covered it up. Then he dozed a while, from his weak condition, seeming insensible to the cold.

The sound of an approaching train woke him, and he started to his feet, remembering only his resolution, and afraid lest he should be too late. He stood watching the approaching locomotive, his teeth chattering, his lips drawn away from them in a frightened smile; once or twice he glanced nervously sidewise, as though he were being watched. When the right moment came, he jumped. As he fell, the folly of his haste occurred to him with merciless clearness, the vastness of what he had left undone. There flashed through his brain, clearer than ever before, the blue of Adriatic water, the yellow of Algerian sands.

He felt something strike his chest,—his body was being thrown swiftly through the air, on and on, immeasurably far and fast, while his limbs gently relaxed. Then, because the picture-making mechanism was crushed, the disturbing visions flashed into black, and Paul dropped back into the immense design of things.

❋

A MIND THAT FOUND ITSELF

Clifford Beers

[The mental and emotional state of the manic-depressive has perhaps never been more vividly and minutely described than by Clifford Beers, whose autobiography, *A Mind That Found Itself,* gave tremendous impetus to the movement for more intelligent and sympathetic treatment of the mentally ill. The cycle of depression is marked in the case of Beers, as in other victims of this illness, by the wish for death. This is accompanied by cannily devised plans for suicide and the delusion that his relatives are officers of the law who plan to indict him for a criminal offense which he unwittingly committed before his incarceration in the mental hospital. When he is freed of the delu-

From *A Mind That Found Itself* by Clifford Beers. By permission of the American Foundation for Mental Hygiene.

sion of being persecuted by the law and given irrefutable proof that his visitor is his brother, a manic state sets in. In this phase of the cycle his tremendous emotional energy is poured into elaborate plans for reform and into attempts at literary and artistic creation.]

My commitment occurred on June 11th, 1901. The institution to which I was committed was a chartered, private institution, but not run for personal profit. It was considered one of the best of its kind in the country and was pleasantly situated. Though the view was a restricted one, a vast expanse of lawn, surrounded by groups of trees, like patches of primeval forest, gave the place an atmosphere which was not without its remedial effect. My quarters were comfortable, and after a little time I adjusted myself to my new environment.

Breakfast was served about half-past seven, though the hour varied somewhat according to the season—earlier in summer and later in winter. In the spring, summer, and autumn, when the weather was favorable, those able to go out of doors were taken after breakfast for walks within the grounds, or were allowed to roam about the lawn and sit under the trees, where they remained for an hour or two at a time. Dinner was usually served shortly after noon, and then the active patients were again taken out of doors, where they remained an hour or two doing much as they pleased, but under watchful eyes. About half-past three they returned to their respective wards, there to remain until the next day—except those who cared to attend the religious service which was held almost every afternoon in an endowed chapel.

In all institutions those confined in different kinds of wards go to bed at different hours. The patients in the best wards retire at nine or ten o'clock. Those in the wards where more troublesome cases are treated go to bed usually at seven or eight o'clock. I, while undergoing treatment, have retired at all hours, so that I am in the better position to describe the mysteries of what is, in a way, one of the greatest secret societies in the world. I soon became accustomed to the rather agreeable routine, and had I not been burdened with the delusions which held me a prisoner of the police, and kept me a stranger to my old world, I should have been able to enjoy a comparatively happy existence in spite of all.

This new feeling of comparative contentment had not been brought about by any marked improvement in health. It was due directly and entirely to an environment more nearly in tune with my ill-tuned mind. While surrounded by sane people my mental inferiority had been painfully apparent to me, as well as to others. Here a feeling of superiority easily asserted itself, for many of my associates were, to my mind, vastly inferior to myself. But this stimulus did not affect me at once. For several weeks I believed the institution to be peopled by detectives, feigning insanity. The government was still operating the Third Degree, only on a grander scale. Nevertheless, I did soon come to the conclusion that the institution was what it purported to be—still cherishing the idea, however, that certain patients and attachés were detectives.

For a while after my arrival I again abandoned my new-found reading habit. But as I became accustomed to my surroundings I grew bolder and resumed the reading of newspapers and such books as were at hand. There was a bookcase in the ward, filled with old numbers of standard English periodicals; among them: *Westminster Review, Edinburgh Review, London Quarterly,* and *Blackwood's.* There were also copies of *Harper's* and *The Atlantic Monthly,* dated a generation or more before my first reading days. Indeed, some of the reviews were over fifty years old. But I had to read their heavy contents or go without reading, for I would not yet ask even for a thing I ardently desired. In the room of one of the patients were thirty or forty books belonging to him. Time and again I walked by his door and cast longing glances at those books, which at first I had not the courage to ask for or to take. But during the summer, about the time I was getting desperate, I finally managed to summon enough courage to take them surreptitiously. It was usually while the owner of these books was attending the daily service in the chapel that his library became a circulating one.

The contents of the books I read made perhaps a deeper impression on my memory than most books make on the minds of normal readers. To assure myself of the fact, I have since reread 'The Scarlet Letter,' and I recognize it as an old friend. The first part of the story, however, wherein Hawthorne describes his work as a Custom House official and portrays his literary personality, seems to have made scarcely any impression. This I attribute to my utter lack of interest at that time in writers and their methods. I then had no desire to write a book, nor any thought of ever doing so.

Letters I looked upon with suspicion. I never read them at the time they were received. I would not even open them; but generally, after a week or sometimes a month, I would secretly open and read them—forgeries of the detectives.

I still refused to speak, and exhibited physical activity only when the patients were taken out of doors. For hours I would sit reading books or newspapers, or apparently doing nothing. But my mind was in an active state and very sensitive. As the event proved, almost everything done or said within the range of my senses was making indelible impressions, though these at the time were frequently of such a character that I experienced great difficulty in trying to recall incidents which I thought I might find useful at the time of my appearance in court.

My ankles had not regained anything like their former strength. It hurt to walk. For months I continued to go flat-footed. I could not sustain my weight with heels lifted from the floor. In going downstairs I had to place my insteps on the edge of each step, or go one step at a time, like a child. Believing that the detectives were pampering me into prime condition, as a butcher fattens a beast for slaughter, I deliberately made myself out much weaker than I really was; and not a little of my inactivity was due to a desire to prolong my fairly comfortable existence, by deferring as long as possible the day of trial and conspicuous disgrace.

But each day still had its distressing incidents. Whenever the attendants were wanted at the office, an electric bell was rung. During the fourteen months that I remained in this hospital in a depressed condition, the bell in my ward rang several hundred times. Never did it fail to send through me a mild shock of terror, for I imagined that at last the hour had struck for my transportation to the scene of trial. Relatives and friends would be brought to the ward—heralded, of course, by a warning bell—and short interviews would be held in my room, during which the visitors had to do all the talking. My eldest brother, whom I shall refer to hereafter as my conservator, called often. He seldom failed to use one phrase which worried me.

'You are looking better and getting stronger,' he would say. 'We shall straighten you out yet.'

To be 'straightened out' was an ambiguous phrase which might refer to the end of the hangman's rope or to a fatal electric shock.

I preferred to be let alone, and the assistant physician in charge of my case, after several ineffectual attempts to engage me in conversation, humored my persistent taciturnity. For more than a year his only remarks to me were occasional conventional salutations. Subsequent events have led me to doubt the wisdom of his policy.

For one year no further attention was paid to me than to see that I had three meals a day, the requisite number of baths, and a sufficient amount of exercise. I was, however, occasionally urged by an attendant to write a letter to some relative, but that, of course, I refused to do. As I shall have many hard things to say about attendants in general, I take pleasure in testifying that, so long as I remained in a passive condition, those at this institution were kind, and at times even thoughtful. But

there came a time when diplomatic relations with doctors and attendants became so strained that war promptly ensued.

It was no doubt upon the gradual but sure improvement in my physical condition that the doctors were relying for my eventual return to normality. They were not without some warrant for this. In a way I had become less suspicious, but my increased confidence was due as much to an increasing indifference to my fate as to an improvement in health. And there were other signs of improved mental vigor. I was still watchful, however, for a chance to end my life, and, but for a series of fortunate circumstances, I do not doubt that my choice of evils would have found tragic expression in an overt act.

Having convinced myself that most of my associates were really insane, and therefore (as I believed) disqualified as competent witnesses in a court of law, I would occasionally engage in conversation with a few whose evident incompetency seemed to make them safe confidants. One, a man who during his life had more than once been committed to an institution, took a very evident interest in me and persisted in talking to me, often much against my will. His persistent inquisitiveness seemed to support his own statement that he had formerly been a successful life-insurance agent. He finally gained my confidence to such a degree that months before I finally began to talk to others I permitted myself to converse frequently with him—but only when we were so situated as to escape observation. I would talk to him on almost any subject, but would not speak about myself. At length, however, his admirable persistence overcame my reticence. During a conversation held in June, 1902, he abruptly said, 'Why you are kept here I cannot understand. Apparently you are as sane as anyone. You have never made any but sensible remarks to me.' Now for weeks I had been waiting for a chance to tell this man my very thoughts. I had come to believe him a true friend who would not betray me.

'If I should tell you some things which you apparently don't know, you would understand why I am held here,' I said.

'Well, tell me,' he urged.

'Will you promise not to repeat my statements to any one else?'

'I promise not to say a word.'

'Well,' I remarked, 'you have seen certain persons who have come here, professing to be relatives of mine.'

'Yes, and they are your relatives, aren't they?'

'They look like my relatives, but they're not,' was my reply.

My inquisitive friend burst into laughter and said, 'Well, if you mean *that,* I shall have to take back what I just said. You are really the craziest person I have ever met, and I have met several.'

'You will think differently some day,' I replied; for I believed that when my trial should occur, he would appreciate the significance of my remark. I did not tell him that I believed these callers to be detectives; nor did I hint that I thought myself in the hands of the police.

Meanwhile, during July and August, 1902, I redoubled my activity in devising suicidal schemes; for I now thought my physical condition satisfactory to my enemies, and was sure that my trial could not be postponed beyond the next opening of the courts in September. I even went

so far as to talk to one of the attendants, a medical student, who during the summer worked as an attendant at the hospital. I approached him artfully. First I asked him to procure from the library for me 'The Scarlet Letter,' 'The House of the Seven Gables,' and other books; then I talked medicine and finally asked him to lend me a textbook on anatomy which I knew he had in his possession. This he did, cautioning me not to let anyone know that he had done so. The book once secured, I lost no time in examining that part which described the heart, its functions, and especially its exact position in the body. I had scarcely begun to read when the young man returned and took the book from me, giving as his reason that an attendant had no right to let a patient read a medical work. Maybe his change of heart was providential.

As is usual in these institutions, all knives, forks, and other articles that might be used by a patient for a dangerous purpose were counted by the attendants after each meal. This I knew, and the knowledge had a deterrent effect. I dared not take one. Though I might at any time during the night have hanged myself, that method did not appeal to me, and I kept it in mind only as a last resort. To get possession of some sharp daggerlike instrument which I could plunge into my heart at a moment's notice—this was my consuming desire. With such a weapon I felt that I could, when the crisis came, rob the detectives of their victory. During the summer months an employé spent his entire time mowing the lawn with a large horse-drawn machine. This, when not in use, was often left outdoors. Upon it was a square wooden box, containing certain necessary tools, among them a sharp, spike-like instrument, used to clean the oil-holes when they became clogged. This bit of steel was five or six inches long, and was shaped like a pencil. For at least three months, I seldom went out of doors that I did not go with the intention of purloining that steel spike. I intended then to keep it in my room against the day of my anticipated transfer to jail.

It was now that my delusions protected me from the very fate they had induced me to court. For had I not believed that the eye of a detective was on me every moment, I could have taken that spike a score of times. Often, when it was not in use, I walked to the lawnmower and even laid my hand upon the tool-box. But I dared not open it. My feelings were much like those of Pandora about a certain other box. In my case, however, the box upon which I looked with longing had Hope without, and not within. Instinctively, perhaps, I realized this, for I did not lift the lid.

One day, as the patients were returning to their wards, I saw, lying directly in my path (I could even now point out the spot), the coveted weapon. Never have I seen anything that I wanted more. To have stooped and picked it up without detection would have been easy; and had I known, as I know now, that it had been carelessly dropped there, nothing could have prevented me from doing so and perhaps using it with fatal effect. But I believed it had been placed there deliberately and as a test, by those who had divined my suicidal purpose. The eye of the imagined detective, which, I am inclined to believe, and like to believe, was the eye of the real God, was upon me; and though I stepped directly over it, I did not pick up that thing of death.

* * *

A few days before Christmas my most galling deprivation was at last removed. That is, my clothes were restored. These I treated with great respect. Not so much as a thread did I destroy. Clothes, as is known, have a sobering and civilizing effect, and from the very moment I was again provided with presentable outer garments my conduct rapidly improved. The assistant physician with whom I had been on such variable terms of friendship and enmity even took me for a sleigh-ride. With this improvement came other privileges or, rather, the granting of my rights. Late in December I was permitted to send letters to my conservator. Though some of my blood-curdling letters were confiscated, a few detailing my experiences were forwarded. The account of my sufferings naturally distressed my conservator, but, as he said when he next visited me: 'What could I have done to help you? If the men in this State whose business it is to run these institutions cannot manage you, I am at a loss to know what to do.' True, he could have done little or nothing, for he did not then know the ins and outs of the baffling situation into which the ties of blood had drawn him.

About the middle of January the doctor in charge of my case went for a two weeks' vacation. During his absence an older member of the staff took charge of the violent ward. A man of wider experience and more liberal ideas than his predecessor, he at once granted me several real privileges. One day he permitted me to pay a brief visit to the best ward—the one from which I had been transferred two months earlier. I thus was able again to mingle with many seemingly normal men, and though I enjoyed this privilege upon but one occasion, and then only a few hours, it gave me intense satisfaction.

Altogether the last six weeks of the fourteen during which I was confined in the violent ward were comfortable and relatively happy. I was no longer subjected to physical abuse, though this exemption was largely due to my own skill in avoiding trouble. I was no longer cold and hungry. I was allowed a fair amount of outdoor exercise which, after my close confinement, proved to be a delightful shock. But, above all, I was again given an adequate supply of stationery and drawing materials, which became as tinder under the focused rays of my artistic eagerness. My mechanical investigations were gradually set aside. Art and literature again held sway. Except when out of doors taking my allotted exercise, I remained in my room reading, writing, or drawing. This room of mine soon became a Mecca for the most irrepressible and loquacious characters in the ward. But I soon schooled myself to shut my ears to the incoherent prattle of my unwelcome visitors. Occasionally, some of them would become obstreperous—perhaps because of my lordly order to leave the room. Often did they threaten to throttle me; but I ignored the threats, and they were never carried out. Nor was I afraid that they would be. Invariably I induced them to obey.

The drawings I produced at this time were crude. For the most part they consisted of copies of illustrations which I had cut from magazines that had miraculously found their way into the violent ward. The heads of men and women interested me most, for I had decided to take up portraiture. At first I was content to draw in black and white, but I soon procured some colors and from that time on devoted my attention to mastering pastel.

In the world of letters I had made little progress. My compositions were for the most part epistles addressed to relatives and friends and to those in authority at the hospital. Frequently the letters addressed to the doctors were sent in sets of three—this to save time, for I was very busy. The first letter of such a series would contain my request, couched in friendly and polite terms. To this I would add a postscript, worded about as follows: 'If, after reading this letter, you feel inclined to refuse my request, please read letter number two.' Letter number two would be severely formal—a business-like repetition of the request made in letter number one. Again a postscript would advise the reader to consult letter number three, if the reading of number two had failed to move him. Letter number three was invariably a brief philippic in which I would consign the unaccommodating doctor to oblivion.

In this way I expended part of my prodigious supply of feeling and energy. But I had also another way of reducing my creative pressure. Occasionally, from sheer excess of emotion, I would burst into verse, of a quality not to be doubted. Of that quality the reader shall judge, for I am going to quote a 'creation' written under circumstances which, to say the least, were adverse. Before writing these lines I had never attempted verse in my life—barring intentionally inane doggerel. And, as I now judge these lines, it is probably true that even yet I have never written a poem. Nevertheless, my involuntary, almost automatic outburst is at least suggestive of the fervor that was in me. These fourteen lines were written within thirty minutes of the time I first conceived the idea; and I present them substantially as they first took form. From a psychological standpoint at least, I am told, they are not without interest.

LIGHT

Man's darkest hour is the hour before he's
  born,
Another is the hour just before the Dawn;
From Darkness unto Life and Light he
  leaps,
To Life but once,—to Light as oft as God
  wills he should.
'Tis God's own secret, why
Some live long, and others early die;
For Life depends on Light, and Light on
  God,
Who hath given to Man the perfect
  knowledge
That Grim Despair and Sorrow end in
  Light
And Life everlasting, in realms
Where darkest Darkness becomes Light;
But not the Light Man knows,
Which only is Light
Because God told Man so.

These verses, which breathe religion, were written in an environment which was anything but religious. With curses of ward-mates ringing in my ears, some subconscious part of me seemed to force me to write at its dictation. I was far from being in a pious frame of mind myself, and the quality of my thought surprised me then—as it does now.

* * *

Though I continued to respect my clothes, I did not at once cease to tear such material as would serve me in my scientific investigations. Gravity being conquered, it was inevitable that I should devote some of my time to the invention of a flying-machine.

This was soon perfected—in my mind; and all I needed, that I might test the device, was my liberty. As usual I was unable to explain how I should produce the result which I so confidently foretold. But I believed and proclaimed that I should, ere long, fly to St. Louis and claim and receive the one-hundred-thousand-dollar reward offered by the Commission of the Louisiana Purchase Exposition for the most efficient airship to be exhibited. The moment the thought winged its way through my mind, I had not only a flying-machine, but a fortune in the bank. Being where I could not dissipate my riches, I became a lavish verbal spender. I was in a mood to buy anything, and I whiled away many an hour planning what I should do with my fortune. The St. Louis prize was a paltry trifle. I reasoned that the man who could harness gravity had at his beck and call the world and all that therein is. This sudden accession of wealth made my vast humanitarian projects seem only the more feasible. What could be more delightful, I thought, than the furnishing and financing of ideas of a magnitude to stagger humanity. My condition was one of ecstatic suspense. Give me my liberty and I would show a sleepy old world what could be done to improve conditions, not only among the insane, but along every line of beneficent endeavor.

The city of my birth was to be made a garden-spot. All defiling, smoke-begriming factories were to be banished to an innocuous distance. Churches were to give way to cathedrals; the city itself was to become a paradise of mansions. Yale University was to be transformed into the most magnificent—yet efficient—seat of learning in the world. For once, college professors were to be paid adequate salaries, and alluring provision for their declining years was to be made. New Haven should become a very hotbed of culture. Art galleries, libraries, museums and theatres of a dreamlike splendor were to rise whenever and wherever I should will. Why absurd? Was it not I who would defray the cost? The famous buildings of the Old World were to be reproduced, if, indeed, the originals could not be purchased, brought to this country and reassembled. Not far from New Haven there is a sandy plain, once the bed of the Connecticut River, but now a kind of miniature desert. I often smile as I pass it on the train; for it was here, for the edification of those who might never be able to visit the Valley of the Nile, that I planned to erect a pyramid that should out-Cheops the original. My harnessed gravity, I believed, would not only enable me to overcome existing mechanical difficulties, but it would make the quarrying of immense monoliths as easy as the slicing of bread, and the placing of them in position as easy as the laying of bricks.

After all, delusions of grandeur are the most entertaining of toys. The assortment which my imagination provided was a comprehensive one. I had tossed aside the blocks of childhood days. Instead of laboriously piling small squares of wood one upon another in an endeavor to build the tiny semblance of a house, I now, in this second childhood of mine, projected against thin air phantom edifices planned and completed in the twinkling of an eye. To be sure, such houses of cards almost immediately superseded one another, but the vanishing of one could not disturb a mind that had ever another interesting bauble to take its place. And therein lies part of the secret of the happiness peculiar to that stage of elation which is distinguished by delusions of grandeur—always provided that he who is possessed by them be not subjected to privation and abuse. The sane man who can prove that he is rich in material wealth is not nearly so happy as the mentally disordered man whose delusions trick him into believing himself a modern Croesus. A wealth of Midas-like delusions is no burden. Such a fortune, though a misfortune in itself, bathes the world in a golden glow. No clouds obscure the vision. Optimism reigns supreme. 'Failure' and 'impossible' are as words from an unknown tongue. And the unique satisfaction about a fortune of this fugitive type is that its loss occasions no regret. One by one the phantom ships of treasure sail away for parts unknown; until when the last ship has become but a speck on the mental horizon, the observer makes the happy discovery that his pirate fleet has left behind it a priceless wake of Reason!

✳

PORPHYRIA'S LOVER

ROBERT BROWNING

[In *Porphyria's Lover* by Browning we find an example of dissociation of the personality culminating in murder. Here the lover, who has previously been rejected and his pride sorely wounded, exults in his murder of Porphyria, believing that thus he may keep forever the perfect moment when she reveals her love for him.]

The rain set early in to-night,
  The sullen wind was soon awake,
It tore the elm-tops down for spite,
  And did its worst to vex the lake:
I listened with heart fit to break.
When glided in Porphyria; straight
  She shut the cold out and the storm,
And kneeled and made the cheerless grate
  Blaze up, and all the cottage warm;
Which done, she rose, and from her form
Withdrew the dripping cloak and shawl,
  And laid her soiled gloves by, untied
Her hat and let the damp hair fall,
  And, last, she sat down by my side
And called me. When no voice replied,
She put my arm about her waist,
  And made her smooth white shoulder bare
And all her yellow hair displaced,
  And, stooping, made my cheek lie there,
And spread, o'er all, her yellow hair,
Murmuring how she loved me—she
  Too weak, for all her heart's endeavor,
To set its struggling passion free
  From pride, and vainer ties dissever,
And give herself to me forever.
But passion sometimes would prevail,
  Nor could to-night's gay feast restrain
A sudden thought of one so pale
  For love of her, and all in vain:

So, she was come through wind and rain.
Be sure I looked up at her eyes
  Happy and proud; at last I knew
Porphyria worshipped me; surprise
  Made my heart swell, and still it grew
While I debated what to do.
That moment she was mine, mine, fair,
  Perfectly pure and good: I found
A thing to do, and all her hair
  In one long yellow string I wound
Three times her little throat around,
And strangled her. No pain felt she;
  I am quite sure she felt no pain.
As a shut bud that holds a bee,
  I warily oped her lids: again
Laughed the blue eyes without a stain.
And I untightened next the tress
  About her neck; her cheek once more
Blushed bright beneath my burning kiss:
  I propped her head up as before,
Only, this time my shoulder bore
Her head, which droops upon it still:
  The smiling rosy little head,
So glad it has its utmost will,
  That all it scorned at once is fled,
And I, its love, am gained instead!
Porphyria's love: she guessed not how
  Her darling one wish would be heard.
And thus we sit together now,
  And all night long we have not stirred,
And yet God has not said a word!

✻

THE SON OF RIZAL
José Garcia Villa

[In Villa's *The Son of Rizal,* a poor outcast finds compensation for his suffering at the hands of his father and for the poverty and misery of his life

(Author's Note: Doctor José Rizal, the national hero of the Philippines, died a martyr's death. Accused of sedition against the mother country, Spain, Rizal was deported, imprisoned, and finally shot. He was married on the morning of his execution. The day of his death is observed annually in the Philippines as an official holiday. *Doctor Rizal left no son.*)

From *Footnote to Youth* by José Villa. By permission of Charles Scribner's Sons.

in the delusion that he is the son of a great national hero. In his fantasy life he is enabled to forget the cruelty of the father whom he hated and to accept a life which is in reality one of barren poverty and ignominy.]

I

Last December 30 I boarded the last afternoon train for Lucena, Tayabas. I had waited until the afternoon to leave, for in the morning my wife, my children and I had gone to the Luneta to view the annual Rizal Day parade. On the morning of the 31st I had to close an important land deal in Lucena.

From my compartment in the train I could see that the third-class cars were filling with returning provincials who had come to the city—Manila—to celebrate the day. They formed a clumsy, motley, obstreperous group and crowded both the station platform and the steps to the cars. They bustled and palavered loudly like little, unruly children. Some were students going home for a day or two, and they were easily and contrastingly distinguishable from the rest by their modern, flashy clothes. There was a short, ducklike fellow among them who hummed 'Ramona,' but nobody listened to him for another was cracking a joke about women.

There was much pushing and jostling on the steps to the cars, and a woman who was invisible, whose feet had been injudiciously stepped upon, issued a string of shrill invectives. She called the persons about her 'Goats! . . . Pigs! . . . Brutes!' She cried to them: did they have no regard for women, did they have no conscience, and, oh! of what advantage being a woman if you had to be trampled upon like an old, useless mat! . . .

But there was one person of all this crowd who caught my true attention—or was it a feeling of pity? I felt guilty that I should think myself so superior as to bestow compassion on a fellow creature. Yet there I was, feeling it, and unable to help myself . . . He was a small, debile, bark-colored man, lugging a long, narrow buri bag which in the native tongue is called *bayong*. He found difficulty in pushing through the group on the steps to the car, and finally retreated quietly to the platform. On his sallow, thin face was written the fear he had that the train might start before he had got on. The black-green, shapeless, old felt hat that he wore was too small for his head, and he pulled it in deeper. Then the locomotive bell began to ring its slow, awing, annunciative notes, and the man got nervous. He was pitifully helpless like a lost animal as he stood there not knowing where to get on.

In my pocket I had two tickets, for not quite fifteen minutes ago my eldest son had insisted on going along with me, but had later on desisted. The tickets had been bought, and I could not find the nerve to return the other. In such little things I am most conscious and sensitive, and would feel myself brazen and shameless, if I returned with indifference the things already paid for . . . Caritatively again (and I hated myself for it) I thought of offering the other ticket to the man.

Half guiltily I whistled to him, and he glanced confusedly in my direction. I beckoned him to approach, which I saw he was reluctant to do—so afraid was he that he would lose more time and not get on the train at all. But I raised my two tickets for him to see, and I surmised that he understood my intention, for he hobbled hurriedly to my window. In brief words I explained to him that I had an extra ticket, and would he be kind enough to share my company in my compartment? I was alone, I said. Timidly yet eagerly he accepted my invitation.

The steps to the first-class cars are often, if not always, clear, and soon he was at the door of my compartment. He mumbled a ceremonious, deferential greeting, removing the black-green hat. I told him to step in, and he did so, silently lifting the buri bag and depositing it on the iron net above our heads; beside it he placed the hat. Then he settled himself awkwardly on the seat opposite mine, and regarded me with soft, friendly, pathetic eyes . . . The train started.

He was sparely built and poorly dressed. He wore the poor man's *camisa-chino*, but it was clean and freshly starched. He had on white drill trousers and red velvet slippers.

He smiled shyly at me and I smiled in return.

'You see, I've got my ticket,' he tried to explain, pulling it out of his *camisa-chino's* pocket, 'but it was hard to get in. I cannot afford to ride in *here*, you know,' he confessed half embarrassed. His thick lips moved slowly, docilely, and his voice was thin, slow and sad. His small, round, melancholy eyes were lowered in humility.

I told him I was glad to help him. I said I was bound for Lucena, and he where?

'Calamba. That is where I live . . . I have three children—two little girls and a boy. Their mother—she died at childbirth.'

I expressed my sympathy and told him I hoped the children were well.

'They are good children,' he said contentedly.

We fell into a warm, friendly chat. He was well-mannered in speech, and although he did not talk fluently— sometimes he was tongue-tied—yet he managed to convey his thoughts.

We became confidential in each other, and I spoke to him of my business. I said I was married and had more children than he had, and was a commercial agent. I said I was tired of the work but was not sure I would be more successful in other lines.

He was sympathetic and in return spoke to me about himself and his trade. His name was Juan Rizal and he was a shoemaker. He had a little shop in the front of his house. 'It is not a big house,' he said.

I said: 'You have a good name: Juan Rizal.'

'My father is Rizal,' he answered.

'Then maybe you are a relative of the hero,' I said inferentially. 'Near relation, I suppose.'

'No. Rizal is my *father*,' he said. 'Rizal. Doctor Rizal,' he emphasized, and I saw a brilliant light of pride in his small buttonlike eyes. 'Yes,' he affirmed himself with not a little bombast.

I said I had not heard and did not know that Rizal had a son.

'Yes, he *has*,' he said matter-of-factly. 'I am *he*.' And he looked at me superiorly.

'The books do not speak of Rizal having a son,' I said.

'They don't know,' he negated with perfect self-confidence. 'They don't know—at all. I *am* the son of Rizal.'

As he said this, he sat himself erect, lifted his chest out, and plaited together his fingers on his lap. He was little and thin, and when he stretched himself to look great and dignified, he became pathetically distorted. Now he looked elongated, disconcertingly elongated, like an extending, crawling, loathsome leech.

And I was moved and I lied:

'I am glad to know you. I am glad to know the son of Rizal,' I said.

'Rizal had only *one* son,' he explained. '*I* am he, that son—yes, *I* am he. But people won't believe me—they are *envious* of me.'

There was a slight whimpering, protestive note in his voice. His thick lips quivered and a film covered his eyes. I thought he was going to cry and I began to feel uncomfortable.

'They are *envious* of me,' he repeated, and could not say more—a choking emotion had seized him. He swayed lightly as though he would fall.

I realized the intensity of his feeling and I kept quiet. When he regained himself, he asked me in a half fearful, half apologetic tone:

'Do you believe me?'

I faltered: 'Y-yes.'

A happy light beamed in his dumb, doglike eyes.

He said: 'Thank you. Thank you. *Thank you.*' He said this, straining himself, for he was greatly excited with gratitude.

There passed moments of silence, and we looked through the window at the passing scenes. The greenery in the soft sunlight was beautiful and healthy, imparting to the eyes a sense of coolness, of vastness. The air, though rather warm, we felt cool and soothing. The train moved smoothly, like a vessel on a very peaceful sea.

It was I who broke the silence. I said I had gone to the Luneta that morning to see the parade. The sun had been hot, and my wife, the chil-

dren and I had perspired a lot. 'It is a trial, waiting for and watching a parade,' I said.

He said I was right and that he too had seen the parade. He had come to Manila for that purpose only. 'I go once a year. It is a sort of—pilgrimage. But—I *love* my father, you see . . .'

It was a naive, full-souled statement, and he said it with contagious tenderness. His eyes ceased for the moment being dull and inexpressive—the soft warmth of gentleness, of a supreme devotional love, filled them—and they became the eyes of a dove.

'I love my father,' he repeated wistfully, softly, as though he were chanting a most holy, sacred song.

But I (and may God punish me for my cruelty!) remarked inadvertently that he *didn't* look like his father.

A look of great, immeasurable hurt stole into his eyes, and he looked at me imploringly, questioned me with those small, melancholy eyes that but a moment ago had been so happy, so inspired, so tender. Struggling out of impending defeat, clamoring to be saved, to be believed in, those eyes looked at me so that a lump rose unwillingly to my throat.

But he said as though he bore me no grudge at all for my cruel remark —said it softly, lowly, as though in solemn prayer:

'I take—after my mother.'

Yet he was disturbed, completely broken by my remark, I realized. It had cut him deeply, struck his very core, although he wanted to appear composed. And his efforts were futile: his unrest was visible everywhere in his person: his eyes grew painfully feverish, his nostrils quivered, his lips trembled. And he gave it up with a twitch of his lips, let himself be as he felt, discoursed, to dispel my doubts, on his mother and his birth: [1]

'My father and my mother—they lived together before they were married. They lived in Talisay, during my father's deportation, but I was born in Dapitan. People don't know that. When I was born they thought —*thought*—I was dead. Dead. But that is not true. I was *alive*. People thought I was born so, because when my mother was in a delicate condition before my birth, my father played a prank on her and she sprang forward and struck against an iron stand. She became sick—I was born prematurely. But I *was* alive. Do you understand? I was born, and *alive— and I lived.*' There was galvanic energy in his excited voice. 'My mother, she was Irish—Josefina Bracken.' He gazed deeper into my eyes. 'I don't remember her well,' he said. 'I don't remember her. She had brown eyes and a little nose.' He blew his nose with a cheap, colored handkerchief.

'My father liked her but maybe he did not love her. He loved Leonora. Leonora was his cousin. They were separated when my father went to Europe. Leonora's mother intercepted his letters—she withheld them from Leonora. When my father came back she was married.' He stopped and brooded.

'I ran away from my mother when I was old enough to do so. I ran away to Calamba. My father was born there. I wanted to go there—to live there. I have lived there ever since . . . Have you ever been to Calamba?'

I said: 'No.'

'My father married my mother on

[1] For veracity of facts mentioned in the following paragraph, consult Austin Craig's *Lineage, Life and Labors of José Rizal, Philippine Patriot*, pages 215-17.

the morning of his execution,' he pursued. 'My father was brave,' he said. 'He was not afraid of the Spaniards. He fell forward when they shot him—they wanted to shoot him in the back, but he turned around and fell forward.'

He was greatly excited. His face was flushed. 'They shot him—*my father*— the white scoundrels! They shot *my father*—as they would—a dog!' He was indignant and a string of tirades left his lips. He shook with fuming rage. His thin, sticklike fingers closed and opened frantically. He was so vituperative I was afraid he did not realize what he was saying.

I stretched a comforting hand to his to calm him down. He looked at me with quivering lips and I realized his helplessness. He told me with rising, apologetic consciousness that he had not meant to upset me. He begged tearfully for my forgiveness, clutching my hands tightly in his. 'Please forgive me,' he said. 'Please forgive me.'

I was afraid he would kneel down, so I moved over to his side and said I understood.

'Do you?' he said. 'Do you?' His voice was pleading, full of internal ache.

'I do,' I said.

He quieted down. He turned his face away from mine, ashamed that he had let his feelings run loose.

We were silent again. Only the *chug-chug-chug* of the train could be heard, and the wind-tossed laughter of those in the neighboring compartments. The air had grown cooler, dusk was fast approaching, and only a lone bird flitted in the sky. There was a sweet, flowing sound as we crossed a rivulet.

My companion turned to me and made me understand that he was desirous of asking a question. I encouraged him.

'His books—you have read my father's books, the *Noli* and the *Filibusterismo?*' There was still a tremor in his voice, and he mispronounced the last title, calling it 'Plisterismo.'

'Only the *Noli*,' I said. 'I have not had the time to read the other.'

He kept his questioning gaze, and I gathered that he wanted me to talk on the book.

'It is a good book,' I said. 'Only a keen, observant mind could have written it.'

He beamed and showed happiness at my words. Peace and repose spread over his face.

'I am glad you like it. I have—never read it. That is why I asked you. I have—never learned to read.'

We were approaching the station of Calamba, Laguna.

'We are nearing your place,' I said.

'Yes,' he said, and a sadness was now in his voice. 'I wish,' he murmured, 'I could invite you home.'

'I will drop in some day.'

The train slackened speed and finally stopped.

I helped the son of Rizal lift the buri bag from the net.

'For my children,' he explained, smiling. 'I bought them fruits.'

He asked me before he alighted:

'Do you *really* believe me?'

'I do.'

He was very happy and shook my hands effusively.

'Good-bye,' he said.

'Good-bye.'

The train moved again.

II

The following month I went to Calamba on the invitation of a friend. It had been a long time, about six years, since we had last met in the city, and now I was to be godfather to his firstborn. The choosing of the name depended on me, he had written, and I was elated by it. Aside from the customary baptismal gift, I brought with me a plaster bust of Rizal which I intended to present to Juan Rizal; I purposed to drop in on him for a while.

After the ceremony I asked my host if he knew anything about Juan Rizal.

'Yes,' he said. 'You mean Juan Kola.'

I told him to explain.

'He is a shoemaker—owns a little shop near the edge of the town. The children call him Juan Sirá. You know what that means: nutty.'

'Tell me more.'

'Well, he calls himself Juan Rizal —tells that to people whom he meets . . . There is a sad story behind it. I will tell it to you:

'When Juan Kola was a small boy, his father was very cruel to him: he used to beat him for any or no reason at all. Naturally the boy grew to dislike his father—learned to hate him as much as he feared him. But when the boy was twelve or thereabouts, the father died. The boy knew no *happiness* so great so that he *cried*. Otherwise the boy would *not* have wept: he was so used to his father's meanness and cruelty that any sorrow, any pain, could not make him cry—he had forgotten how to cry—had learned to stifle that surging in the breast that brings tears to the eyes—and he would merely whine, dry-eyed, like a kicked puppy. But this time he wept, and for a long time afterwards you could see him in the streets crying. And when people asked him why he cried, he replied, "I don't know. I just want to cry." He was not evading the truth, the boy simply had no words for it. But the people knew.

'Then the boy began thinking of Rizal. Rizal was born here, you know, and that makes him closer to us than to you who live elsewhere. Rizal to us is a reality, a magnificent, potent reality, but to you he is only a myth, a golden legend. He is to you a star, far-away, bright, unreachable. To us he is not unreachable for he is among us. We feel him, breathe with him, live with him. *Juan Kola lived with him—lives with him.* In his untutored mind he knew that if Rizal were *his* father he would be a good father, a supremely beautiful father—and he, Juan Kola, would always be happy. And so Juan Kola, the little unhappy boy, made José Rizal his father.

'He was a poor boy, Juan Kola, and he could not go to school. He had to work and earn his living. He does not read nor write, but he knows much about Rizal's life from the school teacher who boarded with the shoemaker to whom he was apprenticed. Of nights, when work was over, he would go to her, to this school teacher, and ask her questions—and she, filled with sympathy for the boy, gave him of her time.

'When Juan's father died, he destroyed all his father's things. There was a picture left of his father, but he burned it, not wishing to remember anything of his true parent. He wanted to be *fully* the son of his adopted father. From then on he was the son of Rizal.

'And that,' concluded my friend, 'is the story of Juan Sirá. The children have misnamed him: it is cruel, unjust. He who can dream of beautiful things, and live in them, surely he is great—and wise.'

'Take me to Juan Rizal,' I said.

* * *

I presented my gift to Juan Rizal in his shabby little nipa home. Juan Rizal was exultant when he opened the package containing Rizal's bust. 'I have always wanted one, but I could not afford it,' he said with tremulous lips and adoring eyes.

And when I was to leave, he kissed my hands fervently and told his children to do the same. His eyes were wet but happy.

'God will reward you,' he said, as I descended the narrow, rickety bamboo steps.

❊

THE BROTHERS KARAMAZOV

FYODOR DOSTOYEVSKY

[Few men have written with such insight as has Dostoyevsky of the schizophrenic or split personality, its terrors, dreams, hallucinations, and torments. For Dostoyevsky knew only too well the agonies of the mental state he describes. In this dramatization of the inner conflict of Ivan Karamazov we see the struggle of a man of powerful emotions and intellect to protect himself from the burden of guilt his Super-ego would impose upon him. Techni-

From *The Brothers Karamazov* by Fyodor Dostoyevsky. Reprinted by permission of Random House, Inc.

cally, Ivan is guiltless of the murder of his father, for which he is soon to be tried. But he cannot escape the self-doubt and the torturous questioning of the reality of good and evil within his own spirit, for he feels that his wish for the death of the vile old man makes him an accomplice in the crime. The evil potentialities in his own nature, his heritage from his father, struggle for supremacy with the ideals his intellectual integrity and social responsibility have imposed upon him.]

The Devil. Ivan's Nightmare

I am not a doctor, but yet I feel that the moment has come when I must inevitably give the reader some account of the nature of Ivan's illness. Anticipating events I can say at least one thing: he was at that moment on the very eve of an attack of brain fever. Though his health had long been affected, it had offered a stubborn resistance to the fever which in the end gained complete mastery over it. Though I know nothing of medicine, I venture to hazard the suggestion that he really had perhaps, by a terrible effort of will, succeeded in delaying the attack for a time, hoping, of course, to check it completely. He knew that he was unwell, but he loathed the thought of being ill at that fatal time, at the approaching crisis in his life, when he needed to have all his wits about him, to say what he had to say boldly and resolutely and 'to justify himself to himself.'

He had, however, consulted the new doctor, who had been brought from Moscow by a fantastic notion of Katerina Ivanovna's to which I have referred already. After listening to him and examining him the doctor came to the conclusion that he was actually suffering from some disorder of the brain, and was not at all surprised by an admission which Ivan had reluctantly made him. 'Hallucinations are quite likely in your condition,' the doctor opined, 'though it

would be better to verify them . . . you must take steps at once, without a moment's delay, or things will go badly with you.' But Ivan did not follow this judicious advice and did not take to his bed to be nursed. 'I am walking about, so I am strong enough, if I drop, it'll be different then, any one may nurse me who likes,' he decided, dismissing the subject.

And so he was sitting almost conscious himself of his delirium and, as I have said already, looking persistently at some object on the sofa against the opposite wall. Some one appeared to be sitting there, though goodness knows how he had come in, for he had not been in the room when Ivan came into it, on his return from Smerdyakov. This was a person or, more accurately speaking, a Russian gentleman of a particular kind, no longer young, *qui faisait la cinquantaine,* as the French say, with rather long, still thick, dark hair, slightly streaked with grey, and a small pointed beard. He was wearing a brownish reefer jacket, rather shabby, evidently made by a good tailor though, and of a fashion at least three years old, that had been discarded by smart and well-to-do people for the last two years. His linen and his long scarf-like neck-tie were all such as are worn by people who aim at being stylish, but on closer inspection his linen was not over clean and his wide scarf was very threadbare. The visitor's check trousers were of excellent cut, but were too light in colour and too tight for the present fashion. His soft fluffy white hat was out of keeping with the season.

In brief there was every appearance of gentility on straitened means. It looked as though the gentleman belonged to that class of idle landowners who used to flourish in the times of serfdom. He had unmistakably been, at some time, in good and fashionable society, had once had good connections, had possibly preserved them indeed, but, after a gay youth, becoming gradually impoverished on the abolition of serfdom, he had sunk into the position of a poor relation of the best class, wandering from one good old friend to another and received by them for his companionable and accommodating disposition and as being, after all, a gentleman who could be asked to sit down with any one, though, of course, not in a place of honour. Such gentlemen of accommodating temper and dependent position, who can tell a story, take a hand at cards, and who have a distinct aversion for any duties that may be forced upon them, are usually solitary creatures, either bachelors or widowers. Sometimes they have children, but if so, the children are always being brought up at a distance, at some aunt's, to whom these gentlemen never allude in good society, seeming ashamed of the relationship. They gradually lose sight of their children altogether, though at intervals they receive a birthday or Christmas letter from them and sometimes even answer it.

The countenance of the unexpected visitor was not so much good-natured as accommodating and ready to assume any amiable expression as occasion might arise. He had no watch, but he had a tortoise-shell lorgnette on a black ribbon. On the middle finger of his right hand was a massive gold ring with a cheap opal stone in it.

Ivan was angrily silent and would not begin the conversation. The visitor waited and sat exactly like a poor relation who had come down from his room to keep his host company at tea, and was discreetly silent, seeing that his host was frowning and preoccupied. But he was ready for any affable conversation as soon as his host should begin it. All at once his face expressed a sudden solicitude.

'I say,' he began to Ivan, 'excuse me, I only mention it to remind you. You went to Smerdyakov's to find out about Katerina Ivanovna, but you came away without finding out anything about her, you probably forgot . . .'

'Ah, yes,' broke from Ivan and his face grew gloomy with uneasiness. 'Yes, I'd forgotten . . . but it doesn't matter now, never mind, till tomorrow,' he muttered to himself, 'and you,' he added, addressing his visitor, 'I should have remembered that myself in a minute, for that was just what was tormenting me! Why do you interfere, as if I should believe that you prompted me, and that I didn't remember it of myself?'

'Don't believe it then,' said the gentleman, smiling amicably, 'what's the good of believing against your will? Besides, proofs are no help to believing, especially material proofs. Thomas believed, not because he saw Christ risen, but because he wanted to believe, before he saw. Look at the spiritualists, for instance . . . I am very fond of them . . . only fancy, they imagine that they are serving the cause of religion, because the devils show them their horns from the other world. That, they say, is a material proof, so to speak, of the existence of another world. The other world and material proofs, what next! And if you come to that, does proving there's a devil prove that there's a God? I want to join an idealist society, I'll lead the opposition in it, I'll say I'm a realist, but not a materialist, he-he!'

'Listen,' Ivan suddenly got up from the table. 'I seem to be delirious . . . I am delirious, in fact, talk any nonsense you like, I don't care! You won't drive me to fury, as you did last time. But I feel somehow ashamed . . . I want to walk about the room . . . I sometimes don't see you and don't even hear your voice as I did last time, but I always guess what you are prating, for it's I, *I myself speaking, not you*. Only I don't know whether I was dreaming last time or whether I really saw you. I'll wet a towel and put it on my head and perhaps you'll vanish into air.'

Ivan went into the corner, took a towel, and did as he said, and with a wet towel on his head began walking up and down the room.

'I am so glad you treat me so familiarly,' the visitor began.

'Fool,' laughed Ivan, 'do you suppose I should stand on ceremony with you? I am in good spirits now, though I've a pain in my forehead . . . and in the top of my head . . . only please don't talk philosophy, as you did last time. If you can't take yourself off, talk of something amusing. Talk gossip, you are a poor relation, you ought to talk gossip. What a nightmare to have! But I am not afraid of you. I'll get the better of you. I won't be taken to a madhouse!'

'*C'est charmant*, poor relation. Yes, I am in my natural shape. For what am I on earth but a poor relation?

By the way, I am listening to you and am rather surprised to find you are actually beginning to take me for something real, not simply your fancy, as you persisted in declaring last time . . .'

'Never for one minute have I taken you for reality,' Ivan cried with a sort of fury. 'You are a lie, you are my illness, you are a phantom. It's only that I don't know how to destroy you and I see I must suffer for a time. You are my hallucination. You are the incarnation of myself, but only of one side of me . . . of my thoughts and feelings, but only the nastiest and stupidest of them. From that point of view you might be of interest to me, if only I had time to waste on you . . .'

'Excuse me, excuse me, I'll catch you. When you flew out at Alyosha under the lamp-post this evening and shouted to him. "You learnt it from *him*! How do you know that *he* visits me?" You were thinking of me then. So for one brief moment you did believe that I really exist,' the gentleman laughed blandly.

'Yes, that was a moment of weakness . . . but I couldn't believe in you. I don't know whether I was asleep or awake last time. Perhaps I was only dreaming then and didn't see you really at all . . .'

'And why were you so surly with Alyosha just now? He is a dear; I've treated him badly over Father Zossima.'

'Don't talk of Alyosha! How dare you, you flunkey!' Ivan laughed again.

'You scold me, but you laugh—that's a good sign. But you are ever so much more polite than you were last time and I know why: that great resolution of yours . . .'

'Don't speak of my resolution,' cried Ivan, savagely.

'I understand, I understand, *c'est noble, c'est charmant*, you are going to defend your brother and to sacrifice yourself . . . *C'est chevaleresque.*'

'Hold your tongue, I'll kick you!'

'I shan't be altogether sorry, for then my object will be attained. If you kick me, you must believe in my reality, for people don't kick ghosts. Joking apart, it doesn't matter to me, scold if you like, though it's better to be a trifle more polite even to me, "Fool, flunkey!" what words!'

'Scolding you, I scold myself,' Ivan laughed again, 'you are myself, myself, only with a different face. You just say what I am thinking . . . and are incapable of saying anything new!'

'If I am like you in my way of thinking, it's all to my credit,' the gentleman declared, with delicacy and dignity.

'You choose out only my worst thoughts, and what's more, the stupid ones. You are stupid and vulgar. You are awfully stupid. No, I can't put up with you! What am I to do, what am I to do!' Ivan said through his clenched teeth.

'My dear friend, above all things I want to behave like a gentleman and to be recognised as such,' the visitor began in an access of deprecating and simple-hearted pride, typical of a poor relation. 'I am poor, but . . . I won't say very honest, but . . . it's an axiom generally accepted in society that I am a fallen angel. If I ever was, it must have been so long ago that there's no harm in forgetting it. Now I only prize the reputation of being a gentlemanly person and live as I can, trying to make myself agreeable. I love men genuinely, I've been greatly calumniated! Here when I stay with you from time to time, my life gains a kind of reality and that's what I like most of all. You see, like you, I suffer from the fantastic and so I love the realism of earth. Here, with you, everything is circumscribed, here all is formulated and geometrical, while we have nothing but indeterminate equations! I wander about here dreaming. I like dreaming. Besides, on earth I become superstitious. Please don't laugh, that's just what I like, to become superstitious. I adopt all your habits here: I've grown fond of going to the public baths, would you believe it? and I go and steam myself with merchants and priests. What I dream of is becoming incarnate once for all and irrevocably in the form of some merchant's wife weighing eighteen stone, and of believing all she believes. My ideal is to go to church and offer a candle in simple-hearted faith, upon my word it is. Then there would be an end to my sufferings. I like being doctored too; in the spring there was an outbreak of smallpox and I went and was vaccinated in a foundling hospital—if only you knew how I enjoyed myself that day. I subscribed ten roubles to the cause of the Slavs! . . . But you are not listening. Do you know, you are not at all well this evening? I know you went yesterday to that doctor . . . well, what about your health? What did the doctor say?'

'Fool!' Ivan snapped out.

'But you are clever, anyway. You are scolding again? I didn't ask out of sympathy. You needn't answer. Now rheumatism has come in again . . .'

'Fool!' repeated Ivan.

'You keep saying the same thing; but I had such an attack of rheumatism last year that I remember it to this day.'

'The devil have rheumatism!'

'Why not, if I sometimes put on fleshly form? I put on fleshly form and I take the consequences. Satan *sum et nihil humanum a me alienum puto.*'

'What, what? Satan *sum et nihil humanum* . . . that's not bad for the devil!'

'I am glad I've pleased you at last.'

'But you didn't get that from me,' Ivan stopped suddenly, seeming struck. 'That never entered my head, that's strange.'

'*C'est du nouveau, n'est ce pas?* This time I'll act honestly and explain to you. Listen, in dreams and especially in nightmares, from indigestion or anything, a man sees sometimes such artistic visions, such complex and real actuality, such events, even a whole world of events, woven into such a plot, with such unexpected details from the most exalted matters to the last button on a cuff, as I swear Leo Tolstoy has never invented. Yet such dreams are sometimes seen not by writers, but by the most ordinary people, officials, journalists, priests . . . The subject is a complete enigma. A statesman confessed to me, indeed, that all his best ideas came to him when he was asleep. Well, that's how it is now, though I am your hallucination, yet just as in a nightmare, I say original things which had not entered your head before. So I don't repeat your ideas, yet I am only your nightmare, nothing more.'

❄

THE BROTHERS KARAMAZOV
FYODOR DOSTOYEVSKY

[Dostoyevsky's picture of Lise, the daughter of the wealthy, dominating Madame Hohlakov, is a terrifying study of an unbalanced sixteen-year-old girl. The possessiveness of the mother may be held partially responsible for the girl's invalidism, her hysteria, and her lack of responsibility in all personal relationships. Her sadistic and masochistic impulses seem at first merely playfully capricious, but later we recognize their basis in the sex frustrations of her violently passionate nature. In her appalling conversation with Aloysha, with whom she had once fancied herself in love, she reveals the completely amoral reactions of one far advanced in a psychotic state.]

A Little Demon

Going in to Lise, he found her half reclining in the invalid chair, in which she had been wheeled when she was unable to walk. She did not move to meet him, but her sharp keen eyes were simply riveted on his face. There was a feverish look in her eyes, her face was pale and yellow. Alyosha was amazed at the change that had taken place in her in three

From *The Brothers Karamazov* by Fyodor Dostoyevsky. Reprinted by permission of Random House, Inc.

days. She was positively thinner. She did not hold out her hand to him . . . He touched the thin, long fingers which lay motionless on her dress, then he sat down facing her, without a word.

'I know you are in a hurry to get to the prison,' Lise said curtly, 'and mamma's kept you there for hours, she's just been telling you about me and Yulia.'

'How do you know?' asked Alyosha.

'I've been listening. Why do you stare at me? I want to listen and I do listen, there's no harm in that. I don't apologise.'

'You are upset about something?'

'On the contrary, I am very happy. I've only just been reflecting for the thirtieth time what a good thing it is I refused you and shall not be your wife. You are not fit to be a husband. If I were to marry you and give you a note to take to the man I loved after you, you'd take it and be sure to give it to him and bring an answer back, too. If you were forty, you would still go on taking my love-letters for me.'

She suddenly laughed.

'There is something spiteful and yet open-hearted about you,' Alyosha smiled to her.

'The open-heartedness consists in my not being ashamed of myself with you. What's more, I don't want to feel ashamed with you, just with you. Alyosha, why is it I don't respect you? I am very fond of you, but I don't respect you. If I respected you, I shouldn't talk to you without shame, should I?'

'No.'

'But do you believe that I am not ashamed with you?'

'No, I don't believe it.'

Lise laughed nervously again; she spoke rapidly.

'I sent your brother, Dmitri Fyodorovitch, some sweets in prison. Alyosha, you know, you are quite pretty! I shall love you awfully for having so quickly allowed me not to love you.'

'Why did you send for me to-day, Lise?'

'I wanted to tell you of a longing I have. I should like some one to torture me, marry me and then torture me, deceive me and go away. I don't want to be happy.'

'You are in love with disorder?'

'Yes, I want disorder. I keep wanting to set fire to the house. I keep imagining how I'll creep up and set fire to the house on the sly. They'll try to put it out, but it'll go on burning. And I shall know and say nothing. Ah, what silliness! And how bored I am!'

She waved her hand with a look of repulsion.

'It's your luxurious life,' said Alyosha, softly.

'Is it better then to be poor?'

'Yes, it is better.'

'That's what your monk taught you. That's not true. Let me be rich and all the rest poor, I'll eat sweets and drink cream and not give any to any one else. Ach, don't speak, don't say anything,' she shook her hand at him, though Alyosha had not opened his mouth. 'You've told me all that before, I know it all by heart. It bores me. If I am ever poor, I shall murder somebody, and even if I am rich, I may murder some one, perhaps—why do nothing! But do you know, I should like to reap, cut the rye? I'll marry you, and you shall become a peasant, a real peasant; we'll keep a colt, shall we? Do you know Kalganov?'

'Yes.'

'He is always wandering about,

dreaming. He says, why live in real life, it's better to dream. One can dream the most delightful things, but real life is a bore. But he'll be married soon for all that, he's been making love to me already. Can you spin tops?'

'Yes.'

'Well, he's just like a top: he wants to be wound up and set spinning and then to be lashed, lashed, lashed with a whip. If I marry him, I'll keep him spinning all his life. You are not ashamed to be with me?'

'No.'

'You are awfully cross, because I don't talk about holy things. I don't want to be holy. What will they do to one in the next world for the greatest sin? You must know all about that.'

'God will censure you.' Alyosha was watching her steadily.

'That's just what I should like. I would go up and they would censure me and I would burst out laughing in their faces. I should dreadfully like to set fire to the house, Alyosha, to our house, you still don't believe me?'

'Why? There are children of twelve years old who have a longing to set fire to something and they do set things on fire too. It's a sort of disease.'

'That's not true, that's not true, there may be children, but that's not what I mean.'

'You take evil for good; it's a passing crisis, it's the result of your illness, perhaps.'

'You do despise me though! It's simply that I don't want to do good, I want to do evil, and it has nothing to do with illness.'

'Why do evil?'

'So that everything might be destroyed. Ah, how nice it would be if everything were destroyed! You know, Alyosha, I sometimes think of doing a fearful lot of harm and everything bad, and I should do it for a long while on the sly and suddenly every one would find it out. Every one will stand round and point their fingers at me and I would look at them all. That would be awfully nice. Why would it be so nice, Alyosha?'

'I don't know. It's a craving to destroy something good or as you say, to set fire to something. It happens sometimes.'

'I not only say it, I shall do it.'

'I believe you.'

'Ah, how I love you for saying you believe me. And you are not lying one little bit. But perhaps you think that I am saying all this on purpose to annoy you?'

'No, I don't think that . . . though perhaps there is a little desire to do that in it, too.'

'There is a little. I never can tell lies to you,' she declared, with a strange fire in her eyes.

What struck Alyosha above everything was her earnestness. There was not a trace of humour or jesting in her face now, though, in old days, fun and gaiety never deserted her even at her most 'earnest' moments.

'There are moments when people love crime,' said Alyosha thoughtfully.

'Yes, yes! You have uttered my thought, they love crime, every one loves crime, they love it always, not at some "moments." You know, it's as though people have made an agreement to lie about it and have lied about it ever since. They all declare that they hate evil, but secretly they all love it.'

'And are you still reading nasty books?'

'Yes, I am. Mamma reads them and

hides them under her pillow and I steal them.'

'Aren't you ashamed to destroy yourself?'

'I want to destroy myself. There's a boy here who lay down between the railway lines when the train was passing. Lucky fellow! Listen, your brother is being tried now for murdering his father and every one loves his having killed his father.'

'Loves his having killed his father?'

'Yes, loves it, every one loves it! Everybody says it's so awful, but secretly they simply love it. I for one love it.'

'There is some truth in what you say about every one,' said Alyosha softly.

'Oh, what ideas you have!' Lise shrieked in delight. 'And you a monk, too! You wouldn't believe how I respect you, Alyosha, for never telling lies. Oh, I must tell you a funny dream of mine. I sometimes dream of devils. It's night, I am in my room with a candle and suddenly there are devils all over the place, in all the corners, under the table, and they open the doors, there's a crowd of them behind the doors and they want to come and seize me. And they are just coming, just seizing me. But I suddenly cross myself and they all draw back, though they don't go away altogether, they stand at the doors and in the corners, waiting. And suddenly I have a frightful longing to revile God aloud, and so I begin, and then they come crowding back to me, delighted, and seize me again and I cross myself again and they all draw back. It's awful fun, it takes one's breath away.'

'I've had the same dream, too,' said Alyosha suddenly.

'Really?' cried Lise, greatly surprised. 'I say, Alyosha, don't laugh, that's awfully important. Could two different people have the same dream?'

'It seems they can.'

'Alyosha, I tell you, it's awfully important,' Lise went on, with really excessive amazement. 'It's not the dream that's important, but your having the same dream as me. You never lie to me, don't lie now: is it true? You are not laughing?'

'It's true.'

Lise seemed extraordinarily impressed and for half a minute she was silent.

'Alyosha, come and see me, come and see me more often,' she said suddenly, in a supplicating voice.

'I'll always come to see you, all my life,' answered Alyosha firmly.

'You are the only person I can talk to, you know,' Lise began again. 'I talk to no one but myself and you. Only you in the whole world. And to you more readily than to myself. And I am not a bit ashamed with you, not a bit. Alyosha, why am I not ashamed with you, not a bit? Alyosha, is it true that at Easter the Jews steal a child and kill it?'

'I don't know.'

'There's a book here in which I read about the trial of a Jew, who took a child of four years old and cut off the fingers from both hands, and then crucified him on the wall, hammered nails into him, and crucified him, and afterwards, when he was tried, he said that the child died soon, within four hours. That was "soon"! He said the child moaned, kept on moaning and he stood admiring it. That's nice!'

'Nice?'

'Nice, I sometimes imagine that it was I who crucified him. He would hang there moaning and I would sit opposite him eating pineapple compote. I am awfully fond of pineapple compote. Do you like it?'

Alyosha looked at her in silence. Her pale, sallow face was suddenly contorted, her eyes burned.

'You know, when I read about that Jew I shook with sobs all night. I kept fancying how the little thing cried and moaned (a child of four years old understands, you know) and all the while the thought of pineapple compote haunted me. In the morning I wrote a letter to a certain person, begging him *particularly* to come and see me. He came and I suddenly told him all about the child and the pineapple compote. *All* about it, *all,* and said that it was nice. He laughed and said it really was nice. Then he got up and went away. He was only here five minutes. Did he despise me? Did he despise me? Tell me, tell me, Alyosha, did he despise me or not?' She sat up on the couch with flashing eyes.

'Tell me,' Alyosha asked anxiously, 'did you send for that person?'

'Yes, I did.'

'Did you send him a letter?'

'Yes.'

'Simply to ask about that, about that child?'

'No, not about that at all. But when he came, I asked him about that at once. He answered, laughed, got up and went away.'

'That person behaved honourably,' Alyosha murmured.

'And did he despise me? Did he laugh at me?'

'No, for perhaps he believes in the pineapple compote himself. He is very ill now, too, Lise.'

'Yes, he does believe in it,' said Lise, with flashing eyes.

'He doesn't despise any one,' Alyosha went on. 'Only he does not believe any one. If he doesn't believe in people, of course, he does despise them.'

'Then he despises me, me?'

'You, too.'

'Good.' Lise seemed to grind her teeth. 'When he went out laughing, I felt that it was nice to be despised. The child with fingers cut off is nice and to be despised is nice . . .'

And she laughed in Alyosha's face, a feverish malicious laugh.

'Do you know, Alyosha, do you know, I should like . . . Alyosha save me!' she suddenly jumped from the couch, rushed to him and seized him with both hands. 'Save me!' she almost groaned. 'Is there any one in the world I could tell what I've told you? I've told you the truth, the truth. I shall kill myself, because I loathe everything, everything. Alyosha, why don't you love me in the least?' she finished in a frenzy.

'But I do love you!' answered Alyosha warmly.

'And will you weep over me, will you?'

'Yes.'

'Not because I won't be your wife, but simply weep for me?'

'Yes.

'Thank you! It's only your tears I want. Every one else may punish me and trample me under foot, every one, every one, not excepting *any one.* For I don't love any one. Do you hear, not any one! On the contrary, I hate him! Go, Alyosha, it's time you went to your brother,' she tore herself away from him suddenly.

'How can I leave you like this?' said Alyosha, almost in alarm.

'Go to your brother, the prison will be shut, go, here's your hat. Give my love to Mitya, go, go!'

And she almost forcibly pushed Alyosha out of the door. He looked at her with pained surprise, when he was suddenly aware of a letter in his right hand, a tiny letter folded up tight and sealed. He glanced at it and instantly read the address 'to Ivan Fyodorovitch Karamazov.' He looked quickly at Lise. Her face had become almost menacing.

'Give it to him, you must give it to him!' she ordered him, trembling and beside herself. 'To-day, at once, or I'll poison myself! That's why I sent for you.'

And she slammed the door quickly. The bolt clicked. Alyosha put the note in his pocket and went straight downstairs, without going back to Madame Hohlakov, forgetting her, in fact. As soon as Alyosha had gone, Lise unbolted the door, opened it a little, put her finger in the crack and slammed the door with all her might, pinching her finger. Ten seconds after, releasing her finger, she walked softly, slowly to her chair, sat up straight in it and looked intently at her blackened finger and at the blood that oozed from under the nail. Her lips were quivering and she kept whispering rapidly to herself:

'I am a wretch, wretch, wretch, wretch!'

Bibliography

❉

THE PHYSICAL HERITAGE

Asch, Sholem, *Three Cities.* New York, Putnam, 1933.

The novel contains excellent passages for the psychic effects of hunger, which induces a split in the personality of a proud, aristocratic man for the first time experiencing the physical deprivations of the poor and eager to identify himself with others.

Conrad, Joseph, *The Nigger of the Narcissus.* New York, Doubleday, Doran, 1921.

This work represents an individual's hysterical manufacturing of symptoms to escape from work or to get attention and later the reverse reaction of hysterical behavior to hide from himself the seriousness of the disease.

Hampson, John, 'Good Food,' in *New Writing*, ed. by John Lehmann. New York, Penguin Books, 1941.

Hunger induces in a boy a strong emotional conflict which is greatly intensified by his determination not to yield to the will of his father, whom he fears and believes unjust.

Hull, Helen, *Through the House Door.* New York, Coward-McCann, 1940.

A man's neurotic withdrawal from life because of blindness is the main theme of this novel. The emotional conflicts involved, the wife's failure to understand, her rationalizations of her own conduct, the effect of the parents' strained relations on the adolescent daughter, are penetratingly observed.

Ibsen, Henrik, *Ghosts.* Boston, Baker, 1938.

The play reveals the effect on the personality of a young man of his discovery that he has hereditary syphilis.

Keats, John, *Letters.* New York, Oxford University Press, 1935.

Many evidences may be found of the effects of the poet's illness: his withdrawal from normal relationships, his attitude toward Fanny Brawne, and his intense jealousy.

Mann, Thomas, 'Tristan,' in *Stories of Three Decades.* New York, Knopf, 1941.

Many of the themes of *The Magic Mountain* are presented here more incisively. The psychological reactions of the consumptive are of especial interest.

—— *The Magic Mountain.* New York, Knopf, 1938.

Under the abnormal conditions of a mountain retreat for consumptives one sees various neuroses induced by ill health: the desire to escape the responsibilities of life, the death urge, the absence of the repressions of ordinary life in emotional relationships.

Mansfield, Katherine, *Journal and Letters.* New York, Knopf, 1927.

We may trace the effect of tuberculosis on a writer's personality in her intense craving for life, fear of death, passion for creation and fear of her own inadequacy.

Rostand, Edmond, *Cyrano de Bergerac.* New York, Doubleday, 1898.

The play reveals the effect of physical unattractiveness in conditioning emotional life. The hero finds compensation in physical prowess, poetic expression, exhibitionism, barbed wit, and the sublimation of his personal desires in sacrifice for the happiness of the girl he loves.

369

Schauffler, Robert, *The Mad Musician.* New York, Doubleday, Doran, 1932.

The biography reveals the influence of Beethoven's physical handicap on his emotional and creative life and shows the restoration of his powers through love.

Steele, Wilbur Daniel, 'Footfalls,' in *A Book of Modern Short Stories,* ed. by Dorothy Brewster, New York, Macmillan, 1928.

The handicap of blindness is compensated by acute development of other senses, especially hearing, in this old man whose pursuit of revenge for the death of his son forms the dominant theme.

Stevenson, Robert Louis, 'The Manse,' in *Works.* New York, Macrae Smith, 1930.

In these sketches of his family, the author analyzes various hereditary strains in his own temperament and physical make-up.

Stone, Irving, *Lust for Life.* New York, Grosset and Dunlap, 1934.

This biographical study of Van Gogh indicates the relation between his physical states and his creative power and neurosis.

Tchekov, Anton, 'Old Age,' in *Stories of Tchekov.* New York, Modern Library, 1932.

The theme of this story is the psychological reaction of the character to physical debility and approaching death.

Trumbo, Dalton, *Johnny Got His Gun.* New York, Lippincott, 1939.

Through a stream-of-consciousness technique the novel shows how a man, blinded and crippled in the first World War, tries to re-orient himself to life.

Turgenev, Ivan, 'The District Doctor,' in *Best Russian Short Stories,* ed. by Thomas Seltzer. New York, Boni and Liveright, 1917.

The effect of physical illness on the emotional life of a young girl desperately seeking to establish the normal sex experiences of healthy adulthood is objectively revealed by the doctor.

Walpole, Hugh, *Jeremy.* New York, George H. Doran, 1919.

Especially interesting is the picture of Jeremy's unattractive little sister and the emotional conflicts induced in her by the neglect of her family and the indifference of her adored brother. Jeremy's development is a fascinating picture of a child's expanding personality and his social adjustments.

Walworth, Dorothy, *Feast of Reason.* New York, Farrar and Rinehart, 1941.

The novel is valuable in showing how one's feeling about a physical handicap, even more than the defect itself, may condition an individual's emotional adjustment to life.

THE INFLUENCE OF THE FAMILY

Aksakoff, Sergei, *Years of Childhood.* New York, Oxford University Press, 1923.

The development of a neurotic attachment to the mother may be traced to lack of understanding accorded to a sensitive boy. His fantasy life is interesting.

Bennett, Arnold, *Clayhanger.* New York, Dutton, 1910.

The novel affords a significant study of a father-son relationship, and the projec-

tion by the dominant father of his ambitions and desires upon the son.

Burnett, Whit, 'Sherrel,' in *50 Best American Short Stories,* ed. by Edward O'Brien. Boston, Houghton Mifflin, 1939.

The memory of his rivalry with his younger brother and an unconscious death wish are responsible for a boy's oppressive feelings of guilt when his brother dies of a contagious disease.

Carroll, Gladys Hasty, *As the Earth Turns*. New York, Macmillan, 1933.

In this novel of life on a New England farm the interest is focused on the happy marriage of two people of different culture patterns. Jen represents an individual perfectly adjusted to life, and the family centers about her rich personality.

Chase, Mary Ellen, *Mary Peters*. New York, Macmillan, 1936.

The broad tolerance and understanding of a mother stand out in contrast to the circumscribed way of life in a small New England community. Both forces are important in shaping a sensitive girl's personality.

De Jong, David Cornel, 'Mama Is a Lady,' in *Best Short Stories of* 1941, ed. by Edward O'Brien. Boston, Houghton Mifflin, 1941.

The effect of example on a child is stronger than precept.

Deland, Margaret, *If This Be I*. New York, Appleton, 1935.

This autobiography treats of a child's realization of the adult world and the emotional conflicts involved in the normal process of growth in a happy family life.

De La Roche, Mazo, *Whiteoaks of Jalna*. New York, Macmillan, 1935. *The Master of Jalna*. New York, Macmillan, 1937.

The conflicts and loyalties within the family circle, the domination of an aged grandmother, the role of parent assumed by the older brothers and sisters, are vigorously portrayed in this family saga.

Dell, Floyd, *Janet March*. New York, George H. Doran, 1927.

An adolescent girl's attachment to her father becomes a handicap in establishing a normal love relationship.

Ewald, Carl, 'My Little Boy,' in *The Woollcott Reader*. New York, Viking, 1935.

A father-son relationship in which the father learns from his son as he permits him to make choices is presented with psychological insight and tenderness.

Ferber, Edna, 'The Gay Old Dog,' in *Cheerful by Request*. New York, Doubleday, 1918.

This story illustrates the effect of repression on the personality of a man whose sisters' demands have prevented him from establishing a home of his own.

Galsworthy, John, *The Forsyte Saga*. New York, Scribner, 1933.

The student will find here a wealth of material on family relationships, problems of youth, maturity, and old age against a background of social patterns which impinge upon the individual's consciousness and determine action.

Gerould, Katherine Fullerton, 'The Bird in the Bush,' in *Great Tradition*. New York, Scribner, 1915.

This narrative presents the effect on sensitive, unselfish parents of their feeling of responsibility to a deformed child.

Gibbs, Angelica, 'Father Was a Wit.' *Story Magazine*, vol. x, no. 54.

Rejection by her father forms the main theme in this picture of an adolescent girl in boarding school. The similarity in temperament of father and daughter, the introversion of both, are significant.

Gosse, Edmund, *Father and Son*. New York, Scribner, 1916.

This biographical account traces the gradual breaking of the too dominant influence of a father on a sensitive son.

Grahame, Kenneth, *The Golden Age*. London, John Lane, 1937.

The adult world and the world of childhood are memorably viewed through the eyes of a group of sensitive, imaginative children, who frequently reveal uncanny resourcefulness in protecting themselves from the well-meaning stupidities and inanities of their elders.

Hahn, Emily, 'My Sister Frances,' in *Short Stories from the New Yorker*. New York, Simon & Schuster, 1940.

The intense jealousy of a girl for her more attractive and romantically successful sister results in an hysterical outburst through which the girl loses her lover.

Heyse, Paul, *L'Arrabiata*. New York, Allyn and Bacon, 1916.

A violent emotional revulsion from the approaches of a lover is the result of a girl's hatred of her father.

Horton, Philip, *Hart Crane*. New York, Norton, 1937.

The roots of Crane's neurosis are found in the lack of understanding accorded him by his family and associates.

Lagerlöf, Selma, *Memories of Childhood*. New York, Doubleday, Doran, 1934.

The author's autobiography presents delightful pictures of home life and of wise, imaginative guidance of a child.

Mann, Thomas, *Buddenbrooks*. New York, Knopf, 1928.

The novel affords opportunity to study the interaction of introvert and extrovert, idealist and materialist, within the pattern of a bourgeois German family.

—— 'Disorder and Early Sorrow,' in *Stories of Three Decades*. New York, Knopf, 1941.

The intense emotions of a little girl who longs to enter into the circle of adult relationships are understood by a sympathetic father.

Masters, Edgar Lee, *Spoon River Anthology*. New York, Macmillan, 1923.

These poetic sketches are valuable for studies of family conflicts. The frustration, hate, and tragedy of incompatible married people are especially well portrayed in the poems about the Pantiers and the Blisses.

Maurois, André, *The Family Circle*. New York, Appleton, 1932.

Interactions within a family group are of interest in this novel.

Meredith, George, *Richard Feverel*. New York, Modern Library, 1927.

The main theme is the reaction of a youth from the rationalistic educational system of his dominating father, a system which produces results very different from those intended.

O'Neill, Eugene, *Ah, Wilderness!* New York, Random House, 1933.

An adolescent's awakening to poetry and love, and the attendant conflicts within the family and without, are no less valid because they are entertaining. The father-son relationship is a wholesome one.

Rawlings, Marjorie Kinnan, *The Yearling*. New York, Scribner, 1940.

Under the guidance of a wise though unlearned father a little boy learns life's lessons of courage, resourcefulness, and social co-operation as a natural part of the joys and pains of a life close to nature.

Santayana, George, *The Last Puritan*. New York, Scribner, 1936.

The influence of a rigid, puritanic mother is a dominant factor in creating the repressions and emotional conflicts of adulthood.

Sinclair, May, *The Three Brontës*. London, Hutchinson, 1933.

The emotional frustrations of the Brontë household and the probable effect of the father's personality on the sensitive, talented children are analyzed from a psychological point of view.

—— *Mary Olivier*. New York, Macmillan, 1919.

A sensitive girl's early realization of her mother's obvious partiality for her brother leads her to make various unsuccessful escapes into fantasy and metaphysics. Her inability to realize a satisfactory adult emotional relationship may be traced to her childhood feeling of insecurity.

Turgenev, Ivan, *Fathers and Sons*. New York, Dutton, 1922.

A moving study of the breach between two generations is reflected in the complete contempt which Bazarov expresses for his parents and their consequent bewilderment.

Undset, Sigrid, *The Longest Years*. London, Cassel, 1940.

The author's account of her childhood is especially valuable for its illustrations of a child's emotional conflicts, her problems in learning, and her relationship with understanding parents and a younger sister of whom she is jealous.

Wescott, Glenway, *The Grandmothers.* New York, Harper, 1927.

The cycles of life that merge within a family circle are sympathetically revealed through the eyes of a sensitive child. The recurrence of traits, mental and physical, the interactions of various individuals, the neurotic manifestations, the emotional conflicts and happy adjustments that are a part of family life, are brought together in a complex pattern.

Winslow, Thyra, 'The Old Lady,' in *Blueberry Pie and Other Stories.* New York, Knopf, 1932.

This story of an elderly mother who wants her room left untouched reminds us poignantly that children may thwart

and violate the personalities of their parents.

Wunsch, W. Robert, and Albers, Edna, *Thicker Than Water.* New York, Appleton, 1939.

The short stories in this collection all focus upon the family unit as it may constrict the personality; such themes as overprotection, neurotic substitutions on the part of the mother, rejection of the child, incompatibility of the parents, the effects of a broken home on the child, are all illustrated.

Zugsmith, Leane, *Home Is Where You Hang Your Childhood.* New York, Random House, 1937.

This group of stories sensitively portrays children's problems in a world of adults. The effect of parental strife and divorce on the child is the theme of several sketches.

SOCIAL AND ECONOMIC PRESSURES

Browning, Robert, 'The Statue and the Bust,' in *Complete Poetical Works of Robert Browning.* Boston, Houghton Mifflin, 1895.

A life-long barrier between lovers is caused by their sense of social expediency and fear of public opinion.

—— 'Fra Lippo Lippi,' *op. cit.*

Physical want and fear condition a child of the streets to acute observation of others, a faculty basic to his later success as a realistic painter.

Caldwell, Erskine, *Tobacco Road.* New York, Scribner, 1932.

The close relationship between belowsubsistence standards of living and amoral attitudes is graphically presented in terms of the animal behavior of the members of the Lester family.

—— *God's Little Acre.* New York, Viking, 1933.

The relationship between poverty and

the emotional orgies of the main characters is implied in this novel of infantilism, perversion, and violence.

Cather, Willa, 'The Sculptor's Funeral,' in *Youth and the Bright Medusa.* New York, Knopf, 1920.

An artist's bitter struggle to free himself from the frustrations induced by an unsympathetic mother and a critical, materialistic small-town environment is implied.

Clark, Walter Van Tilburg, *The Ox-Bow Incident.* New York, Random House, 1940.

We experience the shocking realization that men can be murdered by a mob which, although individually repudiating the action of the group, collectively places the saving of face above humane considerations. Ironically, the sadistic leader cannot bear to live with his guilt and subsequently commits suicide.

De la Mora, Constancia, *In Place of Splendor*. New York, Harcourt, Brace, 1939.

The autobiography of a Spanish aristocrat who supported the cause of the Loyalists reveals the effects on a sensitive personality of her recognition of the role of her family and class in oppressing other human beings.

Di Donato, Pietro, *Christ in Concrete*. New York, Bobbs-Merrill, 1939.

The effects of economic deprivation and insecurity are traced in the personality of the main character.

Dos Passos, John, *U.S.A.* New York, Modern Library, 1930.

The impact on various individuals of contemporary world events and social and economic forces in the changing pattern of American life is seen from varying points of view. Problems of emotional adjustment within the American family may be profitably studied here.

Dostoyevsky, Fyodor, 'The Christmas Tree and the Wedding,' in *Best Russian Short Stories*. New York, Boni and Liveright, 1917.

Rigid social stratifications forced upon the awareness of young children determine their later emotional patterns.

Farrell, James, *Studs Lonigan*. New York, Vanguard Press, 1935.

The values of a group of youngsters in Chicago are affected by a machine civilization. The lessons they learn on the streets of an American city are not those the home, school, and church would have them learn.

Faulkner, William, *Sanctuary*. New York, Random House, 1931.

The inter-relationship between poverty and degeneracy is grimly reviewed in this novel in which man's expression of his animal nature seems to have no curbs put upon it.

Gellhorn, Martha, *The Trouble I've Seen*. New York, William Morrow, 1936.

These stories of people on relief suggest the dire effects upon the personality of poverty and of unemployment.

Gissing, George, *The Private Papers of Henry Ryecroft*. New York, Boni and Liveright, 1918.

The effects of poverty and social pressures on the personality are reflected in this journal of an introverted writer.

Glasgow, Ellen, *They Stooped to Folly*. New York, The Literary Guild, 1929.

The effect of emotional repression as a result of social mores affords a focal point for this ironic novel of changing sex attitudes.

Gogol, Nikolai, *Dead Souls*. New York, Crowell, 1886.

Motivated by a desire for social prestige synonymous with ownership of land and serfs, an expelled Russian customs officer, Tchitchikoff, travels through the country buying up titles for the souls of deceased serfs.

Gorki, Maxim, *Mother*. New York, Appleton, 1920.

This novel portrays the sterility and sadism that may characterize the lives of people whose energy is sapped by overwork and extreme poverty.

Hardy, Thomas, *Tess of the d'Urbervilles*. New York, Harper, 1920.

The love of Tess and Angel is modified and finally destroyed as the pressure of the mores of their age impinges upon them. Angel's dream when he is about to renounce Tess affords an interesting problem for Freudian interpretation.

Hellman, Lillian, 'The Little Foxes,' in *Four Plays*. New York, Modern Library, 1942.

A neurotic woman's drive for power, sharpened by greed, is etched against a background of decadence as this Southern family disintegrates in the violence of its conflicting passions.

Herbst, Josephine, *The Executioner Waits*. New York, Harcourt, Brace, 1934.

The emotional conflicts reflected in the jealousy, love, hate, and fear within a family group result from economic deprivation and fear, on the one hand, and on the other, a desire for power fed by economic success.

Hughes, Langston, *The Ways of White Folks.* New York, Knopf, 1934.

These stories afford valuable studies of Negro-white relationships and the unfortunate psychological effects of prejudice and injustice on members of both races.

Ibsen, Henrik, *A Doll's House.* New York, Modern Library, 1935.

The mores which decreed that women should be decorative and doll-like postpone and threaten Nora's emergence as an adult personality capable of making free choices.

Kingsley, Sidney, *Dead End.* New York, Random House, 1936.

The play shows how environmental forces shape children's personalities and how criminals are made in the slums of a modern city.

Lewis, Sinclair, *Babbitt.* New York, Harcourt, Brace, 1922.

The tremendous drive to keep up with and outshine the Joneses is reflected here. Babbitt partially satisfies the demands of his ego through identification with successful groups and clubs, but his personal frustrations are revealed in a conversation with his son in which he confesses he has never done anything he really wanted to do.

—— *Main Street,* New York, Harcourt, Brace, 1921.

The intolerance that small-town people may show for mores and ideas different from their own and the effects of such intolerance on a sensitive woman are graphically presented.

—— *It Can't Happen Here.* Garden City, N. Y., The Sun Dial Press, 1936.

The author demonstrates the invidious power of group pressure under demagogic leadership upon individuals who would ordinarily resist threats to democratic institutions.

Lewisohn, Ludwig, *Upstream.* New York, Boni and Liveright, 1923.

We follow the emotional conflicts of an individual in the process of adjusting to a new culture pattern.

Marquand, John, *The Late George Apley.* Boston, Little, Brown, 1937.

Social conventions, family pride, and class consciousness govern the personal and public life of the elder Apleys, but the children rebel and partially escape from the circumscribing effects.

Morley, Christopher, *Thunder on the Left.* New York, Grosset and Dunlap, 1928.

In this fantasy it is suggested that the impingement of convention and routine upon one's life has a stultifying effect upon the individual's personality.

O'Neill, Eugene, 'The Hairy Ape,' in *Nine Plays of Eugene O'Neill,* New York, Liveright, 1932.

A stoker's feeling of insecurity, originating in early childhood persecution by his family, is renewed by the terrified scorn of a wealthy girl. He tries desperately and vainly to regain his self-respect through identification with various groups, but when he is rejected by all of them, his behavior becomes psychotic.

—— 'The Great God Brown,' *op. cit.*

Dion, the artist, is crushed by a succession of forces which he cannot combat—chiefly the pressure put upon him to conform to standardized patterns of behavior.

Rice, Elmer, *Street Scene.* New York, Samuel French, Inc., 1929.

Conflicting social mores and individual needs in a crowded tenement district ultimately lead to tragic violence. The central problem is that of the ability of the individual to escape the limitations of his social and economic environment.

Sayre, Joel, 'Love in the Snow,' in *Short Stories from the New Yorker.* New York, Simon & Schuster, 1940.

The first love of two thirteen-year-olds is sensitively portrayed. It is destroyed by the boy's mother, who makes him recognize the force of class distinctions.

Slade, Caroline, *The Triumph of Willie Pond.* New York, Vanguard Press, 1940.

The effects of economic need on the

various personalities of a family on relief are vigorously portrayed—the drive toward crime, prostitution, and suicide to avoid humiliation.

Steinbeck, John, *The Grapes of Wrath*. New York, Viking, 1939.

Interesting contrasts in psychological reaction are afforded by the portraits of the Joads and their friends, driven from the land in which they were rooted to wander in search of work and a home.

Thoreau, Henry David, 'On Imprisonment,' in *Complete Works*. New York, Houghton Mifflin, 1929.

Rebelling against what he felt was a violation of his freedom, Thoreau points out the price one must pay for refusal to conform to the laws of society and comments on the effects of imprisonment on mind and spirit.

Trollope, Anthony, *An Autobiography*. London, Oxford University Press, 1923.

The creative drive may be motivated by a desire for recognition and material gain. Trollope shows how the personality is warped when the individual's quest for self-realization is circumscribed by economic need; conversely, he reveals how the personality reaches fruition when it is permitted to expand without fear of privation.

Wassermann, Jacob, *The World's Illusion*. New York, Harcourt, Brace, 1920.

The gradual socializing of an egoist whose aristocratic background has left him impotent to cope with reality is traced through various experiences which pierce the outward shell of hardness and make him a complete human being capable of suffering.

Wharton, Edith, *Ethan Frome*. New York, Scribner, 1911.

The effect of economic status and Puritanical attitudes upon the love of two individuals is the theme of this short novel. The wife's use of the conversion mechanism, her recovery after the accident, and her sadistic domination are interesting.

—— *The Old Maid*. New York, Grosset & Dunlap, 1939.

Although somewhat anachronistic, the play, adapted by Zoë Akins, throws into clear relief the conditioning of emotional life by the social attitudes of one's time, the effect of repressions, and the drive for domination.

Wright, Richard, 'Almos' a Man,' in *Best Short Stories of 1941*, ed. by Edward O'Brien. Boston, Houghton Mifflin, 1941.

An adolescent Negro boy's misunderstood attempt to assert his feeling of manhood gets him into difficulty with his family and the community and drives him to run away, probably to a life of defiance of society.

Zugsmith, Leane, 'Room in the World,' in *Home Is Where You Hang Your Childhood*. New York, Random House, 1937.

A small girl suffers hurt pride and a feeling of inferiority when an older girl whom she admires sees her bearing a picket sign.

—— 'To Be Alive,' *op. cit.*

Inbred respect for an artificial and outworn social code destroys the love of husband and wife when it is subjected to a test.

EMOTIONAL CONFLICTS

Anderson, Sherwood, *Tar*. New York, Boni and Liveright, 1926.

The emotional life of a sensitive boy is traced from childhood to adolescence.

—— *Winesburg, Ohio*. New York, Boni and Liveright, 1919.

Although all of the stories contain acute emotional insights, the student will find these especially illuminating pictures of introverted or neurotic personalities reacting to individual or group pressures: 'Hands,' for a study of effects of conventional village attitudes on a sensitive man believed to be homosexual; 'Mother,' for its treatment of a mother-son relationship and rivalry between parents for determination of the boy's future; 'The Strength of God,' for repression and neurotic manifestations; 'The Teacher,' for repression; 'The Thinker' and 'Sophistication,' for studies of adolescent awareness of the opposite sex; 'Terror,' for a study of a psychotic individual obsessed by a passion for identification with Biblical patriarchs.

—— 'I Am a Fool,' in *Horses and Men*. New York, Viking, 1923.
This story portrays an adolescent boy's sense of shame and frustration over a brief flirtation in which he becomes acutely conscious of his inferior economic and social status.

Canfield, Dorothy, *The Deepening Stream*. New York, Harcourt, Brace, 1930.
The novel is interesting as a study of a marriage which grows with the ripening experience of a man and woman and their participation in the life of their times. The tendency of the sisters to withdraw from life because of their early family conditioning affords a significant problem, satisfactorily solved in marriage by one, less successfully by the other.

Cather, Willa, *My Mortal Enemy*. New York, Knopf, 1926.
A fascinating study of emotional ambivalence is presented in the turbulent married life of the Henshawes. Myra's passion for domination, threatened by Oswald's interest in other women, eventually takes the form of an illness through which she is able to bind him in a servile devotion to her needs and whims.

Coates, Robert M., 'The Net,' in *Short Stories from the New Yorker*. New York, Simon & Schuster, 1940.
The story presents a man's psychological reactions to his deed of violent mur-

der while under the influence of an overwhelming jealousy.

Crane, Stephen, 'The Open Boat,' in *Twenty Stories by Stephen Crane*. New York, Knopf, 1940.
Human emotions under stress of great physical effort and danger of death may undergo transfer from concentration on personal safety to identification with the group. The story is also interesting for fantasy and hallucination.

Culver, Janet, 'The Hand of God,' in *A Book of Contemporary Short Stories*, ed. by Dorothy Brewster. New York, Macmillan, 1937.
An adolescent girl's first moments of awakening to the emotional life of adulthood are here developed through a fusion of reverie and sense impressions.

Dostoyevsky, Fyodor, *Crime and Punishment*. New York, Modern Library, 1932.
The novel presents a powerful portrait of a conflict between a murderer's fear and his sense of guilt and the working out of a neurosis in confession and acceptance of the social consequences of his crime.

Hale, Nancy, 'Midsummer,' in *Short Stories from the New Yorker*. New York, Simon & Schuster, 1940.
In this interesting portrait of adolescent emotion, the neglected daughter of rich parents seeks emotional satisfaction in an affair with the riding master.

Hardy, Thomas, *Jude the Obscure*. New York, Harper, 1895.
The contrast is effectively pointed between the aspirations of Jude and the squalid realities of his life. Social and economic pressures from without combined with frustrations from within keep him in a perpetual state of emotional upheaval.

Hemingway, Ernest, 'My Old Man,' in *Men Without Women*. New York, Scribner, 1928.
This picture of a boy's bewilderment and disillusionment over the ways of the

adult world, especially those of the father whom he idolized, is ironic and moving.

Hemingway, Ernest, *For Whom the Bell Tolls.* **New York, Scribner, 1941.**

The emotional conflict between an intense love that promises life and an idealistic sense of duty involving acceptance of certain death is the central theme of this novel; subordinate characters afford interesting studies of a number of neuroses.

Joyce, James, 'Araby,' in *Dubliners.* **New York, Viking, 1916.**

An adolescent boy's worship of an older girl and his bitter disappointment because of adult stupidity are presented. Other stories in this volume will also be valuable.

—— *A Portrait of the Artist as a Young Man.* New York, Modern Library, 1928.

The emotional conflicts of a sensitive artistic youth trying to adjust himself to life will be found worthy of study from many points of view: the effects of poverty, family bickering, and physical handicaps on the child; the scorn and persecution inflicted by schoolmates and teachers on an introverted boy; escape in religious hysteria; the awakening of adolescent emotions and a first love affair; the effort to extend the sway of the rational faculties over emotion.

Lawrence, D. H., *The Rainbow.* **New York, Modern Library, 1915.**

The marriage relationships within three generations of a family are traced here with stress on the physical aspects of marriage and the psychological conflicts attendant upon the struggle to preserve the individual identity.

Lehmann, Rosamond, *Dusty Answer.* **London, Chatto and Windus, 1933.**

The conflicts of the adolescent girl in boarding school are sympathetically presented against a background of family and social pressures.

Le Sueur, Meridel, 'I Was Marching,' in *Proletarian Literature in the United States.* **New York, International Publishers, 1935.**

The story describes a woman's identification with mob emotion as she becomes part of a marching strike group.

Lewisohn, Ludwig, *The Island Within.* **New York, Harper, 1928.**

The conflicts and problems of the Jew are suggested as he endeavors to combat racial consciousness through the employment of various escape mechanisms.

Malraux, André, *Man's Hope.* **New York, Random House, 1938.**

Each of the representative volunteers for the Loyalists struggles with the problem of his relation to the cause for which he is fighting. Like Magnin, who heads the guerilla air force, all are torn between loyalty to the ideal of a free humanity and disgust over the suffering which men inflict upon their fellows.

Mansfield, Katherine, 'Marriage à la Mode,' in *Short Stories of Katherine Mansfield.* **New York, Knopf, 1937.**

An emotional conflict which destroys a marriage results from the wife's acceptance of the superficial standards of a group in opposition to the desires of her husband and the welfare of her children.

—— 'A Cup of Tea,' *op. cit.*

A well-to-do, pampered young woman finds her exhibitionist impulses toward charity waning when her husband admires too evidently the girl she has brought in from the streets.

—— 'Psychology,' *op. cit.*

The story illustrates emotional repression. Although the reasons for the repression are not made evident to the reader, fear is apparently stronger than love and does not permit the love to be given recognition. The emotions that should find outlet in a happy human relationship are thwarted and turned inward toward a barren introspection and an identification with objects and surroundings. The emotional response to a passing friend reveals an unconscious transfer of repressed emotion.

Meredith, George, 'Modern Love,' in *Poetical Works*. New York, Scribner, 1912.

A portrait of an egoist primarily concerned with building up a defense for his own wounded pride is reflected in this group of poems.

Odets, Clifford, 'Golden Boy,' in *Six Plays of Clifford Odets*. New York, Modern Library, 1933.

A sensitive introverted young musician is driven by economic forces and a need for social approval to extrovert activities as a prize fighter. The violation of his personality has tragic results.

Scott, Evelyn, *The Wave*. New York, Literary Guild, 1929.

The author traces, frequently through a stream-of-consciousness technique, the reactions of various individuals under the tensions of war.

Sholokoff, Mikhail, *And Quiet Flows the Don*. New York, Knopf, 1941.

Plunged into the chaos of world war, revolution, and counter-revolution, the young Cossack struggles to determine his place in the battle of the revolutionaries against the old order. His unhappy marriage and his passionate love affair with a neighbor's wife afford interesting material for analysis.

Stegner, Wallace, 'Goin' to Town,' in *Best Short Stories of 1941*, ed. by Edward O'Brien. Boston, Houghton Mifflin, 1941.

A boy's intense disappointment over a promised trip and the father's intolerant failure to understand the violence of the child's emotions are effectively narrated.

Tolstoy, Leo, *Anna Karénina*. London, Oxford University Press, 1918.

The novel will be found especially valuable for study of the impact of social attitudes and realities upon emotional states.

—— *Resurrection*. London, Oxford University Press, 1916.

The awareness of the discrepancy between the demands of his conscience and his self-indulgent life leads the hero to a searching of self and a new life of deprivation in which he endeavors to resolve the warring elements in his personality.

THE LEARNING PROCESS

Adams, Henry, *The Education of Henry Adams*. Boston, Houghton Mifflin, 1935.

The author pictures the various often irreconcilable elements which made up his childhood environment and conditioned his development. He presents an indictment of the nineteenth century American educational system and social-economic mores as largely responsible for his later maladjustments.

De la Mare, Walter, *Early One Morning*. New York, Macmillan, 1935.

This delightful miscellany of childhood stresses early memories of precocious children and their learning habits and attainments.

Dickens, Charles, *Hard Times*. London, Oxford University Press, 1925.

The famous Gradgrind system with its emphasis on the merely factual and its denial of imagination and emotion is shown as responsible for children's later emotional conflicts.

Mill, John Stuart, *Autobiography*. New York, Oxford University Press, 1924.

Stress on precocity and training in analytical reasoning at an early age probably led to the author's later emotional maladjustments and neuroses.

Pater, Walter, *The Child in the House*. New York, Mosher, 1902.

The development of mind and emotions is traced from earliest sense impres-

sions and emotional realizations of childhood to a mature philosophy of life
grounded upon these early impressions.

Ruskin, John, *Praeterita*. New York, J.
Wiley and Sons, 1887.

Early chapters of this autobiography
reveal the dominant influence of the author's mother and her vigorous training
with its stress on discipline, memory, and
fact, and the complete denial of emotional satisfactions. The material is significant as it suggests the basis for Ruskin's
later neurosis.

Steffens, Lincoln, *Autobiography of Lincoln Steffens*. New York, Harcourt,
Brace, 1931.

Permitted an unusual degree of freedom, young Steffens grew in sense of
responsibility, judgment, and experience
as naturally as the colt whose care he was
given. As his horizon expanded he sought
contact with varied types of people,
learning from all of them, even those not
ordinarily included in the acquaintance

of a well-brought-up small boy. The gang
and its code succeeded his period of individualism, and we can see the beginning
of awareness of girls in his bid for attention through drinking exploits.

Wells, H. G., *Experiment in Autobiography*. London, Victor Gollancz,
1937.

The author applies psychoanalytic techniques to a study of his own emotional
development and gives interesting reve-
lations of the conflict induced by his background.

Wordsworth, William, 'The Prelude,' in
Poetical Works. London, Oxford University Press, 1936.

In his poetic autobiography Wordsworth traces the development of a poet's
mind from childhood—the formative influences of school, home, associates, nature.
The influence of Hartley's associational
psychology is evident throughout, especially in the 'spots of time' passages.

DREAMS AND THE UNCONSCIOUS

[The editors have not considered it per-
tinent to the scope or intention of this
anthology to go into the extensive dream
material in literature, for apart from context such passages can have little value.
A few have been included which seem
interesting in themselves.]

De la Mare, Walter, *Behold This
Dreamer*. New York, Knopf, 1939.

This miscellany of dreams of real and
fictional characters of various periods of
history affords interesting psychological
insights.

Dostoyevsky, Fyodor, *Crime and Punishment*. New York, Modern Library,
1932.

The dream of Raskolnikov before he

commits the murder is a significant projection of his feelings of guilt and fear.

Hazlitt, William, 'An Essay on Dreams,'
in *Essays of Hazlitt*. London, The
Walter Scott Publishing Company,
1889.

The essay contains startling anticipations of Freudian conclusions on certain
aspects of dream life.

Reid, Forrest, *Apostate*. Boston, Houghton Mifflin, 1926.

This autobiography vividly suggests the
relation between a child's fears and his
dreams, and indicates the origin of his
later creative impulses in his dream life.

THE NEUROSES

Aldington, Richard, *Death of a Hero.* London, Heinemann, 1938.
Excellent chapters in this novel describe adolescent love and economic and social pressures. But the main interest of the book lies in the portrayal of the emotional conflicts of a sensitive youth in war, the disintegration of his personality under the abnormal stresses of terror and brutality.

Anderson, Sherwood, 'Nice Girl,' in *Short Stories from the New Yorker.* New York, Simon & Schuster, 1940.
An introverted girl's intense jealousy of her older sister, preferred by the family, leads her to scheme to take the sister's husband.

Asch, Sholem, *Three Cities.* New York, Putnam, 1933.
Zachary's childhood relationship with his mother conditions his later attitude toward women and renders him powerless to extend his love beyond the mother image.

Bellamann, Henry, *Kings Row.* New York, Simon & Schuster, 1940.
An almost incredible number of neurotic people move through these pages of horror and despair. Sadism, incest, sharp hatred and persecution, within the family and outside of it, leave their indelible imprint on the personalities of the victims. There is also an interesting study of a violinist prodigy who loses her orientation to reality.

Benson, Sally, 'Little Woman,' in *Short Stories from the New Yorker.* New York, Simon & Schuster, 1940.
The regression to childhood of a small woman, who in youth has been pampered and admired for her frailty, causes the withdrawal of the husband, who now wants a mate instead of a doll.

Besier, Rudolph, *The Barretts of Wimpole Street.* Boston, Little, Brown, 1931.
The jealous over-protection accorded Elizabeth Barrett by her neurotic father induces in her a neurasthenia, which is relieved when she finds companionship and acceptance by her impetuous lover, Robert Browning.

Boswell, James, *The Life of Samuel Johnson.* New York, Oxford University Press, 1933.
The neurotic manifestations of Dr. Johnson may possibly be traced to factors in his childhood: his devotion to his mother, a feeling of resentment against his father, sensitiveness to his scrofula, his unattractive physical appearance, and the poverty of his family. A pervading sense of guilt and distrust of self is projected upon society in moods of alternate sadism and masochism, intense rebellion and abject subservience to authority, and a haunting fear of death.

Boyle, Kay, 'Rest Cure,' in *The First Lover and Other Stories.* New York, Harrison Smith and Robert Haas, 1933.
Through interesting symbolism the emotional conflicts of an invalid writer are presented. We are interested especially in his reactions of hate and jealousy for the healthy. In his fear of death he turns for security to childhood memories of his father, from whose limiting influence he has spent his life escaping.

Callaghan, Morley, 'Big Jules,' in *Best Short Stories of 1941,* ed. by Edward O'Brien. Boston, Houghton Mifflin, 1941.
Fear and guilt because of a childhood crime impel a boy to violence until he recognizes friendliness instead of hate in the attitude of others toward him.

Coignard, John, *The Spectacle of a Man.* New York, Morrow, 1937.

A shy, introspective man, inhibited in social intercourse by his stammering and his sense of inferiority, goes to a psychoanalyst for help. We see into the causes of his maladjustment and follow his progress to emotional maturity.

de Montalant, Katherine, 'Là-Bas,' *Story Magazine,* vol. XIV, no. 75.

The love of brother and sister in two generations of a family constitutes the theme of this story. Although the sexual character of the love is in neither case overtly expressed, one brother finds it possible to sublimate his emotion, whereas the other finds that the only escape is suicide.

Dostoyevsky, Fyodor, *Crime and Punishment.* New York, Modern Library, 1932.

In this powerful portrait of the mind of a murderer we find illustrations of innumerable defense mechanisms, rationalization, projection of guilt, conversion, as well as dreams and hallucinations which represent the images of an overwrought mind on the verge of insanity.

Frost, Robert, 'Home Burial,' in *Collected Poems.* New York, Holt, 1939.

This poem reveals the death wish of a grief-stricken woman who nourished her sorrow and refused to take any measures to adjust herself to reality.

Gerould, Katherine Fullerton, 'An Army with Banners,' *Harper's Magazine,* 1925.

A good illustration of Adler's theory of the masculine protest is found in the character of a woman whose need to dominate is greater than her need to love or be loved, a passion evident in her final subjugation of her husband in his illness.

Gide, André, *The Counterfeiters.* New York, Modern Library, 1931.

The novel affords a frank study in various problems of love, both homosexual and heterosexual.

Gorki, Maxim, 'Her Lover,' in *Best Russian Short Stories.* New York, Boni and Liveright, 1917.

An ugly woman finds compensation for the hardships of her life by creating an imaginary lover.

Howard, Sidney, *The Silver Cord.* New York, Samuel French, 1928.

A mother finds in her sons the romantic fulfillment which her marriage failed to bring. When full possession of her sons' affection is threatened by their marriages, an imaginary heart attack becomes a convenient weapon with which to attempt to hold it. Mrs. Phelps calls into play the mechanisms of projection, rationalization, hysteria, and sadism in her desperate efforts to bind her sons.

Huxley, Aldous, *Point Counter Point.* New York, Doubleday, Doran, 1928.

The novel is a compendium of portraits of neurotic, restless people who constantly seek new escapes from their boredom.

—— 'The Rest Cure,' in *Brief Candles.* New York, Doubleday, Doran, 1930.

Moira's regression to infantilism, her fears, her recurrent illnesses, hysteria, narcissism, and unwillingness to assume the responsibilities of adult heterosexuality may be traced to her family pattern. The failure of the marriage is due no less to her husband's emotional immaturity, his escape from reality in research, than to her inadequacy as a wife.

Ibsen, Henrik, *Hedda Gabler.* New York, Modern Library, 1935.

In Hedda we see the neurotic substitutions of a woman unable to cope with reality. Her final resort to suicide represents the breakdown of a personality whose drive for domination was frustrated.

James, Henry, 'The Altar of the Dead,' in *Novels and Tales of Henry James.* New York, Scribner, 1909.

Escape from reality and the responsibilities of human relationships takes the form of a ritualistic worship of the past and the dead.

Kees, Weldon, 'The Life of the Mind,' in *Best Short Stories of* 1941, ed. by Edward O'Brien. Boston, Houghton Mifflin, 1941.

A frustrated professor, unsuccessful in his marriage with a younger woman, escapes in sponsoring college athletes, projects his failure on to others, and compensates by pompous display of authority over subordinates.

Lagerlöf, Selma, *Jerusalem*. New York, Doubleday, Page, 1916.

Karin's paralysis came upon her the morning after a terrifying dream about her dead husband. Repressed feelings of guilt in regard to the brutal, drunken husband whom she hated are apparently at the root of the woman's functional paralysis. The cure after the visit of a faith-healing preacher is to be understood as a result of the power of suggestion combined with the pressure of emergency when she alone is present to save her child from the fire.

Mann, Thomas, 'Little Lizzie,' in *Stories of Three Decades*. New York, Knopf, 1941.

The sadism of a woman in her treatment of an ineffectual husband is powerfully portrayed.

March, William, 'The Little Wife,' in *The Little Wife and Other Stories*. New York, Random House, 1935.

A man escapes temporarily from reality by refusal to admit into his consciousness his knowledge of his wife's death. He protects himself by distortion of fact and hysterical flow of irrelevant talk.

Maugham, Somerset, 'Miss Thompson,' in *The Trembling of a Leaf*. New York, Doubleday, Doran, 1921.

The preacher's repression and sublimation of his physical desires end in the seduction of his convert and suicide.

Molnar, Ferenc, *Liliom*. New York, Liveright, 1921.

Sadistic and masochistic impulses impel actions which a youth alternately repents and repeats. The submissiveness of his wife goads him to torment her despite a genuine feeling of affection.

O'Neill, Eugene, *Beyond the Horizon*. New York, Random House, 1920.

Robert, a frail young man with poetic interests, seeks to escape from the problems of the real world by dreaming of a land 'beyond the horizon.' When faced with an adult's responsibilities he is unable to contend adequately with the forces set up against him: a nagging wife, a hypochondriac mother-in-law, and economic privation.

—— *Mourning Becomes Electra*. New York, Liveright, 1931.

The morbid inversion of the personality, repression, incest, and violence constitute the Freudian groundwork for this modern adaptation of the Electra theme.

Schulberg, Budd, *What Makes Sammy Run?* New York, Random House, 1941.

No inhibitions on his aggressive drive for power are found in this character. We recoil from Sammy's ruthlessness but understand the mechanisms employed to compensate for the feelings of inferiority induced by his childhood experience.

Steinbeck, John, *Of Mice and Men*. New York, Viking, 1937.

The tragedy of a simple individual who suffers from a compulsion neurosis and kills what he loves best is the theme of the story.

Tchekov, Anton, 'The Darling,' in *Best Russian Short Stories*. New York, Boni and Liveright, 1917.

Impelled to escape from herself in identification with the life of another, Olenka must always be in love with someone. The infantile character of her love is cumulatively suggested through the story of her three marriages and her final attachment to a young school boy.

Wolfe, Thomas, *Of Time and the River*. New York, Grosset and Dunlap, 1935.

The hero's sensitiveness to the attitude of others toward him becomes almost obsessional in nature, leading to a persecutory complex in which he projects responsibility upon family and friends.

THE PSYCHOSES

Aiken, Conrad, 'Silent Snow, Secret Snow,' in *A Book of Contemporary Short Stories*, ed. by Dorothy Brewster. New York, Macmillan, 1937.

A boy's retreat from reality into a fantasy world and finally into a complete psychosis is developed with remarkable insight and effective sense imagery.

Coates, Robert M., 'The Fury,' in *Short Stories from the New Yorker*. New York, Simon & Schuster, 1940.

The story presents a study of a sex maniac for whom discovery and fear of social condemnation lead to final escape in madness and suicide.

Conrad, Joseph, 'The Secret Sharer,' in *'Twixt Land and Sea*. New York, Doubleday, Doran, 1912.

A projection of the inner conflicts of a schizophrenic personality is revealed in an objective narrative. The man's feelings of guilt, his withdrawal from others, and his hallucinations are finally resolved in his assumption of responsibility.

Frost, Robert, 'A Servant to Servants,' in *Collected Poems*. New York, Holt, 1939.

A life of economic privation, routine, and duty, devoid of companionship and joy, is leading a woman to insanity. Her fears concerning her own mental state are aggravated by memories of an insane uncle and the inhuman treatment accorded him.

Gerould, Katherine Fullerton, 'Bluebonnet,' in *Valiant Dust*. New York, Scribner, 1922.

A lonely woman's craving for companionship drives her to conjure up a large family of guests.

Green, Julian, *The Closed Garden*. New York, Harper, 1928.

This is a powerful picture of the disintegration of a young girl's personality through isolation from normal contacts.

Hauptmann, Gerhart, *The Fool in Christ*. New York, Viking, 1926.

Emanuel comes to identify himself with Jesus, whose birth was also surrounded with mystery and who suffered likewise from the contempt of others. This imagined parallel becomes the driving force in his life and induces a complete split in his personality.

Hull, Helen, 'Clay Shuttered Doors,' in *A Book of Modern Short Stories*, ed. by Dorothy Brewster. New York, Macmillan, 1928.

The theme of this story, sometimes interpreted as supernaturalism, seems to be hallucinations of a return from the dead. It is interesting also for study of a narcissistic personality.

Isherwood, Christopher, 'I Am Waiting,' in *Short Stories from the New Yorker*. New York, Simon & Schuster, 1940.

The hallucinations of a neurotic bachelor in this story are apparently traceable to sexual frustration and feelings of inferiority, and we are led to anticipate his complete mental breakdown.

Lawrence, D. H., 'The Rocking Horse Winner,' in *The Lovely Lady*. New York, Viking, 1933.

A mother's indifference to her children provides the background for a boy's compensatory delusion that he has been granted powers of divination. His behavior becomes regressive as his personality disintegrates.

Morris, I. V., 'Marching Orders,' in *50 Best Short Stories*, ed. by Edward O'Brien. Boston, Houghton Mifflin, 1939.

The story illustrates the death wish of a man with schizophrenic tendencies. His 'marching orders' represent the impulses toward self-destruction unconsciously fulfilled in his determination to fly an ancient plane.

O'Neill, Eugene, 'All God's Chillun Got Wings,' in *Nine Plays*. New York, Liveright, 1932.

The play presents the progressive disintegration of the personality of a white woman who has married a Negro. Her love cannot cope with persistent social pressure, and she seeks the destruction of her husband's pride as evidence of her personal superiority.

Rolvaag, O. E., *Giants in the Earth*. New York, Harper, 1927.

Psychological interest focuses on the inner conflicts induced when an introverted woman, unadapted to pioneer life, is married to an extrovert who delights in the hardships of the frontier. The novel gives remarkable pictures of the approach of insanity and the effects upon the children of a growing awareness of their mother's state.

Schnitzler, Arthur, *Flight into Darkness*. New York, Simon & Schuster, 1931.

This novel portrays a man who suffers from schizophrenia with paranoid manifestations. Robert suffers from the delusion that his brother is insane and craftily plans and executes his death, despite the brother's obviously sincere expressions of sympathy and love.

Scott, Evelyn, *The Lover*. Scribner's *Magazine*, Oct., 1930.

The author portrays a frustrated middle-aged woman who has never been emotionally satisfied. She takes pride in the memory of her pure martyr-like devotion to an invalid husband, but an unconscious realization of the lack of fulfillment in her sexual life preys upon her and leads to dreams and hallucinations of pursuit by a Negro, symbol of the primitive desires she has denied.

Tchekov, Anton, *The Black Monk*. New York, Modern Library, 1932.

Hallucinations develop out of a writer's morbid sensitivity. The Freudian death wish is evident.

Walpole, Hugh, *Portrait of a Man with Red Hair*. New York, Doran, 1925.

A passion for power over other lives and sadistic means of achieving it may here be traced to an individual's frustration as an unattractive child and the cruel punishment inflicted by his father.

Wells, H. G., *Christina Alberta's Father*. New York and London, Collins, 1934.

An ineffectual little clerk compensates for a life of subservience to others in delusions of grandeur. In his fantasy life he becomes Sargon the Great.

White, E. B., 'The Door,' in *Short Stories from the New Yorker*. New York, Simon & Schuster, 1940.

The story gives a stream-of-consciousness study of schizophrenia developing under the pressures of modern life.

Zweig, Stefan, 'Buchmendel,' in *Kaleidoscope*. New York, Viking, 1934.

A picture of monomania is here presented. A man has retreated from reality in a phenomenal mastery of bibliographical details. When his powers are broken by violent contact with the world from which he has escaped, a complete breakdown of the personality takes place.

Index

❊

Titles of selections are in italics, names of authors of selections in capitals. Other entries are section headings, proper names, concepts, and psychological terms. Numbers in parentheses refer to especially good specific illustrations of concepts in same selection.

Adler, Alfred, theory of inferiority, 18; drive for power, 223
Adolescence, physical and emotional growth in, 11; homosexual phase, 153, 282; first love, 165; gang stage, 172
Adult infantilism, 283
AIKEN, CONRAD, 263
ALDINGTON, RICHARD, 233
Ambivalence, 142, 294, 295, 315
American Tragedy, An, 88
And Man, 11
ANDREYEV, LEONID, 177
Anger, 141-2
Association of ideas, 36 (43), 64 (72), 123 (127), 183, 230, 239, 250, 264, 266, 274

BEERS, CLIFFORD, 340
BENÉT, STEPHEN VINCENT, 281
BENSON, SALLY, 103
Blue Voyage, 263
BRAND, MILLEN, 250
Brave New World, 239
BROMFIELD, LOUIS, 73
Brothers Karamazov, The, 355, 360
BROWNING, ROBERT, 314, 348
BUTLER, SAMUEL, 36, 281

CATHER, WILLA, 326
Censor, 249, 255 (262)
Chapter on Dreams, A, 255
Circle, The, 305
Compensation, 9, 12, 64, 193, 309, 349
Compulsion neurosis, 305
Conditioned response, 229, 239
Confessions of an English Opium-eater, 266
Confessions of Jean-Jacques Rousseau, 237
Conquering hero, fantasies of, 118 (122), 123 (125, 137), 161, 164, 172 (176), 212, 227

Conversion, 283 (287), 298, 309, 312
CRANE, STEPHEN, 212
Criminality, 238

Day-dreams, 263, 266, 325. *See also* Fantasy and Dreams.
Death of a Hero, 233
DELL, FLOYD, 123
Delusion of grandeur, 348, 351
Delusion of persecution, 266, 340, 341
DE MAUPASSANT, GUY, 300
DE QUINCEY, THOMAS, 266
Diary of Cotton Mather, 302
Dissociation of personality, 325, 348. *See also* Schizophrenia.
DOSTOYEVSKY, FYODOR, 355, 360
Dreams, 74 (76); nightmares, 189, 256; Dreams and the Unconscious, 249-80; relation to creation, 258; relation between dreams and awakened state, 261-2, 266 (267), 274
DREISER, THEODORE, 87
Dry September, 110
Dual personality, 234

Economic pressures, 118, 123, 193 (206), 309. *See also* Social and Economic Pressures.
Ego, Freud's theory of the, 315, 326
Egocentricity, 44, 64 (67), 307, 314
Eidetic imagery, 267
Emotional Conflicts, 141-228
Emotions, development of child's, 12, 18, 35, 281-2, 307
Escapes from reality, 36, 64 (66), 283, 309, 314, 325, 326
Exhibitionism, 18 (28), 307, 326
Extroversion, 172

Family, Influence of the, 35-79
Fanaticism, 302

387